That reaper of unseen harvests, th[a]
moulder of raw youth, that mem[ber]
of the noblest of professions,
TEACHER, receives fitting trib[ute]
[in th]is first anthology of its kin[d]
[a treas]ure chest of literatu[re]
[teach]ing.

Unseen Harvests

A TREASURY OF TEACHING

Edited by

CLAUDE M. FUESS

and

EMORY S. BASFORD

THE MACMILLAN COMPANY

NEW YORK · 1947

But now Oswald was realizing for the first time the eternal tragedy of the teacher, that sower of unseen harvests, that reaper of thistles and the wind, that serf of custom, that subjugated rebel, that feeble, persistent antagonist of the triumphant things that rule him. And behind that immediate tragedy Oswald was now apprehending for the first time something more universally tragic, an incessantly recurring story of high hopes and a grey ending; the story of boys and girls, clean and sweet-minded, growing up into life, and of the victory of world inertia, of custom drift and the tarnishing years.

H. G. Wells

I admit that your vocation is labourious, but I utterly deny that it is tragic or deplorable, as you call it. To be a schoolmaster is next to being a king. Do you count it a mean employment to imbue the minds of your fellow-citizens in their earnest years with the best literature and with the love of Christ, and to return them to their country honest and virtuous men? In the opinion of fools it is a humble task, but in fact it is the noblest of occupations. Even among the Heathen it was always a noble thing to deserve well of the State, and no one serves it better than the moulders of raw boys.

Erasmus

Foreword

THIS is a collection of miscellaneous writing clustered around the focal magnet of education. Although some of the material is obviously erudite, those who are hunting for a solemn history of educational theory or practice will certainly be disappointed in this book. Fortunately for them, there is an abundance of such treatises already on the market or at least gathering dust on library shelves. We have tried to select discreetly from authors, great and not-so-great, passages which have some bearing on educational policy or procedure, or which, because of their content or purpose, might be conceived of as especially entertaining to teachers. Inevitably the contents have a wide range. It is a far cry from Confucius to Mr. Dooley, and there is a vast difference in tone between John Milton and Max Beerbohm. The selections have been chosen deliberately to reflect different periods and attitudes. We have included some nuggets from educational philosophers like A. N. Whitehead and William James, and from two Presidents of the United States, Thomas Jefferson and Woodrow Wilson; a few stimulating comments on their profession by such ripe and talented practitioners as "Billy" Phelps, Bliss Perry, and Horace D. Taft; and even more obscure paragraphs and stanzas which describe eminent instructors and their pupils. Here will be found chapters from *Jane Eyre* and *Nicholas Nickleby*, from Thomas Wolfe and Booth Tarkington, from Hazlitt and Stephen Leacock. Nor should the inclusion of a few school stories be regarded as evidence of frivolous intent on the part of the editors, for from these may be derived some of the most searching comment on pedagogues and their victims. Think, for example, of the portrayal of the small English boarding school in Walpole's *The Gods and Mr. Perrin* or of the hidebound faculty conservatism in Bradby's *The Lanchester Tradition!*

We hope, then, that this volume may be picked up at random by professors and "schoolmarms" seeking for recreation, and that they may find in it faithfully limned some of the hazards, the annoyances, and the durable satisfactions of their profession. It is true that we meet in these pages Wackford Squeers, Ichabod Crane, and other none-too-creditable schoolmasters of tradition; but no one can dip into this anthology without making again the discovery that teachers as a group possess to a high degree the virtues of idealism, self-sacrifice, and human sympathy. Furthermore it can do teachers no harm to peruse some of that criticism, implied or direct, which they need as a corrective to the perils inherent in their autocratic positions.

vii

And even those who are not teachers, indeed never expect or wish to be, may be entertained by this presentation of pedagogues and their occasional tribulations. We, as editors, have cherished the hope that our work might even appeal to everybody who has sat in a classroom or lecture hall—and this means all literate men and women. Most Americans are familiar from personal experience with teachers and teaching, and have emerged with a tendency to ridicule or reverence, depending on their temperaments and adventures. At any rate here is what has been said about the subject, from many points of view.

Finally this is an anthology without any basic system, and certainly with no continuity or cumulativeness. The choice of material has cost us many thoughtful and discursive hours and involved a vast amount of reading. Much of our task was as inevitable as it was delightful. It was obvious that we could not omit *Good-bye, Mr. Chips* or *Of Human Bondage,* or some well-worn poems from Whittier and Kipling. In a few regrettable instances we have not been able to secure permission to include items which we desired. But the collection is varied and should have something for every taste. We trust that *Unseen Harvests* may be consulted not only for diversion but even for inspiration.

Claude M. Fuess

Emory S. Basford

Andover, Massachusetts

Acknowledgments

THE editors wish to express their personal thanks to all those who have assisted in any way in the preparation of this anthology for publication: in particular to the members of the English Department of Phillips Academy, Andover, for useful suggestions and help in choosing selections on education; to Mr. Edward Mayo for the loan of his copy of *The Babees' Book;* to Messrs. Allan Cook, Norman Étienne Vuilleumier, and Dudley Fitts for help and advice; to Mr. Guy J. Forbush for his translation of *La Dernière Classe;* to Dr. R. I. W. Westgate for the selection from Quintilian; to Mrs. Theresa Walley Richardson and the staff of the Oliver Wendell Holmes Library for indefatigable research; to Miss Georgia R. MacDonald for secretarial help; to Mrs. Richard Custer and Miss Nettie I. Crosby for meticulous typing; to Mr. R. L. De Wilton of The Macmillan Company for invaluable editorial advice.

Contents

Contents

Contents

Contents

Contents

UNSEEN HARVESTS

Philip Enters King's School

W. SOMERSET MAUGHAM

W. SOMERSET MAUGHAM, English novelist and dramatist, was born in Paris in 1874. Before his tenth year, both his parents had died, and the orphaned child was sent to live with his paternal uncle, a clergyman in England. The account of his life in the cold and stern environment of his uncle's house is told in Of Human Bondage. *At this time Maugham was small, shy, and unable to speak without a stammer—the latter an infirmity the equivalent of Philip Carey's clubfoot.*

He attended Kings' School, Canterbury, and after graduation went to Heidelberg, where he lived a carefree life. After his return to England, he studied medicine at St. Thomas's Hospital. He was duly qualified as a physician, but he actually practiced medicine only one year.

He returned to Paris and there for ten years wrote and starved. In 1907 he completed a successful play, Lady Frederick. *Soon he was well known as a dramatist. Today he is better known as a novelist and short story writer.*

The following selections are from Of Human Bondage, *Maugham's great autobiographical novel.*

THE Careys made up their minds to send Philip to King's School at Tercanbury. The neighbouring clergy sent their sons there. It was united by long tradition to the Cathedral: its headmaster was an honorary Canon, and a past headmaster was the Archdeacon. Boys were encouraged there to aspire to Holy Orders, and the education was such as might prepare an honest lad to spend his life in God's service. A preparatory school was attached to it, and to this it was arranged that Philip should go. Mr. Carey took him into Tercanbury one Thursday afternoon towards the end of September. All day Philip had been excited and rather frightened. He knew little of school life but what he had read in the stories of *The Boy's Own Paper*. He had also read *Eric, or Little by Little*.

When they got out of the train at Tercanbury, Philip felt sick with apprehension, and during the drive in to the town sat pale and silent. The high brick wall in front of the school gave it the look of a prison. There was a little door in it, which opened on their ringing; and a clumsy, untidy man came out and fetched Philip's tin trunk and his play-box. They were shown

Chapters X, XI, XII, are from *Of Human Bondage*, by W. Somerset Maugham; copyright, 1915, by Doubleday, Doran and Company, Inc.; reproduced here by permission of the publishers.

into the drawing-room; it was filled with massive, ugly furniture, and the chairs of the suite were placed round the walls with a forbidding rigidity. They waited for the headmaster.

"What's Mr. Watson like?" asked Philip, after a while.

"You'll see for yourself."

There was another pause. Mr. Carey wondered why the headmaster did not come. Presently Philip made an effort and spoke again.

"Tell him I've got a club-foot," he said.

Before Mr. Carey could speak, the door burst open and Mr. Watson swept into the room. To Philip he seemed gigantic. He was a man of over six feet high, and broad, with enormous hands and a great red beard; he talked loudly in a jovial manner; but his aggressive cheerfulness struck terror in Philip's heart. He shook hands with Mr. Carey, and then took Philip's small hand in his.

"Well, young fellow, are you glad to come to school?" he shouted.

Philip reddened and found no word to answer.

"How old are you?"

"Nine," said Philip.

"You must say sir," said his uncle.

"I expect you've got a good lot to learn," the headmaster bellowed cheerily.

To give the boy confidence he began to tickle him with rough fingers. Philip, feeling shy and uncomfortable, squirmed under his touch.

"I've put him in the small dormitory for the present. . . . You'll like that, won't you?" he added to Philip. "Only eight of you in there. You won't feel so strange."

Then the door opened, and Mrs. Watson came in. She was a dark woman with black hair, neatly parted in the middle. She had curiously thick lips and a small round nose. Her eyes were large and black. There was a singular coldness in her appearance. She seldom spoke and smiled more seldom still. Her husband introduced Mr. Carey to her, and then gave Philip a friendly push towards her.

"This is a new boy, Helen. His name's Carey."

Without a word she shook hands with Philip and then sat down, not speaking, while the headmaster asked Mr. Carey how much Philip knew and what books he had been working with. The Vicar of Blackstable was a little embarrassed by Mr. Watson's boisterous heartiness, and in a moment or two got up.

"I think I'd better leave Philip with you now."

"That's all right," said Mr. Watson. "He'll be safe with me. He'll get on like a house on fire. Won't you, young fellow?"

Without waiting for an answer from Philip the big man burst into a great bellow of laughter. Mr. Carey kissed Philip on the forehead and went away.

"Come along, young fellow," shouted Mr. Watson. "I'll show you the school-room."

He swept out of the drawing-room with giant strides, and Philip hurriedly limped behind him. He was taken into a long, bare room with two tables that ran along its whole length; on each side of them were wooden forms.

"Nobody much here yet," said Mr. Watson. "I'll just show you the play-ground, and then I'll leave you to shift for yourself."

Mr. Watson led the way. Philip found himself in a large play-ground with high brick walls on three sides of it. On the fourth side was an iron railing through which you saw a vast lawn and beyond this some of the buildings of King's School. One small boy was wandering disconsolately, kicking up the gravel as he walked.

"Hulloa, Venning," shouted Mr. Watson. "When did you turn up?"

The small boy came forward and shook hands.

"Here's a new boy. He's older and bigger than you, so don't you bully him."

The headmaster glared amicably at the two children, filling them with fear by the roar of his voice, and then with a guffaw left them.

"What's your name?"

"Carey."

"What's your father?"

"He's dead."

"Oh! Does your mother wash?"

"My mother's dead, too."

Philip thought this answer would cause the boy a certain awkwardness, but Venning was not to be turned from his facetiousness for so little.

"Well, did she wash?" he went on.

"Yes," said Philip indignantly.

"She was a washerwoman then?"

"No, she wasn't."

"Then she didn't wash."

The little boy crowed with delight at the success of his dialectic. Then he caught sight of Philip's feet.

"What's the matter with your foot?"

Philip instinctively tried to withdraw it from sight. He hid it behind the one which was whole.

"I've got a club-foot," he answered.

"How did you get it?"

"I've always had it."

"Let's have a look."

"No."

"Don't then."

The little boy accompanied the words with a sharp kick on Philip's shin, which Philip did not expect and thus could not guard against. The pain was so great that it made him gasp, but greater than the pain was the surprise. He did not know why Venning kicked him. He had not the presence of mind to give him a black eye. Besides, the boy was smaller than he, and he had read in *The Boy's Own Paper* that it was a mean thing to hit anyone smaller than yourself. While Philip was nursing his shin a third boy appeared, and his tormentor left him. In a little while he noticed that the pair were talking about him, and he felt they were looking at his feet. He grew hot and uncomfortable.

But others arrived, a dozen together, and then more, and they began to talk about their doings during the holidays, where they had been, and what wonderful cricket they had played. A few new boys appeared, and with these presently Philip found himself talking. He was shy and nervous. He was anxious to make himself pleasant, but he could not think of anything to say. He was asked a great many questions and answered them all quite willingly. One boy asked him whether he could play cricket.

"No," answered Philip. "I've got a club-foot."

The boy looked down quickly and reddened. Philip saw that he felt he had asked an unseemly question. He was too shy to apologize and looked at Philip awkwardly.

Philip's First Days at School

NEXT morning when the clanging of a bell awoke Philip he looked round his cubicle in astonishment. Then a voice sang out, and he remembered where he was.

"Are you awake, Singer?"

The partitions of the cubicle were of polished pitch-pine, and there was a green curtain in front. In those days there was little thought of ventilation, and the windows were closed except when the dormitory was aired in the morning.

Philip got up and knelt down to say his prayers. It was a cold morning, and he shivered a little; but he had been taught by his uncle that his prayers were more acceptable to God if he said them in his nightshirt than if he waited till he was dressed. This did not surprise him, for he was beginning to realise that he was the creature of a God who appreciated the discomfort of his worshippers. Then he washed. There were two baths for the fifty boarders, and each boy had a bath once a week. The rest of his washing was done in a small basin on a wash-stand, which, with the bed and a chair, made up the furniture of each cubicle. The boys chatted gaily while they dressed. Philip was all ears. Then another bell sounded, and they ran downstairs. They took their seats on the forms on each side of the two long tables in the school-room; and Mr. Watson, followed by his wife and the servants, came in and sat down. Mr. Watson read prayers in an impressive manner, and the supplications thundered out in his loud voice as though they were threats personally addressed to each boy. Philip listened with anxiety. Then Mr. Watson read a chapter from the Bible, and the servants trooped out. In a moment the untidy youth brought in two large pots of tea and on a second journey immense dishes of bread and butter.

Philip had a squeamish appetite, and the thick slabs of poor butter on the bread turned his stomach, but he saw other boys scraping it off and followed their example. They all had potted meats and such like, which they had brought in their play-boxes; and some had "extras," eggs or bacon, upon which Mr. Watson made a profit. When he had asked Mr. Carey whether Philip was to have these, Mr. Carey replied that he did not think boys should be spoilt. Mr. Watson quite agreed with him—he considered nothing was better than bread and butter for growing lads—but some parents, unduly pampering their offspring, insisted on it.

Philip noticed that "extras" gave boys a certain consideration and made up his mind, when he wrote to Aunt Louisa, to ask for them.

After breakfast the boys wandered out into the play-ground. Here the day-boys were gradually assembling. They were sons of the local clergy, of the officers at the Depot, and of such manufacturers or men of business as the old town possessed. Presently a bell rang, and they all trooped into school. This consisted of a large, long room at opposite ends of which two under-masters conducted the second and third forms, and of a smaller one, leading out of it, used by Mr. Watson, who taught the first form. To attach the preparatory to the senior school these three classes were known officially, on speech days and in reports, as upper, middle, and lower second. Philip was put in the last. The master, a red-faced man with a pleasant voice, was called Rice; he had a jolly manner with boys, and the time passed quickly. Philip was surprised when it was a quarter to eleven and they were let out for ten minutes' rest.

The whole school rushed noisily into the play-ground. The new boys were told to go into the middle, while the others stationed themselves along opposite walls. They began to play *Pig in the Middle*. The old boys ran from wall to wall while the new boys tried to catch them: when one was seized and the mystic words said—one, two, three, and a pig for me— he became a prisoner and, turning sides, helped to catch those who were still free. Philip saw a boy running past and tried to catch him, but his limp gave him no chance; and the runners, taking their opportunity, made straight for the ground he covered. Then one of them had the brilliant idea of imitating Philip's clumsy run. Other boys saw it and began to laugh; then they all copied the first; and they ran round Philip, limping grotesquely, screaming in their treble voices with shrill laughter. They lost their heads with the delight of their new amusement, and choked with helpless merriment. One of them tripped Philip up and he fell, heavily as he always fell, and cut his knee. They laughed all the louder when he got up. A boy pushed him from behind, and he would have fallen again if another had not caught him. The game was forgotten in the entertainment of Philip's deformity. One of them invented an odd, rolling limp that struck the rest as supremely ridiculous, and several of the boys lay down on the ground and rolled about in laughter: Philip was completely scared. He could not make out why they were laughing at him. His heart beat so that he could hardly breathe, and he was more frightened than he had ever been in his life. He stood still stupidly while the boys ran round him, mimicking and laughing; they shouted to him to try and catch them; but he did not move. He did not want them to see him run any more. He was using all his strength to prevent himself from crying.

Suddenly the bell rang, and they all trooped back to school. Philip's knee was bleeding, and he was dusty and dishevelled. For some minutes Mr. Rice could not control his form. They were excited still by the strange novelty, and Philip saw one or two of them furtively looking down at his feet. He tucked them under the bench.

In the afternoon they went up to play football, but Mr. Watson stopped Philip on the way out after dinner.

"I suppose you can't play football, Carey?" he asked him.

Philip blushed self-consciously.

"No, sir."

"Very well. You'd better go up to the field. You can walk as far as that, can't you?"

Philip had no idea where the field was, but he answered all the same.

"Yes, sir."

The boys went in charge of Mr. Rice, who glanced at Philip and, seeing he had not changed, asked why he was not going to play.

"Mr. Watson, said I needn't, sir," said Philip.

"Why?"

There were boys all round him, looking at him curiously, and a feeling of shame came over Philip. He looked down without answering. Others gave the reply.

"He's got a club-foot, sir."

"Oh, I see."

Mr. Rice was quite young; he had only taken his degree a year before; and he was suddenly embarrassed. His instinct was to beg the boy's pardon, but he was too shy to do so. He made his voice gruff and loud.

"Now then, you boys, what are you waiting about for? Get on with you."

Some of them had already started and those that were left now set off, in groups of two or three.

"You'd better come along with me, Carey," said the master. "You don't know the way, do you?"

Philip guessed the kindness, and a sob came to his throat.

"I can't go very fast, sir."

"Then I'll go very slow," said the master, with a smile.

Philip's heart went out to the red-faced, commonplace young man who said a gentle word to him. He suddenly felt less unhappy.

But at night when they went up to bed and were undressing, the boy who was called Singer came out of his cubicle and put his head in Philip's.

"I say, let's look at your foot," he said.

"No," answered Philip.

He jumped into bed quickly.

"Don't say no to me," said Singer. "Come on, Mason."

The boy in the next cubicle was looking round the corner, and at the words he slipped in. They made for Philip and tried to tear the bed-clothes off him, but he held them tightly.

"Why can't you leave me alone?" he cried.

Singer seized a brush and with the back of it beat Philip's hands clenched on the blanket. Philip cried out.

"Why don't you show us your foot quietly?"

"I won't."

In desperation Philip clenched his fist and hit the boy who tormented him, but he was at a disadvantage, and the boy seized his arm. He began to turn it.

"Oh, don't, don't," said Philip. "You'll break my arm."

"Stop still then and put out your foot."

Philip gave a sob and a gasp. The boy gave the arm another wrench. The pain was unendurable.

"All right. I'll do it," said Philip.

He put out his foot. Singer still kept his hand on Philip's wrist. He looked curiously at the deformity.

"Isn't it beastly?" said Mason.

Another came in and looked too.

"Ugh," he said, in disgust.

"My word, it is rum," said Singer, making a face. "Is it hard?"

He touched it with the tip of his forefinger, cautiously, as though it were something that had a life of its own. Suddenly they heard Mr. Watson's heavy tread on the stairs. They threw the clothes back on Philip and dashed like rabbits into their cubicles. Mr. Watson came into the dormitory. Raising himself on tiptoe he could see over the rod that bore the green curtain, and he looked into two or three of the cubicles. The little boys were safely in bed. He put out the light and went out.

Singer called out to Philip, but he did not answer. He had got his teeth in the pillow so that his sobbing should be inaudible. He was not crying for the pain they had caused him, nor for the humiliation he had suffered when they looked at his foot, but with rage at himself because, unable to stand the torture, he had put out his foot of his own accord.

And then he felt the misery of his life. It seemed to his childish mind that this unhappiness must go on for ever. For no particular reason he remembered that cold morning when Emma had taken him out of bed and put him beside his mother. He had not thought of it once since it happened, but now he seemed to feel the warmth of his mother's body against his and her arms around him. Suddenly it seemed to him that his life was a dream, his mother's death, and the life at the vicarage, and these two wretched days at school, and he would awake in the morning and be back again at home. His tears dried as he thought of it. He was too unhappy, it must be nothing but a dream, and his mother was alive, and Emma would come up presently and go to bed. He fell asleep.

But when he awoke next morning it was to the clanging of a bell, and the first thing his eyes saw was the green curtain of his cubicle.

Philip Escapes a Thrashing

As time went on Philip's deformity ceased to interest. It was accepted like one boy's red hair and another's unreasonable corpulence. But meanwhile he had grown horribly sensitive. He never ran if he could help it, because he knew it made his limp more conspicuous, and he adopted a peculiar walk. He stood still as much as he could, with his club-foot behind the other, so that it should not attract notice, and he was constantly on the look out for any reference to it. Because he could not join in the games which other boys played, their life remained strange to him; he only interested himself from the outside in their doings; and it seemed to him that there was a barrier between them and him. Sometimes they seemed to think that it was his fault if he could not play football, and he was unable to make them understand. He was left a good deal to himself. He had been inclined to talkativeness, but gradually he became silent. He began to think of the difference between himself and others.

The biggest boy in his dormitory, Singer, took a dislike to him, and Philip, small for his age, had to put up with a good deal of hard treatment. About half-way through the term a mania ran through the school for a game called Nibs. It was a game for two, played on a table or a form with steel pens. You had to push your nib with the finger-nail so as to get the point of it over your opponent's, while he manoeuvred to prevent this and to get the point of his nib over the back of yours; when this result was achieved you breathed on the ball of your thumb, pressed it hard on the two nibs, and if you were able then to lift them without dropping either, both nibs became yours. Soon nothing was seen but boys playing this game, and the more skilful acquired vast stores of nibs. But in a little while Mr. Watson made up his mind that it was a form of gambling, forbade the game, and confiscated all the nibs in the boys' possession. Philip had been very adroit, and it was with a heavy heart that he gave up his winnings; but his fingers itched to play still, and a few days later, on his way to the football field, he went into a shop and bought a pennyworth of J pens. He carried them loose in his pocket and enjoyed feeling them. Presently Singer found out that he had them. Singer had given up his nibs too, but he had kept back a very large one, called a Jumbo, which was almost unconquerable, and he could not resist the opportunity of getting Philip's Js out of him. Though Philip knew that he was at a disadvantage with his small nibs, he had an adventurous disposition and was willing to take the risk; besides, he was aware that Singer would not allow him to refuse. He had not played for a week and sat down to the game now with a thrill of excitement. He lost two of his small nibs quickly, and Singer was jubilant, but the third time by some change the Jumbo slipped round and Philip was able to push his J across it. He crowed with triumph. At that moment Mr. Watson came in.

"What are you doing?" he asked.

He looked from Singer to Philip, but neither answered.

"Don't you know that I've forbidden you to play that idiotic game?"

Philip's heart beat fast. He knew what was coming and was dreadfully frightened, but in his fright there was a certain exultation. He had never been swished. Of course it would hurt, but it was something to boast about afterwards.

"Come into my study."

The headmaster turned, and they followed him side by side. Singer whispered to Philip:

"We're in for it."

Mr. Watson pointed to Singer.

"Bend over," he said.

Philip, very white, saw the boy quiver at each stroke, and after the third he heard him cry out. Three more followed.

"That'll do. Get up."

Singer stood up. The tears were streaming down his face. Philip stepped forward. Mr. Watson looked at him for a moment.

"I'm not going to cane you. You're a new boy. And I can't hit a cripple. Go away, both of you, and don't be naughty again."

When they got back into the school-room a group of boys, who had learned in some mysterious way what was happening, were waiting for them. They set upon Singer at once with eager questions. Singer faced them, his face red with the pain and marks of tears still on his cheeks. He pointed with his head at Philip, who was standing a little behind him.

"He got off because he's a cripple," he said angrily.

Philip stood silent and flushed. He felt that they looked at him with contempt.

"How many did you get?" one boy asked Singer.

But he did not answer. He was angry because he had been hurt.

"Don't ask me to play Nibs with you again," he said to Philip.

"It's jolly nice for you. You don't risk anything."

"I didn't ask you."

"Didn't you!"

He quickly put out his foot and tripped Philip up. Philip was always rather unsteady on his feet, and he fell heavily to the ground.

"Cripple," said Singer.

For the rest of the term he tormented Philip cruelly, and, though Philip tried to keep out of his way, the school was so small that it was impossible; he tried being friendly and jolly with him; he abased himself so far as to buy him a knife; but though Singer took the knife he was not placated. Once or twice, driven beyond endurance, he hit and kicked the bigger boy, but Singer was so much stronger that Philip was helpless, and he was always forced after more or less torture to beg his pardon. It was that which rankled with Philip; he could not bear the humiliation of apologies, which were wrung from him by pain greater than he could bear. And what made it worse was that there seemed no end to his wretchedness; Singer was only eleven and would not go to the upper school till he was thirteen. Philip realised that he must live two years with a tormentor from whom there was no escape. He was only happy while he was working and when he got into bed. And often there recurred to him then that queer feeling that his life with all its misery was nothing but a dream, and that he would awake in the morning in his own little bed in London.

A School Song

RUDYARD KIPLING

RUDYARD KIPLING (1865-1936) was born in Bombay and educated in England. At seventeen, rejecting the parental offer of a University education, he returned to India and engaged in journalism. In 1886 he published in India a collection of poems called Departmental Ditties, *most of which had already appeared in the Lahore* Civil and Military Gazette. *This book marked the beginning of a long and successful career as a writer. Three years later Kipling returned to England, where except for five years spent in the United States and frequent periods of travel, he lived until his death in 1936.*

"A School Song" and "A Little Prep" are taken from Stalky & Co., *a series of tales of schoolboy life based upon Kipling's own schooldays at the United Services College, Westward Ho!*

*L*et us now praise famous men"—
    Men of little showing—
For their work continueth,
And their work continueth,
Broad and deep continueth,
    Greater than their knowing!

Western wind and open surge
    Took us from our mothers—
Flung us on a naked shore
(Twelve bleak houses by the shore!
Seven summers by the shore!)
    'Mid two hundred brothers.

There we met with famous men
    Set in office o'er us;
And they beat on us with rods—
Faithfully with many rods—
Daily beat us on with rods,
    For the love they bore us!

Out of Egypt unto Troy—
    Over Himalaya—
Far and sure our bands have gone—
Hy-Brazil or Babylon,
Islands of the Southern Run,
    And Cities of Cathaia!

And we all praise famous men—
    Ancients of the College;
For they taught us common sense—
Tried to teach us common sense—
Truth and God's Own Common Sense,
    Which is more than knowledge!

Each degree of Latitude
    Strung about Creation
Seeth one or more of us
(Of one muster each of us),
Diligent in that he does,
    Keen in his vocation.

This we learned from famous men,
    Knowing not its uses,
When they showed, in daily work,
Man must finish off his work—
Right or wrong, his daily work—
    And without excuses.

Servants of the Staff and chain,
    Mine and fuse and grapnel—
Some, before the face of Kings,
Stand before the face of Kings;
Bearing gifts to divers Kings—
    Gifts of case and shrapnel.

This we learned from famous men
    Teaching in our borders,
Who declared it was best,
Safest, easiest, and best—
Expeditious, wise, and best—
    To obey your orders.

Some beneath the further stars
    Bear the greater burden:
Set to serve the lands they rule,

(Save he serve no man may rule),
Serve and love the lands they rule;
    Seeking praise nor guerdon.

This we learned from famous men,
    Knowing not we learned it.
Only, as the years went by—
Lonely, as the years went by—
Far from help as years went by,
    Plainer we discerned it.

Wherefore praise we famous men
    From whose bays we borrow—
They that put aside To-day—
All the joys of their To-day—
And with toil of their To-day
    Bought for us To-morrow!

Bless and praise we famous men—
    Men of little showing—
For their work continueth,
And their work continueth,
Broad and deep continueth,
    Great beyond their knowing!

A Little Prep

THE Easter term was but a month old when Stettson major, a day-boy, contracted diphtheria, and the Head was very angry. He decreed a new and narrower set of bounds—the infection had been traced to an outlying farm-house—urged the prefects severely to lick all trespassers, and promised extra attentions from his own hand. There were no words bad enough for Stettson major, quarantined at his mother's house, who had lowered the school-average of health. This he said in the gymnasium after prayers. Then he wrote some two hundred letters to as many anxious parents and guardians, and bade the school carry on. The trouble did not spread, but, one night, a dog-cart drove to the Head's door, and in the morning the Head had gone, leaving all things in charge of Mr. King, senior housemaster. The Head often ran up to town, where the school devoutly believed he bribed officials for early proofs of the Army Examination papers; but this absence was unusually prolonged.

"Downy old bird!" said Stalky to the allies, one wet afternoon, in the study. "He must have gone on a bend an' been locked up, under a false name."

"What for?" Beetle entered joyously into the libel.

"Forty shillin's a month for hackin' the chucker-out of the Pavvy on the shins. Bates always has a spree when he goes to town. Wish he was back, though. I'm about sick o' King's 'whips an' scorpions' an' lectures on public-school spirit—yah!—and scholarship!"

" 'Crass an' materialised brutality of the middle-classes—readin' solely for marks. Not a scholar in the whole school,'" McTurk quoted, pensively boring holes in the mantelpiece with a hot poker.

"That's rather a sickly way of spending an afternoon. Stinks, too. Let's come out an' smoke. Here's a treat." Stalky held up a long Indian cheroot. " 'Bagged it from my pater last holidays. I'm a bit shy of it, though; it's heftier than a pipe. We'll smoke it palaver-fashion. Hand it round, eh? Let's lie up behind the old harrow on the Monkey-farm Road."

"Out of bounds. Bounds beastly strict these days, too. Besides, we shall cat." Beetle sniffed the cheroot critically. "It's a regular Pomposo Stinka-dore."

"You can; I sha'n't. What d'you say, Turkey?"

"Oh, may's well, I s'pose."

"Chuck on your cap, then. It's two to one. Beetle, out you come!"

They saw a group of boys by the notice-board in the corridor; little Foxy, the school-sergeant, among them.

"More bounds, I expect," said Stalky. "Hullo, Foxibus, who are you in mournin' for?" There was a broad band of crape round Foxy's arm.

"He was in my old regiment," said Foxy, jerking his head towards the notices, where a newspaper cutting was thumb-tacked between call-over lists.

"By gum!" quoth Stalky, uncovering as he read. "It's old Duncan—Fat-Sow Duncan—killed on duty at something or other Kotal. '*Rallyin' his men with conspicuous gallantry.*' He would, of course. '*The body was recovered.*' That's all right. They cut 'em up sometimes, don't they, Foxy?"

"Horrid," said the sergeant, briefly.

"Poor old Fat-Sow! I was a fag when he left. How many does that make to us, Foxy?"

"Mr. Duncan, he is the ninth. He came here when he was no bigger than little Grey tertius. My old regiment, too. Yiss, nine to us, Mr. Corkran, up to date."

The boys went out into the wet, walking swiftly.

"Wonder how it feels—to be shot and all that," said Stalky, as they splashed down a lane. "Where did it happen, Beetle?"

"Oh, out in India somewhere. We're always rowin' there. But look here, Stalky, what *is* the good o' sittin' under a hedge an' cattin'? It's be-eastly cold. It's be-eastly wet, and we'll be collared as sure as a gun."

"Shut up! Did you ever know your Uncle Stalky get you into a mess yet?" Like many other leaders, Stalky did not dwell on past defeats.

They pushed through a dripping hedge, landed among water-logged clods, and sat down on a rust-coated harrow. The cheroot burned with sputterings of saltpetre. They smoked it gingerly, each passing to the other between closed forefinger and thumb.

"Good job we hadn't one apiece, ain't it?" said Stalky, shivering through set teeth. To prove his words he immediately laid all before them, and they followed his example. . . .

"I told you," moaned Beetle, sweating clammy drops. "Oh, Stalky, you *are* a fool!"

"*Je cat, tu cat, il cat. Nous cattons!*" McTurk handed up his contribution and lay hopelessly on the cold iron.

"Something's wrong with the beastly thing. I say, Beetle, have you been droppin' ink on it?"

But Beetle was in no case to answer. Limp and empty, they sprawled across the harrow, the rust marking their ulsters in red squares and the abandoned cheroot-end reeking under their very cold noses. Then—they had heard nothing—the Head himself stood before them—the Head who should have been in town bribing examiners—the Head fantastically attired in old tweeds and a deer-stalker!

"Ah," he said, fingering his moustache. "Very good. I might have guessed who it was. You will go back to the College and give my compliments to Mr. King and ask him to give you an extra-special licking. You will then do me five hundred lines. I shall be back to-morrow. Five hundred lines by five o'clock to-morrow. You are also gated for a week. This is not exactly the time for breaking bounds. *Extra*-special, please."

He disappeared over the hedge as lightly as he had come. There was a murmur of women's voices in the deep lane.

"Oh, you Prooshan brute," said McTurk as the voices died away. "Stalky, it's all your silly fault."

"Kill him! Kill him!" gasped Beetle.

"I ca-an't. I'm going to cat again. . . . I don't mind that, but King'll gloat over us horrid. Extra-special, ooh!"

Stalky made no answer—not even a soft one. They went to College and received that for which they had been sent. King enjoyed himself most thoroughly, for by virtue of their seniority the boys were exempt from his hand, save under special order. Luckily, he was no expert in the gentle art.

"'Strange, how desire doth outrun performance,'" said Beetle, irreverently, quoting from some Shakespeare play that they were cramming that term. They regained their study and settled down to the imposition.

"You're quite right, Beetle." Stalky spoke in silky and propitiating tones. "Now, if the Head had sent us up to a prefect, we'd have got something to remember!"

"Look here," McTurk began with cold venom, "we aren't goin' to row you about this business, because it's too bad for a row; but we want you to understand you're jolly well excommunicated, Stalky. You're a plain ass."

"How was I to know that the Head 'ud collar us? What was he doin' in those ghastly clothes, too?"

"Don't try to raise a side-issue," Beetle grunted severely.

"Well, it was all Stettson major's fault. If he hadn't gone an' got diphtheria 'twouldn't have happened. But don't you think it rather rummy—the Head droppin' on us that way?"

"Shut up! You're dead!" said Beetle. "We've chopped your spurs off your beastly heels. We've cocked your shield upside down and—and I don't think you ought to be allowed to brew for a month."

"Oh, stop jawin' at me. I want—"

"Stop? Why—why, we're gated for a week." McTurk almost howled as the agony of the situation overcame him. "A lickin' from King, five hundred lines, *and* gatin'. D'you expect us to kiss you, Stalky, you beast?"

"Drop rottin' for a minute. I want to find out about the Head bein' where he was."

"Well, you have. You found him quite well and fit. Found him makin' love to Stettson major's mother. That was her in the lane—I heard her. And *so* we were ordered a lickin' before a day-boy's mother. Bony old widow, too," said McTurk. "Anything else you'd like to find out?"

"I don't care. I swear I'll get even with him some day," Stalky growled.

"Looks like it," said McTurk. "Extra-special, week's gatin', and five hundred . . . and now you're goin' to row about it! Help scrag him, Beetle!" Stalky had thrown his Virgil at them.

The Head returned next day without explanation, to find the lines waiting for him and the school a little relaxed under Mr. King's viceroyalty. Mr. King had been talking at and round and over the boys' heads, in a lofty and promiscuous style, of public-school spirit and the traditions of ancient seats; for he always improved an occasion. Beyond waking in two hundred and fifty young hearts a lively hatred of all other foundations, he accomplished little—so little, indeed, that when, two days after the Head's return, he chanced to come across Stalky & Co., gated but ever resourceful, playing marbles in the corridor, he said that he was not surprised—not in the least surprised. This was what he had expected from persons of their *morale*.

"But there isn't any rule against marbles, sir. Very interestin' game," said Beetle, his knees white with chalk and dust. Then he received two hundred lines for insolence, besides an order to go to the nearest prefect for judgment and slaughter.

This is what happened behind the closed doors of Flint's study, and Flint was then Head of the Games:—

"Oh, I say, Flint. King has sent me to you for playin' marbles in the corridor an' shoutin' 'alley tor' an' 'knuckle down.'"

"What does he suppose I have to do with that?" was the answer.

"Dunno. Well?" Beetle grinned wickedly. "What am I to tell him? He's rather wrathy about it."

"If the Head chooses to put a notice in the corridor forbiddin' marbles, I can do something; but I can't move on a house-master's report. He knows that as well as I do."

The sense of this oracle Beetle conveyed, all unsweetened, to King, who hastened to interview Flint.

Now Flint had been seven and a half years at the College, counting six months with a London crammer, from whose roof he had returned, home-sick, to the Head for the final Army polish. There were four or five other seniors who had gone through much the same mill, not to mention boys, rejected by other establishments on account of a certain overwhelming-ness, whom the Head had wrought into very fair shape. It was not a Sixth to be handled without gloves, as King found.

"Am I to understand it is your intention to allow board-school games under your study windows, Flint? If so, I can only say—" He said much, and Flint listened politely.

"Well, sir, if the Head sees fit to call a prefects' meeting we are bound to take the matter up. But the tradition of the school is that the prefects can't move in any matter affecting the whole school without the Head's direct order."

Much more was then delivered, both sides a little losing their temper.

After tea, at an informal gathering of prefects in his study, Flint related the adventure.

"He's been playin' for this for a week, and now he's got it. You know as well as I do that if he hadn't been gassing at us the way he has, that young devil Beetle wouldn't have dreamed of marbles."

"We know that," said Perowne, "But that isn't the question. On Flint's showin' King has called the prefects names enough to justify a first-class row. Crammers' rejections, ill-regulated hobble-de-hoys, wasn't it? Now it's impossible for prefects—"

"Rot," said Flint. "King's the best classical cram we've got; and 'tisn't fair to bother the Head with a row. He's up to his eyes with extra-tu. and Army work as it is. Besides, as I told King, we *aren't* a public school. We're a limited liability company payin' four per cent. My father's a shareholder, too."

"What's that got to do with it?" said Venner, a red-headed boy of nine-teen.

"Well, it seems to me that we should be interferin' with ourselves. We've got to get into the Army or—get out, haven't we? King's hired by the Coun-cil to teach us. All the rest's flumdiddle. Can't you see?"

It might have been because he felt the air was a little thunderous that the Head took his after-dinner cheroot to Flint's study; but he so often began an evening in a prefect's room that nobody suspected when he drifted in pensively, after the knocks that etiquette demanded.

"Prefects' meeting?" A cock of one wise eyebrow.

"Not exactly, sir; we're just talking things over. Won't you take the easy-chair?"

"Thanks. Luxurious infants, you are." He dropped into Flint's big half-couch and puffed for a while in silence. "Well, since you're all here, I may confess that I'm the mute with the bowstring."

The young faces grew serious. The phrase meant that certain of their number would be withdrawn from all further games for extra-tuition. It might also mean future success at Sandhurst; but it was present ruin for the First Fifteen.

"Yes, I've come for my pound of flesh. I ought to have had you out before the Exeter match; but it's our sacred duty to beat Exeter."

"Isn't the Old Boys' match sacred, too, sir?" said Perowne. The Old Boys' match was the event of the Easter term.

"We'll hope they aren't in training. Now for the list. First I want Flint. It's the Euclid that does it. You must work deductions with me. Perowne, extra mechanical drawing. Dawson goes to Mr. King for extra Latin, and Venner to me for German. Have I damaged the First Fifteen much?" He smiled sweetly.

"Ruined it, I'm afraid, sir," said Flint. "Can't you let us off till the end of the term?"

"Impossible. It will be a tight squeeze for Sandhurst this year."

"And all to be cut up by those vile Afghans, too," said Dawson. "Wouldn't think there'd be so much competition, would you?"

"Oh, that reminds me. Crandall is coming down with the Old Boys—I've asked twenty of them, but we sha'n't get more than a weak team. I don't know whether he'll be much use, though. He was rather knocked about, recovering poor old Duncan's body."

"Crandall major—the Gunner?" Perowne asked.

"No, the minor—'Toffee' Crandall—in a native infantry regiment. He was almost before your time, Perowne."

"The papers didn't say anything about him. We read about Fat-Sow, of course. What's Crandall done, sir?"

"I've brought over an Indian paper that his mother sent me. It was rather a—hefty, I think you say—piece of work. Shall I read it?"

The Head knew how to read. When he had finished the quarter-column of close type they thanked him politely.

"Good for the old Coll!" said Perowne. "Pity he wasn't in time to save Fat-Sow, though. That's nine to us, isn't it, in the last three years?"

"Yes. . . . And I took old Duncan off all games for extra-tu. five years ago this term," said the Head. "By the way, who do you hand over the Games to, Flint?"

"Haven't thought yet. Who'd you recommend, sir?"

"No, thank you. I've heard it casually hinted behind my back that the Prooshan Bates is a downy bird, but he isn't going to make himself responsible for a new Head of the Games. Settle it among yourselves. Good night."

"And that's the man," said Flint, when the door shut, "that you want to bother with a dame's school row."

"I was only pullin' your fat leg," Perowne returned hastily. "You're so easy to draw, Flint."

"Well, never mind that. The Head's knocked the First Fifteen to bits, and we've got to pick up the pieces, or the Old Boys will have a walk-over. Let's promote all the Second Fifteen and make Big Side play up. There's heaps of talent somewhere that we can polish up between now and the match."

The case was represented so urgently to the school that even Stalky and McTurk, who affected to despise football, played one Big-Side game seriously. They were forthwith promoted ere their ardor had time to cool, and the dignity of their Caps demanded that they should keep some show of virtue. The match-team was worked at least four days out of seven, and the school saw hope ahead.

With the last week of the term the Old Boys began to arrive, and their welcome was nicely proportioned to their worth. Gentlemen cadets from Sandhurst and Woolwich, who had only left a year ago, but who carried enormous side, were greeted with a cheerful "Hullo! What's the Shop like?" from those who had shared their studies. Militia subalterns had more consideration, but it was understood they were not precisely of the true metal. Recreants who, failing for the Army, had gone into business or banks were received for old sake's sake, but in no way made too much of. But when the real subalterns, officers and gentlemen full-blown—who had been to the ends of the earth and back again and so carried no side—came on the scene strolling about with the Head, the school divided right and left in admiring silence. And when one laid hands on Flint, even upon the Head of the Games, crying, "Good Heavens! What do you mean by growing in this way? You were a beastly little fag when I left," visible haloes encircled Flint. They would walk to and fro in the corridor with the little red school-sergeant, telling news of old regiments; they would burst into form-rooms sniffing the well-remembered smells of ink and whitewash; they would find nephews and cousins in the lower forms and present them with enormous wealth; or they would invade the gymnasium and make Foxy show off the new stock on the bars.

Chiefly, though, they talked with the Head, who was father-confessor and agent-general to them all; for what they shouted in their unthinking youth, they proved in their thoughtless manhood—to wit, that the Prooshan Bates was "a downy bird." Young blood who had stumbled into an entanglement with a pastry-cook's daughter at Plymouth; experience who had come into a small legacy but mistrusted lawyers; ambition halting at cross-roads, anxious to take the one that would lead him farthest; extravagance pursued by the money-lender; arrogance in the thick of a regimental row—

each carried his trouble to the Head; and Chiron showed him, in language quite unfit for little boys, a quiet and safe way round, out, or under. So they overflowed his house, smoked his cigars, and drank his health as they had drunk it all the earth over when two or three of the old school had fore-gathered.

"Don't stop smoking for a minute," said the Head. "The more you're out of training the better for us. I've demoralised the First Fifteen with extra-tu."

"Ah, but we're a scratch lot. Have you told 'em we shall need a substitute even if Crandall can play?" said a Lieutenant of Engineers with a D.S.O. to his credit.

"He wrote me he'd play, so he can't have been much hurt. He's coming down to-morrow morning."

"Crandall minor that was, and brought off poor Duncan's body?" The Head nodded. "Where are you going to put him? We've turned you out of house and home already, Head Sahib." This was a Squadron Commander of Bengal Lancers, home on leave.

"I'm afraid he'll have to go up to his old dormitory. You know Old Boys can claim that privilege. Yes, I think leetle Crandall minor must bed down there once more."

"Bates Sahib"—a Gunner flung a heavy arm round the Head's neck—"you've got something up your sleeve. Confess! I know that twinkle."

"Can't you see, you cuckoo?" a Submarine Miner interrupted: "Crandall goes up to the dormitory as an object-lesson, for moral effect and so forth. Isn't that true, Head Sahib?"

"It is. You know too much, Purvis. I licked you for that in '79."

"You did, sir, and it's my private belief you chalked the cane."

"N-no. But I've a very straight eye. Perhaps that misled you."

That opened the flood-gates of fresh memories, and they all told tales out of school.

When Crandall minor that was—Lieutenant R. Crandall of an ordinary Indian regiment—arrived from Exeter on the morning of the match, he was cheered along the whole front of the College, for the prefects had repeated the sense of that which the Head had read them in Flint's study. When Prout's house understood that he would claim his Old Boy's right to a bed for one night, Beetle ran into King's house next door and executed a public "gloat" up and down the enemy's big form-room, departing in a haze of ink-pots.

"What d'you take any notice of these rotters for?" said Stalky, playing substitute for the Old Boys, magnificent in black jersey, white knickers, and black stockings. "I talked to *him* up in the dormitory when he was changin'. Pulled his sweater down for him. He's cut about all over the arms—horrid purply ones. He's goin to tell us about it tonight. I asked him to when I was lacin' his boots."

"Well, you *have* got cheek," said Beetle, enviously.

"Slipped out before I thought. But he wasn't a bit angry. He's no end of a chap. I swear I'm going to play up like beans. Tell Turkey!"

The technique of that match belongs to a by-gone age. Scrimmages were tight and enduring; hacking was direct and to the purpose; and around the scrimmage stood the school, crying, "Put down your heads and shove!" Towards the end everybody lost all sense of decency, and mothers of day-boys too close to the touch-line heard language not included in the bills. No one was actually carried off the field, but both sides felt happier when time was called, and Beetle helped Stalky and McTurk into their over-coats. The two had met in the many-legged heart of things, and, as Stalky said, had "done each other proud." As they swaggered woodenly behind the teams—substitutes do not rank as equals of hairy men—they passed a pony-carriage near the wall, and a husky voice cried, "Well played. Oh, played indeed!" It was Stettson major, white-cheeked and hollow-eyed, who had fought his way to the ground under escort of an impatient coachman.

"Hullo, Stettson," said Stalky, checking. "Is it safe to come near you yet?"

"Oh, yes. I'm all right. They wouldn't let me out before, but I had to come to the match. Your mouth looks pretty plummy."

"Turkey trod on it accidental-done-a-purpose. Well, I'm glad you're better, because we owe you something. You and your membranes got us into a sweet mess, young man."

"I heard of that," said the boy, giggling. "The Head told me."

"Dooce he did! When?"

"Oh, come on up to Coll. My shin'll stiffen if we stay jawin' here."

"Shut up, Turkey. I want to find out about this. Well?"

"He was stayin' at our house all the time I was ill."

"What for? Neglectin' the Coll that way? 'Thought he was in town."

"I was off my head, you know, and they said I kept on callin' for him."

"Cheek! You're only a day-boy."

"He came just the same, and he about saved my life. I was all bunged up one night—just goin' to croak, the doctor said—and they stuck a tube or somethin' in my throat, and the Head sucked out the stuff."

"Ugh! 'Shot if *I* would!"

"He ought to have got diphtheria himself, the doctor said. So he stayed on at our house instead of going back. I'd ha' croaked in another twenty minutes, the doctor says."

Here the coachman, being under orders, whipped up and nearly ran over the three.

"My Hat!" said Beetle. "That's pretty average heroic."

"Pretty average!" McTurk's knee in the small of his back cannoned him into Stalky, who punted him back. "You ought to be hung!"

"And the Head ought to get the V.C.," said Stalky. "Why, he might have been dead *and* buried by now. But he wasn't. But he didn't. Ho! ho! He just nipped through the hedge like a lusty old blackbird. Extra-special, five hundred lines, an' gated for a week—all sereno!"

"I've read o' somethin' like that in a book," said Beetle. "Gummy, what a chap! Just think of it!"

"I'm thinking," said McTurk; and he delivered a wild Irish yell that made the team turn round.

"Shut your fat mouth," said Stalky, dancing with impatience. "Leave it to your Uncle Stalky, and he'll have the Head on toast. If you say a word, Beetle, till I give you leave, I swear I'll slay you. *Habeo Capitem crinibus minimis.* I've got him by the short hairs! Now look as if nothing had happened."

There was no need of guile. The school was too busy cheering the drawn match. It hung round the lavatories regardless of muddy boots while the team washed. It cheered Crandall minor whenever it caught sight of him, and it cheered more wildly than ever after prayers, because the Old Boys in evening dress, openly twirling their moustaches, attended, and instead of standing with the masters, ranged themselves along the wall immediately before the prefects; and the Head called them over, too—majors, minors, and tertiuses, after their old names.

"Yes, it's all very fine," he said to his guests after dinner, "but the boys are getting a little out of hand. There will be trouble and sorrow later, I'm afraid. You'd better turn in early, Crandall. The dormitory will be sitting up for you. I don't know to what dizzy heights you may climb in your profession, but I do know you'll never get such absolute adoration as you're getting now."

"Confound the adoration. I want to finish my cigar, sir."

"It's all pure gold. Go where glory waits, Crandall—minor."

The setting of the apotheosis was a ten-bed attic dormitory, communicating through doorless openings with three others. The gas flickered over the raw pine washstands. There was an incessant whistling of draughts, and outside the naked windows the sea beat on the Pebbleridge.

"Same old bed—same old mattress, I believe," said Crandall, yawning. "Same old everything. Oh, but I'm lame! I'd no notion you chaps could play like this." He caressed a battered shin. "You've given us all something to remember you by."

It needed a few minutes to put them at their ease; and, in some way they could not understand, they were more easy when Crandall turned round and said his prayers—a ceremony he had neglected for some years.

"Oh, I *am* sorry. I've forgotten to put out the gas."

"Please don't bother," said the prefect of the dormitory. "Worthington does that."

A nightgowned twelve-year-old, who had been waiting to show off, leaped from his bed to the bracket and back again, by way of a washstand.

"How d'you manage when he's asleep?" said Crandall, chuckling.

"Shove a cold cleek down his neck."

"It was a wet sponge when *I* was junior in the dormitory. . . . Hullo! What's happening?"

The darkness had filled with whispers, the sound of trailing rugs, bare feet on bare boards, protests, giggles, and threats such as:

"Be quiet, you ass! . . . *Squattez-vous* on the floor, then! . . . I swear you aren't going to sit on *my* bed! . . . Mind the tooth-glass," etc.

"Sta—Corkran said," the prefect began, his tone showing his sense of Stalky's insolence, "that perhaps you'd tell us about that business with Duncan's body."

"Yes—yes—yes," ran the keen whispers. "Tell us."

"There's nothing to tell. What on earth are you chaps hoppin' about in the cold for?"

"Never mind us," said the voices. "Tell about Fat-Sow."

So Crandall turned on his pillow and spoke to the generation he could not see.

"Well, about three months ago he was commanding a treasure-guard—a cart full of rupees to pay troops with—five thousand rupees in silver. He was comin' to a place called Fort Pearson, near Kalabagh."

"I was born there," squeaked a small fag. "It was called after my uncle."

"Shut up—you and your uncle! Never mind *him*, Crandall."

"Well, ne'er mind. The Afridis found out that this treasure was on the move, and they ambushed the whole show a couple of miles before he got to the fort, and cut up the escort. Duncan was wounded, and the escort hooked it. There weren't more than twenty Sepoys all told, and there were any amount of Afridis. As things turned out, I was in charge at Fort Pearson. Fact was, I'd heard the firing and was just going to see about it, when Duncan's men came up. So we all turned back together. They told me something about an officer, but I couldn't get the hang of things till I saw a chap under the wheels of the cart out in the open, propped up on one arm, blazing away with a revolver. You see, the escort had abandoned the cart, and the Afridis—they're an awfully suspicious gang—thought the retreat was a trap—sort of draw, you know—and the cart was the bait. So they had left poor old Duncan alone. 'Minute they spotted how few *we* were, it was a race across the flat who should reach old Duncan first. We ran, and they ran, and we won, and after a little hackin' about they pulled off. I never knew it was one of us till I was right on top of him. There are heaps of Duncans in the service and of course the name didn't remind me. He wasn't changed at all hardly. He'd been shot through the lungs, poor old man, and he was pretty thirsty. I gave him a drink and sat down beside him, and—funny thing, too—he said, 'Hullo, Toffee!' and I said, 'Hullo, Fat-Sow! hope you aren't hurt,' or something of the kind. But he died in a minute or two—never lifted his head off my knees. . . . I say, you chaps out there will get your death of cold. Better go to bed."

"All right. In a minute. But your cuts—your cuts. How did you get wounded?"

"That was when we were taking the body back to the Fort. They came on again, and there was a bit of a scrimmage."

"Did you kill any one?"

"Yes. Shouldn't wonder. Good night."

"Good night. Thank you, Crandall. Thanks awf'ly, Crandall. Good night."

The unseen crowds withdrew. His own dormitory rustled into bed and lay silent for a while.

"I say, Crandall"—Stalky's voice was tuned to a wholly foreign reverence.

"Well, what?"

"Suppose a chap found another chap croaking with diphtheria—all bunged up with it—and they stuck a tube in his throat and the chap sucked the stuff out, what would you say?"

"Um," said Crandall, reflectively. "I've only heard of one case, and that was a doctor. He did it for a woman."

"Oh, this wasn't a woman. It was just a boy."

"Makes it all the finer, then. It's about the bravest thing a man can do. Why?"

"Oh, I heard of a chap doin' it. That's all."

"Then he's a brave man."

"Would *you* funk it?"

"Ra-ather. Anybody would. Fancy dying of diphtheria in cold blood."

"Well—ah! Er! Look here!" The sentence ended in a grunt, for Stalky had leaped out of bed and with McTurk was sitting on the head of Beetle, who would have sprung the mine there and then.

Next day, which was the last of the term and given up to a few wholly unimportant examinations, began with wrath and war. Mr. King had discovered that nearly all his house—it lay, as you know, next door but one to Prout's in the long range of buildings—had unlocked the doors between the dormitories and had gone in to listen to a story told by Crandall. He went to the Head, clamorous, injured, appealing; for he never approved of allowing so-called young men of the world to contaminate the morals of boyhood. Very good, said the Head. He would attend to it.

"Well, I'm awf'ly sorry," said Crandall, guiltily. "I don't think I told 'em anything they oughtn't to hear. Don't let them get into trouble on my account."

"Tck!" the Head answered, with the ghost of a wink. "It isn't the boys that make trouble; it's the masters. However, Prout and King don't approve of dormitory gatherings on this scale, and one must back up the housemasters. Moreover, it's hopeless to punish two houses only, so late in the term. We must be fair and include everybody. Let's see. They have a holiday task for the Easters, which, of course, none of them will ever look at. We will give the whole school, except prefects and study-boys, regular prep. tonight; and the Common-room will have to supply a master to take it. We must be fair to all."

"Prep. on the last night of the term. Whew!" said Crandall, thinking of his own wild youth. "I fancy there will be larks."

The school, frolicking among packed trunks, whooping down the corridor, and "gloating" in form-rooms, received the news with amazement and rage. No school in the world did prep. on the last night of the term. This thing was monstrous, tyrannical, subversive of law, religion, and morality. They would go into the form-rooms, and they would take their degraded holiday task with them, but here they smiled and speculated what manner of man the Common-room would send up against them. The lot fell on Mason, credulous and enthusiastic, who loved youth. No other master was anxious to take that "prep.," for the school lacked the steadying influence of tradition; and men accustomed to the ordered routine of ancient foundations found it occasionally insubordinate. The four long form-rooms, in which all below the rank of study-boys worked, received him with thunders of applause. Ere he had coughed twice they favoured him with a metrical summary of the marriage-laws of Great Britain, as recorded by the High Priest of the Israelites and commented on by the leader of the host. The lower forms reminded him that it was the last day, and that therefore he must "take it all in play." When he dashed off to rebuke them, the Lower Fourth and Upper Third began with one accord to be sick, loudly and realistically. Mr. Mason tried, of all vain things under heaven, to argue with them, and a bold soul at a back desk bade him "take fifty lines for not 'olding up 'is 'and before speaking." As one who prided himself upon the precision of his English this cut Mason to the quick, and while he was trying to discover the offender, the Upper and Lower Second, three form-rooms away, turned out the gas and threw ink-pots. It was a pleasant and stimulating "prep." The study-boys and prefects heard the echoes of it far off, and the Common-room at dessert smiled.

Stalky waited, watch in hand, till half-past eight.

"If it goes on much longer the Head will come up," said he. "We'll tell the studies first, and then the form-rooms. Look sharp!"

He allowed no time for Beetle to be dramatic or McTurk to drawl. They poured into study after study, told their tale, and went again so soon as they saw they were understood, waiting for no comment; while the noise of that unholy "prep." grew and deepened. By the door of Flint's study they met Mason flying towards the corridor.

"He's gone to fetch the Head. Hurry up! Come on!"

They broke into Number Twelve form-room abreast and panting.

"The Head! The Head! The Head!" That call stilled the tumult for a minute, and Stalky, leaping to a desk, shouted, "He went and sucked the diphtheria stuff out of Stettson major's throat when we thought he was in town. Stop rotting, you asses! Stettson major would have croaked if the Head hadn't done it. The Head might have died himself. Crandall says it's the bravest thing any livin' man can do, and I"—his voice cracked—"the Head don't know we know!"

McTurk and Beetle, jumping from desk to desk, drove the news home among the junior forms. There was a pause, and then, Mason behind him, the Head entered. It was in the established order of things that no boy should speak or move under his eye. He expected the hush of awe. He was received with cheers—steady, ceaseless cheering. Being a wise man, he went away, and the forms were silent and a little frightened.

"It's all right," said Stalky. "He can't do much. 'Tisn't as if you'd pulled the desks up like we did when old Carleton took prep. once. Keep it up! Hear 'em cheering in the studies!" He rocketed out with a yell, to find Flint and the prefects lifting the roof off the corridor.

When the Head of a limited liability company, paying four per cent., is cheered on his saintly way to prayers, not only by four form-rooms of boys waiting punishment, but by his trusted prefects, he can either ask for an explanation or go his road with dignity, while the senior house-master glares like an excited cat and points out to a white and trembling mathematical master that certain methods—not his, thank God—usually produce certain results. Out of delicacy the Old Boys did not attend that call-over; and it was to the school drawn up in the gymnasium that the Head spoke icily.

"It is not often that I do not understand you; but I confess I do not to-night. Some of you, after your idiotic performances at prep., seem to think me a fit person to cheer. I am going to show you that I am not."

Crash—crash—crash—came the triple cheer that disproved it, and the Head glowered under the gas.

"That is enough. You will gain nothing. The little boys [the Lower School did not like that form of address] will do me three hundred lines apiece in the holidays. I shall take no further notice of them. The Upper School will do me one thousand lines apiece in the holidays, to be shown up the evening of the day they come back. And further—"

"Gummy, what a glutton!" Stalky whispered.

"For your behaviour towards Mr. Mason I intend to lick the whole of the Upper School tomorrow when I give you your journey-money. This will include the three study-boys I found dancing on the form-room desks when I came up. Prefects will stay after call-over."

The school filed out in silence, but gathered in groups by the gymnasium door waiting what might befall.

"And now, Flint," said the Head, "will you be good enough to give me some explanation of your conduct?"

"Well, sir," said Flint, desperately, "if you save a chap's life at the risk of your own when he's dyin' of diphtheria, and the Coll finds it out, wha-what *can* you expect, sir?"

"Um, I see. Then that noise was not meant for—ah, cheek. I can connive at immorality, but I cannot stand impudence. However, it does not excuse their insolence to Mr. Mason. I'll forego the lines this once, remember; but the lickings hold good."

When this news was made public, the school, lost in wonder and admiration, gasped at the Head as he went to his house. Here was a man to be reverenced. On the rare occasions when he caned he did it very scientifically, and the execution of a hundred boys would be epic—immense.

"It's all right, Head Sahib. *We* know," said Crandall, as the Head slipped off his gown with a grunt in his smoking-room. "I found out just now from our substitute. He was gettin' my opinion of your performance last night in the dormitory. I didn't know then that it was you he was talkin' about. Crafty young animal. Freckled chap with eyes—Corkran, I think his name is."

"Oh, I know *him*, thank you," said the Head, and reflectively. "Ye-es, I should have included them even if I hadn't seen 'em."

"If the old Coll weren't a little above themselves already, we'd chair you down the corridor," said the Engineer. "Oh, Bates, how could you? You might have caught it yourself, and where would we have been, then?"

"I always knew you were worth twenty of us any day. Now I'm sure of it," said the Squadron Commander, looking round for contradictions.

"He isn't fit to manage a school, though. Promise you'll never do it again, Bates Sahib. We—we can't go away comfy in our minds if you take these risks," said the Gunner.

"Bates Sahib, you aren't ever goin' to cane the whole Upper School, are you?" said Crandall.

"I can connive at immorality, as I said, but I can't stand impudence. Mason's lot is quite hard enough even when I back him. Besides, the men at the Golf-club heard them singing 'Aaron and Moses.' I shall have complaints about that from the parents of day-boys. Decency must be preserved."

"We're coming to help," said all the guests.

❀   ❀   ✻

The Upper School were caned one after the other, their overcoats over their arms, the brakes waiting in the road below to take them to the station, their journey-money on the table. The Head began with Stalky, McTurk, and Beetle. He dealt faithfully by them.

"And here's your journey-money. Good-by, and pleasant holidays."

"Good-by. Thank you, sir. Good-by."

They shook hands.

"Desire don't outrun performance—*much*—this mornin'. We got the cream of it," said Stalky. "Now wait till a few chaps come out, and we'll really cheer him."

"Don't wait on our account, please," said Crandall, speaking for the Old Boys. "We're going to begin now."

It was very well so long as the cheering was confined to the corridor, but when it spread to the gymnasium, when the boys awaiting their turn cheered, the Head gave it up in despair, and the remnant flung themselves upon him to shake hands.

Then they seriously devoted themselves to cheering till the brakes were hustled off the premises in dumb-show.

"Didn't I say I'd get even with him?" said Stalky on the box-seat, as they swung into the narrow Northam street. "Now all together—takin' time from your Uncle Stalky:

> *"It's a way we have in the Army,*
> *It's a way we have in the Navy,*
> *It's a way we have at the Public Schools,*
> *Which nobody can deny!"*

A Note on Stalky & Co.

ARTHUR CHRISTOPHER BENSON

FEW men are so well qualified to write about school life as ARTHUR CHRISTOPHER BENSON (1862-1925). He was born at Wellington College, England, where his father was then headmaster. He took a degree at King's College, Cambridge, taught at Eton, and for the last decade of his life was a master of Magdalen College, Cambridge. His essays on education are the result of an entire life spent in an academic environment.

The Upton Letters, from which the following essay is taken, is a series of essays on schoolmastering written in the easy, informal style of personal correspondence.

Upton, May 15, 1904.

MY DEAR HERBERT,—You ask if I have read anything lately? Well, I have been reading *Stalky and Co.* with pain, and, I hope, profit. It is an amazing book; the cleverness, the freshness, the incredible originality of it all; the careless ease with which scene after scene is touched off, and a picture brought before one at a glance, simply astounds me, and leaves me gasping. But I don't want now to discourse about the literary merits of the book, great as they are. I want to relieve my mind of the thoughts that disquiet me. I think, to start with, it is not a fair picture of school life at all. If it is really reminiscent,—and the life-likeness and verisimilitude of the book is undeniable,—the school must have been a very peculiar one. In the first place, the interest is concentrated upon a group of very unusual boys. The Firm of Stalky is, I humbly thank God, a combination of boys of a rare species. The other figures of boys in the book form a mere background, and the deeds of the central heroes are depicted like the deeds of the warriors of the *Iliad.* They dart about, slashing and hewing, while the rank and file run hither and thither like sheep, their only use being in the numerical tale of heads that they can afford to the flashing blades of the protagonists; and even so the chief figures, realistic though they are, remind me not so much of spirited pictures as of Gilray's caricatures. They are highly coloured, fantastic, horribly human and yet, somehow, grotesque. Everything is elongated, widened, magnified, exaggerated. The difficulty is, to my mind, to imagine boys so lawless, so unbridled, so fond at intervals of low delights, who are yet so obviously wholesome-minded and manly. I can only humbly say that it is my belief, confirmed by experience, that boys of so unconventional and daring a type would not be content without dipping into darker pleasures. But Kipling is a great magician, and, in reading the book, one can thankfully believe that in this case it was not so; just as one can also believe that, in this particular case, the boys were as mature and shrewd, and of as complete and trenchant a wit as they appear. My own experience here again is that no boys could keep so easily on so high a level of originality and sagacity. The chief characteristic of all the boys I have ever known is that they are so fitful, so unfinished. A clever boy will say incredibly acute things, but among a dreary tract of wonderfully silly ones. The most original boys will have long lapses into conventionality, but the heroes of Kipling's book are never conventional, never ordinary; and then there is an absence of restfulness which is one of the greatest merits of *Tom Brown*.

But what has made the book to me into a kind of Lenten manual is the presentation of the masters. Here I see, portrayed with remorseless fidelity, the faults and foibles of my own class; and I am sorry to say that I feel deliberately, on closing the book, that schoolmastering must be a dingy trade. My better self cries out against this conclusion, and tries feebly to say that it is one of the noblest of professions; and then I think of King and Prout, and all my highest aspirations die away at the thought that I may be even as these.

I suppose that Kipling would reply that he has done full justice to the profession by giving us the figures of the Headmaster and the Chaplain. The Headmaster is obviously a figure which his creator regards with respect. He is fair-minded, human, generous; it is true that he is enveloped with a strange awe and majesty; he moves in a mysterious way, and acts in a most inconsequent and unexpected manner. But he generally has the best of the situation; and though there is little that is pastoral about him, yet he is obviously a wholesome-minded, manly sort of person, who whips the right person at the right time, and generally scores in the end. But he is a Roman father, at best. He has little compassion and no tenderness; he is acute, brisk, and sensible; but he has (at least to me) neither grace nor wisdom; or, if he has, he keeps them under a polished metallic dish-cover, and only lifts it in private. I do not feel that the Headmaster has any religion, except the religion of all sensible men. In seeming to despise all sentiment, Kipling seems to me to throw aside several beautiful flowers, tied carelessly up in the same bundle. There should be a treasure in the heart of a wise schoolmaster; not to be publicly displayed nor drearily recounted; but at the right moment, and in the right way, he ought to be able to show a boy that there are sacred and beautiful things which rule or ought to rule the heart. If the Head has such a treasure, he keeps it at the bank and only visits it in the holidays.

The "Padre" is a very human figure—to me the most attractive in the book; he has some wisdom and tenderness, and his little vanities are very gently touched. But (I dare say I am a very pedantic person) I don't really like his lounging about and smoking in the boys' studies. I think that what he would have called tolerance is rather a deplorable indolence, a desire to be above all things acceptable. He earns his influence by giving his colleagues away, and he seems to me to think more of the honour of the boys than of the honour of the place.

But King and Prout, the two principal masters—it is they who spoil the taste of my food and mingle my drink with ashes. They are, in their way, well-meaning and conscientious men. But is it not possible to love discipline without being a pedant, and to be vigilant without being a sneak? I fear in the back of my heart that Kipling thinks that the trade of a schoolmaster is one which no generous or self-respecting man can adopt. And yet it is a useful and necessary trade; and we should be in a poor way if it came to be regarded as a detestable one. I wish with all my heart that Kipling had used his genius to make our path smoother instead of rougher. The path of the schoolmaster is indeed set round with pitfalls. A man who is an egotist and a bully finds rich pasturage among boys who are bound to listen to him, and over whom he can tyrannise. But, on the other hand, a man who is both brave and sensitive—and there are many such—can learn as well as teach abundance of wholesome lessons, if he comes to his task with some hope and love. King is, of course, a verbose bully; he delights in petty triumphs; he rejoices in making himself felt; he is a cynic as well, a greedy and low-minded man; he takes a disgusting pleasure in detective work; he begins by believing the worst of boys; he is vain, shy, irritable; he is cruel, and likes to see his victim writhe. I have known many schoolmasters, and I have never known a Mr. King, except perhaps at a private school. But even King has done me good; he has confirmed me in my belief that more can be done by courtesy and decent amiability than can ever be done by discipline enforced by hard words. He teaches me not to be pompous, and not to hunger and thirst after finding things out. He makes me feel sure that the object of detection is to help boys to be better, and not to have the satisfaction of punishing them.

Prout is a feeble sentimentalist, with a deep belief in phrases. He is a better fellow than King, and is only an intolerable goose. Both the men make me wish to burst upon the scene, when they are grossly mishandling some simple situation; but while I want to kick King, when he is retreating with dignity, my only desire is to explain to Prout as patiently as I can what an ass he is. He is a perfect instance of absolutely ineffective virtue, a plain dish unseasoned with salt.

There are, of course, other characters in the book, each of them grotesque and contemptible in his own way, each of them a notable example of what not to be. But I would pardon this if the book were not so unjust; if Kipling had included in his gathering of masters one kindly, serious gentleman, whose sense of vocation did not make him a prig. And if he were to reply that the Headmaster fulfills these conditions, I would say that the Headmaster is a prig in this one point, that he is so desperately afraid of priggishness. The manly man to my mind, is the man who does not trouble his head as to whether he is manly or not, not the man who wears clothes too big for him, and heavy boots, treads like an ox, and speaks gruffly; that is a pose, not better or worse than other poses. And what I want in the book is a man of simple and direct character, interested in his work, and not ashamed of his interest; attached to the boys, and not ashamed of seeming to care.

My only consolation is that I have talked to a good many boys who have read the book; they have all been amused, interested, delighted. But they say frankly that the boys are not like any boys they ever knew, and, when I timidly inquire about the masters, they laugh rather sheepishly, and say that they don't know about that.

I am sure that we schoolmasters have many faults; but we are really trying to do better, and, as I said before, I only wish that a man of Kipling's genius had held out to us a helping hand, instead of giving us a push back into the ugly slough of usherdom, out of which many good fellows my friends and colleagues, have, however feebly, been struggling to emerge.— Ever yours,

T. B.

University Days

JAMES THURBER

JAMES THURBER was born in Columbus, Ohio, in 1894. He took a degree at Ohio State University in 1919 after a year out for reading and another for war service. He has had wide newspaper experience, including work on the Columbus Dispatch *and the Paris edition of the* Chicago Tribune. *He has been associated with the* New Yorker *both as contributor and as managing editor.*

The following essay is a fair sample of Thurber's humor. This selection well illustrates his own definition of humor: "Humor is a kind of emotional chaos told about calmly and quietly in retrospect."

I PASSED all the other courses that I took at my University, but I could never pass botany. This was because all botany students had to spend several hours a week in a laboratory looking through a microscope at plant cells, and I could never see through a microscope. I never once saw a cell through a microscope. This used to enrage my instructor. He would wander around the laboratory pleased with the progress all the students were making in drawing the involved and, so I am told, interesting structure of flower cells, until he came to me. I would just be standing there. "I can't see anything," I would say. He would begin patiently enough, explaining how anybody can see through a microscope, but he would always end up in a fury, claiming that I could *too* see through a microscope but just pretended that I couldn't. "It takes away from the beauty of flowers anyway," I used to tell him. "We are not concerned with beauty in this course," he would say. "We are concerned solely with what I may call the *mechanics* of flars." "Well," I'd say, "I can't see anything." "Try it just once again," he'd say, and I would put my eye to the microscope and see nothing at all, except now and again a nebulous milky substance—a phenomenon of maladjustment. You were supposed to see a vivid, restless clockwork of sharply defined plant cells. "I see what looks like a lot of milk," I would tell him. This, he claimed, was the result of my not having adjusted the microscope properly, so he would readjust it for me, or rather, for himself. And I would look again and see milk.

I finally took a deferred pass, as they called it, and waited a year and tried

"University Days" is from *My Life and Hard Times*, by James Thurber; copyright, 1933, by James Thurber; reprinted by permission of Harper & Brothers and of the author.

again. (You had to pass one of the biological sciences or you couldn't graduate.) The professor had come back from vacation brown as a berry, bright-eyed, and eager to explain cell-structure again to his classes. "Well," he said to me, cheerily, when we met in the first laboratory hour of the semester, "we're going to see cells this time, aren't we?" "Yes, sir," I said. Students to right of me and to left of me and in front of me were seeing cells; what's more, they were quietly drawing pictures of them in their notebooks. Of course, I didn't see anything.

"We'll try it," the professor said to me, grimly, "with every adjustment of the microscope known to man. As God is my witness, I'll arrange this glass so that you see cells through it or I'll give up teaching. In twenty-two years of botany, I—" He cut off abruptly for he was beginning to quiver all over, like Lionel Barrymore, and he genuinely wished to hold onto his temper; his scenes with me had taken a great deal out of him.

So we tried it with every adjustment of the microscope known to man. With only one of them did I see anything but blackness or the familiar lacteal opacity, and that time I saw, to my pleasure and amazement, a variegated constellation of flecks, specks, and dots. These I hastily drew. The instructor, noting my activity, came back from an adjoining desk, a smile on his lips and his eyebrows high in hope. He looked at my cell drawing. "What's that?" he demanded, with a hint of a squeal in his voice. "That's what I saw," I said. "You didn't, you didn't, you *didn't*!" he screamed, losing control of his temper instantly, and he bent over and squinted into the microscope. His head snapped up. "That's your eye!" he shouted. "You've fixed the lens so that it reflects! You've drawn your eye!"

Another course that I didn't like, but somehow managed to pass, was economics. I went to that class straight from the botany class, which didn't help me any in understanding either subject. I used to get them mixed up. But not as mixed up as another student in my economics class who came there direct from a physics laboratory. He was a tackle on the football team, named Bolenciecwcz. At that time Ohio State University had one of the best football teams in the country, and Bolenciecwcz was one of its outstanding stars. In order to be eligible to play it was necessary for him to keep up in his studies, a very difficult matter, for while he was not dumber than an ox he was not any smarter. Most of his professors were lenient and helped him along. None gave him more hints, in answering questions, or asked him simpler ones than the economics professor, a thin timid man named Bassum. One day when we were on the subject of transportation and distribution, it came Bolenciecwcz's turn to answer a question. "Name one means of transportation," the professor said to him. No light came into the big tackle's eyes. "Just any means of transportation," said the professor. Bolenciecwcz sat staring at him. "That is," pursued the professor, "any medium, agency, or method of going from one place to another." Bolenciecwcz had the look of a man who is being led into a trap. "You may choose among steam, horse-drawn, or electrically propelled vehicles," said the instructor. "I might suggest the one which we commonly take in making long journeys across land." There was a profound silence in which everybody stirred uneasily, including Bolenciecwcz and Mr. Bassum. Mr. Bassum abruptly broke this silence in an amazing manner. "Choo-choo-choo," he said, in a low voice, and turned instantly scarlet. He glanced appealingly around the room. All of us, of course, shared Mr. Bassum's desire that Bolenciecwcz should stay abreast of the class in economics, for the Illinois game, one of the hardest and most important of the season, was only a week off. "Toot, toot, too-toooooot!" some student with a deep voice moaned, and we all looked encouragingly at Bolenciecwcz. Somebody else gave a fine imitation of a locomotive letting off steam. Mr. Bassum himself rounded off the little show. "Ding, dong, ding, dong," he said, hopefully. Bolenciecwcz was staring at the floor now, trying to think, his great brow furrowed, his huge hands rubbing together, his face red.

"How did you come to college this year, Mr. Bolenciecwcz?" asked the professor. "*Chuf*fa chuffa, *chuf*fa chuffa."

"M'father sent me," said the football player.

"What on?" asked Bassum.

"I git an 'lowance," said the tackle, in a low, husky voice, obviously embarrassed.

"No, no," said Bassum. "Name a means of transportation. What did you *ride* here on?"

"Train," said Bolenciecwcz.

"Quite right," said the professor. "Now, Mr. Nugent, will you tell us—"

If I went through anguish in botany and economics—for different reasons—gymnasium work was even worse. I don't even like to think about it. They wouldn't let you play games or join in the exercises with your glasses on and I couldn't see with mine off. I bumped into professors, horizontal bars, agricultural students, and swinging iron rings. Not being able to see, I could take it but I couldn't dish it out. Also, in order to pass gymnasium (and you had to pass it to graduate) you had to learn to swim if you didn't know how. I didn't like the swimming pool, I didn't like swimming, and I didn't like the swimming instructor, and after all these years I still don't. I never swam but I passed my gym work anyway, by having another student give my gymnasium number (978) and swim across the pool in my place. He was a quiet, amiable blonde youth, number 473, and he would have seen through a microscope for me if we could have got away with it, but we couldn't get away with it. Another thing I didn't like about gymnasium work was that they made you strip the day you registered. It is impossible for me to be happy when I am stripped and being asked a lot of questions. Still, I did better than a lanky agricultural student who was cross-examined just before I was. They asked each student what college he was in—that is, whether Arts, Engineering, Commerce, or

Agriculture. "What college are you in?" the instructor snapped at the youth in front of me. "Ohio State University," he said promptly.

It wasn't that agricultural student but it was another a whole lot like him who decided to take up journalism, possibly on the ground that when farming went to hell he could fall back on newspaper work. He didn't realize, of course, that that would be very much like falling back full-length on a kit of carpenter's tools. Haskins didn't seem cut out for journalism, being too embarrassed to talk to anybody and unable to use a typewriter, but the editor of the college paper assigned him to the cow barns, the sheep house, the horse pavilion, and the animal husbandry department generally. This was a genuinely big "beat," for it took up five times as much ground and got ten times as great a legislative appropriation as the College of Liberal Arts. The agricultural student knew animals, but nevertheless his stories were dull and colorlessly written. He took all afternoon on each of them, on account of having to hunt for each letter on the typewriter. Once in a while he had to ask somebody to help him hunt. "C" and "L," in particular, were hard letters for him to find. His editor finally got pretty much annoyed at the farmer-journalist because his pieces were so uninteresting. "See here, Haskins," he snapped at him one day, "why is it we never have anything hot from you on the horse pavilion? Here we have two hundred head of horses on this campus—more than any other university in the Western Conference except Purdue—and yet you never get any real low down on them. Now shoot over to the horse barns and dig up something lively." Haskins shambled out and came back in about an hour: he said he had something. "Well, start it off snappily," said the editor. "Something people will read." Haskins set to work and in a couple of hours brought a sheet of typewritten paper to the desk; it was a two-hundred word story about some disease that had broken out among the horses. Its opening sentence was simple but arresting. It read: "Who has noticed the sores on the tops of the horses in the animal husbandry building?"

Ohio State was a land grant university and therefore two years of military drill was compulsory. We drilled with old Springfield rifles and studied the tactics of the Civil War even though the World War was going on at the time. At 11 o'clock each morning thousands of freshmen and sophomores used to deploy over the campus, moodily creeping up on the old chemistry building. It was good training for the kind of warfare that was waged at Shiloh but it had no connection with what was going on in Europe. Some people used to think there was German money behind it, but they didn't dare say so or they would have been thrown in jail as German spies. It was a period of muddy thought and marked, I believe, the decline of higher education in the Middle West.

As a soldier I was never any good at all. Most of the cadets were glumly indifferent soldiers, but I was no good at all. Once General Littlefield, who was commandant of the cadet corps, popped up in front of me during regimental drill and snapped, "You are the main trouble with this university!" I think he meant that my type was the main trouble with the university but he may have meant me individually. I was mediocre at drill, certainly— that is, until my senior year. By that time I had drilled longer than anybody else in the Western Conference, having failed at military at the end of each preceding year so that I had to do it all over again. I was the only senior still in uniform. The uniform which, when new, had made me look like an interurban railway conductor, now that it had become faded and too tight made me look like Bert Williams in his bellboy act. This had a definitely bad effect on my morale. Even so, I had become by sheer practise little short of wonderful at squad manoeuvres.

One day General Littlefield picked our company out of the whole regiment and tried to get it mixed up by putting it through one movement after another as fast as we could execute them: squads right, squads left, squads on right into line, squads right about, squads left front into line, etc. In about three minutes one hundred and nine men were marching in one direction and I was marching away from them at an angle of forty degrees, all alone. "Company, halt!" shouted General Littlefield, "That man is the only man who has it right!" I was made a corporal for my achievement.

The next day General Littlefield summoned me to his office. He was swatting flies when I went in. I was silent and he was silent too, for a long time. I don't think he remembered me or why he had sent for me, but he didn't want to admit it. He swatted some more flies, keeping his eyes on them narrowly before he let go with the swatter. "Button up your coat!" he snapped. Looking back on it now I can see that he meant me although he was looking at a fly, but I just stood there. Another fly came to rest on a paper in front of the general and began rubbing its hind legs together. The general lifted the swatter cautiously. I moved restlessly and the fly flew away. "You startled him!" barked General Littlefield, looking at me severely. I said I was sorry. "That won't help the situation!" snapped the General, with cold military logic. I didn't see what I could do except offer to chase some more flies toward his desk, but I didn't say anything. He stared out the window at the faraway figures of co-eds crossing the campus toward the library. Finally, he told me I could go. So I went. He either didn't know which cadet I was or else he forgot what he wanted to see me about. It may have been that he wished to apologize for having called me the main trouble with the university; or maybe he had decided to compliment me on my brilliant drilling of the day before and then at the last minute decided not to. I don't know. I don't think about it much any more.

The District School

CLARENCE S. DARROW

WELL known for his defense of labor organizations and for his skill as a criminal lawyer, Ohio-born CLARENCE S. DARROW (1857-1938) has told the story of his youth in Ohio in Farmington, *the autobiography from which* "The District School," "The School Readers" *and* "The Last Day of School" *are taken.*

THE first school that I remember was not in the little town near which we lived, but about half a mile away in the opposite direction. Our house must have stood just outside the limits of the little village; at any rate, I was sent to the country school. Every morning we children were given a dinner-pail packed full of pie and cake, and now and then a piece of bread and butter (which I always let the other children eat), and were sent off to school. As we passed along the road we were joined by other little boys and girls, and by the time we reached the building our party contained nearly all the children on the road travelling in the direction from which we came. We were a boisterous, thoughtless crowd,—that is, the boys; the girls were generally quieter and more reserved, which we called "proud."

Almost as soon as the snow was off the ground in the spring, we boys took off our shoes (or, rather, boots) and went barefooted to the school. It was hard for us to wait until our parents said the ground was warm enough for us to take off our boots; we felt so light and free, and could run so fast barefooted, that we always begged our mother to let us leave them off at the very earliest chance. The chief disadvantage was that we often stubbed our toes. This was sometimes serious, when we were running fast and would bring them full tilt against a stone. Most of the time we managed to have one or more toes tied up in rags; and we always found considerable occupation in comparing our wounds, to see whose were the worst, or which were getting well the fastest. The next most serious trouble connected with going barefoot was the necessity for washing our feet every night before we went to bed. This seemed a grievous hardship; sometimes we would forget it, when we could, and I remember now and then being called up out of bed after I thought I had safely escaped and

Farmington, by Clarence S. Darrow; reprinted by permission of Charles Scribner's Sons.

seemed to be sound asleep, and when my feet were clean enough without being washed.

It seemed to us children that our mother was unreasonably particular about this matter of washing our feet before we went to bed. She always required it when we had been barefoot through the day, even though it had been raining and we had wiped our feet in the grass. Still the trouble of washing our feet was partly compensated by our not being obliged to put on or take off our stockings and our boots. This was a great relief, especially in the morning; for this part of our toilet took longer than all the rest, and when the time came around to go barefoot we had only to get up and jump into a few clothes and start away.

In the summer-time it took a long while for us children to travel the short half-mile to the district school. No matter how early we left home, it was nearly always past the hour of nine when we reached the door. For there were always birds in the trees and stones in the road, and no child ever knew any pain except his own. There were little fishes in the creek over which we slid in winter and through which we always waded in the summer-time; then there were chipmunks on the fences and woodchucks in the fields, and no boy could ever manage to go straight to school, or straight back home after the day was done. The procession of barefoot urchins laughed and joked, and fought, and ran, and bragged, and gave no thought to study or to books until the bell was rung and they were safely seated in the room. Then we watched and waited eagerly for recess; and after that, still more anxiously for the hour of noon, which was always the best time by far of all the day, not alone because of the pie and cake and apples and cheese which the more prudent and obedient of us saved until this time, but also because of the games, in which we always had enough boys to go around.

In these games the girls did not join to any great extent; in fact, girls seemed of little use to the urchins who claimed everything as their own. In the school they were always seated by themselves on one side of the room, and sometimes when we failed to study as we should we were made to go and sit with them. This was when we were very young. As we grew older, this form of punishment seemed less and less severe, until some other was substituted in its stead. Most of the boys were really rather bashful with the girls,—those who bragged the loudest and fought the readiest somehow never knew just what to say when they were near. We preferred rather to sit and look at them, and wonder how they could be so neat and clean and well "fixed up." I remember when quite a small boy how I used to look over toward their side of the room, especially at a little girl with golden hair that was always hanging in long curls about her head; and it seemed to me then that nothing could ever be quite so beautiful as this curly head; which may explain the fact that all my life nothing has seemed quite so beguiling as golden hair—unless it were black, or brown, or some other kind.

To the boys, school had its chief value, in fact its only value, in its games and sports. Of course our parents and teachers were always urging us to work. In their efforts to make us study, they resorted to every sort of means—headmarks, presents, praise, flattery, Christmas cards, staying in at recess, staying after school, corporal punishment, all sorts of persuasion, threats, and even main force—to accomplish this result. No like rewards or punishments were required to make us play; which fact, it seems to me, should have shown our teachers and parents that play, exercise, activity, and change are the law of life, especially the life of a little child; and that study, as we knew it, was unnatural and wrong. Still, nothing of this sort ever dawned upon their minds.

I cannot remember much real kindness between the children of the school; while we had our special chums, we never seemed to care for them, except that boys did not like to be alone. There were few things a boy could do alone, excepting tasks, which of course we avoided if we could. On our way to and from the school, or while together at recess and noon, while we played the ordinary games a very small matter brought on a quarrel, and we always seemed to be watching for a chance to fight. In the matter of our quarrels and fights we showed the greatest impartiality, as boys do in almost all affairs of life.

While our books were filled with noble precepts, we never seemed to remember them when we got out of doors, or even to think that they had any application to our lives. In this respect the boy and the grown-up man seem wonderfully alike.

But really, school was not all play. Our teachers and parents tried their best to make us learn,—that is, to make us learn the lessons in the books. The outside lessons we always seemed to get without their help,—in fact, in spite of their best endeavors to prevent our knowing what they meant.

The fact that our teachers tried so hard to make us learn was no doubt one of the chief reasons why we looked on them as our natural enemies. We seldom had the same teacher for two terms of school, and we always wondered whether the new one would be worse or better than the old. We always started in prepared to find her worse; and the first kind words we ever had for our teacher were spoken after she was gone and we compared her with the new one in her place. Our teachers seemed to treat us pretty well for the first few days. They were then very kind and sweet; they hardly ever brought switches to the school until the second week, but we were always sure that they would be called into service early in the term. No old-time teacher would have dreamed that she could get through a term of school without a whip, any more than a judge would believe that society could get along without a jail. The methods that were used to make us learn, and the things we were taught, seem very absurd as I look back upon them now; and still, I presume, they were not different from the means employed to-day.

Most of us boys could learn arithmetic fairly well,—in this, indeed, we always beat the girls. Still, some parts of arithmetic were harder than the rest. I remember that I mastered the multiplication-table up to "twelve times twelve," backwards and forwards and every other way, at a very early age, and I fancy that this knowledge has clung to me through life; but I cannot forget the many weary hours I spent trying to learn the tables of weights and measures, and how much vexation of spirit I endured before my task was done. However, after weary weeks and months I learned them so well that I could say them with the greatest ease. This was many, many years ago; since that time I have found my place in the world of active life, but I cannot now remember that even once have I had occasion to know or care about the difference between "Troy weight" and "Apothecaries' weight," if, in fact, there was any difference at all. And one day, last week I think it was, for the first time in all these endless years I wished to know how many square rods made an acre, and I tried to call back the table that I learned so long ago at school; but as to this my mind was an utter blank, and all that I could do was to see the little girl with the golden locks sitting at her desk—and, by the way, I wonder where she is to-day. But I took a dictionary from the shelf, and there I found it plain and straight, and I made no effort to keep it in my mind, knowing that if perchance in the uncertain years that may be yet to come I may need to know again, I shall find it there in the dictionary safe and sound.

And all those examples that I learned to cipher out! I am sure I know more to-day than the flaxen-haired barefoot boy who used to sit at his little desk at school and only drop his nibbled slate-pencil to drive the flies away from his long bare legs, but I could not do those sums to-day even if one of my old-time teachers should come back from her long-forgotten grave and threaten to keep me in for the rest of my life unless I got the answer right.

And then the geography! How hard they tried to make us learn this book, and how many recesses were denied us because we were not sure just which river in Siberia was the longest! Of course we knew nothing about Siberia, or whether the rivers ran water or blood; but we were forced to know which was the largest and just how long it was. And so all over the great round world we travelled, to find cities, towns, rivers, mountain ranges, peninsulas, oceans, and bays. How important it all was! I remember that one of the ways they took to make us learn this book was to have us sing geography in a chorus of little voices. I can recall to-day how one of those old tunes began, but I remember little beyond the start. The song was about the capitals of all the States, and it began, "State of Maine, Augusta, is on the Kennebec River," and so on through the whole thirty-three or four, or whatever the number was when I was a little child. Well, many, many years have passed away since then, and I have wandered far and wide from my old-time country home. There are few places in the United States that I have not seen, in my quest for activity and change. I have even stood on some of the highest peaks of the Alps, and looked down upon its quiet valleys and its lovely lakes; but I have never yet been to Augusta on the Kennebec River in the State of Maine, and it begins to look as if I never should. Still, if Fortune ever takes me there, I shall be very glad that I learned when yet a child at school that Augusta was the capital of Maine and on the Kennebec River. So, too, I have never been to Siberia, and, not being a Russian, I presume that I shall never go. And in fact, wherever I have wandered on the earth I have had to learn my geography all over new again.

But, really, grammar made me more trouble than any other study. Somehow I never could learn grammar, and it always made me angry when I tried. My parents and teachers told me that I could never write or speak unless I learned grammar, and so I tried and tried, but even now I can hardly tell an adverb from an adjective, and I do not know that I care. When a little boy, I used to think that if I really had anything to tell I could make myself understood; and I think so still. The longer I live the surer I am that the chief difficulty of writers and speakers is the lack of interesting thoughts, and not of proper words. Certainly grammar was a hideous nightmare to me when a child at school. Of all the parts of speech the verb was the most impossible to get. I remember now how difficult it was to conjugate the verb "to love," which the books seemed always to put first. How I stumbled and blundered as I tried to learn that verb! I might possibly have mastered the present tense, but when it came to all the different moods and various tenses it became a hopeless task. I am much older now, but somehow that verb has never grown easier with the fleeting years. The past-perfect tense has always been well-nigh impossible to learn. I never could tell when it left off, or whether it ever left off or not. Neither have I been able to keep it separate from the present, or, for that matter, from the future. A few years after the district school, I went for a brief time to the Academy on the hill, where I studied Latin; and I remember that this same verb was there, with all the old complications and many that were new, to greet me when I came. To be sure, it had been changed to "Amo, Amas, Amat," but it was the old verb just the same, and its various moods and tenses caused me the same trouble that I had experienced as a little child. My worry over this word has made me wonder whether this verb, in all its moods and tenses, was not one of the many causes of the downfall of the Roman Republic, of which we used to hear so much. At any rate, I long since ceased trying to get it straight or keep it straight; indeed, I am quite sure that it was designed only to tangle and ensnare.

The School Readers

IF we scholars did not grow up to be exemplary men and women, it surely was not the fault of our teachers or our parents,—or of the school-book publishers.

When I look back to those lessons that we learned, I marvel that I ever wandered from the straight path in the smallest possible degree. Whether we were learning to read or write, studying grammar or composition, in whatever book we chanced to take, there was the moral precept plain on every page. Our many transgressions could have come only from the fact that we really did not know what these lessons meant; and doubtless our teachers also never thought they had any sort of relation to our lives.

How these books were crammed with noble thoughts! In them every virtue was extolled and every vice condemned. I wonder now how the book publishers could ever have printed such tales, or how they reconciled themselves to the hypocrisy they must have felt when they sold the books.

This moral instruction concerned certain general themes. First of all, temperance was the great lesson taught. I well remember that we children believed that the first taste of liquor was the fatal one; and we never even considered that one drop could be taken without leading us to everlasting ruin and despair. There were the alms-house, the jail, and the penitentiary square, in front of every child who even considered taking the first drink; while all the rewards of this world and the next were freely promised to the noble lad who should resist.

As I look back to-day, it seems as if every moral lesson in the universe must have grown into my being from those books. How could I have ever wandered from the narrow path? I look back to those little freckled, trifling boys and girls, and I hear them read their lessons in their books so long ago. The stories were all the same, from the beginning to the end. We began in the primer, and our instruction in reading and good conduct did not end until the covers of the last book were closed.

It seems to me today that I can hear those little urchins reading about the idle lazy boy who tried to get the bee and the cow and the horse to play with him,—though what he wanted of the bee I could never understand,—but they were all too busy with their work, and so he ran away from school and had a most miserable day alone. How could we children ever stay away from school after we had read this lesson? And yet, I cannot now recall that it made us love our books, or think one whit less of the free breeze, the waving grass and trees, or the alluring coaxing sun.

We were taught by our books that we must on all accounts speak the truth; that we must learn our lessons; that we must love our parents and our teachers; must enjoy work; must be generous and kind; must despise riches; must avoid ambition; and then, if we did all these things, some fairy godmother would come along at just the darkest hour and give us everything our hearts desired. Not one story in the book told how any good could ever come from wilfulness, or selfishness, or greed, or that any possible evil ever grew from thrift, or diligence, or generosity, or kindness. And yet, in spite of all these precepts, we were young savages, always grasping for the best, ever fighting and scheming to get the advantage of our playmates, our teachers, and our tasks.

A quarter of a century seems not to have wrought much change; we still believe in the old moral precepts, and teach them to others, but we still strive to get the best of everything for ourselves.

I wonder if the old school-readers have been changed since I was a boy at school. Are the same lessons there to-day? We were such striking examples of what the books would not do that one would almost think the publishers would drop the lessons out.

I try to recall the feelings of one child who read those stories in the little white schoolhouse by the country road. What did they mean to me? Did I laugh at them, as I do to-day? Or did I really think that they were true, and try and try, and then fail in all I tried, as I do now? I presume the latter was the case; yet for my life I cannot recall the thoughts and feelings that these stories brought to me. But I can still recall the stories.

I remember, as if it were yesterday, the story about the poor widow of Pine Cottage, in the winter, with her five ragged children hovering around her little table. Widows usually had large families then, and most of their boys were lame. This poor widow had at last reached the point where starvation faced her little brood. She had tasted no food for twenty-four hours. Her one small herring was roasting on the dying coals. The prospect was certainly very dark; but she had faith, and somehow felt that in the end she would come out all right. A knock is heard at the back door. A ragged stranger enters and asks for food; the poor widow looks at her five starving children, and then she gives the visitor the one last herring; · he eats it, and lo and behold! the stranger is her long-lost son,—probably one that was left over from the time when she was a widow before. The long-lost son came in this disguise to find out whether or not his mother really loved him. He was, in fact, rich; but he had borrowed the rags at the tavern, and had just arrived from India with a shipload of gold, which he at once divided among his mother and brothers and sisters. How could any child fail to be generous after this? And yet I venture to say that if any of us took a herring to school for dinner the day that we read this story in our class, we clung to it as tenaciously as a miser to his gold.

Then there was the widow with her one lame son, who asks the rich merchant for a little charity. He listens to her pathetic story, and believes she tells the truth. He asks her how much she needs. She tells him that five dollars will be enough. He writes a check, and tells her to go across the street to the bank. She takes it over without reading it. The banker counts out fifty dollars. She says, "There is a mistake; I only asked for five dollars." The banker goes across the street to find out the truth, and the merchant says: "Yes, there was a mistake, I should have made it five hundred,"—which he straightway does. Thus honesty and virtue are rewarded once again. I have lived many years and travelled in many lands, and have seen more or less of human nature and of suffering and greed; I have seen many poor widows,—but have never yet come across the generous merchant.

There was no end to the good diligent boys and girls of whom the readers told; they were on every page we turned, and every one of them received his or her reward and received it right away in cash. There never was the slightest excuse or need for us to be anything but diligent and kind,—and still our young hearts were so perverse and hard that we let the lessons pass unheeded, and clutched at the smallest piece of pie or cake, or the slightest opportunity to deceive some good kind teacher, although we must have known that we missed a golden chance to become President of the United States and have money in the bank besides.

One story of a contented boy stands out so clearly in my mind that I could not refrain from hunting up the old schoolbook and reading it once more. It must have made a wonderful impression on my mind, for there it is, "The Contented Boy." I cannot recall that I ever was contented in my life, and I am sure that I have never seen a boy like this one in the reader; but it is not possible that I knew my schoolbooks were clumsy, stupid lies. After all this time there is the story, clear and distinct; and this is the way it runs:

THE CONTENTED BOY

Mr. Lenox was riding by himself. He got off from his horse to look at something on the roadside. The horse broke away from him and ran off. Mr. Lenox ran after him, but could not catch him.

A little boy at work in a field, near the road, heard the horse. As soon as he saw him running from his master, the boy ran very quickly to the middle of the road, and catching the horse by the bridle, stopped him till Mr. Lenox came up.

Mr. Lenox. Thank you, my good boy. What shall I give you for your trouble?

Boy. I want nothing, sir.

Mr. L. You want nothing? Few men can say as much. But what were you doing in the field?

Boy. I was rooting up weeds, and tending the sheep that were feeding on turnips.

Mr. L. Do you like to work?

Boy. Yes, sir, very well, this fine weather.

Mr. L. But would you not rather play?

Boy. This is not hard work. It is almost as good as play.

Mr. L. Who set you to work?

Boy. My father, sir.

Mr. L. What is your name?

Boy. Peter Hurdle, sir.

Mr. L. How old are you?

Boy. Eight years old next June.

Mr. L. How long have you been here?

Boy. Ever since six o'clock this morning.

Mr. L. Are you not hungry?

Boy. Yes, sir, but I shall go to dinner soon.

Mr. L. If you had a dime now, what would you do with it?

Boy. I don't know, sir. I never had so much.

Mr. L. Have you no playthings?

Boy. Playthings? What are they?

Mr. L. Such things as ninepins, marbles, tops, and wooden horses.

Boy. No, sir. Tom and I play at football in winter, and I have a jumping-rope. I had a hoop, but it is broken.

Mr. L. Do you want nothing else?

Boy. I have hardly time to play with what I have.

Mr. L. You could get apples and cakes if you had money, you know.

Boy. I can have apples at home. As for cake, I don't want that. My mother makes me a pie now and then, which is as good.

Mr. L. Would you not like a knife to cut sticks?

Boy. I have one. Here it is. Brother Tom gave it to me.

Mr. L. Your shoes are full of holes. Don't you want a new pair?

Boy. I have a better pair for Sundays.

Mr. L. But these let in water.

Boy. I do not mind that, sir.

Mr. L. Your hat is all torn, too.

Boy. I have a better one at home.

Mr. L. What do you do if you are hungry before it is time to go home?

Boy. I sometimes eat a raw turnip.

Mr. L. But if there are none?

Boy. Then I do as well as I can without. I work on and never think of it.

Mr. L. I am glad to see that you are so contented. Were you ever at school?

Boy. No, sir. But father means to send me next winter.

Mr. L. You will want books then.

Boy. Yes, sir; each boy has a spelling-book, a reader, and a Testament.

Mr. L. Then I will give them to you. Tell your father so, and that it is because you are an obliging, contented little boy.

Boy. I will, sir. Thank you.

Mr. L. Good-bye, Peter.

Boy. Good-morning, sir.

One other story that has seemed particularly to impress itself upon my mind was about two boys, one named James and the other named John. I believe that these were their names, though possibly one was William and the other Henry. Anyhow, their uncle gave them each a parcel of books. James took out his pocket-knife and cut the fine whipcord that bound his package, but John slowly and patiently untied his string and then rolled it into a nice little ball (the way a nice little boy would do) and carefully put it in his pocket. Some years after, there was a great shooting tournament, and James and John were both there with their bows and arrows; it was late in the game, and so far it was a tie. James seized his last arrow and bent his bow; the string broke and the prize was lost. The book does not tell us that in this emergency John offered his extra piece of whipcord to his brother; instead, the model prudent brother took up his last arrow, bent his bow, when, lo and behold! his string broke too; whereupon John reached into his pocket and pulled out the identical cord that he had untied so long ago, put it on the bow, and of course won the prize!

That miserable story must have cost me several years of valuable time, for ever since I first read it I have always tried to untie every knot that I could find; and although I have ever carefully tucked away all sorts of odd strings into my pockets, I never attended a shooting-match or won a prize in all my life.

One great beauty of the lessons which our school readers taught was the directness and certainty and promptness of the payment that came as a reward of good conduct. Then, too, the recompense was in no way uncertain or ethereal, but was always paid in cash, or something just as material and good. Neither was any combination of circumstances too remote or troublesome or impossible to be brought about. Everything in the universe seemed always ready to conspire to reward virtue and punish vice.

I well remember one story which thus clearly proved that good deeds must be rewarded, and that however great the trouble, the payment would not be postponed even for a day.

It seems that a good boy named Henry—I believe the book did not give his other name—started out one morning to walk about five miles away to do an errand for his sick father. I think it was his father, though it may possibly have been his mother or grandmother. Well, Henry had only got fairly started on his journey when he met a half-starved dog; and thereupon the boy shared with the dog the dinner that he was carrying in his little basket. Of course I know now that, however great his kindness, he could not have relieved the dog unless he had happened to be carrying his dinner in a little basket; but my childish mind was not subtle enough to comprehend it then. After relieving the dog, Henry went on his way with a lighter heart and a lighter basket. Soon he came upon a sick horse lying upon the ground. Henry feared that if he stayed to doctor the horse he would not get home until after dark; but this made no sort of difference to him, so he pulled some grass and took it to the horse, and then went to the river and got some water in his hat (it must have been a Panama) and gave this to the horse to drink, and having done his duty went on his way. He had gone only a short distance farther when he saw a blind man standing in a pond of water. (How the blind man got into the pond of water the story does not tell,—the business of the story was not getting him in but getting him out.) Thereupon little Henry waded into the pond and led the blind man to the shore. Any other boy would simply have

called out to the man, and let him come ashore himself. Of course, if
Henry had been a bad boy, and his name had been Tom, he would have
been found leading the blind man into the pond instead of out, and then
of course he (Tom) would have taken pneumonia and died.

But Henry's adventures did not end here. He had gone only a little way
farther when he met a poor cripple, who had been fighting in some war
and who was therefore a hero, and this cripple was very hungry. Henry
promptly gave him all the dinner he had saved from his interview with
the dog; and having finished this further act of charity, he at last hurried
on to do his errand. But he had worked so long in the Good Samaritan
business that by the time he started home it began to get dark. Then, of
course, he soon reached a great forest, which added to his troubles. After
wandering about for a long time in the darkness and the woods, he sat
down in hunger and despair. Thereupon his old friend the dog came into
the wood and up to the tree where Henry sat, and he found that the dog
carried some bread and meat nicely pinned up in a napkin in payment for
the breakfast given him in the morning. How the dog had managed to
pin the napkin, the story does not tell. After eating his supper, Henry got
up and wandered farther into the woods. He was just despairing a second
time, when by the light of the moon he saw the horse that he had fed in
the morning. The horse took him on his back and carried him out of the
wood; but the poor boy's troubles were not yet done. He was passing along
a lane, when two robbers seized him and began stripping off his clothes;
then the dog came up and bit one robber, who thereupon left Henry and
ran after the dog (presumably so that he might get bitten again), and
just then some one shouted from the hedge and scared the other robber
off. Henry looked toward the hedge in the darkness, and, behold! there
was the crippled soldier riding on the back of the blind man,—and in this
way they had all come together to save Henry and pay him for being such
a good little boy.

When such efforts as these could be put forth for the instant reward of
virtue, where was there a possible inducement left to tempt the most wayward child to sin?

Not only good conduct, but religion, was taught to us children in
the same direct and simple way. Nothing seemed to pay better than
Sabbath observance, according to the strict rules that obtained when I was
young.

I remember the story of a barber who was doing a "thriving business"
in an English city. He was obliged to shave his customers on Sunday
morning (possibly in order that they might look well at church). However, one Sunday the barber went to church himself; and, as it so happened, the minister that day preached a sermon about Sabbath observance. This made so deep an impression on the barber's mind that he
straightway refused to do any more shaving on Sunday. Thereupon
he was obliged to close his shop in the aristocratic neighborhood where he

had lived, and rent a basement amongst the working people who did not go to church and hence had no need of a Sunday shave.

One Saturday night a "pious lawyer" came to town and inquired in great haste where he could find a barber-shop, and was directed to this basement for a shave. The "pious lawyer" told the barber that he must have his work done that night, as he would not be shaved on the Sabbath day. This at once impressed the barber, who was then so poor that he was obliged to borrow a halfpenny from his customer for a candle before he could give him the shave. When the "pious lawyer" learned of the barber's straits, and what had been the cause, he was so deeply moved that he gave him a half-crown, and asked his name. The barber promptly answered that it was William Reed. At this the lawyer opened his eyes,—doubtless through professional instinct,—and asked from what part of the country the barber had come. When he answered, from Kingston, near Taunton, the lawyer's eyes were opened wider still. Then he asked the name of the barber's father, and if he had other relatives. The barber told his father's name, and said that he once had an "Uncle James," who had gone to India many years before and had not been heard from since. Then the "pious lawyer" answered: "If this is true, I have glorious news for you. Your uncle is dead, and he has left a fortune which comes to you." It is needless to add that the barber got the money,—and of course the death of the uncle and the good luck of the nephew were entirely due to the fact that the barber would not shave a customer on the Sabbath day.

Well, those were marvellous tales on which our young minds fed. I wonder now which is the more real,—the world outside as it seemed to us in our young school-days, or that same enchanted land our childhood knew, as we look back upon the scene through the gathering haze that the fleeting years have left before our eyes!

The Last Day of School

SCHOOL had at least two days that made us as happy as children could well be. One was the first day of the term, and the other was the last. Anxious days and weeks and much nervous expectation led up to the first day of school; we wondered what our teacher would be like, and eagerly picked up and told and retold all the gossip that floated from her last place as to her good points and her bad,—especially her bad. Then there was always the question as to what pupils would be at school; what new faces we should see and what old ones would be gone, and whether or not we should like the new ones better than the old. Our minds were firmly made up on this point before we went to school, and no possible circumstance could make us change the opinion, or rather the determination, we had formed. Then we speculated and negotiated as to who should be our seat-mate for the term, or until we fought. There was always the question of studies and classes, and whether the new teacher would let us begin where the old left off, or whether we should have to commence the book over again. We almost always began again, and thus the first parts of our books were badly worn and thumbed, while the pages in the back were fresh and new.

We looked forward to the last day with all the expectancy of the first. Long before this the work began to drag; the novelty had all worn off, and our life was a constant battle with the teacher to see how much we need not do. As the last day drew near, our minds were filled with visions of how easy life would be when there was no school, and of the pleasure the summer held in store for us. On the last day we had no lessons to recite, and in the afternoon our parents were invited in, and we spoke pieces and read essays,—that is, the boys generally spoke the pieces and the girls read the essays. Somehow a boy never could write an essay, and even if he could manage to write one it would be beneath his dignity to stand up on the platform and read from little sheets of notepaper tied with red or blue ribbon. But this task seemed especially to fit the girls. In the first place, they could write better than the boys,—letters or essays or anything of the kind. In the next place, they could not be thought of as standing bolt upright and facing the whole school, visitors and all; they were too shy to stand out alone with nothing in their hands to hide their faces. So the girls read essays on Success, and Work, and Truthfulness, and Spring, and things like that, while the boys spoke pieces. Sometimes we were afraid, but after a little practice we promptly answered to our names, and went on the platform and spoke with the greatest assurance, holding our heads up and making the gestures according to printed forms laid down in the books.

I fancy that none of us ever really understood anything about the pieces that we spoke. I remember in a general way that they were mainly of our country, and brave boys fighting and winning victories and dying, and about the evils and dangers of strong drink. We had a great many pieces about intemperance, ambition, and the like. I especially remember one boy, with red hair and freckles and a short neck and large warts on his hands, who used always to speak a piece entitled "How have the Mighty Fallen." I don't know who wrote it, or where it came from, or what has become of it; but I remember the piece almost as well as if I heard it yesterday. This boy was the prize speaker of the school, and the piece told about Alexander and Caesar and Napoleon, and how and why they failed. Their lack of success was due to ambition and strong drink. I know this piece made a deep impression on my mind, and I always vowed that I never would fail as Alexander and Caesar and Napoleon had done,—and I never have. I remember that once my father came to school on the last day, in the afternoon, to hear us speak; and when I got home at night he told me that the boy who spoke the piece about How the Mighty had Fallen had all the elements of an orator, and he predicted that some day he would make his mark in the world. I felt that I would have given everything I possessed if only my father had said that about me. I know that in my tactful way I led up again and again to the piece that I had spoken, but about this my father said not a single word.

How I envied that red-headed lad, and how I wondered if there really was any chance that I might come out as well as he! For some years my remembrance of this youth had passed away, until the last time I went back home. Then, as I drove past his house with never a thought of my old-time friend, I looked over into the weed-covered yard,—perhaps it was weedy before, but I did not so remember it,—and there I saw a man with a hoe in his hand cleaning out a drain that ran from the cellar to the ditch in front of the house. I looked closely at him, and I never in the world should have known him; but he came down to the fence, and leaned on his hoe, and hailed me as I passed. No doubt he had heard that I had come to town. Then I remembered the piece about How the Mighty had Fallen, and the little red-headed boy at school; but this boy's hair was white, he was bent, and his clothes were about the color of his hair and hands and face in those far-off years when he spoke the piece. I was shocked, but I tried not to let him know it. I asked him how he was, and how he was getting along; and he told me he was very well, and was doing first-rate. And then I thought of my poor father, who said that he had all the elements of an orator and would make his mark some day. Well, perhaps he had made his mark, even though he was cleaning out a cellar-drain,—and, after all, this is better work than making speeches, however fine.

To go back to the last day of school. I remember one piece that we used to speak, about Marco Bozzaris, and how he got into a fight with some Turks; and first he was killed, and then he killed the Turks, as it seemed to me. I had no idea who the Turks were, or why Marco Bozzaris was fighting them, or what it was all about; but I seemed to think there were certain parts of the piece that should be spoken in a loud voice, and certain others that should be said very softly. The book I learned it from had characters or figures that told us when we should speak softly and when we should speak loudly, and we always followed the instructions of the book. If it had told us to speak loudly when it said softly, and softly instead of loudly, we would have done it that way without a thought that it could make any difference with the piece. I have no doubt that if I should read "Marco Bozzaris" to-day I should read it loudly and softly in just the same places that I did at school, without any more regard for what it meant than I had then.

But there was one piece that I always thought especially fine. It was about Casabianca. The name now sounds to me like a Spanish name, but I am sure I had no thought then of what it was. It might have been a Swedish or an Irish name, for all I knew. I remember that this Casabianca was a lad about my own age, and somehow he was on a ship in a battle, and his father was with him. His father was called away on some important matter, and told Casabianca to stand right there on a certain spot and wait until he got back. Something must have detained him,—as I recall it, he was killed, or something of that kind,—at any rate, he did not get back, and it grew dark, and Casabianca began to cry. Pretty soon, to make matters worse, a fire broke out on board the ship, and the smoke began to smother him and the flames to roll around him. The other people on the ship ran to the shore, and they called to him to run too, and the gang-plank had not been taken in or burned, and he had lots of time to get away; but no, his father had gone off, and had told Casabianca to wait until he returned, and he proposed to wait. So he called wildly for his father a great many times; but his father did not come. Still the boy stood fast, and the flames crept slowly up until he was burned to cinders at his post.

This was a very exciting story, and we used to speak it with voices loud and soft, and with gestures that looked like rolling fire and smoke. I did not really know then, but I know now, that this piece was written by somebody who fancied himself or herself a poet, and that it was written to teach a moral lesson. I remember that the last line read "But the noblest thing that perished there was that young and faithful heart." From this I am sure that the lesson meant to be taught was the great virtue of obeying your parents.

I cannot recall that I ever heard any of our teachers say a word about this poem, so I infer that they must have approved its sentiments. Of course I am old enough now to know that a boy who would stick to a burning ship like that might just as well get burned up and be done with at once. But I cannot exactly make up my mind what punishment should be given to the poet or the book-publisher or the teacher who allowed this sort of heroics to be given to a child.

In our pieces and in our lessons a great deal was said about the duties that children owe their parents, a great deal about how much our parents had done for us, and how kind and obedient we should be to them. But I cannot recall that there was a single line about the duties that parents owe to children, and how much they should do for the child who had nothing to say about his own entrance into the world. It is true that these books were written for children, but just as true that the children were to become parents, and that most of them would get little instruction beyond the district school. Which fact may to some extent account for the great number of bad and foolish parents in the world.

Many of these pieces told how much we owed the country, and of our duty to live for it and fight for it, and if need be to die for it. I cannot recall that a single one ever told of any duty the country owed to us, or anything that should be given in return for our service and our lives. All of which shows what a great handicap we children suffered by being obliged to go to school.

After the last piece had been spoken, the teacher put on her most serious face (she always had a variety of faces to put on) and told us how she loved us all,—although she had never said a word of this sort before,—how good and faithful and studious we had been; she told us how kind our parents were to let us go to school, how sad she felt at the final parting, and how impossible it was that the little group could ever be gathered together again this side of heaven, which she trusted all of us would some day reach, so that she might meet us once again. At this we began to regret that we had not treated her better and been more obedient to her rules. Then we felt sad, and drew our coat-sleeves across our eyes, and wished that she would stop talking and let us go out. Finally she spoke the last words and dismissed the school, and our days of captivity were done. Each child snatched his carefully packed books and slate, and with shouts and laughter rushed through the schoolhouse door into the free open world outside.

School-Teaching and Discipline

WILLIAM LYON PHELPS

*KNOWN as "Billy" Phelps to generations of Yale students, WILLIAM
LYON PHELPS (1865-1943) was professor of English literature at Yale
from 1892 to 1933. Through his lectures, his magazine articles, and his
department "As I Like it" in* Scribner's Magazine, *he made every effort to
introduce good literature to the American public. He had a pungent wit,
a lively sense of humor, and a great many enthusiasms, which he exploited
in his lectures and his writing.*

In his Autobiography *he writes of teaching out of long and successful
experience as one of America's best-known teachers.*

THE disciples called Our Lord "Teacher"—a beautiful word; when
people were in difficulties, they came to Him for help: "Teacher, what
shall we do?" In country schools one hears it to-day, and it is very pretty.
The child, finding the problem too much for its abilities, addresses the pale
woman at the desk: "Teacher, will you help me with this?" The Authorised
Version translated the Greek word "teacher" into "master," the then English equivalent, and the word survives in our private schools even unto this
day. The teacher must be a Leader, a Master, in many cases a Lion-tamer,
a manager of wild beasts. It is essential, then, that the man or woman who
teaches should have a strong personality, a dominant, fearless disposition.
He is the Captain of the ship, and is as much alone in the school-room as
the captain is alone with his crew on the high seas. Those who have never
taught have no idea of the loneliness and responsibility of a school-teacher
shut up in a big schoolroom with a pack of wild boys and girls. The teacher
can consult outside of hours with his superiors or colleagues; he can get
advice and talk over his difficulties. But when he goes into the schoolroom,
shuts the door, takes the lonely seat behind the desk, and looks into the
shining morning faces, then he is thrown back absolutely on himself. No
power on earth can help him, and nothing can save the situation if he
makes a blunder. There he needs all his resources, all his courage, and
infinite patience. I remember when I first taught school, hardly more than
a boy myself, I was sent in evenings to preside over "study hour." This

meant that I was to sit behind a desk in a big room filled with healthy boys, and see that no one spoke or made a noise for an hour. I could not interest them, for I, too, must say nothing. They came jostling, tumbling, hilariously, in; I rang a bell, which meant instant silence. That bell gave forth no uncertain sound; I put my whole personality into my finger as I pressed the electric button, and I tried to make it trill just the psychological length of time, neither too short nor too long. Yet every time I rang that bell I wondered if they would really obey. They did, but I never recovered from my amazement at the miracle. I used to look at them as they sat over their tasks with puckered brow and wonder, since they were so many and united, and I was all alone, why they did not devour me. To-day, when I see in a big public school, a thin, anaemic woman sit behind a desk and control a roomfull of young myrmidons, I marvel at the mysterious force of the individual soul.

For the actual *teaching* in a school is the least of the teacher's difficulties. Children must be led, must be controlled; order and discipline must somehow be maintained, or the teacher must seek another situation. In a private boarding-school the personal contact is much closer and much more prolonged. One cannot leave his task, as the workman drops his hammer at the stroke of twelve. In the school where I learned to teach, I rose at seven, presided over a breakfast-table, taught various classes from half past eight to one, played outdoors with boys in the afternoon (how fortunate for me that I loved sports even more than the pupils did), presided at the dinner-table, presided at study hour, and then went upstairs to see that the smaller boys took their hot baths and retired in good order. Energy, cheerfulness, patience, and sympathy are all helpful.

In teaching a class, either in boarding-school or day-school, or, for that matter, in college, certain practical hints may be not impertinent here. Nothing is too minute or too trivial that concerns the great art of teaching. Constant and tremendous enthusiasm for the subject taught is essential. While one is actually teaching it, this thing, whatever it may be, should seem to be the most important thing in time or eternity. The late President Harper, who was one of the most brilliant teachers I have ever known, told me that he had taught the first verse of the first chapter of Genesis I have forgotten how many thousand times. I remarked that he always seemed enthusiastic. He said: "Sometimes I feel wildly enthusiastic; other times I have no enthusiasm at all. When I have no enthusiasm, then I create it." It is absurd that a teacher should allow a headache or a sleepless night to affect his teaching. If his health will permit him to enter the classroom, he must teach with zeal and vigour.

Just as enthusiasm and force are contagious, so are lassitude and indifference. I asked a student once what was the matter with a certain teacher. "Well," he said, "our classroom is a race." "A race?" "Yes, it's a race to see who will get to sleep first, the class or the teacher." There are men and women engaged in teaching who are such ciphers in the classroom that they might just as well teach by telephone, and have a phonograph on the desk to record the pupils' answers.

And the teacher who emanates force, in some altogether mysterious manner, gets it back. The students react on the man behind the desk. I do not know how many times I have risen in the morning feeling so weary and ill that I wondered if I could get to the college. Then at the end of the hour's teaching, I have felt a veritable glow of life and energy. I know that virtue has gone out of me, but some kind of vigour has taken its place.

A teacher should never begin with an apology—ignorance of the subject, lack of time, ill health, etc. But a teacher should never bluff. Every man or woman should acknowledge a mistake when pointed out to him by a pupil, and be grateful for it. "Every schoolboy knows" things that the teacher has forgotten, or perhaps never knew. Hardly a man on any college faculty could pass all the entrance requirements. And if a student asks a question which the teacher cannot answer, confess ignorance at once. This will sometimes happen in one's own subject. No matter. The students respect a teacher who is truthful, and will believe him when he does speak out of an abundance of knowledge. The very first pupils to see through a teacher who dodges questions or attempts to cover ignorance are the bluffers, for they understand the art of bluffing by experience, and cannot be fooled. Once a teacher has a reputation for bluffing, he is lost. The students who cheat and the students who bluff never forgive a teacher for these sins. They exact a much higher standard of us than they set for themselves. This is quite right. We are their leaders.

Never praise an individual pupil in the presence of the class. This is fatal, for the teacher must not be suspected of having favourites. And it is hard on the one praised, as he will soon find out. It is difficult resolutely to refrain from doing this. There are times when the recitation drags abominably, when a succession of failures or utterly stupid answers makes the teacher's heart sick. Then he calls on the one boy or girl who is always prepared, always attentive, always intelligent. A brilliant answer is balm to the soul, but no comment on it should be made. The way to encourage good pupils, stimulate their ambition, and get the very best out of them, is to ask them singly to remain after class, or to seize an opportunity when it presents itself, and express pleasure in their efforts, suggest a good book to read, or let them see in some way that they have attracted your attention and made an impression on your mind. A student never forgets an encouraging private word, when it is given with sincere respect and admiration. I once asked a college junior to remain a moment as the class was passing out, and when we were alone, I told him how much I appreciated his work. He said that that was the first time in his life either in school or college that any teacher had spoken to him personally and commended his efforts. Of course he outdid himself after that, knowing that I expected great things of him, and he later became a specialist in the subject I was teaching.

If it is important, and I am sure it is, never to praise an individual student in the presence of the class, it is far more important never to make fun of a dull student, or a bad recitation; and it is an absolute rule, to which there are no exceptions under any conceivable circumstances, never to use sarcasm toward an individual student before his mates. This may become a terribly dangerous habit, and it is one that grows with astonishing speed. The teacher is doing a cheap and utterly contemptible thing—raising a laugh at the expense of an individual who is at his mercy. It is an awkward thing to play with souls. You may arouse momentary admiration for your wit, but it is probable that you have killed forever the chance to influence the victim of your tyranny. This boy or girl is lost to you, and sometimes years later he will remember you with a flush of anger. It is difficult to avoid sarcasm and ridicule in certain instances—some students leave such wonderful openings and supply such golden opportunities for your wit. Resist this temptation.

Treat good and bad recitations with apparently equal respect. Teachers are always eager to have their pupils respect them, but how many teachers really respect their pupils? There are teachers who listen to good recitations or to requests for information with grinning condescension, and to poor recitations with contempt. Assume that every pupil is seriously interested and doing his best, and you will have less trouble. We had a teacher at school when I was a boy who began each recitation by calling on two or three, and then wearily remarked, "Now we'll hear from the dunces." These latter felt classified, and made no attempt to rise from the slough. If a student makes systematically bad or stupid recitations, speak to him privately: "This subject seems very difficult to you. I am sorry to be forced every day to give you a low mark. Unless you improve, you must know you cannot possibly pass. Is there any suggestion I can make that will help you?" A little conversation like that cannot do any harm, and may accomplish much good. The pupil will be cured of any suspicion that the teacher is "down on him" (a common superstition among students), he will know that the teacher is not indifferent, but really anxious that he should do better, and he will make that renewed effort that invariably follows personal attention. Always remember that the business of the teacher is not to see how difficult and odious he can make his subject, not to see how many boys and girls he can catch off their guard, not to blow out the lamp of the mind with the chill wind of indifference, but to get the highest results out of each individual student committed to his care.

The teacher should never lose his temper in the presence of the class. If a man, he may take refuge in profane soliloquies; if a woman, she may follow the example of one sweet-faced and apparently tranquil girl—go out in the yard and gnaw a post; but there must be no display of rage before the clear eyes of children. When I taught school, there were times when the indifference, stupidity, flippancy, or silliness of the class brought me suddenly to such a pitch of rage, that I dared not trust myself to speak;

I would clutch the arms of my chair, and swallow foam until I felt complete self-command; then I could speak with quiet gravity. The boys all saw what was the matter with me, and learned something not in the book. I can still feel on my face the claws of a female teacher who put them there forty years ago. I suppose I was inattentive, or whispering to my neighbour, or doing something forbidden: the woman suddenly left the platform, rushed down the aisle, seized me on the mouth, and apparently tried to dislocate my jaw. It was impressive, but not edifying. Every time a teacher flies into a passion in the school-room, he is sure either to do or to say something foolish—something that for the moment brings him below the level of the intelligence of the flock. He will bitterly regret it afterwards, for he will find that it is harder to climb than to fall, and he has all that lost ground to recover.

When penalties must be given, it is better to give them more in sorrow than in anger. I have seen teachers who threw out penalties in impetuous rage, losing all the moral effect of the punishment. I have seen other teachers impose penalties with a triumphant laugh, as though they were playing a game with the children, and had made a clever checkmate. "Ha! ha! that will cost you two marks!" A healthy child then sets his brain to work in the endeavor next time to outwit the antagonist. "Stinking old fool! I'll show him!" says the lad to himself. Penalties should be given as though they hurt the teacher as much as the criminal, as though for the moment the boy had really sunk low in the teacher's good opinion, had done something that only continuous good behaviour could repair. It is well to have a moment of eloquent silence intervene between the offence and the punishment, and then have the penalty fall like fate.

For this reason, bad marks for misbehaviour and disciplinary penalties should be given as seldom as possible. Familiarity breeds contempt. Those teachers who are always handing down demerits are always having trouble. Every penalty should be an event in the life of the pupil. It is interesting to observe how lightly children regard the very same penalty when inflicted by one teacher, and how deeply it hurts when inflicted by another. The reason is that children have no respect for some teachers, while for others they will do everything to stand high in their regard. And while it is important to give penalties very rarely, it is still more important never to take them off. The pupil must realise that when he receives a bad mark, nothing on earth can remove it. I well remember two teachers in the same school. One began the year by giving out demerits very freely and for the most trivial things; then at the end of the school day, the culprits flocked around him, begging him to remove certain of the afflictions, promising to do better, saying they did not mean to be bad. To some he yielded. The result was that for months he had to go through this process every day, and whenever a boy received a penalty, he had the hope of getting it cancelled. The other teacher gave only two or three demerits the first week. Each boy came to him afterward, and asked for their removal. The teacher said, "I am very sorry—I never give a penalty if I can help it, but once given, I shall never under any circumstances take it off. Even if I find I have made a mistake, and given it to an innocent boy, I shall not take it off. And I shall try not to make any mistakes." After the first week, no boy ever asked him to remove a bad mark, but they all endeavoured to avoid receiving one.

Whenever it is possible,—it is not always possible,—it is best not to rebuke an individual by name in the presence of the class. Sometimes this permanently antagonises the victim, sometimes it makes a hero out of him in the estimation of his mates. When there is a little plague spot of irruption in the classroom, when there is individual disorder or inattention, it is better to speak to the class as a whole, rather than to single out one person by name. And if there is one boy or girl who persists in repeated offences of this nature, then it is well to keep the culprit a moment after class, and, after everyone has gone out, to talk very frankly, very earnestly, but never angrily or sarcastically with him. Sometimes this method will result not only in complete reformation, but in transforming the individual from a leader of disturbance into an influence for good order. Very few boys or girls can resist a quiet personal talk. And those who are wilfully and deliberately bad are terribly afraid of it, because they suffer such embarrassment and discomfort. I remember one boys' school where the teacher was famous for these interviews, and the remark of a young villain, "Say, I'd rather he'd lick me any day than talk to me!"

It is a great advantage to a teacher to be physically big and physically strong; and if the teacher be a woman, to have robust health. She will need it all in the course of an average day. One admirable disciplinary officer in a college told me that in his many years of teaching he had always thanked God he was over six feet high. He could generally look down on the offender, while the poor wretch had to look up to him. Still discipline, after all, is a matter of personality rather than avoirdupois. There are men of colossal size who somehow never succeed in enforcing discipline; the worst teacher I had in college was six feet four. There are other men, small and unimpressive at first sight, who would be lost in a crowd, and yet who have no difficulty in enforcing the most rigid discipline. When I was five years old, I was sent to the Webster public school in New Haven, the "toughest" district school I ever saw. The majority of the boys and girls came from streets where no well-dressed boy could walk with impunity. I remember the horrible fear I had of "the micks of Morocco Street," a fear well-founded, for I was small even for my age, and frequently suffered at the hands of these merciless brigands. How my heart aches now for the women who had to teach in that school! The unspeakably obscene language of the boys at recess, the filth and dirt they brought into the school room, the naive gestures of physical necessity they made when they raised the other hand for permission to "go out," the insolent manner in which they answered the teacher's questions, the ribald laughter that resounded on occasions skilfully prepared to produce it! No boy ever rose to recite without finding pins, tacks (and I remember one file) put in his chair to greet his down-sitting—then the howl of rage, the back-handed blow, and the teacher's vain remonstrance. Spitballs, heavy with their damp freight, flew around the room, falling on the just and the unjust. Not a day passed that the teacher did not take out the whip, and lash the boys across the palms.

Over this whirlwind of childish savagery, disorder, corruption, and sin a little man sat enthroned as principal. Mr. Lewis was the supreme court, and no boy, however wicked or fearless, spoke his name above an awed whisper. Once in a while he would walk through our room, very casually, without looking at anybody. The most absolute silence marked his advent. He seemed to me to be about eleven feet high, and to breathe forth threatening and slaughter. Years afterward, when I returned to New Haven, I saw him, and marvelled at his tiny frame and puny appearance. Was this gray-haired little man the terror of my childhood? Yet the biggest, the roughest, and the most daredevil boys in the school regarded him with mortal terror. He stood serene and quiet, the bulwark against anarchy. I remember one terribly tough, strong Irish lad, John Devanney, who was my hero. I secretly sent him a Christmas present at the school celebration, and he waved it at me triumphantly, saying, "Huh! my present is a lot better than yours!" He did not know that I was the donor, and I did not dare tell him. He was my hero, because when I was whipped by the teacher, I cried; when he was whipped, he laughed. I can see him now, standing up before the class, the female teacher hitting his hand with the whip with all her might, while he laughed condescendingly at her feeble efforts. Yet she had her trump card. When everything else failed, she would say, "I will send you to Mr. Lewis," and then the ruddy cheeks of the great John Devanney turned pale with fear. What Mr. Lewis did to these lads no one else ever knew, but strange tales came from those mysterious interviews. He was the one salvation of the teachers, and for over forty years he commanded the situation, and made citizens somehow out of that unpromising material. I remember one day, coming out after school was over, he spoke to me kindly, with a smile. I was in such terror that I could say nothing; but as soon as I got around the corner, I ran for my life, lest he should call me back and eat me. A small man and a great personality!

For the average boy or girl, with ordinary health and ordinary ability, I believe the public school is better than the private. It is true that in a public school there are many undesirable pupils—it is often a school of bad manners. Girls may become vulgar and slangy, boys may become coarse and foul-mouthed. Good home influences, religious training, refinement, and the real companionship of father and mother will more than offset this. The small boy is a naturally dirty little animal, and the language, pictures, and associations in his environment at a public school are often atrociously bad. Still, the public school is an absolute democracy—the only pure democracy to be found in America. He lives in a field of free competition—he rises or falls, swims or sinks on his merits. In scholarship he competes fairly with all his classmates, and the son of the labourer has the same chance as the son of the millionnaire. If he does not keep up to a certain grade, down he goes to the lower room, and no influence or outside aid can save him. The schools are all crowded, and those who cannot or will not study must drop out under the merciless law of competition. His comrades, both boys and girls, are imbued with the spirit of democracy, and God help the little snob! If he is fair and square, asking no special favours, he will form many friendships and stand high with his fellows. If he is selfish, conceited, eccentric, his classmates will take it out of him, or drive him away. He sees all kinds of life, learns the pure and noble along with the vulgar and obscene, and literally fights his way upward. He learns to respect boys and girls for what they are and for what they can do, rather than for the backing they have or the homes that support them. If he does not go to college, he cannot graduate from a high school without some knowledge of all sides of human nature, and he is prepared to meet and to understand all sorts of people. If he does go to college, he will probably go with better habits of study, with more ambition to excel in scholarship, and with more self-reliance than if he came from a private fitting school.

On the other hand, if a boy or girl is in poor health, or very far behind in certain studies, he is perhaps better off in a good private school. He will learn good manners, will associate with children of good breeding for the most part, and will have definite personal moral and religious training. The driving out of the Bible and prayers from many public schools is a narrow-minded, stupid, and silly policy, as the Bible and Christianity are the real foundation of Anglo-Saxon citizenship. In almost all private schools the influences are positively good, and the boys and girls who graduate from them are at home in cultivated society. Then the health of individual students is carefully attended to, and those who are backward in certain studies are personally drilled and coached. If the boy goes to college, he enters with a circle of friends, and his way is easier and less lonely. For this very reason, he may be less self-reliant, less independent, and apt to believe that his little circle really constitutes public opinion. Cowardice and conceit are no more in favour in an exclusive private school than they are elsewhere, though they may not be eliminated by such drastic measures as in a public institution.

If a boy goes to a private school after he has attended a public one, it is sometimes a happy combination. But there are some private schools that will not take pupils after they have reached a certain age. On the other hand, when a child goes to a private school very young, he fails to become really acquainted with his parents, and is sometimes actually unfitted for domestic life. There are boys who go to an exclusive school at the age of ten; they live only with rich men's sons; the summer vacations they do not spend at home, but with houseparties in the country, or camping out luxuriously in the woods, or travelling in Europe. Then they go to college, and then to a professional school; so that there are many cases of boys who from the age of ten to the age of twenty-six have hardly lived at home at all—have practically lived in a bachelors' club for sixteen years, and are unacquainted with their parents. When their parents are lacking in the character, morality, religion, refinement, and good sense necessary to bring up children, this may be not so unfortunate.

When a teacher, either in a public or a private school, discovers and can prove that a boy or girl is deliberately and wilfully bad, and when all means undertaken for improvement have failed, it is the manifest duty of the teacher to see that this individual is permanently expelled from the institution. Every teacher is in a position of trust; he has a duty toward the parents who have entrusted their children to his care. One evil boy or girl can corrupt many others, and can really lower the standard of an entire institution. Expulsion is the sole remedy. I am convinced by observation that it is not applied often enough, expecially in private schools.

Fathers and mothers can help the school principal and the school-teacher immensely not merely by taking an intelligent interest in the studies of their children, talking with them sympathetically about their lessons, their teachers, and the general life of the school, but by loyally supporting the discipline of the institution. There are many foolish parents who take the child's part when he imagines he has a grievance. Although the normal mother loves her child better than she loves herself, better than she loves life, and although nothing fills her with more delight than to have the child make a good record at school, and nothing tortures her more cruelly than to have the child fall into disgrace, it is in nearly all cases a bad thing for the child to have the mother an active partisan against school discipline. The parents can show the utmost tenderness toward their offspring, and the utmost sympathy when misfortunes come, and yet staunchly support the rules of the school. No teacher ever expects that a mother will believe her child to be wilfully bad, or will admit it if she does believe it. I always admire a mother when she comes to me and says that her son has been unfortunate, perhaps, or weak, but surely not evil; if a mother will not stand up for her son, who will? But parents, in the interests of their children, should support school discipline, even when their own lamb is gored. One of the greatest difficulties public school-teachers have to contend with is the visit of an irate father bringing his child, and insisting on better treatment. In Germany when a boy gets a whipping at school, he receives another when he comes home; in America, when a boy gets a whipping, the father goes to school and tries to whip the teacher.

If a teacher occupies a subordinate position either in school or college, subordinate to the head of the department, or subordinate to the principal, he should remember that the obedience he demands from his pupils must be shown by him toward those higher in authority. Obey orders cheerfully, and try to carry out faithfully the policy of your superiors. If your Head is a man you cannot respect, do the best you can under the circumstances, and do not indulge in innuendo: if the circumstances become intolerable, leave as quietly as possible, and seek another field for your efforts. But remember that it is possible you may be mistaken, and the superior officer right. You do not know it all. Work for the good of the institution, and not for yourself. Above all, never try to create a party among the pupils, never organise them into a personal sympathetic bodyguard. In matters of school or college discipline or policy, never take the pupils into your confidence. The business of the teacher is not to give confidences, but to receive them.

The Dream School

SEAN O'CASEY

SEAN O'CASEY, Irish dramatist, was born in Dublin in 1881, the youngest of a large family. Though his formal schooling was meagre, he early taught himself to read and write, and while still a child, had read Shakespeare and Milton and many of the English Romantic poets. At about eighteen he became interested in the Irish National Movement and mastered the Irish language. His first play was written for the National Club. His fourth play, The Shadow of a Gunman, *was produced by the Abbey Theatre in 1923. A later play,* Juno and the Paycock, *received the Hawthornden Prize in 1926 and was considered by Richard Watts of the* New York Herald-Tribune *"just about the richest comic creation since the days of Shakespeare."*

The two selections which follow are taken from I Knock at the Door, *the story of the first twelve years of O'Casey's life. He has continued his autobiography in two more volumes,* Pictures in the Hallway *and* Drums Under the Windows.

Iɴ the dark porch, Johnny pulled back as hard as he could from the clasping hand of his mother, and whimpered, Doctor said I must do nothing but eat well and stay in the open air.

—You might as well be here, said his mother, as to be at home, boring your eyes out looking at the pictures in the books your poor father left behind him. Besides your father would be unhappy in heaven, thinking of his little boy growing up to be nothing but a dunce.

She opened the heavy door that was like the heavy door of a prison, drew Johnny inside, and he found himself fast in the middle of fear. They went up to the desk where the Principal sat correcting the exercises of the seniors. He was a man of sixty years of age, with colourless eyes that looked furtively at everyone and everything. He had a pink bald head surrounded by a tufty halo of white hair, and his face was partly covered with mutton-chop whiskers a little less white than the pallor of his face, brought about, Johnny was told afterwards, by too much quiet whiskey drinking. He was a native Irish speaker from Connemara, and his name was Slogan. He looked up with a quick furtive glance at Johnny and his mother.

—Ah, he said, welcome to the bright little new scholar the rector told me about, as he touched the boy on the head with his thin, pale, bony, bubbly-veined hand. Don't be afraid, little boy, he went on, pulling Johnny nearer to him till his pale eyes stared into the timid eye of the boy. He snatched up a snaky-looking cane from the desk, and held it out in front of Johnny's one good eye. There now, he added, see it for yourself—it's not such a terrible thing, is it?

—Johnny's a delicate boy, murmured the mother, and must be treated gently on account of his poor eyes.

—We correct our boys only when it is necessary, said the master with a tight-lipped grin. He got up from the desk, and catching the mother's arm, he turned her towards the door. Off you go home, my good woman, and give God thanks that your boy is where he can share in what will be for his good.

The master led him over to a class that was droning out tables, and sat him down on a bench between two boys, telling him to be good, keep his eye on the teacher, and repeat with the boys what the teacher was saying.

Four'n one are five, four'n two are six, four'n three are seven, four'n four are eight, went on the singsong chorus, while Johnny's one eye glanced dreamily at the green, brown, yellow, and purple countries on a map of the world, with the British Possessions coloured a vivid red, and all surrounded with the pale-blue waters of the world, as all the children of the whole wide world murmured four'n five are nine, four'n six are ten, four'n seven are eleven in the purple, red, green, and yellow lands that he saw all round him as he walked along murmuring four'n eight are twelve, four'n nine are thirteen—going along a great white road—a road white as the driven snow—that was banked on each side of him with daffodils as big as breakfast-cups nodding and nodding at him as he went along the snow-white road, and stretching their blooms to let in big black bees with crimson bands around their bellies, and big red bees with big black bands around their bellies, and purple butterflies with satiny black dots on the tips of their front wings and golden-satiny dots on the tips of their back wings, having crimson feelers sliding all over the bells of the yellow daffodils, and green butterflies with zigzag shining deep blue decorations on their wings that were bigger than any man's hand, and had their tips bordered with bronze, and bigger butterflies still, with front wings white having green stars on them and hind wings green with white stars on them, flew with all the others in and out and through the lovely sway of the gay and golden daffodils.

The sky above was a far deeper blue than the blue on the wing of the blue-dotted butterfly, while through the deep blue of the sky sailed white clouds so low down that some of them shone with the reflected gold from the blossoms of the daffodils. Many beautiful trees lined the road that Johnny walked on, and from some came the smell of thyme and from others the smell of cinnamon. Some of the trees bent down with the weight of blossoms, and numbers were heavy with plums as big as apples, and cherries bigger than the biggest of plums that hung in hundreds on their branches, so that he ate his fill as he walked along the white road.

Then after turning a bend he came upon a huge high gate of bronze, and on one wing of the huge high gate of bronze were figures in beaten silver, of boys beating drums of gold, and on the other wing of the huge high gate of bronze were figures, in beaten gold, of boys blowing trumpets of silver, and over the heads of the figures of boys blowing trumpets and beating drums was the word SCHOOL. Johnny halted and wondered, and as he wondered, the gates slowly opened as the figures in beaten silver beat on their drums of gold, and the figures of beaten gold blew on their trumpets of silver.

When the gates were fully opened two boys like birds came running out with short-handled sharp-pointed spears in their hands; and they bowed down low before him, saying: Hail to the child of God and to the inheritor of the Kingdom of Heaven. Enter, that wisdom, who sitteth on the seat of the mighty, may prepare the way before thy little mind to understand all the majesty and mystery of life that now is, and of the life that is to come.

And the two boys that were like birds, with the spears in their hands, led him gently through the open gate. And when they felt that he was trembling they said to him, Let not your heart be troubled, little boy. Then they stretched out their spears in front of his eyes, and he saw that the points of the spears were made of a sweet chocolate covered cunningly with the thinnest of silver tissue. And they walked through a lovely avenue of laurestilillium covered with great trumpet-shaped flowers that were a delicate white in the morning, a ruddy gold at midday, and a deep dark crimson when the sun went down; then, through a narrower avenue of crocuaxenillium, to a tiny glade filled with the greenest of grass and newest and freshest of blossoms where, on a bank of primroses, sat a grey-bearded old josser, who asked Johnny his name and where he lived, then wrote it all down with a gold pen, having for its nib a gleaming emerald, on a great big white blackboard trimmed with jewels. Then Johnny was led away to a bath, hidden in blooming hawthorn, in which the water was lovely and hot and fully perfumed. When he had been bathed, he was rubbed smoothly with soft sweet-smelling oils till his flesh became as the flesh of a little child; and then dressed in silks as gentle as newly-risen, dewy-grown meadow grass. Then he was declared to be fit and free to wander about or play with the big or little kids who swarmed everywhere over hill, meadow, and dale.

On every little hill was a tower, and on the top of every tower was a watcher to see if any child had grown tired so that he could be made to sit down and rest in beds of moss; or if a kid was anyway hungry the watcher ordered him a slice of currant bread and jam, and each watcher had a needle ready threaded to act should a seam burst or a button fly among the frolicking children. The paths all about the place were paved with tiles of vivid colours—red, green, lemon, ultramarine, orange, and black—fashioned in divers ways. Johnny found, when he made friends with some of the kids, that very few spoke English because it was hard to learn; so they mostly spoke in Latin saying *quo vadis* when they were coming, and when they were going replying *veenie vaynay vicinity vo.* Away in the distance spreading out for miles and miles to the right and to the left were orange groves and lemon groves, and the oranges were as sweet as the sweetest sugar and the lemons had the taste of honey with a faraway sense of bitterness in them. Pear, apple, plum, and cherry trees abounded, and were so cleverly trained that the highest fruit was well within reach of the tiniest kid that was prowling about, and was steady enough to stand on the tips of his toes. Beech trees, from which swings swung, were everywhere, and, in beds of huge red strawberries, tiny babies were resting on moss in nests of bulrushes. All the kids who were running, jumping, swinging, playing tag, and those little ones lying in their bul-rush-nests who happened to be awake, unified their voices as one man and sang the song, We're happy all the day long here. With canes in their hands, cherry-faced women wandered about keeping a wary eye on the kids. The guides told Johnny in Latin that these women were specially employed to lash out with the canes at any kid who missed for a single second the joy that was to be got out of the things the place provided, and so made it sure that no kid could forget for a moment that he was a member of Christ, a child of God, and an inheritor of the Kingdom of Heaven.

Hidden away in a forest of blossoms were rows of low tiny-seated privies, and between them strutted up and down hundreds of clucking, gorgeous-coloured peacocks, and over the privies were bending boughs of lovely-scented shrubs, and in the midst of these lovely-scented shrubs were multitudes of tiny birds—red, blue, purple, green, and yellow—which immediately commenced to sing in chorus and kept it up the whole time any of the kids happened to be seated on one of the privies doing his duty to himself and to mankind in general.

The sun shone for ever gently, and nothing fell from the blue sky, save little showers of pollen now and again falling from the legs of passing butterflies and bees. Rabbits with black bodies and white heads and rab-bits with black heads and white bodies came out in the evening from thick clumps of purple and white heather, whose every bell was as big as a thimble, and played with the children till the moon came out.

A trumpet blew a soft call, and they all sat down to a meal of fruit and snow-white bread, cooked in china ovens, hid away in little hills, and covered with heaps of wild honey gathered the first thing in the fresh morning from the hives that the bees packed in the hollows of the bigger trees. And when the night really fell, and they were jaded enjoying them-selves, they all gently lay down to sleep in beds of musk and mignonette, with an orange moon in a purple sky staring them in the face, and each corner of the heavens gay with young and jostling stars. And Johnny slept sound.

Suddenly something crawled through the musk and mignonette, and his hand was torn by a bitter pain. He shot himself up and gave vent to a loud cry. He heard the sound of laughter all around him. He shoved the bandage from his good eye, and saw the whitish eyes of the schoolmaster staring down at him. Is this the place for sleep? he asked, while Johnny stuck the burning hand into his mouth so that the moisture might lessen the sting. Is this the place for sleep? the master asked again. Yes or no, boy? No, sir, murmured Johnny.

—Hold out the left hand, said the master, and we'll put a sting into it that'll balance the pain in the right so that both together'll keep you awake for a couple of seconds.

Johnny held out his hand, and the cane came down like lightning across his palm, sending a rending pain through his brain that made him quiver. He thrust the left hand beneath the socket of his right arm, and pressed it tight to stem the pain. He bent his head in an effort to hide the tears that broke out of his eyes.

—That little flip on the palm has made tears come, said the master. He's not much of a hero, boys, is he? And the school answered the question with a titter.

—Put your hands behind your back, boy, said the master. Put them behind your back, raise your head, and look at your teacher, he roared.

Johnny, with a quick glance at the reddening weals dividing both palms into two parts, put them behind his back, and gazed mournfully at the teacher.

Three-times-one are three, three-times-two are six, three-times-three are nine, three-times-four are twelve, hummed the class.

A big-limbed, broad-shouldered boy of nearly fourteen, with a bush of tawny red hair and a face like a bulldog well able to smile, who was named Georgie Middleton, had silently watched, with a snarl on his lips, everything that had passed, and was now glaring at Slogan. He was the one boy in the school whom Slogan was afraid to flog.

Slogan lingered for some minutes listening to the class droning out the lesson. Then he turned away and began to return to resume the teaching of his own class.

—It was a God-damned shame to hit a half-dead kid like that, said Middleton loudly as Slogan passed him by.

Crime and Punishment

'WITHOUT his usual cut of bread for lunch that day Johnny sat on a mangy clump of grass watching, with his good eye, Georgie Middleton and a group of cronies sitting between two church buttresses, playing cards, smoking fags, and arguing vigorously. He looked, came nearer; and Middleton lifted his head, and smiled.

—Come over here, and stand near me for luck, he said to Johnny.

Johnny came nearer, a little shyly, leaned a hand on Georgie's shoulder, and watched the play. They were playing twenty-fives for a penny a game and a ha'penny for the best trump out each deal. After every sixth game a boy took his turn for the following six games to stand aside and keep watch in case they should be suddenly surprised by oul' Slogan coming upon them unawares. Massey was now watching, and impatiently waiting for the six games to pass so that he could get back to the sport again. The cards were dealt, the tricks played and gathered, and Middleton won. Again the cards were dealt, given out, the tricks played and gathered, and again Middleton won.

—That's the third game for me, hand-runnin', said Middleton delightedly. Look alive, Ecret, and deal while the luck's my way.

—I'll deal, ejaculated Massey. That's the sixth game, now, and it's Ecret's turn to stand and keep nix.

—It's only the fifth, responded Ecret, there's another game to go yet.

—Sixth, I tell you, persisted Massey; didn't I count them carefully? So up with you off your hunkers, and take my place here.

—I tell you it's only the fifth game, growled Ecret, as he shuffled the cards.

—Sixth, sixth, sixth, repeated Massey impatiently, and he stretched over to take the pack of cards from Ecret's hands.

—No blasted bickerin', now, while I'm winnin', said Middleton testily.

—But fair's fair, grumbled Massey. I've watched here through the six games; and, accordin' to rules, it's Ecret's turn to take my place and keep nix for the crowd.

—Sit down then, snapped Middleton, eager to get another penny in the pool while he was winning; sit down, if you want a hand so badly, and Johnny, here, will keep nix for us all. He looked up at Johnny, and added, Make yourself useful, Johnny, be keepin' your good eye well peeled, an' if you see oul' balls Slogan turning the corner, give us the tip so that we'll all be talkin' about David watchin' Bathsheba havin' her bath, before he comes close.

Johnny became almost ill with fear that he wouldn't see Slogan quick enough, if he came round the corner. He hadn't the courage to say that his eye wasn't good enough; so he strained this one eye open, and stared fixedly at the corner round which Slogan would probably come, if he came at all. He prayed that he would not come, and that the bell would shortly be heard proclaiming that the time for cards was past, and that all must return to the song of the spelling and the sums.

—Somebody shy in the pool, said Middleton; only ninepence in it, so there's a wing missin'—who's shy?

—I am, said Massey, who was dealing the cards. When he had given them out, he added a penny to the pool. Ecret's lead, and spades is trumps, he added, peering expectantly into his hand.

They led and trumped and took their tricks; shuffled and cut and led and trumped and took their tricks, while Johnny stared and stared at the corner round which danger might come, and longed and longed for the warning bell to ring.

Suddenly there shot into his eyes a pain like the piercing of many needles, flooding into an agony that shocked his brain and flashed a glare of crimson light before him that made him clench his teeth and press his lids tight together till a stream of scalding evil tears forced their way between them, and ran hotly down his cheeks. Then he felt himself jerked back by the shoulders, and heard the sound of scrambling feet. When the pain subsided, he opened the good eye, and saw Slogan taking up the money in the pool, and gathering the cards, with a scowl on his face; while the group of boys looked on embarrassed and silent. When Slogan had gathered up all the money and the cards, without speaking a word, he left them standing there, awkward and resentful.

Middleton turned savagely on Johnny.

—How the hell did you manage to let him sail down on the top of us like that? he snarled, but Johnny, burning with shame and shaking with sensitive fear, gave out no answer.

—Caught us all, like a lot of shaggy sheep, muttered Massey.

Middleton turned and struck Johnny sharply across the mouth with the back of his hand, making the boy's lip bleed, as he shouted, You half-blind, sappy-lidded, dead-in-the-head dummy, you couldn't keep your eyes skinned for a minute or two an' save the few bob we were bettin' from buyin' Bibles for the heathen buggers of Bengal!

—Caught us all, like a lot of shaggy sheep, muttered Massey.

Middleton gave Johnny a vicious shove that sent him reeling.

—Away, for Christ's sake outa me sight, you hand-gropin' pig's-eye-in-a-bottle, you!

The others laughed loud, crowded round Johnny, pushed and pinched him, as he turned and walked slowly away from them.

Turning the corner, he heard Slogan belling the end of the play-hour; and, passing the master, he entered the schoolroom, sat down in his place, and screwed his good eye into a lesson book, while his heart thumped in his breast. The boys poured into the school, and his classmates sat down beside him, whispering excitedly about all that had happened.

Suddenly the hum of the school was hushed, for Slogan, standing at his desk at the upper end of the room, was ringing his bell, and all the boys, save Johnny, knew that when the bell was rung from that place some very important thing was about to be said by the master. All that were in the school heard the master's voice coming out of the stillness, with a dull tone of joy in it, like the quavering notes of a sickening bird.

—As I was walking about the playground today—prowling about, I think you all call it—I caught a number of our more respectable boys deep in a very sinful pastime, a pastime that we can safely associate only with papist corner-boys; to-wit too-whoo videlicet, card-playing, and gambling like good ones in this game with the devil's prayer book, forgetful that they were protestant boys baptised in the brine of the Boyne water giving them a great responsibility to behave blameless before God and man and roman catholics, who are always on the alert to exaggerate any little indiscretion that respectable protestant boys may commit. In the first feeling of righteous indignation that came over me, I was going to make an example of every boy connected with this sin by giving each a sound and thorough whaling; but instead of that, I will leave it to their conscience to punish them more than a firm application of the cane could. But there is a certain boy mixed up with it whom no-one would think, at the first go, could be connected with the card-gambling, and this boy must be punished; and I am going to punish this boy now, and punish him well. I am going to punish him in such a way that he will think twice before he indulges in the vice again. This brave little fellow, on whom I'm going to test the valour of my cane, was on the *qui vive* so that the card-school wouldn't be disturbed by the bold bad teacher, but this brave little boy didn't watch well enough. He fell asleep at his post, and in a few minutes he is going to feel very sorry that he didn't keep a better Spartan watch and ward. That little boy's mother is a widow, so he has no father to take care of him; and it is meet, right, and my bounden duty to do everything possible to make sure that no bad tendencies are allowed to creep into the nature of the widow's little son. And when I have reddened his backside with this cane, I'm sure he'll be a better and more careful little boy for a long time to come, and run a mile away from a card whenever he sees one. He swished the cane through the air, and grinningly asked the school, Who was he who said, spare the rod and spoil the child, boys?

—Solomon, sir, Solomon, sir, shouted a dozen of the boys.

—And in what part of the Bible do we read that counsel?

—Proverbs, chapter thirteen, verse twenty-four, shouted a dozen of the boys.

—And what are the exact words, boys?

There was a dead silence, and only one boy held up his hand.

—Well, Ecret, my boy, tell the dunces the exact words used by the wise man, Solomon, when he advises us to deal in a bright way with bold boys.

—He that spareth his rod hateth his son, sang out Ecret, with his head up.

—And wasn't Solomon inspired of God? asked Slogan.

—Yessir, responded the school.

—How do we prove that? questioned the master.

The school was silent.

—All Holy Scripture is inspired of God, said Slogan, and the Book of
Proverbs is part of Holy Scripture, and chapter thirteen and verse twenty-
four is part of the Book of Proverbs; *ergo,* the counsel in the verse, he that
spareth his rod hateth his son, is holy and inspired of God without a possible doubt. So, boys, wouldn't it be very sinful of me to neglect or despise
the teaching inspired of God, seeing that I stand *in loco parentis* to you
all, and particularly to the widow's little son, brave little Johnny Casside?

—Yessir, Yessir, responded the whole school, all save only Georgie Middleton, for Johnny saw that his head hung down, and that he took no part
in what was going on between the boys and their master.

—The ayes have it, said Slogan, nodding brightly towards the boys; so
come along, Johnny, come along up here to me, my son, till I pay you the
attention counselled of God, which will be painful, but which will, ultimately, add a lot to your moral and, I hope, spiritual progress.

—Slogan's callin' y'up, whispered a boy on Johnny's right; wants to biff
you for playin' cards durin' play-hour, so he does. But Johnny cowered his
head down to the desk, and made no offer to stir.

—Eh, there, said a boy to his left, nudging him in the side, d'ye hear?
He's callin' you. Y'are to g'up to him—d'ye hear?

—Come along, boy, said Slogan, down to Johnny; come along, and get it
over. But Johnny hung his head towards the desk, and made no offer to
stir.

—He hesitates, said Slogan. Thus conscience doth make cowards of us
all; and thus the native hue of resolution is sicklied o'er with the pale cast
of thought. Come on, come up here.

—He's not makin' a single move to stir, sir, said the boy on Johnny's left.

—Come on, come up, come up, come on, chirruped the master. Remember what your godfathers and godmothers promised for you—to submit
yourself lowly and reverently to all your governors, teachers, spiritual pas-
tors, and masters; so up you come; and in later years you'll rejoice when
you remember the caning a good master gave you. Then he looked down
at Johnny, and went on in a voice of quiet and steady sternness: Are you
going to come up quietly, boy, to take your medicine, or must I go down,
and wallop you up to me?

Johnny slowly and fearfully climbed out of the desk, and taking as many
steps as possible, came towards Slogan, his heart thumping hard, and the
sweat breaking out all over his forehead. He felt that Slogan wanted to
beat away on him the fear that made him afraid to lay a hand on the other
and bigger boys; for he had heard Middleton, Massey, and Ecret say that

if Slogan ever tried any thrick of caning them, they'd open his bald skull with a slate. He halted a little distance away from the master, just out of reach of the cane.

—A little nearer, a little nearer, boy, purred Slogan; you've got to get it, so make up your mind to take it like a little Spartan. Tell me, boy, what's a Spartan? He doesn't know what a Spartan is, grinned Slogan, turning towards the school. Well, Spartans lived a long time ago in Greece, and were famous for bearing pain without a murmur. In Sparta every little boy, whether good or bad, was continually caned to make him hardy. So just shut your mouth, close your eyes, take your caning calmly, and all the school will look upon you as a little Spartan. I see your britches are a little threadbare, but that will make it all the more exciting for you. Now all we want are two strong and willing boys to come up here and stand ready to hold you down, if you squirm too much, so that you can get the full benefit of a kindly, if stern, Christian castigation. Whom shall I choose for the honour? And Slogan looked slowly and lovingly at the tense figures sitting in bunched-up lines in the yellow wooden desks.

—Will I do, sir? called out Massey, popping up his hand to attract the master's attention.

—You, Massey, said the master, will do nicely for one. You're pretty strong; and, if the need arises, I'm sure you will do your duty. Now, just one more. The biggest boy in the school ought to have the honour of holding the bold boy down—you, Georgie, come along here, and help.

Middleton's face reddened as he bent his head down to the desk and muttered, I'd rather not, sir.

Slogan put a hand behind a less-deaf ear, bent forward sideways, and said, Eh?

Middleton, keeping his head bent, raised his voice and said doggedly, I'd rather not, sir. I want no hand in any boy's batterin'; an' besides, the kid's too delicate to touch.

Slogan went white to the gills.

—Middleton, he said, with quiet bitterness, you had better learn to give an opinion only when your master asks for one.

Middleton suddenly stood up, and a dirty, dog-like scowl lined his harsh face as he pressed his soiled hands on the top of the desk so hard that the knuckles whitened.

—The kid had nothing to do with it, he rasped out; it was me and the others. He didn' play, an' doesn't know how, an' he kep' nix because we made him.

A deep silence spread over the whole school.

—Georgie Middleton, said Slogan, in a dead level voice, glancing over the whole school with his shallow eyes, will be leaving us all in a month or two to go out and fight his way in the world, and I'm sure we all wish him the best of luck. He is to try for a job in a big store where the manager wishes to give a start to a boy who has just left school. Mr. Middleton has

asked our rector to give Georgie a character, and the rector has asked me
for a general report of his conduct here. If Georgie wants to get on in the
world with the help of a good start, I'd advise him to be careful to make
his master think well of him. Am I right, Georgie Middleton? asked
Slogan, now fixing his eyes on the head-bent boy.

Middleton fought his fear for a moment, then the whole school heard
him murmur, Yessir, as he sank into his seat, shocked into the feeling that
dangers flooded the way of an open courage.

—And don't you think, Georgie, that this boy here should be punished
for his own sake? went on the master. There was a pause, and then the
whole school heard the murmur of Yessir from the mouth of Middleton.

—Come along up here, then, said Slogan, and stand ready to help as
soon as I need you. And Middleton, pale, and a little sick with shame,
slouched up; and, sullen and bitterminded, stood near the radiant, iron-
bowelled, ratty-hearted master, who put his hand out and patted Georgie's
shoulder.

—You're a good boy, Georgie, he said, for you have had the manliness
to acknowledge an error which many of us might very well hesitate to do;
and there is more joy in heaven over one sinner that repenteth than over
ninety and nine that need no repentance. And now, he went on, gripping
Johnny by the collar of his coat, we start to cane a little conscience and a
lot of caution into the soul of a wilful little boy.

Johnny shook when he felt the grip on his shoulder, and his stomach
went a little sick with the foreknowledge of the pain that was to come
upon him.

—Me mother said I wasn't to be touched because me eyes are bad, he
said hurriedly and imploringly. Don't beat me, and I'll promise I'll never
do the like again. Then he felt the searing sting of the cane across his
thighs, and he screamed and tore at the master with his little hands, twisted
his body and lashed out with his feet at the master's shins. Some of the
kicks got home, the master gave a dog's yelp, and a burning glare of
cruelty shot into his paly eyes.

—Here, Massey, and you, Middleton, he yelled, hold his arms stretched
out over the desk till I knock the devil of resistance out of him!

The two boys caught hold of Johnny's arms and pulled him over the
desk, leaving him at the mercy of the smiter, while the panting boy pleaded
please, sir, don't. I didn't mean to watch for the card-playin', really I
didn'—oh, you're cuttin' the skin off me!

But the bastard, sweating and puffing, with rigid snarling face and shining eyes, panted and sliced and cut and cut again and again. Johnny felt
Massey twisting his arm, pretending that he was hard to hold. Slogan, at
last easing off, gave a few more vicious strokes, then stopped to wipe his
face in his handkerchief.

—Up on the chair with you, now, beside the desk, he said to the quivering boy, and let the school have a good look at you. A slice across the legs

sent Johnny, with a suppressed cry, to leap quick on to the chair, chorused by a titter from the school at his haste to get there. Ashamed to rub the maddening sting in his backside and legs before the school, he balanced himself on the chair, with the eyebandage that had loosened in the struggle, hanging round his neck, his eyes torturing him with the ache of the disease and the tears that had poured out of them, and his whole nature shaken with the confused wonder at what people were doing to him and what people were thinking of him; there he stood balancing on the chair, doing his best to check the sobs that tossed about the very beating of his heart.

Slogan looked at him for a minute, and then shook his head, and there was contempt in the shake.

—He wasn't much of a Spartan, after all, he said, turning to the school, with a grin, and the opinion I have of him now is less than the one I had before. Well, we'll have to be careful of him, for one sickly sheep infects the flock, and poisons all the rest. He glanced again at Johnny. We'll give him a minute or two to pull himself together and try to be a man, but if he goes on annoying the school with his baby blubbering, we'll have to cane him quiet—isn't that so?

—Yessir, chorused the school.

A bell rang for change of positions; those who had been seated in desks, formed into standing classes, and those who had been standing, sat themselves down in the desks. Johnny still shook a little with gentle crying till Slogan stood before him, angry, threatening, cane in hand.

—Finish the whinging, finish the whinging, boy, quick, or—and he shook the arm of Johnny. The boy tried to check the sobbing, tried to look calm, and sobbed again.

—Stop it at once. D'ye hear? Are you finished?

—Yessir, murmured Johnny.

—Finished, quite, quite finished, are you?

—Yessir.

—Well, let's hear no more of it. Not a squeak out of you, or the cane'll be twisting round your legs again.

With a steady effort of will, Johnny kept quiet, stood sullen on the chair, and waited and watched Slogan return to his desk, and bend over it to correct exercises. He looked at the thin stream of sunlight flowing in by the door, left open to give air to a room hot with the breath of children and teachers.

Then the bell rang again, and all that were standing filed into the desks. The Regulations of the Board of Education were turned with their face to the wall, and an oblong strip of millboard having written on it, Religious Education, was turned to face the school. Rapping on his desk with a heavy, glossy ebony ruler, Slogan silenced the murmur of the school. He put down the ruler on the desk beside him, and bent his hoary oul' head, saying softly, Let us pray.

There was a clatter of moving bodies as all got down on to their knees. Slogan knelt down too, resting his hoary oul' head on his arms that rested on the seat of the chair from which he had risen to pray. The ebony ruler lay motionless on the desk beside him. O Lord, open Thou our eyes that we may behold wonderful things out of Thy law. The ebony ruler lay quiet on the desk beside him. Our Father which art in heaven. Hallowed be Thy Name. Johnny could see the pink baldy head of him, with its hoary edging, as Slogan bent down over the seat of the chair on which his arms rested.

Johnny suddenly slipped down from the chair he stood on, a flood of mighty rage swept through him; he whipped up the heavy ebony ruler, and with all the hate in all his heart, in all his mind, in all his soul, and in all his strength, and a swift upward swing of his arm, he brought the ebony ruler down on the pink, baldy, hoary oul' head of hoary oul' Slogan, feeling a desperate throb of joy when he heard the agonising yell that Slogan let out of him when the ebony ruler fell.

Still gripping the ebony ruler, he made for the open door and the sun. He saw Georgie Middleton grip Ecret's shoulder as Ecret made a movement to rise and stop his flight. He saw, as he flew past, the hand of Massey stretched out to hinder, and he heard the blasting curse of Massey in his ears as the ebony ruler came down on the outstretched hand. Away out through the door he dashed, across the road, down the narrow mucky Brady's Lane, shinned speedily up the rough-cut stone wall of the railway embankment, dropping the ruler as he climbed, heard in a clitter-clatter way the rush of an oncoming train, cleft by a sudden frightened, piercing whistle, plunged over the rails, checked for a second or two by the rush of the wind carried by the train as it went thundering by, saw dimly as in a mist a white-faced driver's mouth opening and shutting frantically; but pulling violently out of the intaking wind of the passing train, he sliddered down the other side of the embankment, ripping his trousers and tearing a rent in his leg with the jagged end of a jutting stone; rushed up the street opposite, turned down the next on the left, pushed open the hall-door of the house, burst into the room, and fell, exhausted and fainting, at his frightened mother's feet.

When he came to himself, his mother was bathing his body with water soothing and warm. The sting in his legs had ceased, for his mother had softened them with vaseline. He stretched his hand out, and gripped his mother's bodice.

—Don't let oul' Hunter or oul' Slogan come near me, ma, he pleaded.

—They won't be let within an ace of you, she answered; but why did you come dashing in, and why did they beat you till your poor legs were covered with bunches of weals?

—Oul' Slogan bet an' bet me because he said I watched an' kep' nix for boys playin' cards behind the buttresses of the church at playtime. I couldn't get out of it for they were biggern me; an', besides, me eyes 'ud be in the way of me seeing how to use me mits in a fight; 'n I didn't want to, but they made me, 'n oul' Slogan came on top of us; 'n because all the boys were biggern me, he bet 'n bet me till he was tired.

His mother softly fixed the bandage round his bad eye, snuggled him gently under the bed-clothes, bent down and kissed him.

—Rest and sleep sound, she said, and forget all about it till the morning.

And he lay down safe with her who would watch over him, and wended his way into a deep sleep.

Harvard: The Cockpit of Learning

BLISS PERRY

BLISS PERRY has had a long and distinguished career as teacher and editor. Born in Williamstown, Massachusetts, in 1860, he received his education at Williams College and at the Universities of Berlin and Strassburg. For many years he taught English successively at Williams, Princeton, and Harvard. From 1899 to 1909 he was editor of the Atlantic Monthly. *In the following year he was in France as Harvard lecturer there. On his return he resumed his teaching at Harvard until his retirement in 1930. Since then he has lived in Cambridge the quiet and leisurely life of an Emeritus.*

The following selection is taken from Professor Perry's autobiography And Gladly Teach.

> I have been a looker on in the Cockpit of Learning these many years.—Roger Ascham, *The Schoolmaster*
>
> The best and most fruitful conception of a university or college is the ancient one of a society or guild of scholars associated together for preserving, imparting, increasing, and enjoying knowledge.— President A. Lawrence Lowell, *At War with Academic Traditions in America*

I. Looking in at the Window

My grandfather, Baxter Perry, had been graduated from Harvard in President Kirkland's time, but I cannot recall that my father had any special veneration for that seat of learning. In my own undergraduate days, few students in the smaller New England colleges knew anything whatever about Harvard. The "inferior institutions" imagined that Harvard looked down upon them, but the more cruel truth was that she was not thinking of them at all. The first Harvard undergraduates I ever saw were on the porch of a hotel at Bar Harbor in the summer of 1879. Half-a-dozen of us Williams boys, cruising along the Maine coast and held at Mount Desert by a southeaster, fell into conversation with these Harvard youths. They were extremely courteous, but when they asked politely, "Where *is* Williamstown College?" we were young enough to be annoyed.

I suppose I knew at that time the names of a few Harvard professors.

The one most familiar to me was that of Louis Agassiz, who had died in 1873. I had studied Goodwin's Greek Grammar, and was aware that Child was an authority on English Ballads. I had read Professor Lowell's poems and essays, and knew that Longfellow and Holmes had once been professors likewise. Asa Gray, the botanist, was a distant kinsman of ours, and I had seen Charles Eliot Norton at Ashfield. Oddly enough, considering the ineffaceable personal impression which President Eliot usually made, I cannot recall when and where I first saw him.

By 1886, when Harvard was celebrating its two hundred and fiftieth anniversary, I was studying in Germany, and during the nineties, whether at Williams or Princeton, I had very few opportunities of meeting Harvard teachers. When we came to live in Cambridge in 1900, I knew possibly a dozen professors. In the Department of English, for example, I had happened to meet Barrett Wendell and George P. Baker. I knew that Child was dead, and that A. S. Hill, Wendell, and Briggs had devoted much of their energy to teaching undergraduates to write, but the courses offered by the English Department in Linguistics and Literature were then much less known to the general public than the courses in composition.

By the tests of productivity and of interesting personalities the leading department at Harvard, in 1900, was that of Philosophy. In this unrivalled "philosophical menagerie," as Professor Palmer termed it, he was himself the senior exhibit, with William James, Royce, Munsterberg, and Santayana as his associates. All of them except Santayana wrote for the *Atlantic* and were constantly in evidence in Boston and Cambridge circles. Although Norton had retired from active teaching in 1898, he and Shaler— the geologist and professor of things-in-general—were among the best known of the Harvard group. Both men had welcomed me warmly when I first came to Cambridge. I printed Shaler's *Reminiscences* in the *Atlantic,* and Ruskin's letters to Norton, although I objected strongly and without avail to Norton's deletion of many of Ruskin's affectionate personal greetings to his correspondent. I was always a little in awe of Mr. Norton. I saw him occasionally at the Tavern Club and always at the Saturday Club. In his own library at Shady Hill he was a charming host, and like my friend Robert Grant I found Norton's "bent for disillusion" singularly fascinating. "Not only," writes Judge Grant,[1] "did I relish hearing false claims or premises stripped of their glamour, but his judgments, even when most gloomy with respect to immediate values, were compact with infinite riches in a little room—riches of finished speech, however withering."

On two occasions, in his library, after seating me by the fireplace and waiting until the cigars were drawing well, Mr. Norton proceeded to give an elaborate analysis of Theodore Roosevelt. In both instances, his mild opening phrase was this: "Of course the man is a Barbarian." But he said it so gently and with such a disarming smile that I was sure—perhaps mistakenly—that "T. R." would have enjoyed it as much as I did. To his old

[1] *Fourscore; an Autobiography*, 1934.

friends he was finely loyal. I remember dining at Shady Hill one evening with Mr. Howells and Arthur Sedgwick, just after the publication of Henry James's *The American Scene*. After dinner Howells read aloud some passages from it for our delectation. I hope I was not in a controversial mood, but I did not really like this much-discussed "third manner" of Henry James. (Neither, for that matter, did Henry's older brother William. "There *isn't* any third manner," William once remarked to me. "Poor Harry has simply changed his stenographer, and the new one records all of his hesitancies and ellipses.") Whenever Howells paused in his reading of striking passages, Mr. Norton, perhaps mischievously, insisted on asking my opinion of the style. I maintained that with all its marvels, it was artificial and affected, and I could not help contrasting it, in my own mind, with the perfection of Mr. Howells's reminiscent writing in such books as *Literary Friends and Acquaintance*. I did not utter this conviction aloud, however. Arthur Sedgwick, I thought, was on my side, but neither our host nor Mr. Howells would allow that those glittering pages had any flaw. Two or three days later I happened to meet Mr. Norton. "I think I may tell you," he said, with his wonderful and slightly malicious smile, "that Mr. Howells agreed with you entirely about *The American Scene*, but he would not admit it."

Professor Norton's cousin, President Eliot, was likewise a fastidious master of speech, with a mind as inquisitive as Norton's although less subtle and far more vigorous. As I have said of him elsewhere,[2] "he was an *amplificator imperii*, an enlarger of the empire of man's estate. His mind was Roman rather than Greek; he cared little for speculative subtleties, he distrusted introspection, and was deaf to some of the rich voices of the past. He read John Locke rather than Plato, was more interested in Pasteur than in Virgil, and in commenting on the Bible story of Mary and Martha, he made it clear that he preferred Martha. He was primarily an organizer and administrator, with an imperial grasp of fact. . . . It is true, of course, that sculpture cannot suggest all of the fascination which was felt in Mr. Eliot's living, speaking presence: in his flawless courtesy of bearing, his habit of deferential listening, his swift, benignant smile, and above all, the tones of his incomparable voice. It was usually low and grave; sometimes hauntingly wistful; but when he was moved by moral indignation it rang—as someone said of Dryden's couplets—like a bronze coin thrown down on marble."

Mr. Eliot belonged to my father's generation, and from the first year of our settling in Cambridge, his kindness to me could scarcely have been greater if I had been his son. I do not think that he was particularly interested in the purely literary features of the *Atlantic*, but he read all its articles on education, economics, politics, and social reconstruction, and was a frequent contributor. I happened to meet him on the platform of

[2] At the unveiling of the bust of President Eliot at Eliot House, on the one-hundredth anniversary of his birth, March 20, 1934.

various public meetings in Boston and Cambridge, and sometimes had the ill-luck to precede or follow him as a speaker. I say "ill-luck," because all the rest of us must have felt, "What can the man do that cometh after the King?" And yet, as many other men of my generation have testified, we could not have had a more considerate and encouraging listener. How flattered I felt in 1902, when he suddenly found himself unable to give a promised address at the University of California and asked me to take his place! I did my best with a speech on "Poetry and Politics," about which I remember nothing now except the remark of D. O. Mills, the veteran banker and Regent of the University. As soon as the formal exercises were concluded, Mr. Mills poured out for me a very tall glass of whiskey-and-water in President Wheeler's library, and pronounced with finality: "Mr. Perry, Poetry is a fine thing, but Business is *the* thing." That was the voice of a whole era.

Yet if there was one spot in the United States which seemed as yet deaf to such a voice, in the opening years of the twentieth century, it was Old Cambridge; steeped as it was in the traditions of Harvard College and typified by the leisurely charm of Brattle Street. The Graduate School of Business Administration, designed to "establish business as a profession," was not invented until 1908, and did not attain its present prominence until after the World War. In 1900 the gracious outward aspect of Old Cambridge was in harmony with its inner spirit. Brattle Street, and even the streets "just off" Brattle, looked as secure as an English cathedral close, and there was among its old American families the sense of continuity, of assured social position, which was a part of that English tradition which lingered in Boston and Cambridge until well into the twentieth century. Brattle Street was like an island in the stream of new and alien races swarming into Greater Boston; an island also in the stream of suburban Americans attracted to Cambridge by rapid transit, by the development of manufacturing interests, and by the growth of Harvard University. Possibly Old Cambridge could count fewer men of world-wide reputation than in 1850, and yet within half a mile of the Craigie House there were probably as many men of personal distinction as could be found anywhere in a similar radius, outside of the great European capitals. Family still counted for something, but money for very little. A typical figure was President Eliot, riding his bicycle every morning on his way to market or for tranquil exercise. I recall that he once appeared on his bicycle at our house at Mercer Circle at 7:15 A.M. to invite me to lunch with an Englishman who had just arrived. Luckily I was shaved and nearly dressed, and came down to find Mr. Eliot examining curiously some vellum-bound seventeenth-century quartos in my study—about the last things in which I should have supposed him to be interested. There were very few telephones in Cambridge then. Today, if a President of Harvard were arranging an extemporized luncheon party, his secretary would be telephoning the professor's secretary—but it would be much later than 7:15 A.M. There were no motor cars as yet, and but few private carriages, though Mr. Howells could no longer have said, as he did once, that there was but one carriage in Old Cambridge and that was owned by a publisher. Social life was simple. Calling had not yet gone out of fashion, and for such occasions, especially on Saturday and Sunday afternoons, gentlemen were accustomed to don their silk hats. Richard H. Dana the Third, a lover of the old ways, was one of the last dwellers on Brattle Street to wear a silk hat really well.[3]

As newcomers to this Old Cambridge, my wife and I were naturally looking at Harvard from the outside. Yet it was obvious that for generations the college had set its stamp upon the community. There were many Harvard professors, for example, in Saint John's Church—really the Chapel of the Episcopal Theological School—where we sat on Sundays under the preaching of Dean George Hodges. He was a singularly able, liberal, and spiritually minded man, like ourselves an immigrant to Cambridge, and, I suspect, never really at home or happy there. Mrs. Perry, who was born in New Haven, educated at Smith, and had been a professor's wife at Williams and Princeton, was tolerably familiar with the innocent provincialism of typical college communities. In our first year or two in Cambridge, we used to collect Harvard stories. One of hers was the remark of a Cambridge lady upon whom my wife happened to be calling, on the day of a Harvard-Yale football game. Casting about for fruitful topics of conversation, they hit upon the fact that two brothers, one representing Harvard and the other Yale, were that day playing against each other. "Perhaps it isn't so strange as it seems," hazarded the Cambridge lady; "you know that it often happens that one of two brothers is brighter than the other." Her guest, brought up in Yale loyalties, assented politely. I was able to match this with a remark made to me by the Cambridge lady's husband, after a dinner in their house. The men, while taking their coffee. mentioned a then newly published book, *Who's Who in America*. I remarked that I was finding it useful in the *Atlantic* office, inasmuch as it gave biographical information about most of the men who had achieved national prominence. Whereupon our host asked, with entire seriousness, "Wouldn't the *Harvard Quinquennial Catalogue* answer every purpose?"

There was a strong Harvard flavor, naturally, in those "paper, discussion, and supper" clubs in which Cambridge abounded. We joined the Query Club and the Junior Shop Club, and are indebted to them for many enduring friendships. The Query Club still held to the old convention of frock coats and high-necked dresses; the Junior Shop Club, made up almost entirely of young Harvard professors and their wives, ventured boldly upon dinner coats and evening gowns. The "papers," supposed to be the shop-talk of a specialist, were not too technical, and the suppers were excellent. Occasionally we attended dinners in the Back Bay, which was then

[3] In this paragraph I have quoted freely from my *R. H. Dana (1851-1931)*, Boston, 1933.

none too easy of access from Cambridge. I joined a good many—perhaps, in view of the amount of night work which I was carrying, too many—of those agreeable men's dining-clubs which are a peculiar institution of Boston. Aldrich introduced me to the Jury Club, whose twelve members dined monthly at some Boston hotel. We had a bibulous retired Admiral, I remember, and a couple of flaming Irish journalists from the Papyrus group. I had supposed that all the Fenians were dead!

A personification of ancient Boston and Harvard respectability was the Examiner Club, founded in 1863 by some of the contributors to the famous Unitarian organ, *The Christian Examiner*. Its original aim was "the discussion of some topic of general interest," and it met monthly at Young's Hotel. Among the older members were a few survivors of the "Conscience Whigs" and the "Cotton Whigs" of the eighteen-fifties; men who still hated or loved Daniel Webster and liked to talk about him. There were old-school reformers like Edward Atkinson and Gamaliel Bradford, Senior, who shared my father's views on the tariff. Our most picturesque figure was Edward Everett Hale, who had written "The Man Without a Country" for the *Atlantic* in the very year of the founding of the Club. The phrase "grand old sloven"—once applied to Montaigne by Emerson—might with equal affection be applied to Dr. Hale, and the carelessness of his dress was matched by the reckless inaccuracy and vigor of his talk. Our treasurer, who was responsible for the selection of the food and wine, was a venerable librarian and epicure named Denny, who might have stepped straight out of the pages of Charles Lamb. He startled me once by asking the chemical composition of the ink used in the Harvard Library, and when I pleaded ignorance, he remarked with deep satisfaction: "I asked that question once of Justin Winsor, and *he* could not answer. I always said he was destitute of the very first qualification for a librarian."

A more gentle figure of the past was Mr. Josiah Phillips Quincy, who as a boy of six had been the marvellous "little Josiah" of Bronson Alcott's Temple School in 1835. His questions and answers to his teacher are faithfully recorded in Miss Elizabeth Peabody's *Record of a School* and Mr. Alcott's *Conversations with Children on the Gospels*. Emerson, who often visited the Temple School, wrote in his Journal for 1836: "Little Josiah Quincy, now six years, six months old, is a child having something wonderful and divine in him. He is a youthful prophet." But "little Josiah," when I knew him, had long ceased to talk theology. He had even written dramatic poems and worldly fiction for the *Atlantic*. He disliked the cigars selected for us by Mr. Denny, and always brought a supply of his own, which he used to offer me with an Old-World hesitancy and elegance. It was from him that I learned that he happened to be calling upon Emerson on the day when the 1856 edition of *Leaves of Grass* arrived, with its famous "I Greet You at the Beginning of a Great Career. R. W. Emerson" emblazoned in gilt letters upon the cover.[4] Emerson had written those

[4] Reproduced in my *Walt Whitman*, edition of 1906, p. 114.

words to Whitman in a private letter in 1855, and Walt saw no reason why he should not make them public. "At no other time," Mr. Quincy wrote me, "had I seen a cloud of dissatisfaction darken that serene countenance."

Although I was a member of the Examiner Club until 1910, and met there many vigorous men of my own generation. I find that my memories of their talk are vague. That private dining-room in Young's Hotel seems now a dusky, shadowy place, with but a dim light upon the faces of a few old men, who represented something that has long since disappeared from Boston. But perhaps the dimness is only the haze from those cigars presented to me by Bronson Alcott's favorite pupil, "little Josiah" Quincy.

The Harvard coloring in some other Boston clubs was even more marked than in the Examiner. The Saturday Club, which I joined in 1903, had at that time thirty-five members, although some of these, like Mr. Howells and Judge Holmes, were no longer residents of Boston. Yet every member of the Harvard Corporation, save one, was enrolled in the Club, besides ten or a dozen Harvard professors. Mr. Norton was then President. It is obvious that it was a temptation to some members to utilize Club dinners for informal discussion of the various business of Harvard College. In fact, James Russell Lowell had been a sinner in this respect as far back as 1866, when he wrote to Norton concerning a recent dinner of the Club: "With me it was a business meeting. I sat between Hoar and Brimmer [two members of the Corporation] that I might talk over college matters." I confess that as a newcomer to Boston and Cambridge I was amazed at the annihilating frankness with which Harvard men discussed the personalities and policies of their Alma Mater. The phrase "Harvard indifferentism" had already been coined, but though it was accurate enough as describing a small and sophisticated group of undergraduates, indifference was surely not a characteristic of the alumni. If they disliked some fact or tendency pertaining to Harvard, they never hesitated in public or private to express their views. Astonished as I was at first by this broad latitude of criticism, I came gradually to see that it was one of the priceless traditions of a freedom-loving university.

Those leisurely monthly dinners of the Saturday Club opened many doors of friendship. Although I met many of the Saturday Club Group at other clubs also, there were some men like Edward W. Emerson, Alexander Agassiz, William Lawrence and George A. Gordon whom I rarely saw elsewhere and whose conversation was always rewarding. "General conversation," the ideal aim of dining-clubs, is difficult to secure when there are more than ten at the table, but even on crowded days at the Saturday Club and in spite of the "business of Harvard College" which was bound to intrude at times, there was always the chance of sitting next to some real person like Major Higginson or Dr. Henry P. Walcott or President Eliot, members of the Corporation though they were! I recall the touchingly simple question asked by Mr. Howells on the occasion of his very last visit to the Club. He was then an old man, and disinclined to meet strangers. But discovering that he and President Lowell had never met, I asked Mr. Howells if I might not bring Mr. Lowell over to sit next him. "*Is he a friendly person?*" asked the novelist with some anxiety. I could assure him on this point. The two men, thus shaking hands for the first time, had long been members of both the Saturday Club and the Tavern Club, where "friendly persons" do not wait to be introduced; but more than thirty years had gone by since Howells had deserted Boston for New York.

The history of the Saturday Club has been written in two stout volumes,[5] and that of the Tavern Club in one,[6] and I should not naturally allude to these clubs in this chapter, were it not that I am attempting to describe the various indirect paths which I happened to follow in gaining an acquaintance with Harvard men and Harvard ways. The ever delightful Tavern Club, which has long had its home in Boylston Place, Boston, with the Bear for its totem, is as unacademic a retreat from sorrow as can be discovered anywhere. Yet Harvard men are in the majority of its varied membership. Its first President, Mr. Howells, was indeed a perpetual example of the saving truth that a college education is not essential to a real education; but his seven successors in the Presidency of the Tavern all had some association with Harvard. When I joined the Club in 1905, the splendid figure of Major Henry Lee Higginson sat in the Tall Chair. In the immortal line of Mark Howe—official historian and unofficial poet of the Tavern—Higginson was

"The Bear's—the Ursa's—Major."

I was still, in the midsummer of 1905, looking in at the windows of Harvard College from the outside. I knew next to nothing about its graduate schools and the larger problems of Harvard University. But having been for half-a-dozen years in daily contact with Harvard graduates as human beings, and having found that most of them were "friendly persons," I was in a mood to look favorably upon that letter of President Eliot which offered me a professorship. Whatever else might be true of Harvard, I could not believe that an institution headed by Charles W. Eliot was dominated by any considerations of Circulation and Advertising. At No. 4 Park Street one was trained to speak respectfully of Circulation and Advertising, for without the protection of those Twin Deities what would become of the magazine? "When my master goeth into the house of Rimmon to worship there, *and he leaneth on my hand*, and I bow myself in the house of Rimmon; when I bow down myself in the house of Rimmon, the Lord pardon thy servant in this thing."

It is a very human prayer, but I did not wish to be repeating it for the rest of my life.

[5] *Early Years of the Saturday Club (1855-1870)*. By Edward W. Emerson, 1918. *Later Years of the Saturday Club (1870-1920)*. Edited by M. A. DeW. Howe, 1927.
[6] *Semi-Centennial History of the Tavern Club*. By M. A. DeW. Howe, 1934.

II. Lifted In

"I hope it will turn out," President Eliot wrote me on March 21, 1906, "that your pecuniary situation will be fully as good as it is now, and that the nature of your work will be more congenial, comfortable, and influential." With these kindly words he lifted me into the cockpit, on the half-time arrangement.

There were some amusing aspects of this appointment. In the first place, I did not know exactly what I was accepting. The Smith Professorship "of the French and Spanish Languages and Literatures and Professor of Belles Lettres" was the title of the chair which I had been offered in 1905, with the explanation which I have already quoted: "It will be for you to select the work you would prefer to do within this great field of literature—English, French, Italian, and Spanish." I wrote Mr. Eliot at once that though I had a reading knowledge of French and Italian, and a very little Spanish, I did not possess accurate scholarship in any of the Romance languages. In his opinion, however, the previous holders of the Chair had "made it almost entirely a professorship of belles lettres and English literature, with an excursion by Ticknor into Spanish literature, and by Longfellow and Lowell into Italian literature. . . . The Smith Professor could not appropriately be a philologist in the technical sense, literature rather than linguistics being the appropriate field of this professorship." This was an assuredly clear statement, though it may be open to question in its interpretation of the actual courses given long ago. Mr. Eliot was equally clear in his dislike of the term "Belles Lettres" and in his unwillingness to have it perpetuated at Harvard. I think he associated it somehow with the Scottish Presbyterian Universities of the eighteenth century! What label he would invent for me, and whether the Corporation and Overseers would approve, of course I did not know; but as I had already borne (and survived) such awesome titles as Professor of "English and Elocution," of "Oratory and Aesthetic Criticism," and of "English Language and Literature and Belles Lettres," the question of my future academic label did not worry me. Many months went by without any further word from President Eliot.

Finally the University *Gazette* of March 16, 1906, gave the official notice of my appointment as "Professor of English Literature," with an explanatory note which, as I afterward learned, was written by Mr. Eliot himself in the office of the *Gazette*:

"This Professorship of English Literature replaces, and is in succession to, the Professorship of Belles Lettres hitherto attached to the Smith Professorship of the French and Spanish Languages. The incumbents of the combined Professorships have been George Ticknor, from 1817 to 1835, Henry Wadsworth Longfellow, from 1836 to 1854, and James Russell Lowell, from 1855 to 1886."

Up to this time there had never been a chair of "English Literature" at

Harvard, the term "English" being considered elastic enough to cover both linguistic and literary courses; and to my embarrassment the newspapers made a good deal of my election as "the successor of Ticknor, Longfellow, and Lowell." I did not belong in that galley, of course, and though I did not mind the chaffing of a few friends, I had an uncomfortable feeling that the public was getting the impression that Harvard was landing a bigger fish than it had actually caught. Fortunately the situation was soon clarified by the promotion of a brilliant young scholar, J. D. M. Ford, to the Smith Professorship of the French and Spanish Languages; and W. H. Schofield's appointment to a chair of Comparative Literature indicated a growing recognition of the interrelation of various European literatures.

Although President Eliot wrote me, a week after the *Gazette* appeared, that "the appointment meets with cordial and universal approval," I knew well enough that such a miracle was impossible. Without raising the question of my qualifications for a professorship, it was felt by some of my future colleagues that the President had carried through the appointment without due consultation with the Department of English—although as a matter of fact some members of that Department had been taken into his confidence. Barrett Wendell evidently had not, and he talked a good deal about the abuse of Presidential power. A comic situation arose on the very day when the newspapers announced my election. I was lunching at the Tavern Club, as usual in those days, and as I went up to the dining-room several men called out their congratulations. By some ironic fate the only vacant chair at the round table was the one next to Wendell. I did not expect him to welcome me to Harvard, and he was too honest to pretend to do so. He opened the conversation with some reference to Byron, and before long was attacking violently his *Vision of Judgment*, the famous satire written as a parody of Southey's eulogy of King George Third. Wendell maintained (perhaps with his tongue in his cheek; I was not sure) that Southey's poem was better than Byron's, on the ground that Southey was on the side of the established order of society, while Byron's satire was subversive of it. I do not usually care for a literary debate while eating lunch, but I could not let anybody exalt Southey's poetry over Byron's, and I contradicted every assertion that Wendell made. For half an hour this battle was waged, and Wendell told someone as he left the Club that he had not had such an enjoyable conversation for months. But Harvard was not mentioned.

I have described in earlier chapters my first faculty meeting at Williams, before I was twenty-one, and the first faculty meeting at Princeton, a dozen years later. Compared with those experiences, I must confess that my first faculty meeting at Harvard, in the spring of 1907, was disillusionizing. We met at four in the afternoon in that beautiful Bulfinch room in University Hall which in my grandfather's time had served as the college chapel. Tea was served in an anteroom, and after President Eliot had called the Faculty of Arts and Sciences to order and the secretary had begun to drone out the minutes of the previous meeting, professors kept strolling in for the next quarter of an hour, tea-cup in hand and still talking. The older men took seats at the long table; the others sprawled in big chairs or upon the side benches. Trained as I had once been in the punctilious decorum and strict parliamentary procedure of the Princeton faculty, the Harvard customs seemed to me shockingly indecorous. Nothing could spoil Eliot's impeccable dignity as a presiding officer, and I marvelled at the patient courtesy with which he listened to motions and remarks made by men who did not even take the trouble to rise in addressing the chair. And I observed that when a man did rise, it was ominous, for the chances were that he was one of the recognized bores who wanted to make a speech!

Of course, being a stranger to University Hall, I missed the historical key of the situation. The truth was that the faculty meeting had sought to preserve the informality of a committee meeting long after it had outgrown the conditions for effective working. When a community has grown into a city, it can no longer be governed by the admirable methods of the primitive town-meeting. I reflected with amusement upon Mr. Eliot's own behavior at faculty meetings when he was a young assistant professor, for he had told me that in that early period he had no interest whatever in faculty discussions and desired to spend the hour upon his own work. Unluckily the table in the faculty room seated at that time only seventeen men, even with some crowding, so that young Eliot could not find elbow room for writing. With characteristic daring, he asked President Walker if the faculty might not have a larger table. "Why, Mr. Eliot," exclaimed the President, "a new table would cost *money*, and Harvard College *has* no money!"

And now, after more than forty years, there was indeed a little more money and a longer table, but precisely the same indifference to what some members of the faculty might be saying! As Eliot sat there at the head of the table, he looked old and indifferent. No one doubted his ability, even then, to master any assembly if he chose, but he reminded me somehow of Lancelot as umpire of the lists in *The Last Tournament*, when he saw the rules of knighthood broken, but made no sign. By 1907, the real work of the faculty was done off-stage, by small committees, and the talk in the faculty meetings was largely supererogatory. During President Lowell's administration the meetings declined in frequency and significance, and now under President Conant a smaller representative body, the "Council of the Faculty of Arts and Sciences," is functioning in their place—the faculty assembling as a whole only four times a year.

My colleague F. N. Robinson and I have had many a laugh over the deplorable scene which made memorable my first attendance upon a meeting of the English Department. The gentle Dean Briggs was presiding, and the business of the afternoon was the approval of the courses proposed for the next half-year. If accepted by the Department, they were then submitted to the Committee on Instruction, who in turn presented them to the Faculty for final adoption. Professor X indicated his desire to offer again a course on "The English Bible," which he had already given with marked success. But Professor Y, whose nerves were often out of tune, made sudden and violent objection: declaring that Professor X was ignorant of Hebrew, and that it was a disgrace to the Department and to Harvard that a course in the Bible should be taught by a man who could not read the Old Testament in the original. Professor X naturally resented this attack upon his scholarship, particularly as Y was himself ignorant of the Hebrew tongue. I happened to be sitting between X and Y, and as their voices rose higher and higher, while their gesticulating fingers shot across my face and the sweet-natured Briggs writhed in humiliation for his Department, I saw the Cockpit of Learning at its worst. If "rare Ben Jonson" had been presiding instead of Briggs, he might have enjoyed the quarrel for a season, but surely he would have ended by taking X and Y, one in either hand, and knocking their hot heads together.

Both X and Y are dead long ago, but that scene taught me something about the jealousies and animosities that may underlie the decorous surface of a department; and I am tempted to set down another instance of the emotional instability of justly famous teachers. Within a few months after I had begun work at Harvard, the French Ambassador, M. Jusserand, was to receive an honorary degree. It is customary in such ceremonials to appoint some professor to escort the candidate—walking with him in the Commencement procession, and taking him to his assigned seat upon the platform. President Eliot asked me if I would escort the Ambassador. I could not decently decline, although I have little love for the pomps of college Commencements, having seen too much of them all my life. Besides, to wait in Cambridge for Commencement Day meant a loss of three days of fishing! Nevertheless I walked with the friendly M. Jusserand, just as I walked in later years with Henry James and with my brother Lewis, when they in turn were candidates for honorary degrees. Not until autumn did I learn that my endeavor to be courteous had had dire consequences. Another professor, it appeared, had considered that the honor of escorting the Ambassador should have been his, and that President Eliot had passed him over with the deliberate intention of insulting him. For two years he refused to speak to Eliot. He wrote me a letter, however, explaining that he knew that I was innocent of having done him an intentional injury, and that the fault lay wholly with the President. I kept that letter as a curiosity, and should not mention it now except to illustrate the pitiful misunderstandings and rivalries which sometimes fester in the professorial heart. Yet when faced by the real troubles of life—as distinct from imaginary maladies—such men often act with silent and magnificent heroism. Ours is a queer profession.

Hitherto I had known little of departmental psychology. At Williams I had had but one colleague in the field of English, and at Princeton only two or three; and in those colleges, after we had once settled upon a fair division of our labors, each man went his own way. But now I began to perceive that the English problem at Harvard was not so simple. One had to reckon with the "filio-pietistic" royalty to the methods of dead masters: if Child had taught Milton or Bacon in a particular way, that was the way to teach those courses still. One had to reckon also with the prescriptive right to certain authors or fields, claimed by men already giving instruction in them. I remember my surprise when an exceptionally competent young professor wished to offer a new course in one corner of a great field, large enough for half-a-dozen specialists at once. But the cautious Department felt compelled to refuse the request: Professor Z was already lecturing upon that general period, and his feelings would be hurt if any portion of it were assigned to another man.

Obviously, a new member of this Department had to walk delicately. Here was a brilliant array of prima-donnas, each supreme in a chosen role: men like Briggs, Wendell, Copeland, Robinson, Baker, and the famous Kittredge, with younger scholars like Neilson and Greenough coming on. But it was difficult for a stranger to discover any common denominator of their activities. What was the underlying philosophy of the Department, its ideal aim, its relation with liberal studies as a whole? I had no intimate friends in the Department, and there was no one to explain its state of mind, if indeed it had one. Fundamental questions were avoided in our meetings; the precious time was consumed in the discussion of wearisome administrative details. The separate parts of the English machine seemed to be in competent hands, but how were the parts related? One was tempted to think, with the old lady who listened to one of Emerson's discourses, that "it had no connection save in God." Years afterward, when I had grown accustomed to our irresponsible individualism, I remember that a colleague in English said to me gloomily: "We *have* no real Department, and never have had." But we were then six hundred miles from Cambridge, salmon fishing, and he had had no luck that day.

The steel core of the English work at Harvard, then as now, was in the solid linguistic and historical courses covering the period from the earliest Anglo-Saxon writers to the decline of the Elizabethan drama. These courses were essential for candidates for honors in English and for the higher degrees. My own graduate work in Germany had been largely in this field, but I had ceased to teach Anglo-Saxon and Chaucer after going to Princeton, and during the dozen years before coming to Harvard I had fallen quite out of step with the philologists. I had, and still have, deep respect for the science of linguistics, but the very best I could say for myself in 1907 was the remark of the futile Mr. Brooke in *Middlemarch:* "I went into that a good deal at one time." An out-of-date philologist is worse than none.

But I could be trusted, Dean Briggs thought, with "English 7^b," a large lecture course covering the period between the death of Swift and the publication of the *Lyrical Ballads,* for in the eighteenth century I had long felt at home. Then Schofield, desirous of new courses for his Department of Comparative Literature, proposed that I should offer something on "Types of Fiction" in the eighteenth and nineteenth centuries, the material to be drawn partly from Continental and partly from English novelists. The idea was to follow the currents of Realism, Sentimentalism, Romanticism, etc., as they swept from one European country to another. We had to study Russian fiction in translations, but a portion of the assigned reading might be done in French, Italian, or German, at the preference of the student.

It was in these two courses, "English 7^b" and "Comparative Literature 12," that I began my half-time work in February, 1907, after returning from the holiday in Italy. In the next year, 1907-'08, I find that I gave a course in Tennyson, to be given alternately with one on Carlyle; and, for graduate students only, a Comparative Literature course on "Political Satire since the Renaissance." In 1908-'09 I was offering a new course on "Lyric Poetry," and wondering whether my colleagues in the Department would sanction a course on Emerson. Finally they did, with the remark that in their judgment Emerson was the only American author worthy of having a course devoted exclusively to him. Perhaps they were afraid that I might offer a course on Walt Whitman! As far as I am aware, this was the first Emerson course to be given in any American college; and when my friend Dr. George A. Gordon heard of it, he remarked grimly that he had himself been graduated from Emerson's own college, and had heard the seer mentioned at Harvard precisely three times.

But when the year 1909-'10 opened, and Lawrence Lowell was succeeding Eliot as President of Harvard, I found myself, as has been told already, expounding Emerson, not in Seven 11, but in the pleasant land of France.

The Aims of Education

ALFRED NORTH WHITEHEAD

*ALFRED NORTH WHITEHEAD, mathematician and philosopher, was
born in England in 1861. He was educated at Sherburne School and at
Trinity College, Cambridge. He taught mathematics in his native country until 1924, when he became Professor of Philosophy at Harvard. He
retired in 1937 and now lives quietly in Cambridge, Massachusetts.*

*His is a deeply religious nature. A mystic, he regards religious experi-
ence as the rational path to knowledge.*

CULTURE is activity of thought, and receptiveness to beauty and
humane feeling. Scraps of information have nothing to do with it. A
merely well-informed man is the most useless bore on God's earth. What
we should aim at producing is men who possess both culture and expert
knowledge in some special direction. Their expert knowledge will give
them the ground to start from, and their culture will lead them as deep
as philosophy and as high as art. We have to remember that the valuable
intellectual development is self-development, and that it mostly takes
place between the ages of sixteen and thirty. As to training, the most important part is given by mothers before the age of twelve. A saying due
to Archbishop Temple illustrates my meaning. Surprise was expressed at
the success in after-life of a man, who as a boy at Rugby had been somewhat undistinguished. He answered, "It is not what they are at eighteen, it
is what they become afterwards that matters."

In training a child to activity of thought, above all things we must beware of what I will call "inert ideas"—that is to say, ideas that are merely
received into the mind without being utilised, or tested, or thrown into
fresh combinations.

In the history of education, the most striking phenomenon is that schools
of learning, which at one epoch are alive with a ferment of genius, in a
succeeding generation exhibit merely pedantry and routine. The reason
is, that they are overladen with inert ideas. Education with inert ideas is
not only useless: it is, above all things, harmful—*Corruptio optimi, pes-
sima.* Except at rare intervals of intellectual ferment, education in the past
has been radically infected with inert ideas. That is the reason why uneducated clever women, who have seen much of the world, are in middle

life so much the most cultured part of the community. They have been saved from this horrible burden of inert ideas. Every intellectual revolution which has ever stirred humanity into greatness has been a passionate protest against inert ideas. Then, alas, with pathetic ignorance of human psychology, it has proceeded by some educational scheme to bind humanity afresh with inert ideas of its own fashioning.

Let us now ask how in our system of education we are to guard against this mental dryrot. We enunciate two educational commandments, "Do not teach too many subjects," and again, "What you teach, teach thoroughly."

The result of teaching small parts of a large number of subjects is the passive reception of disconnected ideas, not illumined with any spark of vitality. Let the main ideas which are introduced into a child's education be few and important, and let them be thrown into every combination possible. The child should make them his own, and should understand their application here and now in the circumstances of his actual life. From the very beginning of his education, the child should experience the joy of discovery. The discovery which he has to make, is that general ideas give an understanding of that stream of events which pours through his life, which is his life. By understanding I mean more than a mere logical analysis, though that is included. I mean "understanding" in the sense in which it is used in the French proverb, "To understand all, is to forgive all." Pedants sneer at an education which is useful. But if education is not useful, what is it? Is it a talent, to be hidden away in a napkin? Of course, education should be useful, whatever your aim in life. It was useful to Saint Augustine and it was useful to Napoleon. It is useful, because understanding is useful.

I pass lightly over that understanding which should be given by the literary side of education. Nor do I wish to be supposed to pronounce on the relative merits of a classical or a modern curriculum. I would only remark that the understanding which we want is an understanding of an insistent present. The only use of a knowledge of the past is to equip us for the present. No more deadly harm can be done to young minds than by depreciation of the present. The present contains all that there is. It is holy ground; for it is the past, and it is the future. At the same time it must be observed that an age is no less past if it existed two hundred years ago than if it existed two thousand years ago. Do not be deceived by the pedantry of dates. The ages of Shakespeare and of Moliere are no less past than are the ages of Sophocles and of Virgil. The communion of saints is a great and inspiring assemblage, but it has only one possible hall of meeting, and that is, the present; and the mere lapse of time through which any particular group of saints must travel to reach that meeting-place, makes very little difference.

Passing now to the scientific and logical side of education, we remember that here also ideas which are not utilised are positively harmful. By utilising an idea, I mean relating it to that stream, compounded of sense perceptions, feelings, hopes, desires, and of mental activities adjusting thought to thought, which forms our life. I can imagine a set of beings which might fortify their souls by passively reviewing disconnected ideas. Humanity is not built that way—except perhaps some editors of newspapers.

In scientific training, the first thing to do with an idea is to prove it. But allow me for one moment to extend the meaning of "prove"; I mean—to prove its worth. Now an idea is not worth much unless the propositions in which it is embodied are true. Accordingly an essential part of the proof of an idea is the proof, either by experiment or by logic, of the truth of the propositions. But it is not essential that this proof of the truth should constitute the first introduction to the idea. After all, its assertion by the authority of respectable teachers is sufficient evidence to begin with. In our first contact with a set of propositions, we commence by appreciating their importance. That is what we all do in after-life. We do not attempt, in the strict sense, to prove or to disprove anything, unless its importance makes it worthy of that honour. These two processes of proof, in the narrow sense, and of appreciation, do not require a rigid separation in time. Both can be proceeded with nearly concurrently. But in so far as either process must have the priority, it should be that of appreciation by use.

Furthermore, we should not endeavour to use propositions in isolation. Emphatically I do not mean, a neat little set of experiments to illustrate Proposition I and then the proof of Proposition I, a neat little set of experiments to illustrate Proposition II and then the proof of Proposition II, and so on to the end of the book. Nothing could be more boring. Interrelated truths are utilised *en bloc*, and the various propositions are employed in any order, and with any reiteration. Choose some important applications of your theoretical subject; and study them concurrently with the systematic theoretical exposition. Keep the theoretical exposition short and simple, but let it be strict and rigid so far as it goes. It should not be too long for it to be easily known with thoroughness and accuracy. The consequences of a plethora of half-digested theoretical knowledge are deplorable. Also the theory should not be muddled up with the practice. The child should have no doubt when it is proving and when it is utilising. My point is that what is proved should be utilised, and that what is utilised should—so far as is practicable—be proved. I am far from asserting that proof and utilisation are the same thing.

At this point of my discourse, I can most directly carry forward my argument in the outward form of a digression. We are only just realising that the art and science of education require a genius and a study of their own; and that this genius and this science are more than a bare knowledge of some branch of science or of literature. This truth was partially perceived in the past generation; and headmasters, somewhat crudely, were apt to supersede learning in their colleagues by requiring left-hand bowling and a taste for football. But culture is more than cricket, and more than football, and more than extent of knowledge.

Education is the acquisition of the art of the utilisation of knowledge. This is an art very difficult to impart. Whenever a text-book is written of real educational worth, you may be quite certain that some reviewer will say that it will be difficult to teach from it. Of course it will be difficult to teach from it. If it were easy, the book ought to be burned; for it cannot be educational. In education, as elsewhere, the broad primrose path leads to a nasty place. This evil path is represented by a book or a set of lectures which will practically enable the student to learn by heart all the questions likely to be asked at the next external examination. And I may say in passing that no educational system is possible unless every question directly asked of a pupil at any examination is either framed or modified by the actual teacher of that pupil in that subject. The external assessor may report on the curriculum or on the performance of the pupils, but never should be allowed to ask the pupil a question which has not been strictly supervised by the actual teacher, or at least inspired by a long conference with him. There are a few exceptions to this rule, but they are exceptions, and could easily be allowed for under the general rule.

We now return to my previous point, that theoretical ideas should always find important applications within the pupil's curriculum. This is not an easy doctrine to apply, but a very hard one. It contains within itself the problem of keeping knowledge alive, of preventing it from becoming inert, which is the central problem of all education.

The best procedure will depend on several factors, none of which can be neglected, namely, the genius of the teacher, the intellectual type of the pupils, their prospects in life, the opportunities offered by the immediate surroundings of the school, and allied factors of this sort. It is for this reason that the uniform external examination is so deadly. We do not denounce it because we are cranks, and like denouncing established things. We are not so childish. Also, of course, such examinations have their use in testing slackness. Our reason of dislike is very definite and very practical. It kills the best part of culture. When you analyse in the light of experience the central task of education, you find that its successful accomplishment depends on a delicate adjustment of many variable factors. The reason is that we are dealing with human minds, and not with dead matter. The evocation of curiosity, of judgment, of the power of mastering a complicated tangle of circumstances, the use of theory in giving foresight in special cases—all these powers are not to be imparted by a set rule embodied in one schedule of examination subjects.

I appeal to you, as practical teachers. With good discipline, it is always possible to pump into the minds of a class a certain quantity of inert knowledge. You take a text-book and make them learn it. So far, so good. The child then knows how to solve a quadratic equation. But what is the point of teaching a child to solve a quadratic equation? There is a traditional answer to this question. It runs thus: The mind is an instrument, you first sharpen it, and then use it; the acquisition of the power of solving a quadratic equation is part of the process of sharpening the mind. Now there is just enough truth in this answer to have made it live through the ages. But for all its half-truth, it embodies a radical error which bids fair to stifle the genius of the modern world. I do not know who was first responsible for this analogy of the mind to a dead instrument. For aught I know, it may have been one of the seven wise men of Greece, or a committee of the whole lot of them. Whoever was the originator, there can be no doubt of the authority which it has acquired by the continuous approval bestowed upon it by eminent persons. But whatever its weight of authority, whatever the high approval which it can quote, I have no hesitation in denouncing it as one of the most fatal, erroneous, and dangerous conceptions ever introduced into the theory of education. The mind is never passive; it is a perpetual activity, delicate, receptive, responsive to stimulus. You cannot postpone its life until you have sharpened it. Whatever interest attaches to your subject-matter must be evoked here and now; whatever powers you are strengthening in the pupil, must be exercised here and now; whatever possibilities of mental life your teaching should impart, must be exhibited here and now. That is the golden rule of education, and a very difficult rule to follow.

The difficulty is just this: the apprehension of general ideas, intellectual habits of mind, and pleasurable interest in mental achievement can be evoked by no form of words, however accurately adjusted. All practical teachers know that education is a patient process of the mastery of details, minute by minute, hour by hour, day by day. There is no royal road to learning through an airy path of brilliant generalisations. There is a proverb about the difficulty of seeing the wood because of the trees. That difficulty is exactly the point which I am enforcing. The problem of education is to make the pupil see the wood by means of the trees.

The solution which I am urging, is to eradicate the fatal disconnection of subjects which kills the vitality of our modern curriculum. There is only one subject-matter for education, and that is Life in all its manifestations. Instead of this single unity, we offer children—Algebra, from which nothing follows; Geometry, from which nothing follows; Science, from which nothing follows; History, from which nothing follows; a Couple of Languages, never mastered; and lastly, most dreary of all, Literature, represented by plays of Shakespeare, with philological notes and short analyses of plot and character to be in substance committed to memory. Can such a list be said to represent Life, as it is known in the midst of the living of it? The best that can be said of it is, that it is a rapid table of contents which a deity might run over in his mind while he was thinking of creating a world, and had not yet determined how to put it together.

Let us now return to quadratic equations. We still have on hand the unanswered question. Why should children be taught their solution? Unless quadratic equations fit into a connected curriculum, of course there is no reason to teach anything about them. Furthermore, extensive as should be the place of mathematics in a complete culture, I am a little doubtful whether for many types of boys algebraic solutions of quadratic equations do not lie on the specialist side of mathematics. I may here remind you that as yet I have not said anything of the psychology or the content of the specialism, which is so necessary a part of an ideal education. But all that is an evasion of our real question, and I merely state it in order to avoid being misunderstood in my answer.

Quadratic equations are part of algebra, and algebra is the intellectual instrument which has been created for rendering clear the quantitative aspects of the world. There is no getting out of it. Through and through the world is infected with quantity. To talk sense, is to talk in quantities. It is no use saying that the nation is large,—How large? It is no use saying that radium is scarce,—How scarce? You cannot evade quantity. You may fly to poetry and to music, and quantity and number will face you in your rhythms and your octaves. Elegant intellects which despise the theory of quantity, are but half-developed. They are more to be pitied than blamed. The scraps of gibberish, which in their school-days were taught to them in the name of algebra, deserve some contempt.

This question of the degeneration of algebra into gibberish, both in word and in fact, affords a pathetic instance of the uselessness of reforming educational schedules without a clear conception of the attributes which you wish to evoke in the living minds of the children. A few years ago there was an outcry that school algebra was in need of reform, but there was a general agreement that graphs would put everything right. So all sorts of things were extruded, and graphs were introduced. So far as I can see, with no sort of idea behind them, but just graphs. Now every examination paper has one or two questions on graphs. Personally, I am an enthusiastic adherent of graphs. But I wonder whether as yet we have gained very much. You cannot put life into any schedule of general education unless you succeed in exhibiting its relation to some essential characteristic of all intelligent or emotional perception. It is a hard saying, but it is true; and I do not see how to make it any easier. In making these little formal alterations you are beaten by the very nature of things. You are pitted against too skilful an adversary, who will see to it that the pea is always under the other thimble.

Reformation must begin at the other end. First, you must make up your mind as to those quantitative aspects of the world which are simple enough to be introduced into general education; then a schedule of algebra should be framed which will about find its exemplification in these applications. We need not fear for our pet graphs, they will be there in plenty when we once begin to treat algebra as a serious means of studying the world. Some of the simplest applications will be found in the quantities which occur in the simplest study of society. The curves of history are more vivid and more informing than the dry catalogues of names and dates which comprise the greater part of that arid school study. What purpose is effected by a catalogue of undistinguished kings and queens? Tom, Dick, or Harry, they are all dead. General resurrections are failures, and are better postponed. The quantitative flux of the forces of modern society is capable of very simple exhibition. Meanwhile, the idea of the variable, of the function, of rate of change, of equations and their solution, of elimination, are being studied as an abstract science for their own sake. Not, of course, in the pompous phrases with which I am alluding to them here, but with that iteration of simple special cases proper to teaching.

If this course be followed, the route from Chaucer to the Black Death, from the Black Death to modern Labour troubles, will connect the tales of the mediaeval pilgrims with the abstract science of algebra, both yielding diverse aspects of that single theme, Life. I know what most of you are thinking at this point. It is that the exact course which I have sketched out is not the particular one which you would have chosen, or even see how to work. I quite agree. I am not claiming that I could do it myself. But your objection is the precise reason why a common external examination system is fatal to education. The process of exhibiting the applications of knowledge must, for its success, essentially depend on the character of the pupils and the genius of the teacher. Of course I have left out the easiest applications with which most of us are more at home. I mean the quantitative sides of sciences, such as mechanics and physics.

Again, in the same connection we plot the statistics of social phenomena against the time. We then eliminate the time between suitable pairs. We can speculate how far we have exhibited a real causal connection, or how far a mere temporal coincidence. We notice that we might have plotted against the time one set of statistics for one country and another set for another country, and thus, with suitable choice of subjects, have obtained graphs which certainly exhibited mere coincidence. Also other graphs exhibit obvious causal connections. We wonder how to discriminate. And so are drawn on as far as we will.

But in considering this description, I must beg you to remember what I have been insisting on above. In the first place, one train of thought will not suit all groups of children. For example, I should expect that artisan children will want something more concrete and, in a sense, swifter than I have set down here. Perhaps I am wrong, but that is what I should guess. In the second place, I am not contemplating one beautiful lecture stimulating, once and for all, an admiring class. That is not the way in which education proceeds. No; all the time the pupils are hard at work solving examples, drawing graphs, and making experiments, until they have a thorough hold on the whole subject. I am describing the interspersed explanations, the directions which should be given to their thoughts. The pupils have got to be made to feel that they are studying something, and are not merely executing intellectual minuets.

Finally, if you are teaching pupils for some general examination, the problem of sound teaching is greatly complicated. Have you ever noticed the zigzag moulding round a Norman arch? The ancient work is beautiful, the modern work is hideous. The reason is, that the modern work is done to exact measure, the ancient work is varied according to the idiosyncrasy of the workman. Here it is crowded, and there it is expanded. Now the essence of getting pupils through examinations is to give equal weight to all parts of the schedule. But mankind is naturally specialist. One man sees a whole subject, where another can find only a few detached examples. I know that it seems contradictory to allow for specialism in a curriculum especially designed for a broad culture. Without contradictions the world would be simpler, and perhaps duller. But I am certain that in education wherever you exclude specialism you destroy life.

We now come to the other great branch of a general mathematical education, namely Geometry. The same principles apply. The theoretical part should be clear-cut, rigid, short, and important. Every proposition not absolutely necessary to exhibit the main connection of ideas should be cut out, but the great fundamental ideas should be all there. No omission of concepts, such as those of Similarity and Proportion. We must remember that, owing to the aid rendered by the visual presence of a figure, Geometry is a field of unequalled excellence for the exercise of the deductive faculties of reasoning. Then, of course, there follows Geometrical Drawing, with its training for the hand and eye.

But, like Algebra, Geometry and Geometrical Drawing must be extended beyond the mere circle of geometrical ideas. In an industrial neighbourhood, machinery and workshop practice form the appropriate extension. For example, in the London Polytechnics this has been achieved with conspicuous success. For many secondary schools I suggest that surveying and maps are the natural applications. In particular, plane-table surveying should lead pupils to a vivid apprehension of the immediate application of geometric truths. Simple drawing apparatus, a surveyor's chain, and a surveyor's compass, should enable the pupils to rise from the survey and mensuration of a field to the construction of the map of a small district. The best education is to be found in gaining the utmost information from the simplest apparatus. The provision of elaborate instruments is greatly to be deprecated. To have constructed the map of a small district, to have considered its roads, its contours, its geology, its climate, its relation to other districts, the effects on the status of its inhabitants, will teach more history and geography than any knowledge of Perkin Warbeck or of Behren's Straits. I mean not a nebulous lecture on the subject, but a serious investigation in which the real facts are definitely ascertained by the aid of accurate theoretical knowledge. A typical mathematical problem should be: Survey such and such a field, draw a plan of it to such and such a scale, and find the area. It would be quite a good procedure to impart the necessary geometrical propositions without their proofs. Then, concurrently in the same term, the proofs of the propositions would be learnt while the survey was being made.

Fortunately, the specialist side of education presents an easier problem than does the provision of a general culture. For this there are many reasons. One is that many of the principles of procedure to be observed are the same in both cases, and it is unnecessary to recapitulate. Another reason is that specialist training takes place—or should take place—at a more advanced stage of the pupil's course, and thus there is easier material to work upon. But undoubtedly the chief reason is that the specialist study is normally a study of peculiar interest to the student. He is studying it because, for some reason, he wants to know it. This makes all the difference. The general culture is designed to foster an activity of mind; the specialist course utilises this activity. But it does not do to lay too much stress on these neat antitheses. As we have already seen, in the general course foci of special interest will arise; and similarly in the special study, the external connections of the subject drag thought outwards.

Again, there is not one course of study which merely gives general culture, and another which gives special knowledge. The subjects pursued for the sake of a general education are special subjects specially studied; and, on the other hand, one of the ways of encouraging general mental activity is to foster a special devotion. You may not divide the seamless coat of learning. What education has to impart is an intimate sense for the power of ideas, for the beauty of ideas, and for the structure of ideas, together with a particular body of knowledge which has peculiar reference to the life of the being possessing it.

The appreciation of the structure of ideas is that side of a cultured mind which can only grow under the influence of a special study. I mean that eye for the whole chess-board, for the bearing of one set of ideas on another. Nothing but a special study can give any appreciation for the exact formulation of general ideas, for their relations when formulated, for their service in the comprehension of life. A mind so disciplined should be both more abstract and more concrete. It has been trained in the comprehension of abstract thought and in the analysis of facts.

Finally, there should grow the most austere of all mental qualities; I mean the sense for style. It is an aesthetic sense, based on admiration for the direct attainment of a foreseen end, simply and without waste. Style in art, style in literature, style in science, style in logic, style in practical execution have fundamentally the same aesthetic qualities, namely, attainment and restraint. The love of a subject in itself and for itself, where it is not the sleepy pleasure of pacing a mental quarter-deck, is the love of style as manifested in that study.

Here we are brought back to the position from which we started, the utility of education. Style, in its finest sense, is the last acquirement of the educated mind; it is also the most useful. It pervades the whole being. The administrator with a sense for style hates waste; the engineer with a sense for style economises his material; the artisan with a sense for style prefers good work. Style is the ultimate morality of mind.

But above style, and above knowledge, there is something, a vague shape like fate above the Greek gods. That something is Power. Style is the fashioning of power, the restraining of power. But, after all, the power of attainment of the desired end is fundamental. The first thing is to get there. Do not bother about your style, but solve your problem, justify the ways of God to man, administer your province, or do whatever else is set before you.

Where, then, does style help? In this, with style the end is attained without side issues, without raising undesirable inflammations. With style you attain your end and nothing but your end. With style the effect of your activity is calculable, and foresight is the last gift of gods to men. With style your power is increased, for your mind is not distracted with irrelevancies, and you are more likely to attain your object. Now style is the exclusive privilege of the expert. Whoever heard of the style of an amateur painter, of the style of an amateur poet? Style is always the product of specialist study, the peculiar contribution of specialism to culture.

English education in its present phase suffers from a lack of definite aim, and from an external machinery which kills its vitality. Hitherto in this address I have been considering the aims which should govern education. In this respect England halts between two opinions. It has not decided whether to produce amateurs or experts. The profound change in the world which the nineteenth century has produced is that the growth of knowledge has given foresight. The amateur is essentially a man with appreciation and with immense versatility in mastering a given routine. But he lacks the foresight which comes from special knowledge. The object of this address is to suggest how to produce the expert without loss of the essential virtues of the amateur. The machinery of our secondary education is rigid where it should be yielding, and lax where it should be rigid. Every school is bound on pain of extinction to train its boys for a small set of definite examinations. No headmaster has a free hand to develop his general education or his specialist studies in accordance with the opportunities of his school, which are created by its staff, its environment, its class of boys, and its endowments. I suggest that no system of external tests which aims primarily at examining individual scholars can result in anything but educational waste.

Primarily it is the schools and not the scholars which should be inspected. Each school should grant its own leaving certificates, based on its own curriculum. The standards of these schools should be sampled and corrected. But the first requisite for educational reform is the school as a unit, with its approved curriculum based on its own needs, and evolved by its own staff. If we fail to secure that, we simply fall from one formalism into another, from one dung-hill of inert ideas into another.

In stating that the school is the true educational unit in any national system for the safeguarding of efficiency, I have conceived the alternative system as being the external examination of the individual scholar. But every Scylla is faced by its Charybdis—or, in more homely language, there is a ditch on both sides of the road. It will be equally fatal to education if we fall into the hands of a supervising department which is under the impression that it can divide all schools into two or three rigid categories, each type being forced to adopt a rigid curriculum. When I say that the school is the educational unit, I mean exactly what I say, no larger unit, no smaller unit. Each school must have the claim to be considered in relation to its special circumstances. The classifying of schools for some purposes is necessary. But no absolutely rigid curriculum, not modified by its own staff, should be permissible. Exactly the same principles apply, with the proper modifications, to universities and to technical colleges.

When one considers in its length and in its breadth the importance of this question of the education of a nation's young, the broken lives, the defeated hopes, the national failures, which result from the frivolous inertia with which it is treated, it is difficult to restrain within oneself a savage rage. In the conditions of modern life the rule is absolute, the race which does not value trained intelligence is doomed. Not all your heroism, not all your social charm, not all your wit, not all your victories on land or at sea, can move back the finger of fate. To-day we maintain ourselves. To-morrow science will have moved forward yet one more step, and there will be no appeal from the judgment which will then be pronounced on the uneducated.

We can be content with no less than the old summary of educational ideal which has been current at any time from the dawn of our civilisation. The essence of education is that it be religious.

Pray, what is religious education?

A religious education is an education which inculcates duty and reverence. Duty arises from our potential control over the course of events. Where attainable knowledge could have changed the issue, ignorance has the guilt of vice. And the foundation of reverence is this perception, that the present holds within itself the complete sum of existence, backwards and forwards, that whole amplitude of time, which is eternity.

Education

RALPH WALDO EMERSON

RALPH WALDO EMERSON (1803-1882) was born in Boston, educated at the Boston Latin School and at Harvard College, from which he was graduated in 1821. Following his graduation, he taught in a girls' school in Boston until 1825, when he entered the Divinity School at Cambridge. His career as a clergyman was brief. After three years as an associate pastor of the Second (Unitarian) Church in Boston he experienced such a change in his religious views that he resigned his pastorate. He spent the year 1833 in Europe, visiting Italy, France, and Great Britain and making the acquaintance of Wordsworth and Carlyle. In 1834 he settled in Concord, where he made his home for the remainder of his life.

Emerson was a seer and mystic, the chief interpreter to America of the philosophy of transcendentalism. As a mystic he taught the nearness of God to all the affairs of men. In his essays he discusses a wide variety of topics, mystical and practical. His views on education are of interest to all who teach.

I LIKE boys, the masters of the playground and of the streets,—boys, who have the same liberal ticket of admission to all shops, factories, armories, town-meetings, caucuses, mobs, target-shootings, as flies have; quite unsuspected, coming in as naturally as the janitor,—known to have no money in their pockets, and themselves not suspecting the value of this poverty; putting nobody on his guard, but seeing the inside of the show,— hearing all the asides. There are no secrets from them, they know everything that befalls in the fire-company, the merits of every engine and of every man at the brakes, how to work it, and are swift to try their hand at every part; so too the merits of every locomotive on the rails, and will coax the engineer to let them ride with him and pull the handles when it goes to the engine-house. They are there only for fun, and not knowing that they are at school, in the court-house, or the cattle-show, quite as much and more than they were, an hour ago, in the arithmetic class.

They know truth from counterfeit as quick as the chemist does. They detect weakness in your eye and behavior a week before you open your mouth, and have given you the benefit of their opinion quick as a wink. They make no mistakes, have no pedantry, but entire belief on experience. Their elections at baseball or cricket are founded on merit, and are right. They don't pass for swimmers until they can swim, nor for stroke-oar until

103

they can row: and I desire to be saved from their contempt. If I can pass
with them, I can manage well enough with their fathers.

Everybody delights in the energy with which boys deal and talk with
each other; the mixture of fun and earnest, reproach and coaxing, love and
wrath, with which the game is played;—the good-natured yet defiant independence of a leading boy's behavior in the school-yard. How we envy
in later life the happy youths to whom their boisterous games and rough
exercise furnish the precise element which frames and sets off their school
and college tasks, and teaches them, when least they think it, the use and
meaning of these. In their fun and extreme freak they hit on the topmost
sense of Horace. The young giant, brown from his hunting-tramp, tells his
story well, interlarded with lucky allusions to Homer, to Virgil, to college-
songs, to Walter Scott; and Jove and Achilles, partridge and trout, opera
and binomial theorem, Caesar in Gaul, Sherman in Savannah, and hazing
in Holworthy, dance through the narrative in merry confusion, yet the
logic is good. If he can turn his books to such picturesque account in his
fishing and hunting, it is easy to see how his reading and experience, as
he has more of both, will interpenetrate each other. And every one desires
that this pure vigor of action and wealth of narrative, cheered with so
much humor and street rhetoric, should be carried into the habit of the
young man, purged of its uproar and rudeness, but with all its vivacity
entire. His hunting and campings-out have given him an indispensable
base: I wish to add a taste for good company through his impatience of
bad. That stormy genius of his needs a little direction to games, charades,
verses of society, song, and a correspondence year by year with his wisest
and best friends. Friendship is an order of nobility; from its revelations
we come more worthily into nature. Society he must have or he is poor
indeed; he gladly enters a school which forbids conceit, affectation, emphasis and dulness, and requires of each only the flower of his nature and
experience; requires good will, beauty, wit and select information; teaches
by practice the law of conversation, namely, to hear as well as to speak.

Meantime, if circumstances do not permit the high social advantages,
solitude has also its lessons. The obscure youth learns there the practice
instead of the literature of his virtues; and, because of the disturbing effect
of passion and sense, which by a multitude of trifles impede the mind's
eye from the quiet search of that fine horizon-line which truth keeps,—
the way to knowledge and power has ever been an escape from too much
engagement with affairs and possessions; a way, not through plenty and
superfluity, but by denial and renunciation, into solitude and privation;
and, the more is taken away, the more real and inevitable wealth of being
is made known to us. The solitary knows the essence of the thought, the
scholar in society only its fair face. There is no want of example of great
men, great benefactors, who have been monks and hermits in habit. The
bias of mind is sometimes irresistible in that direction. The man is, as it
were, born deaf and dumb, and dedicated to a narrow and lonely life.

Let him study the art of solitude, yield as gracefully as he can to his destiny. Why cannot he get the good of his doom, and if it is from eternity a settled fact that he and society shall be nothing to each other, why need he blush so, and make wry faces to keep up a freshman's seat in the fine world? Heaven often protects valuable souls charged with great secrets, great ideas, by long shutting them up with their own thoughts. And the most genial and amiable of men must alternate society with solitude, and learn its severe lessons.

There comes the period of the imagination to each, a later youth; the power of beauty, the power of books, of poetry. Culture makes his books realities to him, their characters more brilliant, more effective on his mind, than his actual mates. Do not spare to put novels into the hands of young people as an occasional holiday and experiment; but, above all, good poetry in all kinds, epic, tragedy, lyric. If we can touch the imagination, we serve them, they will never forget it. Let him read Tom Brown at Rugby, read Tom Brown at Oxford,—better yet, read Hodson's Life—Hodson who took prisoner the king of Delhi. They teach the same truth,—a trust, against all appearances, against all privations, in your own worth, and not in tricks, plotting, or patronage.

I believe that our own experience instructs us that the secret of Education lies in respecting the pupil. It is not for you to choose what he shall know, what he shall do. It is chosen and foreordained, and he only holds the key to his own secret. By your tampering and thwarting and too much governing he may be hindered from his end and kept out of his own. Respect the child. Wait and see the new product of Nature. Nature loves analogies, but not repetitions. Respect the child. Be not too much his parent. Trespass not on his solitude.

But I hear the outcry which replies to this suggestion:—Would you verily throw up the reins of public and private discipline; would you leave the young child to the mad career of his own passions and whimsies, and call this anarchy a respect for the child's nature? I answer,—Respect the child, respect him to the end, but also respect yourself. Be the companion of his thought, the friend of his friendship, the lover of his virtue, —but no kinsman of his sin. Let him find you so true to yourself that you are the irreconcilable hater of his vice and the imperturbable slighter of his trifling.

The two points in a boy's training are, to keep his *naturel* and train off all but that:—to keep his *naturel*, but stop off his uproar, fooling and horseplay;—keep his nature and arm it with knowledge in the very direction in which it points. Here are the two capital facts, Genius and Drill. The first is the inspiration in the well-born healthy child, the new perception he has of nature. Somewhat he sees in forms or hears in music or apprehends in mathematics, or believes practicable in mechanics or possible in political society, which no one else sees or hears or believes. This is the perpetual romance of new life, the invasion of God into the old dead

world, when he sends into quiet houses a young soul with a thought which
is not met, looking for something which is not there, but which ought to
be there: the thought is dim but it is sure, and he casts about restless for
means and masters to verify it; he makes wild attempts to explain himself
and invoke the aid and consent of the bystanders. Baffled for want of language and methods to convey his meaning, not yet clear to himself, he
conceives that though not in this house or town, yet in some other house
or town is the wise master who can put him in possession of the rules and
instruments to execute his will. Happy this child with a bias, with a
thought which entrances him, leads him, now into deserts now into cities,
the fool of an idea. Let him follow it in good and in evil report, in good or
bad company; it will justify itself; it will lead him at last into the illustrious society of the lovers of truth.

Happy the natural college thus self-instituted around every natural
teacher; the young men of Athens around Socrates; of Alexandria around
Plotinus; of Paris around Abelard; of Germany around Fichte, or Niebuhr,
or Goethe: in short the natural sphere of every leading mind. But the
moment this is organized, difficulties begin. The college was to be the
nurse and home of genius; but, though every young man is born with some
determination in his nature, and is a potential genius; is at last to be one;
it is, in the most, obstructed and delayed, and, whatever they may hereafter be, their senses are now opened in advance of their minds. They
are more sensual than intellectual. Appetite and indolence they have, but
no enthusiasm. These come in numbers to the college: few geniuses: and
the teaching comes to be arranged for these many, and not for those few.
Hence the instruction seems to require skilful tutors, of accurate and systematic mind, rather than ardent and inventive masters. Besides, the
youth of genius are eccentric, won't drill, are irritable, uncertain, explosive, solitary, not men of the world, not good for every-day association.
You have to work for large classes instead of individuals; you must lower
your flag and reef your sails to wait for the dull sailors; you grow departmental, routinary, military almost with your discipline and college
police. But what doth such a school to form a great and heroic character?
What abiding Hope can it inspire? What Reformer will it nurse? What
poet will it breed to sing to the human race? What discoverer of Nature's
laws will it prompt to enrich us by disclosing in the mind the statute which
all matter must obey? What fiery soul will it send out to warm a nation
with his charity? What tranquil mind will it have fortified to walk with
meekness in private and obscure duties, to wait and to suffer? Is it not
manifest that our academic institutions should have a wider scope; that
they should not be timid and keep the ruts of the last generation, but that
wise men thinking for themselves and heartily seeking the good of mankind, and counting the cost of innovation, should dare to arouse the young
to a just and heroic life; that the moral nature should be addressed in

the school-room, and children should be treated as the high-born candidates of truth and virtue?

So to regard the young child, the young man, requires, no doubt, rare patience: a patience that nothing but faith in the remedial forces of the soul can give. You see his sensualism; you see his want of those tastes and perceptions which make the power and safety of your character. Very likely. But he has something else. If he has his own vice, he has its correlative virtue. Every mind should be allowed to make its own statement in action, and its balance will appear. In these judgments one needs that foresight which was attributed to an eminent reformer, of whom it was said "his patience could see in the bud of the aloe the blossom at the end of a hundred years." Alas for the cripple Practice when it seeks to come up with the bird Theory, which flies before it. Try your design on the best school. The scholars are of all ages and temperaments and capacities. It is difficult to class them, some are too young, some are slow, some perverse. Each requires so much consideration, that the morning hope of the teacher, of a day of love and progress, is often closed at evening by despair. Each single case, the more it is considered, shows more to be done; and the strict conditions of the hours, on one side, and the number of tasks, on the other. Whatever becomes of our method, the conditions stand fast,—six hours, and thirty, fifty, or a hundred and fifty pupils. Something must be done, and done speedily, and in this distress the wisest are tempted to adopt violent means, to proclaim martial law, corporal punishment, mechanical arrangement, bribes, spies, wrath, main strength and ignorance, in lieu of that wise genial providential influence they had hoped, and yet hope at some future day to adopt. Of course the devotion to details reacts injuriously on the teacher. He cannot indulge his genius, he cannot delight in personal relations with young friends, when his eye is always on the clock, and twenty classes are to be dealt with before the day is done. Besides, how can he please himself with genius, and foster modest virtue? A sure proportion of rogue and dunce finds its way into every school and requires a cruel share of time, and the gentle teacher, who wished to be a Providence to youth, is grown a martinet, sore with suspicions; knows as much vice as the judge of a police court, and his love of learning is lost in the routine of grammars and books of elements.

A rule is so easy that it does not need a man to apply it; an automaton, a machine, can be made to keep a school so. It facilitates labor and thought so much that there is always the temptation in large schools to omit the endless task of meeting the wants of each single mind, and to govern by steam. But it is at frightful cost. Our modes of Education aim to expedite, to save labor; to do for masses what cannot be done for masses, what must be done reverently, one by one: say rather, the whole world is needed for the tuition of each pupil. The advantages of this system of emulation and display are so prompt and obvious, it is such a time-saver, it is so energetic on slow and on bad natures, and is of so easy application, needing no sage or poet, but any tutor or schoolmaster in his first term can apply it,—that it is not strange that this calomel of culture should be a popular medicine. On the other hand, total abstinence from this drug, and the adoption of simple discipline and the following of nature, involves at once immense claims on the time, the thoughts, on the life of the teacher. It requires time, use, insight, event, all the great lessons and assistances of God; and only to think of using it implies character and profoundness; to enter on this course of discipline is to be good and great. It is precisely analogous to the difference between the use of corporal punishment and the methods of love. It is so easy to bestow on a bad boy a blow, overpower him, and get obedience without words, that in this world of hurry and distraction, who can wait for the returns of reason and the conquest of self; in the uncertainty too whether that will ever come? And yet the familiar observation of the universal compensations might suggest the fear that so summary a stop of a bad humor was more jeopardous than its continuance.

Now the correction of this quack practice is to import into Education the wisdom of life. Leave this military hurry and adopt the pace of Nature. Her secret is patience. Do you know how the naturalist learns all the secrets of the forest, of plants, of birds, of beasts, of reptiles, of fishes, of the rivers and the sea? When he goes into the woods the birds fly before him and he finds none; when he goes to the river-bank, the fish and the reptile swim away and leave him alone. His secret is patience; he sits down, and sits still; he is a statue; he is a log. These creatures have no value for their time, and he must put as low a rate on his. By dint of obstinate sitting still, reptile, fish, bird and beast, which all wish to return to their haunts, begin to return. He sits still; if they approach, he remains passive as the stone he sits upon. They lose their fear. They have curiosity too about him. By and by the curiosity masters the fear, and they come swimming, creeping and flying towards him; and as he is still immovable, they not only resume their haunts and their ordinary labors and manners, show themselves to him in their work-day trim, but also volunteer some degree of advances towards fellowship and good understanding with a biped who behaves so civilly and well. Can you not baffle the impatience and passion of the child by your tranquillity? Can you not wait for him, as Nature and Providence do? Can you not keep for his mind and ways, for his secret, the same curiosity you give to the squirrel, snake, rabbit, and the sheldrake and the deer? He has a secret; wonderful methods in him; he is,—every child,—a new style of man; give him time and opportunity. Talk of Columbus and Newton! I tell you the child just born in yonder hovel is the beginning of a revolution as great as theirs. But you must have the believing and prophetic eye. Have the self-command you wish to inspire. Your teaching and discipline must have the reserve and taciturnity of Nature. Teach them to hold their tongues by holding your own. Say little; do not snarl; do not chide; but govern by the eye. See what they need, and that the right thing is done.

I confess myself utterly at a loss in suggesting particular reforms in our ways of teaching. No discretion that can be lodged with a school-committee, with the overseers or visitors of an academy, of a college, can at all avail to reach these difficulties and perplexities, but they solve themselves when we leave institutions and address individuals. The will, the male power, organizes, imposes its own thought and wish on others, and makes the military eye which controls boys as it controls men; admirable in its results, a fortune to him who has it, and only dangerous when it leads the workman to overvalue and overuse it and precludes him from finer means. Sympathy, the female force,—which they must use who have not the first,—deficient in instant control and the breaking down of resistance, is more subtle and lasting and creative. I advise teachers to cherish mother-wit. I assume that you will keep the grammar, reading, writing and arithmetic in order; 't is easy and of course you will. But smuggle in a little contraband wit, fancy, imagination, thought. If you have a taste which you have suppressed because it is not shared by those about you, tell them that. Set this law up, whatever becomes of the rules of the school: they must not whisper, much less talk; but if one of the young people says a wise thing, greet it, and let all the children clap their hands. They shall have no book but schoolbooks in the room; but if one has brought in a Plutarch or Shakespeare or Don Quixote or Goldsmith or any other good book, and understands what he reads, put him at once at the head of the class. Nobody shall be disorderly, or leave his desk without permission, but if a boy runs from his bench, or a girl, because the fire falls, or to check some injury that a little dastard is inflicting behind his desk on some helpless sufferer, take away the medal from the head of the class and give it on the instant to the brave rescuer. If a child happens to show that he knows any fact about astronomy, or plants, or birds, or rocks, or history, that interests him and you, hush all the classes and encourage him to tell it so that all may hear. Then you have made your school-room like the world. Of course you will insist on modesty in the children, and respect to their teachers, but if the boy stops you in your speech, cries out that you are wrong and sets you right, hug him!

To whatsoever upright mind, to whatsoever beating heart I speak, to you it is committed to educate men. By simple living, by an illimitable soul, you inspire, you correct, you instruct, you raise, you embellish all. By your own act you teach the beholder how to do the practicable. According to the depth from which you draw your life, such is the depth not only of your strenuous effort, but of your manners and presence.

The beautiful nature of the world has here blended your happiness with your power. Work straight on in absolute duty, and you lend an arm and an encouragement to all the youth of the universe. Consent yourself to be an organ of your highest thought, and lo! suddenly you put all men in your debt, and are the fountain of an energy that goes pulsing on with waves of benefit to the borders of society, to the circumference of things.

In School Days

JOHN GREENLEAF WHITTIER

JOHN GREENLEAF WHITTIER, descendant of Quaker farmers, was born in 1807, in Haverhill, Massachusetts, and died in 1892. He had little formal schooling and during his youth led the austere life of a typical farm boy of the day.

Early in his life he became an Abolitionist and many of his poems were written to further the Abolitionist cause. After the Civil War he resumed his early interest in the New England scene and wrote Snow-Bound, *his greatest work. This poem, published in 1866, is a record of home life on a New England farm in midwinter. The merry schoolmaster described in the second selection was George Haskell, a Dartmouth student.*

STILL sits the school-house by the road,
   A ragged beggar sleeping;
Around it still the sumachs grow,
   And blackberry-vines are creeping.

Within, the master's desk is seen,
   Deep scarred by raps official;
The warping floor, the battered seats,
   The jack-knife's carved initial;

The charcoal frescos on its wall;
   Its door's worn sill, betraying
The feet that, creeping slow to school,
   Went storming out to playing!

Long years ago a winter sun
   Shone over it at setting;
Lit up its western window-panes,
   And low eaves' icy fretting.

It touched the tangled golden curls,
   And brown eyes full of grieving,
Of one who still her steps delayed
   When all the school were leaving.

For near her stood the little boy
  Her childish favor singled:
His cap pulled low upon a face
  Where pride and shame were mingled.

Pushing with restless feet the snow
  To right and left, he lingered:—
As restlessly her tiny hands
  The blue-checked apron fingered.

He saw her lift her eyes; he felt
  The soft hand's light caressing,
And heard the tremble of her voice,
  As if a fault confessing.

"I'm sorry that I spelt the word:
  I hate to go above you,
Because,"—the brown eyes lower fell,—
  "Because, you see, I love you!"

Still memory to a gray-haired man
  That sweet child-face is showing.
Dear girl! the grasses on her grave
  Have forty years been growing!

He lives to learn, in life's hard school,
  How few who pass above him
Lament their triumph and his loss,
  Like her,—because they love him.

The Master of the District School

BRISK wielder of the birch and rule,
The master of the district school
Held at the fire his favored place,
Its warm glow lit a laughing face
Fresh-hued and fair, where scarce appeared
The uncertain prophecy of beard.
He played the old and simple games
Our modern boyhood scarcely names,
Sang songs, and told us what befalls
In classic Dartmouth's college halls.

Born the wild Northern hills among,
From whence his yeoman father wrung
By patient toil subsistence scant,
Not competence and yet not want,
He early gained the power to pay
His cheerful, self-reliant way;
Could doff at ease his scholar's gown
To peddle wares from town to town;
Or through the long vacation's reach
In lonely lowland districts teach,
Where all the droll experience found
At stranger hearths in boarding round,
The moonlit skater's keen delight,
The sleigh-drive through the frosty night,
The rustic party, with its rough
Accompaniment of blind-man's buff,
And whirling plate, and forfeits paid,
His winter task a pastime made.
Happy the snow-locked homes wherein
He tuned his merry violin,
Or played the athlete in the barn,
Or held the good dame's winding yarn,
Or mirth-provoking versions told
Of classic legends rare and old,
Wherein the scenes of Greece and Rome
Had all the commonplace of home,
And little seemed at best the odds
'Twixt Yankee pedlers and old gods;
Where Pindus-born Araxes took
The guise of any grist-mill brook,
And dread Olympus at his will
Became a huckleberry hill.

A careless boy that night he seemed;
But at his desk he had the look
And air of one who wisely schemed,
And hostage from the future took
In trainéd thought and lore of book.
Large-brained, clear-eyed,—of such as he
Shall Freedom's young apostles be,
Who, following in War's bloody trail,
Shall every lingering wrong assail;
All chains from limb and spirit strike,
Uplift the black and white alike;
Scatter before their swift advance

The darkness and the ignorance,
The pride, the lust, the squalid sloth,
Which nurtured Treason's monstrous growth,
Made murder pastime, and the hell
Of prison-torture possible;
The cruel lie of caste refute,
Old forms remould, and substitute
For Slavery's lash the freeman's will,
For blind routine, wise-handed skill;
A school-house plant on every hill,
Stretching in radiate nerve-lines thence
The quick wires of intelligence;
Till North and South together brought
Shall own the same electric thought,
In peace a common flag salute,
And, side by side in labor's free
And unresentful rivalry,
Harvest the fields wherein they fought.

Dr. Johnson on Education

JAMES BOSWELL

JAMES BOSWELL (1740-1795), biographer of Samuel Johnson (1709-1784), was born in Edinburgh, the descendant of a Scotch family of some wealth and distinction. He was educated at Edinburgh University and at Glasgow University, where he was a student of civil law. Before settling down to the practice of law, Boswell spent several years in London, enjoying society and making the acquaintance of celebrated men. He first met Samuel Johnson on May 16, 1763, in a London bookshop kept by an actor named Davies. This introduction afforded Johnson great satisfaction, for he was particularly happy in the company of men of genius.

In 1763 Boswell left London for the continent ostensibly to continue the study of law and thereby give evidence to his father of a serious purpose in life. The law, however, claimed little of his time. He observed, traveled, sought the acquaintance of great men. He visited Berlin and Paris, Geneva and Corsica. He met both Voltaire and Rousseau and in Corsica became a friend of General Paoli, at whose London residence he subsequently spent much of his time. In February 1766 Boswell returned to England and in the following July was admitted to the bar as advocate. In 1768 he published a historical account of Corsica and a year later a volume of "Essays in Favour of the Brave Corsicans." Hoping through his interest in Corsica to gain the acquaintance of English statesmen, he made frequent visits to London. His friendship with Johnson developed and in 1773 he was admitted to the famous Literary Club, which Johnson and Sir Joshua Reynolds had founded. He conceived the idea of writing a biography of Johnson and set about collecting information and making a careful record of Johnson's conversation. In 1773 he made a tour of the Hebrides with Johnson, an account of which he published after Johnson's death.

The famous Life of Samuel Johnson, L.L.D., appeared in 1791. While at work upon a second edition of the Life, Boswell became ill and died on May 19, 1795.

Thanks largely to Boswell's Life Samuel Johnson is still one of the most familiar figures in English literature. Born in Litchfield in 1709 and educated at Pembroke College, Oxford, Johnson had become the most famous man of letters in England before his death in 1784. A man of great wisdom, of shrewdness and wit, of invincible common sense, of deep piety, Johnson has been called "a national institution," "the embodiment of the mind and character of the English people." Without the genius of Boswell, however, Johnson's great fame might have faded into legend and in time *been forgotten. Johnson was, perhaps, the best talker of whom we have record. It is Boswell who has kept this talk alive. The following excerpt from the* Life *is a sample of Johnson's brilliant talk.*

A⊤ night Mr. Johnson and I supped in a private room at the Turk's Head coffee-house, in the Strand. "I encourage this house (said he;) for the mistress of it is a good civil woman, and has not much business."

"Sir, I love the acquaintance of young people; because, in the first place, I don't like to think myself growing old. In the next place, young acquaintances must last longest, if they do last; and then, Sir, young men have more virtue than old men; they have more generous sentiments in every respect. I love the young dogs of this age: they have more wit and humour and knowledge of life than we had; but then the dogs are not so good scholars. Sir, in my early years I read very hard. It is a sad reflection, but a true one, that I knew almost as much at eighteen as I do now. My judgment, to be sure, was not so good; but I had all the facts. I remember very well, when I was at Oxford, an old gentleman said to me, 'Young man, ply your book diligently now, and acquire a stock of knowledge; for when years come upon you, you will find that poring upon books will be but an irksome task.'"

.   .   .

He maintained that a boy at school was the happiest of human beings. I supported a different opinion, from which I have never yet varied, that a man is happier; and I enlarged upon the anxiety and sufferings which are endured at school. JOHNSON. "Ah! Sir, a boy's being flogged is not so severe as a man's having the hiss of the world against him. Men have a solicitude about fame; and the greater share they have of it, the more afraid they are of losing it." I silently asked myself, "Is it possible that the great SAMUEL JOHNSON really entertains any such apprehension, and is not confident that his exalted fame is established upon a foundation never to be shaken?"

.   .   .

We talked of the education of children; and I asked him what he thought was best to teach them first. JOHNSON. "Sir, it is no matter what you teach them first, any more than what leg you shall put into your breeches first. Sir, you may stand disputing which is best to put in first, but in the mean time your breech is bare. Sir, while you are considering which of two things you should teach your child first, another boy has learnt them both."

.   .   .

Talking of a young man who was uneasy from thinking that he was very deficient in learning and knowledge, he said, "A man has no reason to complain who holds a middle place, and has many below him; and perhaps he has not six of his years above him;—perhaps not one. Though he may not know any thing perfectly, the general mass of knowledge that he has acquired is considerable. Time will do for him all that is wanting."

.   .   .

Mr. Langton told us he was about to establish a school upon his estate, but it had been suggested to him, that it might have a tendency to make the people less industrious. JOHNSON. "No, Sir. While learning to read and write is a distinction, the few who have that distinction may be the less inclined to work; but when everybody learns to read and write, it is no longer a distinction. A man who has a laced waistcoat is too fine a man to work; but if every body had laced waistcoats, we should have people working in laced waistcoats. There are no people whatever more industrious, none who work more, than our manufacturers; yet they have all learnt to read and write. Sir, you must not neglect doing a thing immediately good, from fear of remote evil;—from fear of its being abused. A man who has candles may sit up too late, which he would not do if he had not candles; but nobody will deny that the art of making candles, by which light is continued to us beyond the time that the sun gives us light, is a valuable art, and ought to be preserved."

.   .   .

"There is now less flogging in our great schools than formerly, but then less is learned there; so that what the boys get at one end they lose at the other."

"More is learned in publick than in private schools, from emulation; there is the collision of mind with mind, or the radiation of many minds pointing to one centre. Though few boys make their own exercises, yet if a good exercise is given up, out of a great number of boys, it is made by somebody."

"I hate by-roads in education. Education is as well known, and has long been as well known, as ever it can be. Endeavouring to make children prematurely wise is useless labour. Suppose they have more knowledge at five or six years old than other children, what use can be made of it? It will be lost before it is wanted, and the waste of so much time and labour of the teacher can never be repaid. Too much is expected from precocity, and too little performed. Miss ———— was an instance of early cultivation, but in what did it terminate? In marrying a little Presbyterian parson, who keeps an infant boarding-school, so that all her employment now is,

To suckle fools, and chronicle small-beer.

She tells the children, This is a cat, and that is a dog, with four legs and a tail; see there! you are much better than a cat or a dog, for you can speak. If

I had bestowed such an education on a daughter, and had discovered that she thought of marrying such a fellow, I would have sent her to the Congress."

. . .

He allowed very great influence to education. "I do not deny, Sir, but there is some original difference in minds; but it is nothing in comparison of what is formed by education. We may instance the science of *numbers*, which all minds are equally capable of attaining; yet we find a prodigious difference in the powers of different men, in that respect, after they are grown up, because their minds have been more or less exercised in it: and I think the same cause will explain the difference of excellence in other things, gradations admitting always some difference in the first principles."

. . .

We had a quiet comfortable meeting at Mr. Dilly's; nobody there but ourselves. Mr. Dilly mentioned somebody having wished that Milton's *Tractate on Education* should be printed along with his Poems in the edition of *The English Poets* then going on. JOHNSON. "It would be breaking in upon the plan; but would be of no great consequence. So far as it would be any thing, it would be wrong. Education in England has been in danger of being hurt by two of its greatest men, Milton and Locke. Milton's plan is impracticable, and I suppose has never been tried. Locke's, I fancy, has been tried often enough, but is very imperfect; it gives too much to one side, and too little to the other; it gives too little to literature."

. . .

It having been mentioned to Dr. Johnson that a gentleman who had a son whom he imagined to have an extreme degree of timidity, resolved to send him to a publick school, that he might acquire confidence;—"Sir, (said Johnson,) this is a preposterous expedient for removing his infirmity; such a disposition should be cultivated in the shade. Placing him at a publick school is forcing an owl upon day."

Nicholas and His Uncle Wait Upon Mr. Wackford Squeers, the Yorkshire Schoolmaster

CHARLES DICKENS

CHARLES DICKENS (1812-1870) had little formal education. Weak and sickly as a child and left largely to his own resources, he fed his imagination on a little collection of books found in a spare room of a house in Chatham in which five of his boyhood years were spent.

When Charles was eleven, his family moved to London and soon he knew the life of the streets about which he later wrote so vividly. When his father fell into debt and was confined in a debtors' prison, young Charles took a job in a tumble-down blacking warehouse at a salary of six shillings a week. During this year the boy lived in a wretched children's lodging house and consorted daily with vagabonds and street waifs. Though the year was an unhappy one, it was a most important influence in his life. It sharpened his powers of observation and gave him material which he later put to good use in his novels.

A small legacy enabled his father to obtain release from debtors' prison and to send Charles to school for two years. In 1826 Charles began to earn his own living again, and at nineteen he became a parliamentary reporter and journalist.

While working as a journalist, Dickens adopted the pen name of Boz and began writing a series of sketches collected and published in 1836 as Sketches by Boz, Illustrative of Every Day Life and Every Day People. *The year 1836 was a turning point in his fortunes. After Pickwick his novels followed one another in rapid succession.*

The following selections are taken from Nicholas Nickleby. *In this novel Dickens shows his zeal as a reformer in his account of Dotheboys Hall, the cheap Yorkshire school presided over by the unforgettable Mr. Squeers.*

· · ·

Mr. Squeers's appearance was not prepossessing. He had but one eye, and the popular prejudice runs in favour of two. The eye he had, was unquestionably useful, but decidedly not ornamental; being of a greenish grey, and in shape resembling the fanlight of a street-door. The blank side of his face was much wrinkled and puckered up, which gave him a very sinister appearance, especially when he smiled, at which times his expression bordered closely on the villainous. His hair was very flat and shiny, save at the ends, where it was brushed stiffly up from a low protruding forehead, which assorted well with his harsh voice and coarse manner. He was about two or three and fifty, and a trifle below the middle size; he wore a white neckerchief with long ends, and a suit of scholastic black; but his coat sleeves being a great deal too long, and his trousers a great deal too short, he appeared ill at ease in his clothes, and as if he were in a perpetual state of astonishment at finding himself so respectable.

Mr. Squeers was standing in a box by one of the coffee-room fireplaces, fitted with one such table as is usually seen in coffee-rooms, and two of extraordinary shapes and dimensions made to suit the angles of the partition. In a corner of the seat, was a very small deal trunk, tied round with a scanty piece of cord; and on the trunk was perched—his lace-up half-boots and corduroy trousers dangling in the air—a diminutive boy, with his shoulders drawn up to his ears and his hands planted on his knees, who glanced timidly at the schoolmaster, from time to time, with evident dread and apprehension.

"Half-past three," muttered Mr. Squeers, turning from the window, and looking sulkily at the coffee-room clock. "There will be nobody here to-day."

Much vexed by this reflection, Mr. Squeers looked at the little boy to see whether he was doing anything he could beat him for. As he happened not to be doing anything, at all, he merely boxed his ears, and told him not to do it again.

"At Midsummer," muttered Mr. Squeers, resuming his complaint, "I took down ten boys; ten twenties is two hundred pound. I go back at eight o'clock to-morrow morning, and have got only three—three oughts is an ought—three twos is six—sixty pound. What's come of all the boys? what's parents got in their heads? what does it all mean?"

Here the little boy on the top of the trunk gave a violent sneeze.

"Halloa, sir!" growled the schoolmaster, turning round. "What's that, sir?"

"Nothing, please sir," replied the little boy.

"Nothing, sir!" exclaimed Mr. Squeers.

"Please sir, I sneezed," rejoined the boy, trembling till the little trunk shook under him.

"Oh! sneezed, did you?" retorted Mr. Squeers. "Then what did you say 'nothing' for, sir?"

In default of a better answer to this question, the little boy screwed a couple of knuckles into each of his eyes and began to cry, wherefore Mr. Squeers knocked him off the trunk with a blow on one side of his face, and knocked him on again with a blow on the other.

"Wait till I get you down into Yorkshire, my young gentleman," said Mr. Squeers, "and then I'll give you the rest. Will you hold that noise, sir?"

"Ye—ye—yes," sobbed the little boy, rubbing his face very hard with the Beggar's petition in printed calico.

"Then do so at once, sir," said Squeers. "Do you hear?"

As this admonition was accompanied with a threatening gesture, and uttered with a savage aspect, the little boy rubbed his face harder, as if to keep the tears back; and, beyond alternately sniffing and choking, gave no further vent to his emotions.

"Mr. Squeers," said the waiter, looking in at this juncture; "here's a gentleman asking for you at the bar."

"Show the gentleman in, Richard," replied Mr. Squeers, in a soft voice. "Put your handkerchief in your pocket, you little scoundrel, or I'll murder you when the gentleman goes."

The schoolmaster had scarcely uttered these words in a fierce whisper, when the stranger entered. Affecting not to see him, Mr. Squeers feigned to be intent upon mending a pen, and offering benevolent advice to his youthful pupil.

"My dear child," said Mr. Squeers, "all people have their trials. This early trial of yours, that is fit to make your little heart burst, and your very eyes come out of your head with crying, what is it? Nothing; less than nothing. You are leaving your friends, but you will have a father in me, my dear, and a mother in Mrs. Squeers. At the delightful village of Dotheboys, near Greta Bridge in Yorkshire, where youth are boarded, clothed, booked, washed, furnished with pocket-money, provided with all necessaries—"

"It *is* the gentleman," observed the stranger, stopping the schoolmaster in the rehearsal of his advertisement. "Mr. Squeers, I believe, sir?"

"The same, sir," said Mr. Squeers, with an assumption of extreme surprise.

"The gentleman," said the stranger, "that advertised in the Times newspaper?"

—"Morning Post, Chronicle, Herald, and Advertiser, regarding the Academy called Dotheboys Hall at the delightful village of Dotheboys, near Greta Bridge in Yorkshire," added Mr. Squeers. "You come on business, sir. I see by my young friends. How do you do, my little gentleman? and how do *you* do, sir?" With this salutation Mr. Squeers patted the heads of two hollow-eyed, small-boned little boys, whom the applicant had brought with him, and waited for further communications.

"I am in the oil and colour way. My name is Snawley, sir," said the stranger.

Squeers inclined his head as much as to say, "And a remarkably pretty name, too."

The stranger continued. "I have been thinking, Mr. Squeers, of placing my two boys at your school."

"It is not for me to say so, sir," replied Mr. Squeers, "but I don't think you could possibly do a better thing."

"Hem!" said the other. "Twenty pounds per annewum, I believe, Mr. Squeers?"

"Guineas," rejoined the schoolmaster, with a persuasive smile.

"Pounds for two, I think, Mr. Squeers," said Mr. Snawley, solemnly.

"I don't think it could be done, sir," replied Squeers, as if he had never considered the proposition before. "Let me see; four five is twenty, double that, and deduct the—well, a pound either way shall not stand betwixt us. You must recommend me to your connection, sir, and make it up that way."

"They are not great eaters," said Mr. Snawley.

"Oh! that doesn't matter at all," replied Squeers. "We don't consider the boys' appetites at our establishment." This was strictly true; they did not.

"Every wholesome luxury, sir, that Yorkshire can afford," continued Squeers; "every beautiful moral that Mrs. Squeers can instil; every—in short, every comfort of a home that a boy could wish for, will be theirs, Mr. Snawley."

"I should wish their morals to be particularly attended to," said Mr. Snawley.

"I am glad of that, sir," replied the schoolmaster, drawing himself up. "They have come to the right shop for morals, sir."

"You are a moral man yourself," said Mr. Snawley.

"I rather believe I am, sir," replied Squeers.

"I have the satisfaction to know you are, sir," said Mr. Snawley. "I asked one of your references, and he said you were pious."

"Well, sir, I hope I am a little in that line," replied Squeers.

"I hope I am also," rejoined the other. "Could I say a few words with you in the next box?"

"By all means," rejoined Squeers with a grin. "My dears, will you speak to your new playfellow a minute or two? That is one of my boys, sir. Belling his name is,—a Taunton boy that, sir."

"Is he, indeed?" rejoined Mr. Snawley, looking at the poor little urchin as if he were some extraordinary natural curiosity.

"He goes down with me to-morrow, sir," said Squeers. "That's his luggage that he is a sitting upon now. Each boy is required to bring, sir, two suits of clothes, six shirts, six pair of stockings, two nightcaps, two pocket-handkerchiefs, two pair of shoes, two hats, and a razor."

"A razor!" exclaimed Mr. Snawley, as they walked into the next box. "What for?"

"To shave with," replied Squeers, in a slow and measured tone.

There was not much in these three words, but there must have been something in the manner in which they were said, to attract attention; for the schoolmaster and his companion looked steadily at each other for a few seconds, and then exchanged a very meaning smile. Snawley was a sleek, flat-nosed man, clad in sombre garments, and long black gaiters, and bearing in his countenance an expression of much mortification and sanctity; so, his smiling without any obvious reason was the more remarkable.

"Up to what age do you keep boys at your school then?" he asked at length.

"Just as long as their friends make the quarterly payments to my agent in town, or until such time as they run away," replied Squeers. "Let us understand each other; I see we may safely do so. What are these boys;—natural children?"

"No," rejoined Snawley, meeting the gaze of the schoolmaster's one eye. "They ain't."

"I thought they might be," said Squeers, coolly. "We have a good many of them; that boy's one."

"Him in the next box?" said Snawley.

Squeers nodded in the affirmative; his companion took another peep at the little boy on the trunk, and turning round again, looked as if he were quite disappointed to see him so much like other boys, and said he should hardly have thought it.

"He is," cried Squeers. "But about these boys of yours; you wanted to speak to me?"

"Yes," replied Snawley. "The fact is, I am not their father, Mr. Squeers. I'm only their father-in-law."

"Oh! Is that it?" said the schoolmaster. "That explains it at once. I was wondering what the devil you were going to send them to Yorkshire for. Ha! ha! Oh, I understand now."

"You see I married the mother," pursued Snawley; "it's expensive keeping boys at home, and as she has a little money in her own right, I am afraid (women are so very foolish, Mr. Squeers) that she might be led to squander it on them, which would be their ruin, you know."

"*I* see," returned Squeers, throwing himself back in his chair, and waving his hand.

"And this," resumed Snawley, "has made me anxious to put them to some school a good distance off, where there are no holidays—none of those ill-judged comings home twice a year that unsettle children's minds so—and where they may rough it a little—you comprehend?"

"The payments regular, and no questions asked," said Squeers, nodding his head.

"That's it, exactly," rejoined the other. "Morals strictly attended to, though."

"Strictly," said Squeers.

"Not too much writing home allowed, I suppose?" said the father-in-law, hesitating.

"None, except a circular at Christmas, to say they never were so happy, and hope they may never be sent for," rejoined Squeers.

"Nothing could be better," said the father-in-law, rubbing his hands.

"Then, as we understand each other," said Squeers, "will you allow me to ask you whether you consider me a highly virtuous, exemplary, and well-conducted man in private life; and whether as a person whose business it is to take charge of youth, you place the strongest confidence in my unimpeachable integrity, liberality, religious principles and ability?"

"Certainly I do," replied the father-in-law, reciprocating the schoolmaster's grin.

"Perhaps you won't object to say that, if I make you a reference?"

"Not the least in the world."

"That's your sort!" said Squeers, taking up a pen; "this is doing business, and that's what I like."

Having entered Mr. Snawley's address, the schoolmaster had next to perform the still more agreeable office of entering the receipt of the first quarter's payment in advance, which he had scarcely completed, when another voice was heard inquiring for Mr. Squeers.

"Here he is," replied the schoolmaster: "what is it?"

"Only a matter of business, sir," said Ralph Nickleby, presenting himself, closely followed by Nicholas. "There was an advertisement of yours in the papers this morning?"

"There was, sir. This way, if you please," said Squeers, who had by this time got back to the box by the fire-place. "Won't you be seated?"

"Why, I think I will," replied Ralph, suiting the action to the word, and placing his hat on the table before him. "This is my nephew, sir, Mr. Nicholas Nickleby."

"How do you do, sir?" said Squeers.

Nicholas bowed, said he was very well, and seemed very much astonished at the outward appearance of the proprietor of Dotheboys Hall: as indeed he was.

"Perhaps you recollect me?" said Ralph, looking narrowly at the schoolmaster.

"You paid me a small account at each of my half-yearly visits to town, for some years, I think, sir," replied Squeers.

"I did," rejoined Ralph.

"For the parents of a boy named Dorker, who unfortunately—"

"—Unfortunately died at Dotheboys Hall," said Ralph, finishing the sentence.

"I remember very well, sir," rejoined Squeers. "Ah! Mrs. Squeers, sir, was as partial to that lad as if he had been her own; the attention, sir, that was bestowed upon that boy in his illness! Dry toast and warm tea offered him every night and morning when he couldn't swallow anything—a candle in his bed-room on the very night he died—the best dictionary sent up for him to lay his head upon—I don't regret it though. It is a pleasant thing to reflect that one did one's duty by him."

Ralph smiled, as if he meant anything but smiling, and looked round at the strangers present.

"These are only some pupils of mine," said Wackford Squeers, pointing to the little boy on the trunk and the two little boys on the floor, who had been staring at each other without uttering a word, and writhing their bodies into most remarkable contortions, according to the custom of little boys when they first become acquainted. "This gentleman, sir, is a parent who is kind enough to compliment me upon the course of education adopted at Dotheboys Hall, which is situated, sir, at the delightful village of Dotheboys, near Greta Bridge in Yorkshire, where youth are boarded, clothed, booked, washed, furnished with pocket-money—"

"Yes, we know all about that, sir," interrupted Ralph, testily. "It's in the advertisement."

"You are very right, sir; it *is* in the advertisement." replied Squeers.

"And in the matter of fact besides," interrupted Mr. Snawley. "I feel bound to assure you, sir, and I am proud to have this opportunity *of* assuring you, that I consider Mr. Squeers a gentleman highly virtuous, exemplary, well-conducted, and—"

"I make no doubt of it, sir," interrupted Ralph, checking the torrent of recommendation; "no doubt of it at all. Suppose we come to business?"

"With all my heart, sir," rejoined Squeers. " 'Never postpone business,' is the very first lesson we instil into our commercial pupils. Master Belling, my dear, always remember that; do you hear?"

"Yes, sir," repeated Master Belling.

"He recollects what it is, does he?" said Ralph.

"Tell the gentleman," said Squeers.

"Never," repeated Master Belling.

"Very good," said Squeers; "go on."

"Never," repeated Master Belling again.

"Very good indeed," said Squeers. "Yes."

"P," suggested Nicholas, good-naturedly.

"Perform—business!" said Master Belling. "Never—perform—business!"

"Very well, sir," said Squeers, darting a withering look at the culprit. "You and I will perform a little business on our private account by and by."

"And just now," said Ralph, "we had better transact our own, perhaps."

"If you please," said Squeers.

"Well," resumed Ralph, "it's brief enough; soon broached; and I hope easily concluded. You have advertised for an able assistant, sir?"

"Precisely so," said Squeers.

"And you really want one?"

"Certainly," answered Squeers.

"Here he is!" said Ralph. "My nephew Nicholas, hot from school, with everything he learnt there, fermenting in his head, and nothing fermenting in his pocket, is just the man you want."

"I am afraid," said Squeers, perplexed with such an application from a youth of Nicholas's figure, "I am afraid the young man won't suit me."

"Yes, he will," said Ralph; "I know better. Don't be cast down, sir; you will be teaching all the young noblemen in Dotheboys Hall in less than a week's time, unless this gentleman is more obstinate than I take him to be."

"I fear, sir," said Nicholas, addressing Mr. Squeers, "that you object to my youth, and to my not being a Master of Arts?"

"The absence of a college degree *is* an objection," replied Squeers, looking as grave as he could, and considerably puzzled, no less by the contrast between the simplicity of the nephew and the worldly manner of the uncle, than by the incomprehensible allusion to the young noblemen under his tuition.

"Look here, sir," said Ralph; "I'll put this matter in its true light in two seconds."

"If you'll have the goodness," rejoined Squeers.

"This is a boy, or a youth, or a lad, or a young man, or a hobbledehoy, or whatever you like to call him, of eighteen or nineteen, or thereabouts," said Ralph.

"That I see," observed the schoolmaster.

"So do I," said Mr. Snawley, thinking it as well to back his new friend occasionally.

"His father is dead, he is wholly ignorant of the world, has no resources whatever, and wants something to do," said Ralph. "I recommend him to this splendid establishment of yours, as an opening which will lead him to fortune if he turns it to proper account. Do you see that?"

"Everybody must see that," replied Squeers, half imitating the sneer with which the old gentleman was regarding his unconscious relative.

"I do, of course," said Nicholas, eagerly.

"He does, of course, you observe," said Ralph, in the same dry, hard manner. "If any caprice of temper should induce him to cast aside this golden opportunity before he has brought it to perfection, I consider myself absolved from extending any assistance to his mother and sister. Look at him, and think of the use he may be to you in half a dozen ways! Now, the question is, whether, for some time to come at all events, he won't serve your purpose better than twenty of the kind of people you would get under ordinary circumstances. Isn't that a question for consideration?"

"Yes, it is," said Squeers, answering a nod of Ralph's head with a nod of his own.

"Good," rejoined Ralph. "Let me have two words with you."

The two words were had apart; in a couple of minutes Mr. Wackford Squeers announced that Mr. Nicholas Nickleby was, from that moment, thoroughly nominated to, and installed in, the office of first assistant master at Dotheboys Hall.

"Your uncle's recommendation has done it, Mr. Nickleby," said Wackford Squeers.

Nicholas, overjoyed at his success, shook his uncle's hand warmly, and could almost have worshipped Squeers upon the spot.

"He is an odd-looking man," thought Nicholas. "What of that? Porson was an odd-looking man, and so was Doctor Johnson; all these bookworms are."

"At eight o'clock to-morrow morning, Mr. Nickleby," said Squeers, "the coach starts. You must be here at a quarter before, as we take these boys with us."

"Certainly, sir," said Nicholas.

"And your fare down, I have paid," growled Ralph. "So, you'll have nothing to do but keep yourself warm."

Here was another instance of his uncle's generosity! Nicholas felt his unexpected kindness so much, that he could scarcely find words to thank him; indeed, he had not found half enough, when they took leave of the schoolmaster, and emerged from the Saracen's Head gateway.

Mr. and Mrs. Squeers at Home

"Now then!" cried Squeers, poking his head out at the front door. "Where are you, Nickleby?"

"Here, sir," replied Nicholas.

"Come in, then," said Squeers, "the wind blows in, at this door, fit to knock a man off his legs."

Nicholas sighed, and hurried in. Mr. Squeers, having bolted the door to keep it shut, ushered him into a small parlour scantily furnished with a few chairs, a yellow map hung against the wall, and a couple of tables; one of which bore some preparations for supper; while, on the other, a tutor's assistant, a Murray's grammar, half a dozen cards of terms and a worn letter directed to Wackford Squeers, Esquire, were arranged in picturesque confusion.

They had not been in this apartment a couple of minutes, when a female bounced into the room, and seized Mr. Squeers by the throat, gave him two loud kisses: one close after the other, like a postman's knock. The lady, who was of a large rawboned figure, was about half a head taller than Mr. Squeers, and was dressed in a dimity night-jacket; with her hair in papers; she had also a dirty nightcap on, relieved by a yellow cotton handkerchief which tied it under the chin.

"How is my Squeery?" said this lady in a playful manner, and a very hoarse voice.

"Quite well, my love," replied Squeers. "How's the cows?"

"All right, every one of 'em," answered the lady.

"And the pigs?" said Squeers.

"As well as they were when you went away."

"Come; that's a blessing," said Squeers, pulling off his great-coat. "The boys are all as they were, I suppose?"

"Oh, yes, they're well enough," replied Mrs. Squeers, snappishly. "That young Pitcher's had a fever."

"No!" exclaimed Squeers. "Damn that boy, he's always at something of that sort."

"Never was such a boy, I do believe," said Mrs. Squeers; "whatever he has is always catching too. I say it's obstinacy, and nothing shall ever convince me that it isn't. I'd beat it out of him; and I told you that, six months ago."

"So you did, my love," rejoined Squeers. "We'll try what can be done."

Pending these little endearments, Nicholas had stood, awkwardly enough, in the middle of the room: not very well knowing whether he was expected to retire into the passage, or to remain where he was. He was now relieved from his perplexity by Mr. Squeers.

"This is the new young man, my dear," said that gentleman.

"Oh," replied Mrs. Squeers, nodding her head at Nicholas, and eyeing him coldly from top to toe.

"He'll take a meal with us to-night," said Squeers, "and go among the boys to-morrow morning. You can give him a shake-down here, to-night, can't you?"

"We must manage it somehow," replied the lady. "You don't much mind how you sleep, I suppose, sir?"

"No, indeed," replied Nicholas, "I am not particular."

"That's lucky," said Mrs. Squeers. And as the lady's humour was considered to lie chiefly in retort, Mr. Squeers laughed heartily, and seemed to expect that Nicholas should do the same.

After some further conversation between the master and mistress relative to the success of Mr. Squeers's trip, and the people who had paid, and the people who had made default in payment, a young servant girl brought in a Yorkshire pie and some cold beef, which being set upon the table, the boy Smike appeared with a jug of ale.

Mr. Squeers was emptying his great-coat pockets of letters to different boys, and other small documents, which he had brought down in them. The boy glanced, with an anxious and timid expression, at the papers, as if with a sickly hope that one among them might relate to him. The look was a very painful one, and went to Nicholas's heart at once; for it told a long and very sad history.

It induced him to consider the boy more attentively, and he was surprised to observe the extraordinary mixture of garments which formed his dress. Although he could not have been less than eighteen or nineteen years old, and was tall for that age, he wore a skeleton suit, such as is usually put upon very little boys, and which, though most absurdly short in the arms and legs, was quite wide enough for his attenuated frame. In order that the lower part of his legs might be in perfect keeping with this singular dress, he had a very large pair of boots, originally made for tops, which might have been once worn by some stout farmer, but were now too patched and tattered for a beggar. Heaven knows how long he had been there, but he still wore the same linen which he had first taken down; for, round his neck, was a tattered child's frill, only half concealed by a coarse, man's neckerchief. He was lame; and as he feigned to be busy in arranging the table, glanced at the letters with a look so keen, and yet so dispirited and hopeless, that Nicholas could hardly bear to watch him.

"What are you bothering about there, Smike?" cried Mrs. Squeers; "let the things alone, can't you.'"

"Eh!" said Squeers, looking up. "Oh! it's you, is it?"

"Yes, sir," replied the youth, pressing his hands together, as though to control, by force, the nervous wandering of his fingers; "Is there—"

"Well!" said Squeers.

"Have you—did anybody—has nothing been heard—about me?"

"Devil a bit," replied Squeers testily.

The lad withdrew his eyes, and, putting his hand to his face, moved towards the door.

"Not a word," resumed Squeers, "and never will be. Now, this is a pretty sort of thing, isn't it, that you should have been left here, all these years, and no money paid after the first six—nor no notice taken, nor no clue to be got who you belong to? It's a pretty sort of thing that I should have to feed a great fellow like you, and never hope to get one penny for it, isn't it?"

The boy put his hand to his head as if he were making an effort to recollect something, and then, looking vacantly at his questioner, gradually broke into a smile, and limped away.

"I'll tell you what, Squeers," remarked his wife as the door closed, "I think that young chap's turning silly."

"I hope not," said the schoolmaster; "for he's a handy fellow out of doors, and worth his meat and drink, anyway. I should think he'd have wit enough for us though, if he was. But come; let's have supper, for I am hungry and tired, and want to get to bed."

This reminder brought in an exclusive steak for Mr. Squeers, who speedily proceeded to do it ample justice. Nicholas drew up his chair, but his appetite was effectually taken away.

"How's the steak, Squeers?" said Mrs. S.

"Tender as a lamb," replied Squeers. "Have a bit?"

"I couldn't eat a morsel," replied his wife. "What'll the young man take, my dear?"

"Whatever he likes that's present," rejoined Squeers, in a most unusual burst of generosity.

"What do you say, Mr. Knuckleboy?" inquired Mrs. Squeers.

"I'll take a little of the pie, if you please," replied Nicholas. "A very little, for I'm not hungry."

"Well, it's a pity to cut the pie if you're not hungry, isn't it?" said Mrs. Squeers. "Will you try a bit of the beef?"

"Whatever you please," replied Nicholas, abstractedly; "it's all the same to me."

Mrs. Squeers looked vastly gracious on receiving this reply; and nodding to Squeers, as much as to say that she was glad to find the young man knew his station, assisted Nicholas to a slice of meat with her own fair hands.

"Ale, Squeery?" inquired the lady, winking and frowning to give him to understand that the question propounded was, whether Nicholas should have ale, and not whether he (Squeers) would take any.

"Certainly," said Squeers, re-telegraphing in the same manner. "A glassful."

So Nicholas had a glassful, and, being occupied with his own reflections, drank it, in happy innocence of all the foregoing proceedings.

"Uncommon juicy steak that," said Squeers, as he laid down his knife and fork, after plying it, in silence, for some time.

"It's prime meat," rejoined his lady. "I bought a good large piece of it myself on purpose for—"

"For what!" exclaimed Squeers hastily. "Not for the—"

"No, no; not for them," rejoined Mrs. Squeers; "on purpose for you against you came home. Lor! you didn't think I could have made such a mistake as that."

"Upon my word, my dear, I didn't know what you were going to say," said Squeers, who had turned pale.

"You needn't make yourself uncomfortable," remarked his wife, laughing heartily. "To think that I should be such a noddy! Well!"

This part of the conversation was rather unintelligible; but popular rumour in the neighborhood asserted that Mr. Squeers, being amiably opposed to cruelty to animals, not unfrequently purchased for boy consumption the bodies of horned cattle who had died a natural death; possibly he was apprehensive of having unintentionally devoured some choice morsel intended for the young gentlemen.

Supper being over, and removed by a small servant girl with a hungry eye, Mrs. Squeers retired to lock it up, and also to take into safe custody the clothes of the five boys who had just arrived, and who were half-way up the troublesome flight of steps which leads to death's door, in consequence of exposure to the cold. They were then regaled with a light supper of porridge, and stowed away, side by side, in a small bedstead, to warm each other, and dream of a substantial meal with something hot after it, if their fancies set that way: which it is not at all improbable they did.

Mr. Squeers treated himself to a stiff tumbler of brandy-and-water, made on the liberal half-and-half principle, allowing for the dissolution of the sugar; and his amiable helpmate mixed Nicholas the ghost of a small glassful of the same compound. This done, Mr. and Mrs. Squeers drew close up to the fire, and sitting with their feet on the fender, talked confidentially in whispers; while Nicholas, taking up the tutor's assistant, read the interesting legends in the miscellaneous questions, and all the figures into the bargain, with as much thought or consciousness of what he was doing, as if he had been in a magnetic slumber.

At length, Mr. Squeers yawned fearfully, and opined that it was high time to go to bed; upon which signal Mrs. Squeers and the girl dragged in a small straw mattress and a couple of blankets, and arranged them into a couch for Nicholas.

"We'll put you into your regular bed-room to-morrow, Nickleby," said Squeers. "Let me see! Who sleeps in Brooks's bed, my dear?"

"In Brooks's," said Mrs. Squeers, pondering. "There's Jennings, little Bolder, Graymarsh, and what's his name."

"So there is," rejoined Squeers. "Yes! Brooks is full."

"Full!" thought Nicholas. "I should think he was."

"There's a place somewhere, I know," said Squeers; "but I can't at this moment call to mind where it is. However, we'll have that all settled to-morrow. Good night, Nickleby. Seven o'clock in the morning, mind."

"I shall be ready, sir," replied Nicholas, "Good-night."

"I'll come in myself and show you where the well is," said Squeers. "You'll always find a little bit of soap in the kitchen window; that belongs to you."

Nicholas opened his eyes, but not his mouth; and Squeers was again going away, when he once more turned back.

"I don't know, I am sure," he said, "whose towel to put you on; but if you'll make shift with something to-morrow morning, Mrs. Squeers will arrange that in the course of the day. My dear, don't forget."

"I'll take care," replied Mrs. Squeers; "and mind *you* take care, young man, and get first wash. The teacher ought always to have it; but they get the better of him if they can."

Mr. Squeers then nudged Mrs. Squeers to bring away the brandy bottle, lest Nicholas should help himself in the night; and the lady having seized it with great precipitation, they retired together.

Of the Internal Economy of Dotheboys Hall

"DRAT the things," said the lady, opening the cupboard; "I can't find the school spoon anywhere."

"Never mind it, my dear," observed Squeers in a soothing manner; "it's of no consequence."

"No consequence, why how you talk!" retorted Mrs. Squeers sharply; "isn't it brimstone morning?"

"I forgot, my dear," rejoined Squeers; "yes, it certainly is. We purify the boys' bloods now and then, Nickleby."

"Purify fiddlesticks' ends," said his lady. "Don't think, young man, that we go to the expense of flower of brimstone and molasses, just to purify them; because if you think we carry on the business in that way, you'll find yourself mistaken, and so I tell you plainly."

"My dear," said Squeers frowning. "Hem!"

"Oh! nonsense," rejoined Mrs. Squeers. "If the young man comes to be a teacher here, let him understand, at once, that we don't want any foolery about the boys. They have the brimstone and treacle, partly because if they hadn't something or other in the way of medicine they'd be always ailing and giving a world of trouble, and partly because it spoils their appetites and comes cheaper than breakfast and dinner. So, it does them good and us good at the same time, and that's fair enough, I'm sure."

Having given this explanation, Mrs. Squeers put her hand into the closet and instituted a stricter search after the spoon, in which Mr. Squeers assisted. A few words passed between them while they were thus engaged, but as their voices were partially stifled by the cupboard, all that Nicholas could distinguish was, that Mr. Squeers said what Mrs. Squeers had said was injudicious, and that Mrs. Squeers said what Mr. Squeers said was "stuff."

A vast deal of searching and rummaging ensued, and it proving fruitless, Smike was called in, and pushed by Mrs. Squeers, and boxed by Mr. Squeers; which course of treatment brightening his intellects, enabled him to suggest that possibly Mrs. Squeers might have the spoon in her pocket, as indeed turned out to be the case. As Mrs. Squeers had previously protested, however, that she was quite certain she had not got it, Smike received another box on the ear for presuming to contradict his mistress, together with a promise of a sound thrashing if he were not more respectful in future; so that he took nothing very advantageous by his motion.

"A most invaluable woman, that, Nickleby," said Squeers when his consort had hurried away, pushing the drudge before her.

"Indeed, sir!" observed Nicholas.

"I don't know her equal," said Squeers; "I do not know her equal. That woman, Nickleby, is always the same—always the same bustling, lively, active, saving creetur that you see her now."

Nicholas sighed involuntarily at the thought of the agreeable domestic prospect thus opened to him; but Squeers was, fortunately, too much occupied with his own reflections to perceive it.

"It's my way to say, when I am up in London," continued Squeers, "that to them boys she is a mother. But she is more than a mother to them; ten times more. She does things for them boys, Nickleby, that I don't believe half the mothers going, would do for their own sons."

"I should think they would not, sir," answered Nicholas.

Now, the fact was, that both Mr. and Mrs. Squeers viewed the boys in

the light of their proper and natural enemies; or, in other words, they held
and considered that their business and profession was to get as much from
every boy as could by possibility be screwed out of him. On this point
they were both agreed, and behaved in unison accordingly. The only difference between them was, that Mrs. Squeers waged war against the
enemy openly and fearlessly, and that Squeers covered his rascality, even
at home, with a spice of his habitual deceit; as if he really had a notion of
some day or other being able to take himself in, and persuade his own
mind that he was a very good fellow.

"But come," said Squeers, interrupting the progress of some thoughts to
this effect in the mind of his usher; "let's go to the school-room; and lend
me a hand with my school coat, will you?"

Nicholas assisted his master to put on an old fustian shooting-jacket,
which he took down from a peg in the passage; and Squeers, arming himself with his cane, led the way across the yard, to a door in the rear of the
house.

"There," said the schoolmaster as they stepped in together; "this is our
shop, Nickleby!"

It was such a crowded scene, and there were so many objects to attract
attention, that, at first, Nicholas stared about him, really without seeing
anything at all. By degrees, however, the place resolved itself into a bare
and dirty room, with a couple of windows, whereof a tenth part might be
of glass, the remainder being stopped up with old copybooks and paper.
There were a couple of long old rickety desks, cut and notched, and inked,
and damaged, in every possible way; two or three forms; a detached desk
for Squeers; and another for his assistant. The ceiling was supported, like
that of a barn, by cross beams and rafters; and the walls were so stained
and discoloured, that it was impossible to tell whether they had ever been
touched with paint or whitewash.

But the pupils—the young noblemen! How the last faint traces of hope,
the remotest glimmering of any good to be derived from his efforts in this
den, faded from the mind of Nicholas as he looked in dismay around!
Pale and haggard faces, lank and bony figures, children with the countenances of old men, deformities with irons upon their limbs, boys of
stunted growth, and others whose long meagre legs would hardly bear
their stooping bodies, all crowded on the view together; there were the
bleared eye, the hare-lip, the crooked foot, and every ugliness or disortion
that told of unnatural aversion conceived by parents for their offspring, or
of young lives which, from the earliest dawn of infancy, had been one
horrible endurance of cruelty and neglect. There were little faces which
should have been handsome, darkened with the scowl of sullen, dogged
suffering; there was childhood with the light of its eye quenched, its
beauty gone, and its helplessness alone remaining; there were vicious-
faced boys, brooding, with leaden eyes, like malefactors in a jail; and
there were young creatures on whom the sins of their frail parents had

descended, weeping even for the mercenary nurses they had known, and lonesome even in their loneliness. With every kindly sympathy and affection blasted in its birth, with every young and healthy feeling flogged and starved down, with every revengeful passion that can fester in swollen hearts, eating its evil way to their core in silence, what an incipient Hell was breeding here!

And yet this scene, painful as it was, had its grotesque features, which, in a less interested observer than Nicholas, might have provoked a smile. Mrs. Squeers stood at one of the desks, presiding over an immense basin of brimstone and treacle, of which delicious compound she administered a large instalment to each boy in succession: using for the purpose a common wooden spoon, which might have been originally manufactured for some gigantic top, and which widened every young gentleman's mouth considerably: they being all obliged, under heavy corporal penalties, to take in the whole of the bowl at a gasp. In another corner, huddled together for companionship, were the little boys who had arrived on the preceding night, three of them in very large leather breeches, and two in old trousers, a something tighter fit than drawers are usually worn; at no great distance from these was seated the juvenile son and heir of Mr. Squeers—a striking likeness of his father—kicking, with great vigour, under the hands of Smike, who was fitting upon him a pair of new boots that bore a most suspicious resemblance to those which the least of the little boys had worn on the journey down—as the little boy himself seemed to think, for he was regarding the appropriation with a look of most rueful amazement. Besides these, there was a long row of boys waiting, with countenances of no pleasant anticipation, to be treacled; and another file, who had just escaped from the infliction, making a variety of wry mouths indicative of anything but satisfaction. The whole were attired in such motley, ill-assorted, extraordinary garments, as would have been irresistibly ridiculous, but for the foul appearance of dirt, disorder, and disease, with which they were associated.

"Now," said Squeers, giving the desk a great rap with his cane, which made half the little boys nearly jump out of their boots, "is that physicking over?"

"Just over," said Mrs. Squeers, choking the last boy in her hurry, and tapping the crown of his head with the wooden spoon to restore him. "Here, you Smike; take away now. Look sharp!"

Smike shuffled out with the basin, and Mrs. Squeers having called up a little boy with a curly head, and wiped her hands upon it, hurried out after him into a species of wash-house, where there was a small fire and a large kettle, together with a number of little wooden bowls which were arranged upon a board.

Into these bowls, Mrs. Squeers, assisted by the hungry servant, poured a brown composition, which looked like diluted pincushions without the covers, and was called porridge. A minute wedge of brown bread was inserted in each bowl, and when they had eaten their porridge by means of the bread, the boys ate the bread itself, and ·had finished their breakfast; whereupon Mr. Squeers said in a solemn voice, "For what we have received, may the Lord make us truly thankful!"—and went away to his own.

Nicholas distended his stomach with a bowl of porridge, for much the same reason which induces some savages to swallow earth—lest they should be inconveniently hungry when there is nothing to eat. Having further disposed of a slice of bread and butter, allotted to him in virtue of his office, he sat himself down, to wait for school-time.

He could not but observe how silent and sad the boys all seemed to be. There was none of the noise and clamour of a school-room; none of its boisterous play, or hearty mirth. The children sat crouching and shivering together, and seemed to lack the spirit to move about. The only pupil who evinced the slightest tendency towards locomotion or playfulness was Master Squeers, and as his chief amusement was to tread upon the other boys' toes in his new boots, his flow of spirits was rather disagreeable than otherwise.

After some half-hour's delay, Mr. Squeers reappeared, and the boys took their places and their books, of which latter commodity the average might be about one to eight learners. A few minutes having elapsed, during which Mr. Squeers looked very profound, as if he had a perfect apprehension of what was inside all the books, and could say every word of their contents by heart if he only chose to take the trouble, that gentleman called up the first class.

Obedient to this summons there ranged themselves in front of the schoolmaster's desk, half a dozen scarecrows, out at knees and elbows, one of whom placed a torn and filthy book beneath his learned eye.

"This is the first class in English spelling and philosophy, Nickleby," said Squeers, beckoning Nicholas to stand beside him. "We'll get up a Latin one, and hand that over to you. Now, then, where's the first boy?"

"Please, sir, he's cleaning the back parlour window," said the temporary head of the philosophical class.

"So he is, to be sure," rejoined Squeers. "We go upon the practical mode of teaching, Nickleby; the regular education system. C-l-e-a-n, clean, verb active, to make bright, to scour. W-i-n, win, d-e-r, der, winder, a casement. When the boy knows this out of book, he goes and does it. It's just the same principle as the use of the globes. Where's the second boy?"

"Please, sir, he's weeding the garden," replied a small voice.

"To be sure," said Squeers, by no means disconcerted. "So he is. B-o-t, bot, t-i-n, tin, bottin, n-e-y, ney, bottinney, noun substantive, a knowledge of plants. When he has learned that bottinney means a knowledge of plants, he goes and knows 'em. That's our system, Nickleby; what do you think of it?"

"It's a very useful one, at any rate," answered Nicholas.

"I believe you," rejoined Squeers, not remarking the emphasis of his usher. "Third boy, what's a horse?"

"A beast, sir," replied the boy.

"So it is," said Squeers. "Ain't it, Nickleby?"

"I believe there is no doubt of that, sir," answered Nicholas.

"Of course there isn't," said Squeers. "A horse is a quadruped, and quadruped's Latin for beast, as everybody that's gone through the grammar, knows, or else where's the use of having grammars at all?"

"Where, indeed!" said Nicholas abstractedly.

"As you're perfect in that," resumed Squeers, turning to the boy, "go and look after *my* horse, and rub him down well, or I'll rub you down. The rest of the class go and draw water up, till somebody tells you to leave off, for it's washing-day to-morrow, and they want the coppers filled."

So saying, he dismissed the first class to their experiments in practical philosophy, and eyed Nicholas with a look, half cunning and half doubtful, as if he were not altogether certain what he might think of him by this time.

"That's the way we do it, Nickleby," he said, after a pause.

Nicholas shrugged his shoulders in a manner that was scarcely perceptible, and said he saw it was.

"And a very good way it is, too," said Squeers. "Now, just take them fourteen little boys and hear them some reading, because, you know, you must begin to be useful. Idling about here won't do."

Mr. Squeers said this, as if it had suddenly occurred to him, either that he must not say too much to his assistant, or that his assistant did not say enough to him in praise of the establishment. The children were arranged in a semi-circle round the new master, and he was soon listening to their dull, drawling, hesitating recital of those stories of engrossing interest which are to be found in the more antiquated spelling books.

In this exciting occupation, the morning lagged heavily on. At one o'clock, the boys, having previously had their appetites thoroughly taken away by stir-about and potatoes, sat down in the kitchen to some hard salt beef, of which Nicholas was graciously permitted to take his portion to his own solitary desk, to eat it there in peace. After this, there was another hour of crouching in the school-room and shivering with cold, and then school began again.

It was Mr. Squeers's custom to call the boys together, and make a sort of report, after every half-yearly visit to the metropolis, regarding the relations and friends he had seen, the news he had heard, the letters he had brought down, the bills which had been paid, the accounts which had been left unpaid, and so forth. This solemn proceeding always took place in the afternoon of the day succeeding his return; perhaps, because the boys acquired strength of mind from the suspense of the morning, or, possibly, because Mr. Squeers himself acquired greater sternness and inflexibility from certain warm potations in which he was wont to indulge after his early dinner. Be this as it may, the boys were recalled from house-window, garden, stable, and cow-yard, and the school were assembled in full conclave, when Mr. Squeers, with a small bundle of papers in his hand, and Mrs. S. following with a pair of canes, entered the room and proclaimed silence.

"Let any boy speak a word without leave," said Mr. Squeers, mildly, "and I'll take the skin off his back."

This special proclamation had the desired effect, and a deathlike silence immediately prevailed, in the midst of which Mr. Squeers went on to say—

"Boys, I've been to London, and have returned to my family and you, as strong and well as ever."

Accordingly to half-yearly custom, the boys gave three feeble cheers at this refreshing intelligence. Such cheers! Sighs of extra strength with the chill on.

"I have seen the parents of some boys," continued Squeers, turning over his papers, "and they're so glad to hear how their sons are getting on, that there's no prospect at all of their going away, which of course is a very pleasant thing to reflect upon, for all parties."

Two or three hands went to two or three eyes when Squeers said this, but the greater part of the young gentlemen having no particular parents to speak of, were wholly uninterested in the thing one way or other.

"I have had disappointments to contend against," said Squeers, looking very grim; "Bolder's father was two pound ten short. Where is Bolder?"

"Here he is, please, sir," rejoined twenty officious voices. Boys are very like men, to be sure.

"Come here, Bolder," said Squeers.

An unhealthy-looking boy, with warts all over his hands, stepped from his place to the master's desk, and raised his eyes imploringly to Squeers's face; his own, quite white from the rapid beating of his heart.

"Bolder," said Squeers, speaking very slowly, for he was considering, as the saying goes, where to have him. "Bolder, if your father thinks that because—why, what's this, sir?"

As Squeers spoke, he caught up the boy's hand by the cuff of his jacket, and surveyed it with an edifying aspect of horror and disgust.

"What do you call this, sir?" demanded the schoolmaster, administering a cut with the cane to expedite the reply.

"I can't help it, indeed, sir," rejoined the boy, crying. "They will come; it's the dirty work I think, sir—at least I don't know what it is, sir, but it's not my fault."

"Bolder," said Squeers, tucking up his wristbands, and moistening the palm of his right hand to get a good grip of the cane, "you are an incorrigible young scoundrel, and as the last thrashing did you no good, we must see what another will do towards beating it out of you."

With this, and wholly disregarding a piteous cry for mercy, Mr. Squeers fell upon the boy and caned him soundly: not leaving off indeed, until his arm was tired out.

"There," said Squeers, when he had quite done; "rub away as hard as you like, you won't rub that off in a hurry. Oh! you won't hold that noise, won't you? Put him out, Smike."

The drudge knew better from long experience, than to hesitate about obeying, so he bundled the victim out by a side door, and Mr. Squeers perched himself again on his own stool, supported by Mrs. Squeers, who occupied another at his side.

"Now let us see," said Squeers. "A letter for Cobbey. Stand up, Cobbey."

Another boy stood up, and eyed the letter very hard while Squeers made a mental abstract of the same.

"Oh!" said Squeers: "Cobbey's grandmother is dead, and his uncle John has took to drinking, which is all the news his sister sends, except eighteen-pence, which will just pay for that broken square of glass. Mrs. Squeers, my dear, will you take the money?"

The worthy lady pocketed the eighteenpence with a most business-like air, and Squeers passed on to the next boy, as coolly as possible.

"Graymarsh," said Squeers, "he's the next. Stand up, Graymarsh."

Another boy stood up, and the schoolmaster looked over the letter as before.

"Graymarsh's maternal aunt," said Squeers, when he had possessed him-self of the contents, "is very glad to hear he's so well and happy, and sends her respectful compliments to Mrs. Squeers, and thinks she must be an angel. She likewise thinks Mr. Squeers is too good for this world; but hopes he may long be spared to carry on the business. Would have sent the two pair of stockings as desired, but is short of money, so forwards a tract instead, and hopes Graymarsh will put his trust in Providence. Hopes, above all, that he will study in everything to please Mr. and Mrs. Squeers, and look upon them as his only friends; and that he will love Master Squeers; and not object to sleeping five in a bed, which no Christian should. Ah!" said Squeers, folding it up, "a delightful letter. Very affecting indeed."

It was affecting in one sense, for Graymarsh's maternal aunt was strongly supposed, by her more intimate friends, to be no other than his maternal parent; Squeers, however, without alluding to this part of the story (which would have sounded immoral before boys), proceeded with the business by calling out "Mobbs," whereupon another boy rose, and Graymarsh resumed his seat.

"Mobbs's mother-in-law," said Squeers, "took to her bed on hearing that he wouldn't eat fat, and has been very ill ever since. She wishes to know, by an early post, where he expects to go to, if he quarrels with his vittles; and with what feelings he could turn up his nose at the cow's liver broth, after his good master had asked a blessing on it. This was told her in the London newspapers—not by Mr. Squeers, for he is too kind and too good to set anybody against anybody—and it has vexed her so much, Mobbs can't think. She is sorry to find he is discontented, which is sinful and horrid, and hopes Mr. Squeers will flog him into a happier state of mind; with which view, she has also stopped his halfpenny a week pocket-money, and given a double-bladed knife with a corkscrew in it to the Missionaries, which she had bought on purpose for him."

"A sulky state of feeling," said Squeers, after a terrible pause, during which he had moistened the palm of his right hand again, "won't do. Cheerfulness and contentment must be kept up. Mobbs, come to me!"

Mobbs moved slowly towards the desk, rubbing his eyes in anticipation of good cause for doing so; and he soon afterwards retired by the side door, with as good cause as a boy need have.

Mr. Squeers then proceeded to open a miscellaneous collection of letters; some enclosing money, which Mrs. Squeers "took care of"; and others referring to small articles of apparel, as caps and so forth, all of which the same lady stated to be too large, or too small, and calculated for nobody but young Squeers, who would appear indeed to have had most accommodating limbs, since everything that came into the school fitted him to a nicety. His head, in particular, must have been singularly elastic, for hats and caps of all dimensions were alike to him.

This business despatched, a few slovenly lessons were performed, and Squeers retired to his fireside, leaving Nicholas to take care of the boys in the school-room, which was very cold, and where a meal of bread and cheese was served out shortly after dark.

The Education of the Young

FINLEY PETER DUNNE

FINLEY PETER DUNNE (1867-1936) is best known for his humorous essays on American life in which Mr. Dooley, an Irish saloon keeper, criticizes current events, politicians, social leaders, customs, and human foibles in general.

Dunne, a Chicago journalist, began writing the Dooley articles for the Chicago Evening Post in 1893. At that time Dunne had been a newspaper reporter for eight years. When in 1900 he left Chicago and came East, the articles continued to appear in Collier's Weekly *with illustrations by Charles Dana Gibson.*

During the nineties interest in the Irish, their jokes and dialect, was high. There were Irishmen on the stage and an Irishman comedian on every vaudeville and burlesque bill. Chauncy Olcott and Andrew Mack were popular Irish tenors of the day. It is not surprising that the Dooley sketches soon caught general attention and within a year or two were famous.

In the shrewd humor of Irish dialect the Dooley sketches attacked pretense and hypocrisy, injustice and stupidity. Some of the sketches are dated; others are as pertinent today as when they were written.

> "If ye had a boy wud ye sind him to colledge?" asked Mr. Hennessy. "Well," said Mr. Dooley, "at th' age whin a boy is fit to be in colledge I wudden't have him around th' house."

THE troubled Mr. Hennessy had been telling Mr. Dooley about the difficulty of making a choice of schools for Packy Hennessy, who at the age of six was at the point where the family must decide his career. "'Tis a big question," said Mr. Dooley, "an' wan that seems to be worryin' th' people more thin it used to whin ivry boy was designed f'r th' priesthood, with a full undherstandin' be his parents that th' chances was in favor iv a brick yard. Nowadays they talk about th' edycation iv th' child befure they choose th' name. 'Tis: Th' kid talks in his sleep. 'Tis th' fine lawyer he'll make.' Or, 'Did ye notice him admirin' that photygraph? He'll be a gr-reat journalist.' Or, 'Look at him fishin' in Uncle Tim's watch pocket. We must thrain him f'r a banker.' Or, 'I'm afraid he'll niver be sthrong enough to wurruk. He must go into th' church.' Befure he's baptized too, d'ye mind. 'Twill not be long befure th' time comes whin th' soggarth'll christen th' infant: 'Judge Pathrick Aloysius Hinnissy, iv th' Northern District iv Illinye,' or 'Profissor P. Aloysius Hinnissy, LL.D., S.T.D., P.G.N., iv th' faculty iv Nothre Dame.' Th' innocent child in his cradle, wondherin' what ails th' mist iv him an' where he got such funny lookin' parents fr'm, has thim to blame that brought him into th' wurruld if he dayvilops into a second story man befure he's twinty-wan an' is took up be th' polis. Why don't you lade Packy down to th' occylist an' have him fitted with a pair iv eye-glasses? Why don't ye put goloshes on him, give him a blue umbrelly an' call him a doctor at wanst an' be done with it?

"To my mind, Hinnissy, we're wastin' too much time thinkin' iv th' future iv our young, an' thryin' to larn thim early what they oughtn't to know till they've growed up. We sind th' childher to school as if 'twas a summer garden where they go to be amused instead iv a pinitinchry where they're sint f'r th' original sin. Whin I was a la-ad I was put at me ah-bee abs, th' first day I set fut in th' school behind th' hedge an' me head was sore inside an' out befure I wint home. Now th' first thing we larn th' future Mark Hannas an' Jawn D. Gateses iv our naytion is waltzin', singin', an' cuttin' pitchers out iv a book. We'd be much betther teachin' thim th' sthrangle hold, f'r that's what they need in life.

"I know what'll happen. Ye'll sind Packy to what th' Germans call a Kindygartin, an' 'tis a good thing f'r Germany, because all a German knows is what some wan tells him, an' his grajation papers is a certy-ficate that he don't need to think annymore. But we've inthrajooced it into this counthry, an' whin I was down seein' if I cud injooce Rafferty, th' janitor iv th' Isaac Muggs Grammer School, f'r to vote f'r Riordan—an' he's goin' to—I dhropped in on Cassidy's daughter, Mary Ellen, an' see her kindy-gartnin'. Th' childher was settin' ar-round on th' flure an' some was moldin' dachshunds out iv mud an' wipin' their hands on their hair, an' some was carvin' figures iv a goat out iv paste-board an' some was singin' an' some was sleepin' an' a few was dancin' an' wan la-ad was pullin' another la-ad's hair. 'Why don't ye take th' coal shovel to that little barbaryan, Mary Ellen?' says I. 'We don't believe in corporeal punishment,' says she. 'School shud be made pleasant f'r th' childher,' she says. 'Th' child who's hair is bein' pulled is larnin' patience,' she says, 'an' th' child that's pullin' th' hair is discoverin' th' footility iv human indeavor,' says she. 'Well, oh, well,' says I, 'times has changed since I was a boy,' I says. 'Put thim through their exercises,' says I. 'Tommy,' says I, 'spell cat,' I says. 'Go to th' divvle,' says th' cheerub. 'Very smartly answered,' says Mary Ellen. 'Ye shud not ask thim to spell,' she says. 'They don't larn that till they get to colledge,' she says, 'an',' she says, 'sometimes not even thin,' she says. 'An' what do they larn?' says I. 'Rompin',' she says, 'an' dancin',' she says, 'an' inde-pindance iv speech, an' beauty songs, an' sweet thoughts, an' how to make home home-like,' she says. 'Well,' says I, 'I didn't take anny iv thim things at colledge, so ye needn't unblanket thim,' I says. 'I won't put thim through anny exercise to-day,' I says. 'But whisper, Mary Ellen,' says I, 'Don't ye niver feel like bastin' th' seeraphims?' 'Th' teachin's iv Free-bull and Pitzotly is conthrary to that,' she says. 'But I'm goin' to be marrid an' lave th' school on Choosdah, th' twinty-sicond iv Janooary,' she says, 'an' on Mandah, th' twinty-first, I'm goin' to ask a few iv th' little darlin's to th' house an',' she says, 'stew thim over a slow fire,' she says. Mary Ellen is not a German, Hinnissy.

"Well, afther they have larned in school what they ar-re licked f'r larnin' in th' back yard—that is squashin' mud with their hands—they're conducted up through a channel iv free an' beautiful thought till they're r-ready f'r colledge. Mamma packs a few doylies an' tidies into son's bag, an' some silver to be used in case iv throuble with th' landlord, an' th' la-ad throts off to th' siminary. If he's not sthrong enough to look f'r high honors as a middleweight pugilist he goes into th' thought depart-ment. Th' prisidint takes him into a Turkish room, gives him a cigareet an' says: 'Me dear boy, what special branch iv larnin' wud ye like to have studied f'r ye be our compitint profissors? We have a chair iv Beauty an' wan iv Puns an' wan iv Pothry on th' Changin' Hues iv th' Settin' Sun, an' wan on Platonic Love, an' wan on Nonsense Rhymes, an' wan on Sweet Thoughts, an' wan on How Green Grows th' Grass, an' wan on th' Rela-tion iv Ice to th' Greek Idee iv God,' he says. 'This is all ye'll need to equip ye f'r th' perfect life, onless,' he says, 'we won't think much iv ye, but we have a good school where ye can larn that disgraceful thrade,' he says. An' th' la-ad makes his choice, an' ivry mornin' whin he's up in time he takes a whiff iv hasheesh an' goes off to hear Profissor Maryanna tell him that 'if th' dates iv human knowledge must be rejicted as subjictive, how much more must they be subjicted as rejictive if, as I think, we keep our thoughts fixed upon th' inanity iv th' finite in comparison with th' onthink-able truth with th' ondivided an' onimaginable reality. Boys, ar-re ye with me?' . . ."

"I don't undherstand a wurrud iv what ye're sayin'," said Mr. Hennessy.

"No more do I," said Mr. Dooley. "But I believe 'tis as Father Kelly says: 'Childher shuddn't be sint to school to larn, but to larn how to larn. I don't care what ye larn thim so long as 'tis onpleasant to thim.' 'Tis thrainin' they need, Hinnissy. That's all. I niver cud make use iv what I larned in colledge about thrigojoomethry an'—an'—grammar an' th' welts I got on th' skull fr'm th' school-masther's cane I have niver been able to turn to anny account in th' business, but 'twas th' bein' there an' havin' to get things to heart without askin' th' meanin' iv thim an' goin' to school cold an' comin' home hungry, that made th' man iv me ye see befure ye."

"That's why th' good woman's throubled about Packy," said Hennessy.

"Go home," said Mr. Dooley.

Soaring

BOOTH TARKINGTON

BOOTH TARKINGTON, novelist and playwright, was born in 1869 in Indianapolis, Indiana. He received his education at Phillips Exeter Academy, Purdue University, and Princeton. While at Princeton, he contributed to student publications and founded the Princeton Triangle Club. He first won popularity as an author with the publication of The Gentleman from Indiana *in 1899. With the publication of* Monsieur Beaucaire *a year later, his literary reputation was established, and he began in earnest his career as a writer. Since then he has twice won the Pulitzer Prize for fiction, once for* The Magnificent Ambersons *and again for* Alice Adams. *Between 1899 and 1946, when he died, he wrote some forty novels and about twenty plays.*

His novels fall into two groups: his stories about boys, and his novels of American life. Of the former, Penrod, *published in 1914, is perhaps the most famous. The following selections from this novel reveal a remarkable understanding of the nature of the schoolboy.*

HALF the members of the class passed out to a recitation-room, the empurpled Victorine among them, and Miss Spence started the remaining half through the ordeal of trial by mathematics. Several boys and girls were sent to the blackboard, and Penrod, spared for the moment, followed their operations a little while with his eyes, but not with his mind; then, sinking deeper in his seat, limply abandoned the effort. His eyes remained open, but saw nothing; the routine of the arithmetic lesson reached his ears in familiar, meaningless sounds, but he heard nothing; and yet, this time, he was profoundly occupied. He had drifted away from the painful land of facts, and floated now in a new sea of fancy which he had just discovered.

Maturity forgets the marvellous realness of a boy's day-dreams, how colourful they glow, rosy and living, and how opaque the curtain closing down between the dreamer and the actual world. That curtain is almost sound-proof, too, and causes more throat-trouble among parents than is suspected.

The nervous monotony of the schoolroom inspires a sometimes unbear-

Penrod, by Booth Tarkington; copyright, 1914, by Doubleday, Doran & Company, Inc.; excerpts reprinted by permission of Brandt and Brandt.

able longing for something astonishing to happen, and as every boy's fundamental desire is to do something astonishing himself, so as to be the centre of all human interest and awe, it was natural that Penrod should discover in fancy the delightful secret of self-levitation. He found, in this curious series of imaginings, during the lesson in arithmetic, that the atmosphere may be navigated as by a swimmer under water, but with infinitely greater ease and with perfect comfort in breathing. In this mind he extended his arms gracefully, at a level with his shoulders, and delicately paddled the air with his hands, which at once caused him to be drawn up out of his seat and elevated gently to a position about midway between the floor and the ceiling, where he came to an equilibrium and floated; a sensation not the less exquisite because of the screams of his fellow pupils, appalled by the miracle. Miss Spence herself was amazed and frightened, but he only smiled down carelessly upon her when she commanded him to return to earth; and then, when she climbed upon a desk to pull him down, he quietly paddled himself a little higher, leaving his toes just out of her reach. Next, he swam through a few slow somersaults to show his mastery of the new art, and, with the shouting of the dumfounded scholars ringing in his ears, turned on his side and floated swiftly out of the window, immediately rising above the housetops, while people in the street below him shrieked, and a trolley car stopped dead in wonder.

With almost no exertion he paddled himself, many yards at a stroke, to the girls' private school where Marjorie Jones was a pupil—Marjorie Jones of the amber curls and the golden voice! Long before the "Pageant of the Table Round," she had offered Penrod a hundred proofs that she considered him wholly undesirable and ineligible. At the Friday Afternoon Dancing Class she consistently incited and led the laughter at him whenever Professor Bartet singled him out for admonition in matters of feet and decorum. And but yesterday she had chid him for his slavish lack of memory in daring to offer her a greeting on the way to Sunday-school. "Well! I expect you must forgot I told you never to speak to me again! If I was a boy, I'd be too proud to come hanging around people that don't speak to me, even if I *was* the Worst Boy in Town!" So she flouted him. But now, as he floated in through the window of her classroom and swam gently along the ceiling like an escaped toy balloon, she fell upon her knees beside her little desk, and, lifting up her arms toward him, cried with love and admiration:

"Oh, *Penrod!*"

He negligently kicked a globe from the high chandelier, and, smiling coldly, floated out through the hall to the front steps of the school, while Marjorie followed, imploring him to grant her one kind look.

In the street an enormous crowd had gathered, headed by Miss Spence and a brass band; and a cheer from a hundred thousand throats shook the very ground as Penrod swam overhead. Marjorie knelt upon the steps and watched adoringly while Penrod took the drum-major's baton and, performing sinuous evolutions above the crowd, led the band. Then he threw the baton so high that it disappeared from sight; but he went swiftly after it, a double delight, for he had not only the delicious sensation of rocketing safely up and up into the blue sky, but also that of standing in the crowd below, watching and admiring himself as he dwindled to a speck, disappeared and then, emerging from a cloud, came speeding down, with the baton in his hand, to the level of the treetops, where he beat time for the band and the vast throng and Marjorie Jones, who all united in the "Star-spangled Banner" in honour of his aerial achievements. It was a great moment.

It was a great moment, but something seemed to threaten it. The face of Miss Spence looking up from the crowd grew too vivid—unpleasantly vivid. She was beckoning him and shouting, "Come down, Penrod Schofield! Penrod Schofield, come down here!" He could hear her above the band and the singing of the multitude; she seemed intent on spoiling everything. Marjorie Jones was weeping to show how sorry she was that she had formerly slighted him, and throwing kisses to prove that she loved him; but Miss Spence kept jumping between him and Marjorie, incessantly calling his name.

He grew more and more irritated with her; he was the most important person in the world and was engaged in proving it to Marjorie Jones and the whole city, and yet Miss Spence seemed to feel she still had the right to order him about as she did in the old days when he was an ordinary schoolboy. He was furious; he was sure she wanted him to do something disagreeable. It seemed to him that she had screamed "Penrod Schofield!" thousands of times.

From the beginning of his aerial experiments in his own schoolroom, he had not opened his lips, knowing somehow that one of the requirements for air floating is perfect silence on the part of the floater; but, finally, irritated beyond measure by Miss Spence's clamorous insistence, he was unable to restrain an indignant rebuke—and immediately came to earth with a frightful bump.

Miss Spence—in the flesh—had directed toward the physical body of the absent Penrod an inquiry as to the fractional consequences of dividing seventeen apples, fairly, among three boys, and she was surprised and displeased to receive no answer although to the best of her knowledge and belief, he was looking fixedly at her. She repeated her question crisply, without visible effect; then summoned him by name with increasing asperity. Twice she called him, while all his fellow pupils turned to stare at the gazing boy. She advanced a step from the platform.

"Penrod Schofield!"

"Oh, my goodness!" he shouted suddenly, "Can't you keep still a *minute?*"

Uncle John

Miss Spence gasped. So did the pupils. The whole room filled with a swelling conglomerate "O-o-o-o-h!"

As for Penrod himself, the walls reeled with the shock. He sat with his mouth open, a mere lump of stupefaction. For the appalling words that he had hurled at the teacher were as inexplicable to him as to any other who heard them.

Nothing is more treacherous than the human mind; nothing else so loves to play the Iscariot. Even when patiently bullied into a semblance of order and training, it may prove but a base and shifty servant. And Penrod's mind was not his servant; it was a master, with the April wind's whims; and it had just played him a diabolical trick. The very jolt with which he came back to the schoolroom in the midst of his fancied flight jarred his day-dream utterly out of him; and he sat, open-mouthed in horror at what he had said.

The unanimous gasp of awe was protracted. Miss Spence, however, finally recovered her breath, and, returning deliberately to the platform, faced the school. "And then, for a little while," as pathetic stories sometimes recount, "everything was very still." It was so still, in fact, that Penrod's new-born notoriety could almost be heard growing. This grisly silence was at last broken by the teacher.

"Penrod Schofield, stand up!"

The miserable child obeyed.

"What did you mean by speaking to me in that way?"

He hung his head, raked the floor with the side of his shoe, swayed, swallowed, looked suddenly at his hands with the air of never having seen them before, then clasped them behind him. The school shivered in ecstatic horror, every fascinated eye upon him; yet there was not a soul in the room but was profoundly grateful to him for the sensation—including the offended teacher herself. Unhappily, all this gratitude was unconscious and altogether different from the kind which results in testimonials and loving-cups. On the contrary!

"Penrod Schofield!"

He gulped.

"Answer me at once! Why did you speak to me like that?"

"I was——" He choked, unable to continue.

"Speak out!"

"I was just—thinking," he managed to stammer.

"That will not do," she returned sharply. "I wish to know immediately why you spoke as you did."

The stricken Penrod answered helplessly:

"Because I was just thinking."

Upon the very rack he could have offered no ampler truthful explanation. It was all he knew about it.

"Thinking what?"

"Just thinking."

Miss Spence's expression gave evidence that her power of self-restraint was undergoing a remarkable test. However, after taking counsel with herself, she commanded:

"Come here!"

He shuffled forward, and she placed a chair upon the platform near her own.

"Sit there!"

Then (but not at all as if nothing had happened), she continued the lesson in arithmetic. Spiritually the children may have learned a lesson in very small fractions indeed as they gazed at the fragment of sin before them on the stool of penitence. They all stared at him attentively with hard and passionately interested eyes, in which there was never one trace of pity. It cannot be said with precision that he writhed; his movement was more a slow, continuous squirm, effected with a ghastly assumption of languid indifference; while his gaze, in the effort to escape the marble-hearted glare of his schoolmates, affixed itself with apparent permanence to the waistcoat button of James Russell Lowell just above the "U" in "Russell."

Classes came and classes went, grilling him with eyes. Newcomers received the story of the crime in darkling whispers; and the outcast sat and sat and sat, and squirmed and squirmed and squirmed. (He did one or two things with his spine which a professional contortionist would have observed with real interest.) And all this while of freezing suspense was but the criminal's detention awaiting trial. A known punishment may be anticipated with some measure of equanimity; at least, the prisoner may prepare himself to undergo it; but the unknown looms more monstrous for every attempt to guess it. Penrod's crime was unique; there were no rules to aid him in estimating the vengeance to fall upon him for it. What seemed most probable was that he would be expelled from the school in the presence of his family, the mayor, and council, and afterward whipped by his father upon the State House steps, with the entire city as audience by invitation of the authorities.

Noon came. The rows of children filed out, every head turning for a last unpleasingly speculative look at the outlaw. Then Miss Spence closed the door into the cloakroom and that into the big hall, and came and sat at her desk, near Penrod. The tramping of feet outside, the shrill calls and shouting and the changing voices of the older boys ceased to be heard—and there was silence. Penrod, still affecting to be occupied with Lowell, was conscious that Miss Spence looked at him intently.

"Penrod," she said gravely, "what excuse have you to offer before I report your case to the principal?"

The word "principal" struck him to the vitals. Grand Inquisitor, Grand Khan, Sultan, Emperor, Tsar, Cæsar Augustus—these are comparable. He stopped squirming instantly, and sat rigid.

"I want an answer. Why did you shout those words at me?"

"Well," he murmured, "I was just—thinking."

"Thinking what?" she asked sharply.

"I don't know."

"That won't do!"

He took his left ankle in his right hand and regarded it helplessly.

"That won't do, Penrod Schofield," she repeated severely. "If that is all the excuse you have to offer I shall report your case this instant!"

And she rose with fatal intent.

But Penrod was one of those whom the precipice inspired. "Well, I *have* got an excuse."

"Well"—she paused impatiently—"what is it?"

He had not an idea, but he felt one coming, and replied automatically, in a plaintive tone:

"I guess anybody that had been through what *I* had to go through, last night, would think they had an excuse."

Miss Spence resumed her seat, though with the air of being ready to leap from it instantly.

"What has last night to do with your insolence to me this morning?"

"Well, I guess you'd see," he returned, emphasizing the plaintive note, "if you knew what *I* know."

"Now, Penrod," she said, in a kinder voice, "I have a high regard for your mother and father, and it would hurt me to distress them, but you must either tell me what was the matter with you or I'll have to take you to Mrs. Houston."

"Well, ain't I going to?" he cried, spurred by the dread name. "It's because I didn't sleep last night."

"Were you ill?" The question was put with some dryness.

He felt the dryness. "No'm; *I* wasn't."

"Then if someone in your family was so ill that even you were kept up all night, how does it happen they let you come to school this morning?"

"It wasn't illness," he returned, shaking his head mournfully. "It was lots worse'n anybody's being sick. It was—it was—well, it was jest awful."

"*What* was?" He remarked with anxiety the incredulity in her tone.

"It was about Aunt Clara," he said.

"Your Aunt Clara!" she repeated. "Do you mean your mother's sister who married Mr. Farry of Dayton, Illinois?"

"Yes—Uncle John," returned Penrod sorrowfully. "The trouble was about him."

Miss Spence frowned a frown which he rightly interpreted as one of continued suspicion. "She and I were in school together," she said. "I used to know her very well, and I've always heard her married life was entirely happy. I don't——"

"Yes, it was," he interrupted, "until last year when Uncle John took to running with travelling men——"

"What?"

"Yes'm." He nodded solemnly. "That was what started it. At first he was a good, kind husband, but these travelling men would coax him into a saloon on his way from work, and they got him to drinking beer and then ales, wines, liquors, and cigars——"

"Penrod!"

"Ma'am?"

"I'm not inquiring into your Aunt Clara's private affairs; I'm asking you if you have anything to say which would palliate——"

"That's what I'm tryin' to *tell* you about, Miss Spence," he pleaded,—"if you'd jest only let me. When Aunt Clara and her little baby daughter got to our house last night——"

"You say Mrs. Farry is visiting your mother?"

"Yes'm—not just visiting—you see, she *had* to come. Well of course, little baby Clara, she was so bruised up and mauled, where he'd been hittin' her with his cane——"

"You mean that your uncle had done such a thing as *that!*" exclaimed Miss Spence, suddenly disarmed by this scandal.

"Yes'm, and mamma and Margaret had to sit up all night nursin' little Clara—and *Aunt* Clara was in such a state *somebody* had to keep talkin' to *her*, and there wasn't anybody but me to do it, so I——"

"But where was your father?" she cried.

"Ma'am?"

"Where was your father while——"

"Oh—papa?" Penrod paused, reflected; then brightened. "Why, he was down at the train, waitin' to see if Uncle John would try to follow 'em and make 'em come home so's he could persecute 'em some more. I wanted to do that, but they said if he did come I mightn't be strong enough to hold him, and——" The brave lad paused again, modestly. Miss Spence's expression was encouraging. Her eyes were wide with astonishment, and there may have been in them, also, the mingled beginnings of admiration and self-reproach. Penrod, warming to his work, felt safer every moment.

"And so," he continued, "I had to sit up with Aunt Clara. She had some pretty big bruises, too, and I had to——"

"But why didn't they send for a doctor?" However, this question was only a flicker of dying incredulity.

"Oh, they didn't want any *doctor*," exclaimed the inspired realist promptly. "They don't want anybody to *hear* about it because Uncle John might reform—and then where'd he be if everybody knew he'd been a drunkard and whipped his wife and baby daughter?"

"Oh!" said Miss Spence.

"You see, he used to be upright as anybody," he went on explanatively. "It all begun——"

"Began, Penrod."

"Yes'm. It all commenced from the first day he let those travelling men coax him into the saloon." Penrod narrated the downfall of his Uncle John at length. In detail he was nothing short of plethoric; and incident followed incident, sketched with such vividness, such abundance of colour, and such verisimilitude to a drunkard's life as a drunkard's life should be, that had Miss Spence possessed the rather chilling attributes of William J. Burns himself, the last trace of skepticism must have vanished from her mind. Besides, there are two things that will be believed of any man whatsoever, and one of them is that he has taken to drink. And in every sense it was a moving picture which, with simple but eloquent words, the virtuous Penrod set before his teacher.

His eloquence increased with what it fed on; and as with the eloquence so with self-reproach in the gentle bosom of the teacher. She cleared her throat with difficulty once or twice, during his description of his ministering night with Aunt Clara. "And I said to her, 'Why, Aunt Clara, what's the use of takin' on so about it?' And I said, 'Now, Aunt Clara, all the crying in the world can't make things any better.' And then she'd just keep catchin' hold of me, and sob and kind of holler, and I'd say, '*Don't* cry, Aunt Clara—*please* don't cry.'"

Then, under the influence of some fragmentary survivals of the respectable portion of his Sunday adventures, his theme became more exalted; and, only partially misquoting a phrase from a psalm, he related how he had made it of comfort to Aunt Clara, and how he had besought her to seek Higher guidance in her trouble.

The surprising thing about a structure such as Penrod was erecting is that the taller it becomes the more ornamentation it will stand. Gifted boys have this faculty of building magnificence upon cobwebs—and Penrod was gifted. Under the spell of his really great performance, Miss Spence gazed more and more sweetly upon the prodigy of spiritual beauty and goodness before her, until at last, when Penrod came to the explanation of his "just thinking," she was forced to turn her head away.

"You mean, dear," she said gently, "that you were all worn out and hardly knew what you were saying?"

"Yes'm."

"And you were thinking about all those dreadful things so hard that you forgot where you were?"

"I was thinking," he said simply, "how to save Uncle John."

And the end of it for this mighty boy was that the teacher kissed him!

On Teaching Languages

BENJAMIN FRANKLIN

The short excerpt which follows is from the Autobiography *of BENJAMIN FRANKLIN (1706-1790). This book, known as the first American classic, was begun in 1771 when Franklin was at Twyford, England, as the guest of the Reverend Jonathan Shipley, Bishop of St. Asaph. About a third of the* Autobiography *was written at this time. Thirteen years had passed before Franklin found leisure to continue the work. He was then representing his country in Paris and living in Passy. Though a French edition of the* Autobiography *appeared in Paris in 1791 and an English edition in New York in 1794, the version we know today was not published until 1868.*

Franklin owed little to formal schooling. He read widely and learned to write by imitating the Spectator *essays and by long training as a newspaper editor.*

Franklin was a man of many interests, philanthropic, scientific, literary, and political. He initiated projects of many kinds, founded among other organizations the American Philosophical Society and an Academy for the Education of Youth, which was the forerunner of the University of Pennsylvania. Some of his ideas on education are revealed in the following selection from the Autobiography.

I HAD begun in 1732 to study languages; I soon made myself so much a master of the French as to be able to read the books with ease. I then undertook the Italian. An acquaintance, who was also learning it, us'd often to tempt me to play chess with him. Finding this took up too much of the time I had to spare for study, I at length refused to play any more unless on this condition, that the victor in every game should have a right to impose a task, either in parts of the grammar to be got by heart, or in translations, etc., which tasks the vanquish'd was to perform upon honour, before our next meeting. As we played pretty equally, we thus beat one another into that language. I afterwards, with a little painstaking, acquir'd as much of the Spanish as to read their books also. I have already mention'd that I had only one year's instruction in a Latin school, and that when very young after which I neglected that language entirely. But, when I had attained an acquaintance with the French, Italian, and Spanish, I was surpris'd to find, on looking over a Latin Testament, that I understood so much more of that language than I had imagined, which encouraged me to apply myself again to the study of it, and I met with more success, as those preceding languages had greatly smooth'd my way. From these circumstances, I have thought that there is some inconsistency in our common mode of teaching languages. We are told that it is proper to begin first with the Latin, and, having acquir'd that, it will be more easy to attain those modern languages which are derived from it; and yet we do not begin with the Greek, in order more easily to acquire the Latin. It is true that, if you can clamber and get to the top of the staircase without using the steps, you will more easily gain them in descending; but certainly, if you begin with the lowest you will with more ease ascend to the top; and I would therefore offer it to the consideration of those who superintend the education of our youth, whether, since many of those who begin with the Latin quit the same after spending some years without having made any great proficiency, and what they have learnt becomes almost useless, so that their time has been lost, it would not have been better to have begun with the French, proceeding to the Italian, etc.; for, tho', after spending the same time, they should quit the study of languages and never arrive at the Latin, they would, however, have acquired another tongue or two, that, being in modern use, might be serviceable to them in common life.

The Clerk of Oxford

GEOFFREY CHAUCER

GEOFFREY CHAUCER was born in 1340 (?), in London, the son of John Chaucer, vintner. Chaucer, like other young men of his day, finished his education as a page in the household of a nobleman. Two parchment leaves, fragments of a Household Account for the years 1356 to 1359 of Elizabeth, wife of Prince Lionel, third son of Edward III, contain an entry of a suit of clothes bought from one Geoffrey Chaucer, on May 20, 1357. That this was Geoffrey Chaucer, the poet, is almost certain.

In 1359 Chaucer joined the army of Edward III in an invasion of France. After his return from France he held various positions at court and in the course of the next ten years was sent on diplomatic missions to Genoa and Florence. In 1386 he was elected a knight of the shire for Kent; in 1388 he made his merry pilgrimage to Canterbury. A few years later he appears to have been in distressed circumstances. In 1398 the king made him a grant of a tun of wine a year for life. In 1399 Chaucer leased a house in the garden of the Chapel of St. Mary, Westminster, and there on October 25, 1400, he died.

The characterization of the clerk is taken from the Prologue to the Canterbury Tales.

A CLERK ther was of Oxenford also,
That un-to logik hadde longe y-go.
As lene was his hors as is a rake,
And he nas nat right fat, I undertake;
But loked holwe, and ther-to soberly.
Ful thredbar was his overest courtepy;
For he had geten him yet no benefice,
Ne was so worldly for to have office.
For him was levere have at his beddes heed
Twenty bokes, clad in blak or reed
Of Aristotle and his philosophye,
Than robes riche, or fithele, or gay sautrye.
But al be that he was a philosophre,
Yet hadde he but litel gold in cofre;
But al that he mighte of his frendes hente,
On bokes and on leringe he it spente,

And bisily gan for the soules preye
Of hem that yaf him wher-with to scoleye.
Of studie took he most cure and most hede.
Noght o word spak he more than was nede,
And that was seyd in forme and reverence,
And short and quik, and ful of hy sentence.
Sowninge in moral vertu was his speche,
And gladly wolde he lerne, and gladly teche.

The Old and the New Schoolmaster

CHARLES LAMB

CHARLES LAMB (1775-1834) was born in London and at the age of seven was sent to Christ's Hospital, a London charity school, where he began a lifelong friendship with Coleridge. He left school at the age of fourteen and two years later began a life of drudgery at a clerk's desk in the East India House. While still in his teens, Lamb had made sallies into literature by contributing verse to the Morning Chronicle. *With his sister Mary he wrote* Tales from Shakespeare (1807). *Though he continued to publish stories and essays from time to time, it was not until 1820 that Lamb became a regular contributor to the* London Magazine, *in which appeared the first series of essays published in 1823 as* The Essays of Elia. *Excerpts from two of these essays are given here.*

In one of my daily jaunts between Bishopsgate and Shacklewell, the coach stopped to take up a staid-looking gentleman, about the wrong side of thirty, who was giving his parting directions (while the steps were adjusting), in a tone of mild authority, to a tall youth, who seemed to be neither his clerk, his son, nor his servant, but something partaking of all three. The youth was dismissed, and we drove on. As we were the sole passengers, he naturally enough addressed his conversation to me; and we discussed the merits of the fare; the civility and punctuality of the driver; the circumstance of an opposition coach having been lately set up, with the probabilities of its success—to all which I was enabled to return pretty satisfactory answers, having been drilled into this kind of etiquette by some years' daily practice of riding to and fro in the stage aforesaid—when he suddenly alarmed me by a startling question, whether I had seen the show of prize cattle that morning in Smithfield? Now as I had not seen it, and do not greatly care for such sort of exhibitions, I was obliged to return a cold negative. He seemed a little mortified, as well as astonished, at my declaration, as (it appeared) he was just come fresh from the sight, and doubtless had hoped to compare notes on the subject. However, he assured me that I had lost a fine treat, as it far exceeded the show of last year. We were now approaching Norton Falgate, when the sight of some shop-goods *ticketed* freshened him up into a dissertation upon the cheapness of cottons this spring. I was now a little in heart, as the nature of my morning avocations had brought me into some sort of familiarity with the raw material; and I was surprised to find how eloquent

I was becoming on the state of the Indian market—when, presently, he
dashed my incipient vanity to the earth at once, by inquiring whether I
had ever made any calculation as to the value of the rental of all the
retail shops in London. Had he asked of me, what song the Sirens sang,
or what name Achilles assumed when he hid himself among women, I
might, with Sir Thomas Browne, have hazarded a "wide solution." [1] My
companion saw my embarrassment, and, the almshouses beyond Shore-
ditch just coming in view, with great good-nature and dexterity shifted
his conversation to the subject of public charities; which led to the comparative merits of provision for the poor in past and present times, with
observations on the old monastic institutions, and charitable orders; but,
finding me rather dimly impressed with some glimmering notions from old
poetic associations, than strongly fortified with any speculations reducible
to calculation on the subject, he gave the matter up; and, the country
beginning to open more and more upon us, as we approached the turnpike
at Kingsland (the destined termination of his journey), he put a home
thrust upon me, in the most unfortunate position he could have chosen,
by advancing some queries relative to the North Pole Expedition. While
I was muttering out something about the Panorama of those strange
regions (which I had actually seen), by way of parrying the question, the
coach stopping relieved me from any further apprehensions. My companion getting out, left me in the comfortable possession of my ignorance;
and I heard him, as he went off, putting questions to an outside passenger,
who had alighted with him, regarding an epidemic disorder, that had been
rife about Dalston; and which, my friend assured him, had gone through
five or six schools in that neighbourhood. The truth now flashed upon me,
that my companion was a schoolmaster; and that the youth, whom he had
parted from at our first acquaintance, must have been one of the bigger
boys, or the usher.—He was evidently a kind-hearted man, who did not
seem so much desirous of provoking discussion by the questions which
he put, as of obtaining information at any rate. It did not appear that he
took any interest, either, in such kind of inquiries, for their own sake; but
that he was in some way bound to seek for knowledge. A greenish-col-
oured coat, which he had on, forbade me to surmise that he was a
clergyman. The adventure gave birth to some reflections on the difference
between persons of his profession in past and present times.

Rest to the souls of those fine old Pedagogues; the breed, long since
extinct, of the Lilys, and the Linacres: who believing that all learning was
contained in the languages which they taught, and despising every other
acquirement as superficial and useless, came to their task as to a sport!
Passing from infancy to age, they dreamed away all their days as in a
grammar-school. Revolving in a perpetual cycle of declensions, conjuga-
tions, syntaxes, and prosodies; renewing constantly the occupations which
had charmed their studious childhood; rehearsing continually the part of

[1] Urn Burial.

the past; life must have slipped from them at last like one day. They were always in their first garden, reaping harvests of their golden time, among their *Flori-* and their *Spici-legia;* in Arcadia still, but kings; the ferule of their sway not much harsher, but of like dignity with that mild sceptre attributed to kind Basileus; the Greek and Latin, their stately Pamela and their Philoclea; with the occasional duncery of some untoward Tyro, serving for a refreshing interlude of a Mopsa, or a clown Damœtas!

With what a savour doth the Preface to Colet's, or (as it is sometimes called) Paul's "Accidence," set forth! "To exhort every man to the learning of grammar, that intendeth to attain the understanding of the tongues, wherein is contained a great treasury of wisdom and knowledge, it would seem but vain and lost labour; for so much as it is known, that nothing can surely be ended, whose beginning is either feeble or faulty; and no building be perfect, whereas the foundation and ground work is ready to fall, and unable to uphold the burden of the frame." How well doth this stately preamble (comparable to those which Milton commendeth as "having been the usage to prefix to some solemn law, then first promulgated by Solon, or Lycurgus") correspond with and illustrate that pious zeal for conformity, expressed in a succeeding clause, which would fence about grammar-rules with the severity of faith-articles!—"as for the diversity of grammars, it is well profitably taken away by the king's majesties wisdom, who foreseeing the inconvenience, and favourably providing the remedie, caused one kind of grammar by sundry learned men to be diligently drawn, and so to be set out, only everywhere to be taught for the use of learners, and for the hurt in changing of schoolmaisters." What a *gusto* in that which follows: "wherein it is profitable that he (the pupil) can orderly decline his noun and his verb." *His* noun!

The fine dream is fading away fast; and the least concern of a teacher in the present day is to inculcate grammar-rules.

The modern schoolmaster is expected to know a little of everything, because his pupil is required not to be entirely ignorant of anything. He must be superficially, if I may so say, omniscient. He is to know something of pneumatics; of chemistry; of whatever is curious, or proper to excite the attention of the youthful mind; an insight into mechanics is desirable, with a touch of statistics; the quality of soils, etc., botany, the constitution of his country, *cum multis aliis.* You may get a notion of some part of his expected duties by consulting the famous Tractate on Education, addressed to Mr. Hartlib.

All these things—these, or the desire of them—he is expected to instil, not by set lessons from professors, which he may charge in the bill, but at school-intervals, as he walks the streets, or saunters through green fields (those natural instructors), with his pupils. The least part of what is expected from him, is to be done in school-hours. He must insinuate knowledge at the *mollia tempora fandi.* He must seize every occasion—the season of the year—the time of the day—a passing cloud—a rainbow—a waggon of hay—a regiment of soldiers going by—to inculcate something useful. He can receive no pleasure from a casual glimpse of Nature, but must catch at it as an object of instruction. He must interpret beauty into the picturesque. He cannot relish a beggar-man, or a gipsy, for thinking of the suitable improvement. Nothing comes to him, not spoiled by the sophisticating medium of moral uses. The Universe—that Great Book, as it has been called—is to him indeed, to all intents and purposes, a book, out of which he is doomed to read tedious homilies to distasting schoolboys.— Vacations themselves are none to him, he is only rather worse off than before; for commonly he has some intrusive upper-boy fastened upon him at such high times; some cadet of a great family; some neglected lump of nobility, or gentry; that he must drag after him to the play, to the Panorama, to Mr. Bartley's Orrery, to the Panopticon, or into the country, to a friend's house, or his favourite watering-place. Wherever he goes, this uneasy shadow attends him. A boy is at his board, and in his path, and in all his movements. He is boy-rid, sick of perpetual boy.

Boys are capital fellows in their own way, among their mates; but they are unwholesome companions for grown people. The restraint is felt no less on the one side, than on the other.—Even a child, that "plaything for an hour," tires *always*. The noises of children, playing their own fancies— as I now hearken to them by fits, sporting on the green before my window, while I am engaged in these grave speculations at my neat suburban retreat at Shacklewell—by distance made more sweet—inexpressibly take from the labour of my task. It is like writing to music. They seem to modulate my periods. They ought at least to do so—for in the voice of that tender age there is a kind of poetry, far unlike the harsh prose-accents of man's conversation.—I should but spoil their sport, and diminish my own sympathy for them, by mingling in their pastime.

I would not be domesticated all my days, with a person of very superior capacity to my own—not, if I know myself at all, from any considerations of jealousy or self-comparison, for the occasional communion with such minds has constituted the fortune and felicity of my life—but the habit of too constant intercourse with spirits above you, instead of raising you, keeps you down. Too frequent doses of original thinking from others, restrain what lesser portion of that faculty you may possess of your own. You get entangled in another man's mind, even as you lose yourself in another man's grounds. You are walking with a tall varlet, whose strides out-pace yours to lassitude. The constant operation of such potent agency would reduce me, I am convinced, to imbecility. You may derive thoughts from others; your way of thinking, the mould in which your thoughts are cast, must be your own. Intellect may be imparted, but not each man's intellectual fame.—

As little as I should wish to be always thus dragged upwards, as little (or rather still less) is it desirable to be stunted downwards by your associates. The trumpet does not more stun you by its loudness, than a whisper teases you by its provoking inaudibility.

Why are we never quite at our ease in the presence of a schoolmaster?—because we are conscious that he is not quite at his ease in ours. He is awkward, and out of place, in the society of his equals. He comes like Gulliver from among his little people, and he cannot fit the stature of his understanding to yours. He cannot meet you on the square. He wants a point given him, like an indifferent whistplayer. He is so used to teaching, that he wants to be teaching *you*. One of these professors, upon my complaining that these little sketches of mine were anything but methodical, and that I was unable to make them otherwise, kindly offered to instruct me in the method by which young gentlemen in *his* seminary were taught to compose English themes.—The jests of a schoolmaster are coarse, or thin. They do not *tell* out of school. He is under the restraint of a formal and didactive hypocrisy in company, as a clergyman is under a moral one. He can no more let his intellect loose in society, than the other can his inclinations.—He is forlorn among his co-evals; his juniors cannot be his friends.

"I take blame to myself," said a sensible man of this profession, writing to a friend respecting a youth who had quitted his school abruptly, "that your nephew was not more attached to me. But persons in my situation are more to be pitied, than can well be imagined. We are surrounded by young, and, consequently, ardently affectionate hearts, but *we* can never hope to share an atom of their affections. The relation of master and scholar forbids this. *How pleasing this must be to you, how I envy your feelings,* my friends will sometimes say to me, when they see young men, whom I have educated, return after some years' absence from school, their eyes shining with pleasure, while they shake hands with their old master, bringing a present of game to me, or a toy to my wife, and thanking me in the warmest terms for my care of their education. A holiday is begged for the boys; the house is a scene of happiness; I, only, am sad, at heart.—This fine-spirited and warm-hearted youth, who fancies he repays his master with gratitude for the care of his boyish years—this young man—in the eight long years I watched over him with a parent's anxiety, never could repay me with one look of genuine feeling. He was proud, when I praised; he was submissive, when I reproved him; but he did never *love* me—and what he now mistakes for gratitude and kindness for me, is but the pleasant sensation, which all persons feel at revisiting the scene of their boyish hopes and fears; and the seeing on equal terms the man they were accustomed to look up to with reverence. My wife too," this interesting correspondent goes on to say, "my once darling Anna, is the wife of a schoolmaster.—When I married her—knowing that the wife of a schoolmaster ought to be a busy notable creature, and fearing that my gentle Anna would ill supply the loss of my dear bustling mother, just then dead, who never sat still, was in every part of the house in a moment, and whom I was obliged sometimes to threaten to fasten down in a chair, to save her from fatiguing herself to death—I expressed my fears, that I was bringing her into a way of life unsuitable to her; and she, who loved me tenderly, promised for my sake to exert herself to perform the duties of her new situation. She promised, and she has kept her word. What wonders will not a woman's love perform?—My house is managed with a propriety and decorum, unknown in other schools; my boys are well fed, look healthy, and have every proper accommodation; and all this performed with a careful economy, that never descends to meanness. But I have lost my gentle, *helpless* Anna!—When we sit down to enjoy an hour of repose after the fatigue of the day, I am compelled to listen to what have been her useful (and they are really useful) employments through the day, and what she proposes for her to-morrow's task. Her heart and her features are changed by the duties of her situation. To the boys, she never appears other than the *master's wife*, and she looks up to me as the *boys' master;* to whom all show of love and affection would be highly improper, and unbecoming the dignity of her situation and mine. Yet *this* my gratitude forbids me to hint to her. For my sake she submitted to be this altered creature, and can I reproach her for it?"—For the communication of this letter, I am indebted to my cousin Bridget.

Christ's Hospital Five and Thirty Years Ago

THE UPPER and Lower Grammar Schools were held in the same room; and an imaginary line only divided their bounds. Their character was as different as that of the inhabitants on the two sides of the Pyrenees. The Rev. James Boyer was the Upper Master: but the Rev. Matthew Field presided over that portion of the apartment, of which I had the good fortune to be a member. We lived a life as careless as birds. We talked and did just what we pleased, and nobody molested us. We carried an accidence, or a grammar, for form; but, for any trouble it gave us, we might take two years in getting through the verbs deponent, and another two in forgetting all that we had learned about them. There was now and then the formality of saying a lesson, but if you had not learned it, a brush across the shoulders (just enough to disturb a fly) was the sole remonstrance. Field never used the rod; and in truth he wielded the cane with no great good will—holding it "like a dancer." It looked in his hands rather like an emblem than an instrument of authority; and an emblem, too, he was ashamed of. He was a good easy man, that did not care to ruffle his own peace, nor perhaps set any great consideration upon the value of juvenile time. He came among us, now and then, but often stayed away whole days from us; and when he came, it made no difference to us—he had his private room to retire to, the short time he stayed, to be out of the sound of our noise. Our mirth and uproar went on. We had classics of our own, without being beholden to "insolent Greece or haughty Rome," that passed current among us—Peter Wilkins—the Adventures of the Hon. Capt. Robert Boyle—the Fortunate Blue Coat Boy—and the like. Or we cultivated a turn for mechanic or scientific operation; making little sun-dials of paper; or weaving those ingenious parentheses, called *cat-cradles;* or making dry peas to dance upon the end of a tin pipe; or studying the art military over that laudable game "French and English," and a hundred other such devices to pass away the time—mixing the useful with the agreeable—as would have made the souls of Rousseau and John Locke chuckle to have seen us.

Matthew Field belonged to that class of modest divines who affect to mix in equal proportion the *gentleman,* the *scholar,* and the *Christian;* but, I know not how, the first ingredient is generally found to be the predominating dose in the composition. He was engaged in gay parties, or with his courtly bow at some episcopal levée, when he should have been attending upon us. He had for many years the classical charge of a hundred children, during the four or five first years of their education; and his very highest form seldom proceeded further than two or three of the introductory fables of Phædrus. How things were suffered to go on thus, I cannot guess. Boyer, who was the proper person to have remedied these abuses, always affected, perhaps felt, a delicacy in interfering in a province not strictly his own. I have not been without my suspicions, that he was not altogether displeased at the contrast we presented to his end of the school. We were a sort of Helots to his young Spartans. He would sometimes, with ironic deference, send to borrow a rod of the Under Master, and then, with Sardonic grin, observe to one of his upper boys, "how neat and fresh the twigs looked." While his pale students were battering their brains over Xenophon and Plato, with a silence as deep as that enjoined by the Samite, we were enjoying ourselves at our ease in our little Goshen. We saw a little into the secrets of his discipline, and the prospect did but the more reconcile us to our lot. His thunders rolled innocuous for us; his storms came near, but never touched us; contrary to Gideon's miracle, while all around were drenched, our fleece was dry.[1] His boys turned out the better scholars; we, I suspect, have the advantage in temper. His pupils cannot speak of him without something of terror allaying their gratitude; the remembrance of Field comes back with all the soothing images of indolence, and summer slumbers, and work like play, and innocent idleness, and Elysian exemptions, and life itself a "playing holiday."

Though sufficiently removed from the jurisdiction of Boyer, we were near enough (as I have said) to understand a little of his system. We occasionally heard sounds of the *Ulalantes,* and caught glances of Tartarus. B. was a rabid pedant. His English style was cramped to barbarism. His

[1] Cowley.

Easter anthems (for his duty obliged him to those periodical flights) were grating as scrannel pipes.[2]—He would laugh, ay, and heartily, but then it must be at Flaccus's quibble about *Rex*—or at the *tristis servitas in vultu,* or *inspicere in patinas,* of Terence—thin jests, which at their first broaching could hardly have had *vis* enough to move a Roman muscle.—He had two wigs, both pedantic, but of different omen. The one serene, smiling, fresh powdered, betokening a mild day. The other, an old discoloured, unkempt, angry caxon, denoting frequent and bloody execution. Woe to the school, when he made his morning appearance in his *passy,* or *passionate wig.* No comet expounded surer.—J. B. had a heavy hand. I have known him double his knotty fist at a poor trembling child (the maternal milk hardly dry upon its lips) with a "Sirrah, do you presume to set your wits at me?"—Nothing was more common than to see him make a headlong entry into the schoolroom, from his inner recess, or library, and, with turbulent eye, singling out a lad, roar out, "Od's my life, Sirrah" (his favourite adjuration), "I have a great mind to whip you,"—then, with as sudden a retracting impulse, fling back into his lair—and, after a cooling lapse of some minutes (during which all but the culprit had totally forgotten the context) drive headlong out again, piecing out his imperfect sense, as if it had been some Devil's Litany, with the expletory yell—*"and I WILL too."*—In his gentler moods, when the *rabidus furor* was assuaged, he had resort to an ingenious method, peculiar, for what I have heard, to himself, of whipping the boy, and reading the Debates, at the same time; a paragraph, and a lash between; which in those times, when parliamentary oratory was most at a height and flourishing in these realms, was not calculated to impress the patient with a veneration for the diffuser graces of rhetoric.

Once, and but once, the uplifted rod was known to fall ineffectual from his hand—when droll squinting W—— having been caught putting the inside of the master's desk to a use for which the architect had clearly not designed it, to justify himself, with great simplicity averred, that *he did not know that the thing had been forewarned.* This exquisite irrecognition of any law antecedent to the oral or declaratory struck so irresistibly upon the fancy of all who heard it (the pedagogue himself not excepted) that remission was unavoidable.

L. has given credit to B.'s great merits as an instructor. Coleridge, in his literary life, has pronounced a more intelligible and ample encomium on them. The author of the Country Spectator doubts not to compare him with the ablest teachers of antiquity. Perhaps we cannot dismiss him

---

[2] In this and every thing B. was the antipodes of his co-adjutor. While the former was digging his brains for crude anthems, worth a pig-nut, F. would be recreating his gentlemanly fancy in the more flowery walks of the Muses. A little dramatic effusion of his, under the name of Vertumnus and Pomona, is not yet forgotten by the chroniclers of that sort of literature. It was accepted by Garrick, but the town did not give it their sanction—B. used to say of it, in a way of half-compliment, half-irony, that it was *too classical for representation.*

better than with the pious ejaculation of C.—when he heard that his old master was on his death-bed— "Poor J. B.!—may all his faults be forgiven; and may he be wafted to bliss by little cherub boys, all head and wings, with no *bottoms* to reproach his sublunary infirmities."

The German School

DOROTHY RICHARDSON

DOROTHY RICHARDSON, English novelist, was born in 1882 in se-cluded surroundings in late Victorian England. Some of the impressions and inner experiences of her youth are recorded in Pilgrimage, *a novel-cycle begun in 1913 and not yet completed.*

The following excerpt is taken from Pointed Roofs, *one of the novels in the* Pilgrimage *cycle.*

During those early days Miriam realised that school-routine, as she knew it—the planned days—the regular unvarying succession of les-sons and preparations, had no place in this new world. Even the masters' lessons, coming in from outside and making a kind of framework of ap-pointments over the otherwise fortuitously occupied days, were, she soon found, not always securely calculable. Herr Kapellmeister Bossenberger would be heard booming and intoning in the hall unexpectedly at all hours. He could be heard all over the house. Miriam had never seen him, but she noticed that great haste was always made to get a pupil to the saal and that he taught impatiently. He shouted and corrected and mimicked. Only Millie's singing, apparently, he left untouched. You could hear her lilting away through her little high songs as serenely as she did at Vor-spielen.

Miriam was at once sure that he found his task of teaching these girls an extremely tiresome one.

Probably most teachers found teaching tiresome. But there was some-thing peculiar and new to her in Herr Bossenberger's attitude. She tried to account for it . . . German men despised women. Why did they teach them anything at all?

The same impression, the sense of a half-impatient, half-exasperated tuition came to her from the lectures of Herr Winter and Herr Schraub.

Herr Winter, a thin tall withered-looking man with shabby hair and bony hands whose veins stood up in knots, drummed on the table as he taught botany and geography. The girls sat around bookless and politely attentive and seemed, the Germans at least, to remember all the facts for which he appealed during the last few minutes of his hour. Miriam could never recall anything but his weary withered face.

Herr Schraub, the teacher of history, was, she felt, almost openly contemptuous of his class. He would begin lecturing, almost before he was inside the door. He taught from a book, sitting with downcast eyes, his round red mass of face—expressionless save for the bristling spikes of his tiny straw-coloured moustache and the rapid movements of his tight rounded little lips—persistently averted from his pupils. For the last few minutes of his time he would, ironically, his eyes fixed ahead of him at a point on the table, snap questions—indicating his aim with a tapping finger, going round the table like a dealer at cards. Surely the girls must detest him. . . . The Germans made no modification of their polite attentiveness. Amongst the English only Gertrude and the Martins found any answers for him. Miriam, proud of sixth-form history essays and the full marks she had generally claimed for them, had no memory for facts and dates; but she made up her mind that were she ever so prepared with a correct reply, nothing should drag from her any response to these military tappings. Fräulein presided over these lectures from the corner of the sofa out of range of the eye of the teacher and horrified Miriam by voicelessly prompting the girls whenever she could. There was no kind of preparation for these lessons.

2

Miriam mused over the difference between the bearing of these men and that of the masters she remembered and tried to find words. What was it? Had her masters been more—respectful than these Germans were? She felt they had. But it was not only that. She recalled the men she remembered teaching week by week through all the years she had known them . . . the little bolster-like literature master, an albino, a friend of Browning, reading, reading to them as if it were worth while, as if they were equals . . . interested friends—that had never struck her at the time. . . . But it was true—she could not remember ever having felt a schoolgirl . . . or being "talked down" to . . . dear Stroodie, the music-master, and Monsieur—old white-haired Monsieur, dearest of all, she could hear his gentle voice pleading with them on behalf of his treasures . . . the drilling-master with his keen, friendly blue eye . . . the briefless barrister who had taught them arithmetic in a baritone voice, laughing all the time but really wanting them to get on.

What was it she missed? Was it that her old teachers were "gentlemen" and these Germans were not? She pondered over this and came to the conclusion that the whole attitude of the Englishman and of Monsieur, her one Frenchman, towards her sex was different from that of these Germans. It occurred to her once in a flash during these puzzled musings that the lessons she had had at school would not have been given more zestfully, more as if it were worth while, had she and her schoolfellows been boys. Here she could not feel that. The teaching was grave enough. The masters felt the importance of what they taught . . . she felt that they were formal, reverently formal, "pompous" she called it, towards the facts that they flung out down the long schoolroom table, but that the relationship of their pupils to these facts seemed a matter of less than indifference to them.

3

She began to recognise now with a glow of gratitude that her own teachers, those who were enthusiastic about their subjects—the albino, her dear Monsieur with his classic French prose, a young woman who had taught them logic and the beginning of psychology—that strange, new subject—were at least as enthusiastic about getting her and her mates awake and into relationship with something. They cared somehow.

She recalled the albino, his face and voice generally separated from his class by a book held vertically, close to his left eye, while he blocked the right eye with his free hand—his faintly wheezy tones bleating triumphantly out at the end of a passage from "The Ring and the Book," as he lowered his volume and bent beaming towards them all, his right eye still blocked, for response. Miss Donne, her skimpy skirt powdered with chalk, explaining a syllogism from the blackboard, turning quietly to them, her face all aglow, her chalky hands gently pressed together, "Do you *see*? Does anyone *see*?" Monsieur, spoiling them, sharpening their pencils, letting them cheat over their pages of rules, knowing quite well that each learned only one and directing his questioning accordingly, Monsieur dreaming over the things he read to them, repeating passages, wandering from his subject, making allusions here and there—and all of them, she, at any rate, and Lilla—she knew, often—in paradise. How rich and friendly and helpful they all seemed.

4

She began to wonder whether hers had been in some way a specially good school. Things *had* mattered there. Somehow the girls had been made to feel they mattered. She remembered even old Stroodie—the least attached member of the staff—asking her suddenly, once, in the middle of a music-lessons what she was going to do with her life and a day when the artistic vice-principal—who was a connection by marriage of Holman Hunt's and had met Ruskin, Miriam knew, several times—had gone from girl to girl round the collected fifth and sixth forms asking them each what they would best like to do in life. Miriam had answered at once with a conviction born that moment that she wanted to "write a book." It irritated her when she remembered during these reflections that she had not been able to give to Fräulein Pfaff's public questioning any intelligible account of the school. She might at least have told her of the connection with Ruskin and Browning and Holman Hunt, whereas her muddled replies had led Fräulein to decide that her school had been "a kind of high school." She knew it had not been this. She felt there was something questionable about a high school. She was beginning to think that her school had been very good. Pater had seen to that—that was one of the things he had steered and seen to. There had been a school they might have gone to higher up the hill where one learned needlework even in the "first class" as they called it instead of the sixth form as at her school, and "Calisthenics" instead of drilling—and something called elocution—where the girls were "finished." It was an expensive school. Had the teachers there taught the girls . . . as if they had no minds? Perhaps that school was more like the one she found herself in now? She wondered and wondered. What was she going to do with her life after all these years at the good school? She began bit by bit to understand her agony on the day of leaving. It was there she belonged. She ought to go back and go on.

One day she lay twisted and convulsed, face downwards on her bed at the thought that she could never go back and begin. If only she could really begin now, knowing what she wanted. . . . She would talk now with those teachers. . . . Isn't it all wonderful! Aren't things wonderful! Tell me some more. . . . She felt sure that if she could go back, things would get clear. She would talk and think and understand. . . . She did not linger over that. It threatened a storm whose results would be visible. She wondered what the other girls were doing—Lilla? She had heard nothing of her since that last term. She would write to her one day, perhaps. Perhaps not. . . . She would have to tell her that she was a governess. Lilla would think that very funny and would not care for her now that she was so old and worried. . . .

5

Woven through her retrospective appreciations came a doubt. She wondered whether, after all, her school had been right. Whether it ought to have treated them all so seriously. If she had gone to the other school she was sure she would never have heard of the Æsthetic Movement or felt troubled about the state of Ireland and India. Perhaps she would have grown up a Churchwoman . . . and "ladylike." Never.

She could only think that somehow she must be "different"; that a sprinkling of the girls collected in that school were different, too. The school she decided was new—modern—Ruskin. Most of the girls perhaps had not been affected by it. But some had. She had. The thought stirred her. She had. It was mysterious. Was it the school or herself? Herself to begin with. If she had been brought up differently, it could not, she felt sure, have made her very different—for long—nor taught her to be affable —to smile that smile she hated so. The school had done something to her. It had not gone against the things she found in herself. She wondered once or twice during these early weeks what she would have been like if she had been brought up with these German girls. What they were going to do with their lives was only too plain. All but Emma, she had been astounded to discover, had already a complete outfit of house-linen to which

they were now adding fine embroideries and laces. All could cook. Minna
had startled her one day by exclaiming with lit face, "Ach, ich koche so
schrecklich gern!" . . . Oh, I am so frightfully fond of cooking. . . . And
they were placid and serene, secure in a kind of security Miriam had never
met before. They did not seem to be in the least afraid of the future. She
envied that. Their eyes and their hands were serene. . . . They would
have houses and things they could do and understand, always. . . . How
they must want to begin, she mused. . . . What a prison school must
seem.

She thought of their comfortable German homes, of ruling and shop-
ping and directing and being looked up to. . . . German husbands.

That thought she shirked. Emma in particular she could not contemplate
in relation to a German husband.

In any case one day these girls would be middle-aged . . . as Clara
looked now . . . they would look like the German women on the boule-
vards and in the shops.

In the end she ceased to wonder that the German masters dealt out their
wares to these girls so superciliously.

And yet . . . German music, a line of German poetry, a sudden light on
Clara's face. . . .

6

There was one other teacher, a Swiss and some sort of minister she supposed as everyone called him the Herr Pastor. She wondered whether he
was in any sense the spiritual adviser of the school and regarded him with
provisional suspicion. She had seen him once, sitting short and very black
and white at the head of the schoolroom table. His black beard and dark
eyes as he sat with his back to the window made his face gleam like a
mask. He had spoken very rapidly as he told the girls the life-story of
some poet.

The First Skirmish

G. F. BRADBY

G. F. BRADBY, English writer, was born in 1863. He received his education at Rugby and at Balliol College, Oxford. After graduation, he returned to Rugby and taught there until his retirement in 1920.

The following selection is from his novel of school life, The Lanchester Tradition.

M R. FLACGON had come to Chiltern with a determination to do great things for education. He himself had had a hard struggle to win to knowledge, and the phases of the struggle had left their mark deeply imprinted on his character. Born with a thirst for knowledge, he had had to force his way, step by step, to the fountain head; and the narrow circumstances of a Cumberland vicarage had strewn the path with difficulties. Old and musty books spelled out by candlelight in his father's study, then a scholarship at a decaying provincial grammar school, and finally a classical exhibition at a small Oxford College—such had been the stages by which he had made his way up the stream. And, when he reviewed the past, he could not but remember how brackish and unsatisfying the water had often been in the channels where he had been compelled to seek it. If his thirst had been less insatiable, his own experiences might well have cured him of the desire to drink.

To a childhood spent among the Cumbrian Fells he owed a robust constitution and a toughness of fibre that defied fatigue; perhaps, too, a certain gravity and reticence which seem to come naturally to those who are bred among mountains. Rather below middle height, with a clear-cut face and an intellectual forehead, his most striking feature was his eyes—fearless, grey, receptive eyes, which looked out upon the world with a quiet but penetrating interest. A friend, who knew him intimately, described them as seeing, rather than speaking, eyes.

Of public schools he knew nothing from the inside, and he had few opportunities of studying public school men at his own small college. In such as he came across he had noted a certain self-sufficiency and polite lack of interest in things intellectual, which he put down to the narrowness of their training. The circumstances of his own upbringing had thrown him almost entirely among boys and men who had to make their own way

"The First Skirmish" is reprinted from *The Lanchester Tradition* by permission of A. P. Watt & Son and the author.

168

in the world, and who were desperately intent on turning even half a talent to profitable use. Their aims might be low and their ambitions sordid, but there was no trifling with opportunity, no deliberate rejection of golden chances. He had had no practical experience of that large and wealthy class of people who have been well off for two generations and whose children are born with an assured future—the people, in fact, who send their boys to the richer public schools; and he had yet to learn how paralysing to the intellectual life an assured future may be. In a word, he did not yet understand the psychology of the horse who refuses to drink when taken to the water; and, noticing that public school men were, as a class, unintellectual, he assumed that their minds had been starved, and that their teachers set no store by intellect.

The idea of standing for a headmastership had first been suggested to him by an acquaintance whom chance had thrown in his way. After securing his Fellowship, Mr. Flaggon had accepted a post as tutor to a foreign prince, partly because the work was light and he needed a holiday, and partly because the tutorship was a travelling one and he was eager to see something of the world. Ten days of continuous rain and snow on the Riffel Alp had thrown him much into the society of the great man behind the scenes to whom allusion has already been made. The great man was both an enthusiast for education and a firm believer in ability; he even had the hardihood to maintain that ability is of greater value than experience, and experiment more fruitful of results than the accepted method of playing for safety. Being a shrewd judge of men, he soon discerned, beneath the tutor's quiet and unsensational exterior, signs of exceptional power; and he did not lose sight of him. The Welsh appointment was largely his doing, and, when the headmastership of Chiltern fell vacant, it was he who wrote and suggested that Mr. Flaggon should stand.

Mr. Flaggon himself had hardly regarded his candidature even as a forlorn hope. It was intended rather as a *ballon d'essai,* a notice to the scholastic world that he considered himself a possible headmaster, and an opportunity of gauging how that world would regard his claims. Chiltern, as we have seen, had no hesitation in branding his pretensions as presumptuous; and Mr. Flaggon was quite aware that the success of his audacious move, which had come as a surprise to himself, had been more than a disappointment to his future colleagues.

But he was not dismayed by the difficulty of the task that lay before him. His whole life had been spent in overcoming difficulties, and he had the quiet confidence of a man who is sure of his own temper and accustomed to succeed. As has been stated before, he brought with him to his new work a great zeal for the cause of education; but he had no cut-and-dried theories of reform, no patent nostrum of his own. He knew what education *ought* to be, what it had been to himself—an individual renaissance, a quickening of the highest faculties of mind and spirit; and he knew that that was precisely what public school education was *not*. He was determined to study the problem on the spot and to proceed tentatively. The machinery, as he saw it, was antiquated, the bill of fare obsolete, the valley full of dry bones. But the dry bones were only waiting for a revivifying spirit to become clothed with flesh and to start into life again. In his mind's eye he saw the boys as hungry sheep who looked up and were not fed. He had not yet become acquainted with the particular breed of sheep that is born without an appetite.

But ever since his first flying visit to the school, Mr. Flaggon had begun to realise that there were other problems behind the educational one which would claim the attention of a headmaster. He had always taken on trust the virtues that are considered inherent in the public school system—loyalty, discipline, gentlemanly behaviour, and a subordination of the individual will to the interests of the community. In his undergraduate days he had often experienced an absurd sensation of being considered morally, as well as socially, inferior to the more fortunate alumni of the great public schools. Old Boys had talked to him with flashing eyes and genuine conviction of the exceptional merits of their own schools, and of the enhanced value which they gave to life; and he had believed them. And what he believed of other schools he had been taught to believe as pre-eminently true of Chiltern. Chiltern was the only institution of its kind about which nobody had as yet written a schoolboy story; but it ranked amongst the aristocracy of public schools, and, in the eyes of Chilternians, even higher. And it had special characteristics of its own. Somebody had said that Chiltern turned out gentlemen rather than scholars; and somebody else, probably an Old Chilternian, had added that you could always tell a Chiltern boy from the way he behaved in a drawing-room. Wealthy manufacturers sent their sons to Chiltern to acquire the easy manners and social polish which seemed natural to the place; and to be an Old Chilternian was an "open sesame" to any club that was not primarily intellectual.

Mr. Flaggon had expected, therefore, to find a somewhat low level of mental attainments but a high standard of good breeding. But, ever since his first visit, his mind had been haunted by the picture of three vapid youths strolling past their headmaster with insolent unconcern and the blasé voices saying: "Is that the new Gus?"

"Looks like it—unless it's his shuvver."

And then there was the writing on certain walls in Mr. Cox's house.

This unfavourable impression was confirmed as he watched the boys in Chapel on the first Sunday of the Term. There was an air of insolence and swagger about the way in which the bigger boys strolled in last and lounged, instead of kneeling, during the prayers. Signs of intelligence were frequent between block and block; and, even among the smaller boys, there was often a kind of self-consciousness and pose, which, though he could not quite analyse the cause, affected Mr. Flaggon unpleasantly.

He had often heard of the impressiveness of a school-chapel service. There was certainly nothing impressive about the service at Chiltern on the first Sunday of the Term, except, perhaps, the singing of the hymns—and that was much more noisy than reverent.

Mr. Flaggon belonged to no definite party in the Church. A dislike of labels and definitions, coupled with a strong desire to make the Church inclusive rather than exclusive, had won him the easy hatred of the dogmatists and the reputation of being unorthodox. His own religious views had been deeply coloured by the life and example of his father, a man of great but unrecognised power, who had cheerfully sacrificed all personal ambition to work in an obscure Cumbrian parish. At one period of his youth, his father's attitude to life and cheerful acceptance of a lot so far below his merits, had puzzled him; and he had allowed himself to wonder whether such complete self-abnegation was commendable or even right. But the extraordinary manifestations of grief which that father's death provoked in the whole neighbourhood had taught him to judge the value of work by a different standard, and to realise that the things of the spirit can never be adequately measured in terms of the flesh. Hence-forward, the life of duty, and faith in the individual conscience, which had been the secret of the father's influence, became the ideals of the son, and, if he was attracted into the field of education, it was largely because, to him, education in its truest sense meant a lifting of the veil from the spirit. But as he mounted the Chiltern pulpit to deliver his first sermon from the text "The letter killeth, but the spirit maketh alive," he felt conscious, instinctively and with something of a chill, that the note he was going to sound was not a note that would find an echo in the hearts of his congregation. Here were no hungry sheep looking up to be fed, but indifference, inertia, and an unknown something that was probably worse than either and possibly the cause of both.

Mr. Flaggon was an interesting and a distinguished preacher; his worst enemies admitted that. He had the gift of saying what he meant, the happy phrase, and the inevitable word. But, if his manner could not but create a favourable impression, his matter caused serious alarm amongst the staff, and there was much shaking of heads afterwards in the great quadrangle under the shadow of Dr. Lanchester's statue.

"It's not so much the sermon," said Mr. Pounderly in his most confidential tones; "it's the text that frightens me. There were some points in the sermon, but the text was full of innuendo."

"Surely," exclaimed Mr. Bent, "you are not going to hang a dog for his collar?"

"Pardon me!" said Mr. Pounderly, "I hang no man. But, unless my judgment is strangely at fault, that text, considering the time and the place, spells upheaval."

"And the manner!" chimed in Mr. Beadle, "the assured, precocious manner! The air of confidence and authority! I agree with Pounderly that we are marked down for slaughter; it is the death-knell of the Classics!"

And the two men walked off together shaking their heads.

Mr. Chowdler did not content himself with shaking his head afterwards in the great quadrangle. He shook it frequently and emphatically during the sermon, in order that everybody might know that he was in complete disagreement with the preacher. And on him fell the unpleasant duty, as he phrased it, of making a reply and restating the Lanchester position, on the third Sunday of the Term.

For, needless to say, Mr. Chowdler was in orders. No mere laymen could have combined such a capacity for quarrelling with so profound a conviction of his own reasonableness and humility. In Mr. Chowdler's hands religion became a weapon to smite with. For choice, he smote lies, cant, humbug, and Bible critics; but, occasionally, quite innocent and respectable things found themselves floored by Mr. Chowdler's massive fist and trampled under his double-welted heel. For, when Mr. Chowdler mounted the pulpit, necessity was laid upon him to smite something or somebody. There were men, like Mr. Plummer, who doubted whether there would be much scope in Heaven for Mr. Chowdler's type of religion; but, if they did not regard it as the highest form of Christianity, they had to admit that it was manly, and therefore good for the boys.

But, on this third Sunday of the Term, Mr. Chowdler was no ordinary smiter; he was the incarnation of the Lanchester spirit repelling a German invasion. And his text, "Hold fast to that which is good," was not delivered like an ordinary text; it was fired like a six-inch shell full at the stall in which the headmaster was sitting. Mr. Bent said, afterwards, that he fully expected to see Chowdler follow up the discharge of the text by leaving the cover of the pulpit and attacking with the bayonet. However, the preacher spoke daggers but used none. Change? Yes, change was necessary, growth was necessary; but not change in essentials and axioms, not change in the foundations. Hold fast to the foundations, hold fast to that which is good! There was a tendency in a restless, riotous age to imagine that, because a thing lasted, because it was old and venerable, it was therefore obsolete. A fool's mistake! Why, granite lasts, gold lasts. Hold fast to the granite, hold fast to the gold, hold fast to that which is good. Again, there was a tendency in an age of feverish and futile activity to assail whatever is venerable, whatever has withstood the destructiveness of man and the storms of time. You tear up the mighty oak, and replace it by what? Tares? Yes, too often by tares, or at best by some finnikin exotic treelet, such as you may see in gaudy Eastern pots in decadent which is good! Fortunately, and God be praised for it, they had in that place a great example by which to guide their endeavours—Abraham Lanchester, their great headmaster, restorer not destroyer, whose clear, sane intellect and genius, conservative in the best and noblest meaning of the word, had left them an imperishable birthright and a priceless heritage. Hold fast to a priceless heritage, hold fast to a great tradition, hold fast to that which is good! And so on for five-and-twenty minutes.

Mr. Flaggon was conscious that he was being preached at, and he knew that the boys knew it; for they kept turning round continually to see how he was taking it. Mrs. Chowdler, who watched him narrowly, maintained that he had been profoundly impressed and "looked as if a new light had suddenly dawned on him"; but the general opinion among the boys was that he hadn't "turned a hair" and that it was impossible to be sure whether he had really understood what "Old Jowler" was driving at.

It is reasonable to suppose that the sermon gave Mr. Flaggon food for reflection; he certainly sat for some time afterwards in his study, looking into the fire and apparently thinking. But, whatever his thoughts may have been, he kept them to himself and said nothing.

Mr. Chowdler's effort was much appreciated on the staff, even by some who were more prone to criticise than to praise. Mr. Pounderly pronounced it statesmanlike, and Mr. Black went so far as to say that it was inspired. Mr. Bent's was the only voice that called it "bosh," and he received a grave and well-deserved rebuke from Mr. Plummer for his lack of reverence. It was confidently assumed by many that Mr. Chowdler's serious note of warning, voicing, as it did, the general feeling of the staff, would give Mr. Flaggon pause and force him to recognise facts. But their optimism was of short duration; for, within a few days, a notice asking every master to send in a copy of his weekly routine, made it clear to the most sanguine that the era of change and experiment had begun.

The Dream of Eugene Aram

THOMAS HOOD

*THOMAS HOOD (1799-1845) was born in London, the son of a book-
seller. In 1821 he became sub-editor of the* London Magazine, *which
was published by old friends of his father. Through this office he became
acquainted with Lamb, Hazlitt, and De Quincey. He edited various
periodicals and from time to time published both verse and prose. In
1829 he became editor of the* Gem, *in which his poem,* The Dream of
Eugene Aram, *was published.*

'Twas in the prime of summer time,
    An evening calm and cool,
And four and twenty happy boys
    Came bounding out of school:
There were some that ran, and some that leapt
    Like troutlets in a pool.

Away they sped with gamesome minds
    And souls untouched by sin;
To a level mead they came, and there
    They drave the wickets in:
Pleasantly shone the setting sun
    Over the town of Lynn.

Like sportive deer they coursed about,
    And shouted as they ran,—
Turning to mirth all things of earth,
    As only boyhood can;
But the Usher sat remote from all,
    A melancholy man!

His hat was off, his vest apart,
    To catch heaven's blessèd breeze;
For a burning thought was in his brow,
    And his bosom ill at ease:
So he leaned his head on his hands, and read
    The book between his knees!

Leaf after leaf he turned it o'er,
   Nor ever glanced aside,
For the peace of his soul he read that book
   In the golden eventide:
Much study had made him very lean,
   And pale, and leaden-eyed.

At last he shut the ponderous tome,
   With a fast and fervent grasp
He strained the dusky covers close,
   And fixed the brazen hasp:
"O, God! could I so close my mind,
   And clasp it with a clasp!"

Then leaping on his feet upright,
   Some moody turns he took,
Now up the mead, then down the mead,
   And past a shady nook,—
And, lo! he saw a little boy
   That pored upon a book!

"My gentle lad, what is't you read—
   Romance or fairy fable?
Or is it some historic page,
   Of kings and crowns unstable?"
The young boy gave an upward glance,—
   "It is 'The Death of Abel.'"

The Usher took six hasty strides,
   As smit with sudden pain,—
Six hasty strides beyond the place,
   Then slowly back again;
And down he sat beside the lad,
   And talked with him of Cain;

And, long since then, of bloody men,
   Whose deeds tradition saves;
Of lonely folk cut off unseen,
   And hid in sudden graves;
Of horrid stabs in groves forlorn,
   And murders done in caves;

And how the sprites of injured men
   Shriek upward from the sod,—
Ay, how the ghostly hand will point
   To show the burial clod;

And unknown facts of guilty acts
    Are seen in dreams from God!

He told how murderers walk the earth
    Beneath the curse of Cain,—
With crimson clouds before their eyes,
    And flames about their brain;
For blood has left upon their souls
    Its everlasting stain!

"And well," quoth he, "I know, for truth,
    Their pangs must be extreme,—
Woe, woe, unutterable woe,—
    Who spill life's sacred stream!
For why? Methought, last night, I wrought
    A murder, in a dream!

"One that had never done me wrong—
    A feeble man and old;
I led him to a lonely field,—
    The moon shone clear and cold:
Now here, said I, this man shall die,
    And I will have his gold!

"Two sudden blows with a ragged stick,
    And one with a heavy stone,
One hurried gash with a hasty knife,—
    And then the deed was done:
There was nothing lying at my foot
    But lifeless flesh and bone!

"Nothing but lifeless flesh and bone,
    That could not do me ill;
And yet I feared him all the more,
    For lying there so still:
There was a manhood in his look,
    That murder could not kill!

"And, lo, the universal air
    Seemed lit with ghastly flame;—
Ten thousand thousand dreadful eyes
    Were looking down in blame:
I took the dead man by his hand,
    And called upon his name!

"O, God! it made me quake to see
　　Such sense within the slain!
But when I touched the lifeless clay,
　　The blood gushed out amain!
For every clot, a burning spot
　　Was scorching in my brain!

"My head was like an ardent coal,
　　My heart as solid ice;
My wretched, wretched soul, I know,
　　Was at the devil's price:
A dozen times I groaned; the dead
　　Had never groaned but twice!

"And now, from forth the frowning sky,
　　From the heaven's topmost height,
I heard a voice—the awful voice
　　Of the blood-avenging sprite:—
'Thou guilty man! take up thy dead
　　And hide it from my sight!'

"I took the dreary body up,
　　And cast it in a stream,—
A sluggish water, black as ink,
　　The depth was so extreme:—
My gentle Boy, remember this
　　Is nothing but a dream!

"Down went the corse with a hollow plunge,
　　And vanished in the pool;
Anon I cleansed my bloody hands,
　　And washed my forehead cool,
And sat among the urchins young,
　　That evening, in the school.

"O, Heaven! to think of their white souls,
　　And mine so black and grim!
I could not share in childish prayer,
　　Nor join in evening hymn:
Like a devil of the pit I seemed,
　　'Mid holy cherubim!

"And peace went with them, one and all,
　　And each calm pillow spread;
But Guilt was my grim chamberlain

That lighted me to bed;
And drew my midnight curtains round,
  With fingers bloody red!

"All night I lay in agony,
  In anguish dark and deep;
My fevered eyes I dared not close,
  But stared aghast at Sleep:
For Sin had rendered unto her
  The keys of hell to keep!

"All night I lay in agony,
  From weary chime to chime,
With one besetting horrid hint,
  That racked me all the time;
A mighty yearning, like the first
  Fierce impulse unto crime!

"One stern tyrannic thought, that made
  All other thoughts its slave;
Stronger and stronger every pulse
  Did that temptation crave,—
Still urging me to go and see
  The Dead Man in his grave!

"Heavily I rose up, as soon
  As light was in the sky,
And sought the black accursèd pool
  With a wild misgiving eye;
And I saw the Dead in the river bed,
  For the faithless stream was dry.

"Merrily rose the lark, and shook
  The dew-drop from its wing;
But I never marked its morning flight,
  I never heard it sing:
For I was stooping once again
  Under the horrid thing.

"With breathless speed, like a soul in chase,
  I took him up and ran;—
There was no time to dig a grave
  Before the day began:
In a lonesome wood, with heaps of leaves,
  I hid the murdered man!

"And all that day I read in school,
    But my thought was other where;
As soon as the mid-day task was done,
    In secret I was there:
And a mighty wind had swept the leaves,
    And still the corse was bare!

"Then down I cast me on my face,
    And first began to weep,
For I knew my secret then was one
    That earth refused to keep:
Or land or sea, though he should be
    Ten thousand fathoms deep.

"So wills the fierce avenging Sprite,
    Till blood for blood atones!
Ay, though he's buried in a cave,
    And trodden down with stones,
And years have rotted off his flesh,—
    The world shall see his bones!

"O, God! that horrid, horrid dream
    Besets me now awake!
Again—again, with dizzy brain,
    The human life I take;
And my red right hand grows raging hot,
    Like Cranmer's at the stake.

"And still no peace for the restless clay
    Will wave or mould allow;
The horrid thing pursues my soul,—
    It stands before me now!"
The fearful Boy looked up, and saw
    Huge drops upon his brow.

That very night, while gentle sleep
    The urchin eyelids kissed,
Two stern-faced men set out from **Lynn**,
    Through the cold and heavy mist:
And Eugene Aram walked between,
    With gyves upon his wrist.

A Letter on Education

BEN JONSON

AFTER leaving Westminster School, BEN JONSON (1572-1637) worked for a time as a bricklayer's apprentice but soon joined the army and saw military service in Flanders. He returned to London and in 1597 began to write plays and to act. A quarrel which resulted in his killing a fellow actor sent him to prison in 1598. In the same year his comedy, Every Man in his Humor, *was performed at the Globe with Shakespeare in the cast. His first extant tragedy,* Sejanus, *was performed at the Globe by Shakespeare's company in 1603. From 1605 onwards he was constantly producing masques for the court, a form of entertainment which reached a high development in his hands. In 1616 he was unofficial poet laureate and the recipient of a pension by James I. When he died in 1637, he was buried in Westminster Abbey. The inscription upon his tomb is "O rare Ben Jonson."*

In A Letter on Education *Jonson gives good advice to teachers.*

IT pleased your Lordship of late to ask my opinion touching the education of your sons, and especially to the advancement of their studies. To which, though I returned somewhat for the present, which rather manifested a will in me than gave any just resolution to the thing propounded, I have upon better cogitation called those aids about me, both of mind and memory, which shall venter my thoughts clearer, if not fuller, to your Lordship's demand. I confess, my Lord, they will seem but petty and minute things I shall offer to you, being writ for children, and of them. But studies have their infancy as well as creatures. We see in men even the strongest compositions had their beginnings from milk and the cradle; and the wisest tarried sometimes about apting their mouths to letters and syllables. In their education, therefore, the care must be the greater had of their beginnings, to know, examine, and weigh their natures; which, though they be proner in some children to some disciplines, yet are they naturally prompt to taste all by degrees, and with change. For change is a kind of refreshing in studies, and infuseth knowledge by way of recreation. Thence the school itself is called a play or game, and all letters are so best taught to scholars. They should not be affrighted or deterred in their entry, but drawn on with exercise and emulation. A youth should not be made to hate study before he know the causes to love it, or taste the bitterness before the sweet; but called on and allured, entreated and praised: yea, when he deserves it not. For which cause I wish

180

them sent to the best school, and a public, which I think the best. Your Lordship, I fear, hardly hears of that, as willing to breed them in your eye and at home, and doubting their manners may be corrupted abroad. They are in more danger in your own family, among ill servants (allowing they be safe in their schoolmaster), than amongst a thousand boys, however immodest. Would we did not spoil our own children, and overthrow their manners ourselves by too much indulgence! To breed them at home is to breed them in a shade, whereas in a school they have the light and heat of the sun. They are used and accustomed to things and men. When they come forth into the commonwealth, they find nothing new, or to seek. They have made their friendships and aids, some to last till their age. They hear what is commanded to others as well as themselves; much approved, much corrected; all which they bring to their own store and use, and learn as much as they hear. Eloquence would be but a poor thing if we should only converse with singulars, speak but man and man together. Therefore I like no private breeding. I would send them where their industry should be daily increased by praise, and that kindled by emulation. It is a good thing to inflame the mind; and though ambition itself be a vice, it is often the cause of great virtue. Give me that wit whom praise excites, glory puts on, or disgrace grieves; he is to be nourished with ambition, pricked forward with honor, checked with reprehension, and never to be suspected of sloth. Though he be given to play, it is a sign of spirit and liveliness, so there be a mean had of their sports and relaxations. And from the rod or ferule I would have them free, as from the menace of them; for it is both deformed and servile.

Mr. Vincent Perrin Drinks His Tea and Gives Mr. Traill Sound Advice

HUGH WALPOLE

HUGH WALPOLE was born in 1884, in Auckland, New Zealand, where his father had gone as a clergyman soon after his graduation from Cambridge. When Hugh was nine years old, he was sent to school in England. In 1903 he entered Emmanuel College, Cambridge. After leaving Cambridge, he worked for a short time in the Mersey Mission to Seamen at Liverpool but found the work uncongenial and soon left it for a year of study in France. On his return to England he became a schoolmaster in a provincial school. His experiences as a schoolmaster are vividly set forth in his novel, The Gods and Mr. Perrin, *from which the following selections are taken.*

Schoolmastering proving uncongenial, Walpole went to London with £30 in his pocket and the manuscript of a novel, determined to become a writer. In 1913 he published Fortitude, *his first successful novel. From that date until his death in 1941 he was a successful and prolific writer.*

VINCENT PERRIN said to himself again and again as he climbed the hill: "It shall be all right this term"—and then, "It *shall* be"—and then, "*This* term." A cold wintry sun watched him from above the brown shaggy wood on the horizon; the sky was a pale and watery blue, and on its surface white clouds edged with gray lay like saucers. A little wind sighed and struggled amongst the hedges, because Mr. Perrin had nearly reached the top of the hill, and there was always a breeze there. He stopped for a moment and looked back. The hill on which he was stood straight out from the surrounding country; it was shaped like a sugar-loaf, and the red-brown earth of its field seemed to catch the red light of the sun; behind it was green, undulating country, in front of it the blue, vast sweep of the sea.

"It shall be all right this term," said Mr. Perrin, and he pulled his rather faded greatcoat about his ears, because the little wind was playing with the short bristly hairs at the back of his neck. He was long and gaunt; his face might have been considered strong had it not been for the weak chin and a shaggy, unkempt mustache of a nondescript pale brown. His hands were long and bony, and the collar that he wore was too high, and propped his neck up, so that he had the effect of someone who strained to overlook something. His eyes were pale and watery, and his eyebrows of the same sandy color as his mustache. His age was about forty-five, and he had been a master at Moffatt's for over twenty years. His back was a little bent as he walked; his hands were folded behind his back, and carried a rough, ugly walking-stick that trailed along the ground.

His eyes were fixed on the enormous brown block of buildings on the top of the hill in front of him: he did not see the sea, or the sky, or the distant Brown Wood.

The air was still with the clear suspense of an early autumn day. The sound of a distant mining stamp drove across space with the ring of a hammer, and the tiny whisper—as of someone who tells eagerly, but mysteriously, a secret—was the beating of the waves far at the bottom of the hill against the rocks.

Faint blue smoke hung against the saucer-shaped clouds above the chimneys of Moffatt's; in the air there was a sharp scented smell of some hidden bonfire.

The silence was broken by the sound of wheels, and an open cab drove up the hill. In it were seated four small boys, surrounded by a multitude of bags, hockey-sticks, and rugs. The four small boys were all very small indeed, but they all sat up when they saw Mr. Perrin, and touched their hats with a simultaneous movement. Mr. Perrin nodded sternly, glanced at them for a moment, and then switched his eyes back to the brown buildings again.

"Barker Minor, French, Doggett, and Rogers," he said to himself quickly; "Barker Minor, French . . . ;" then his mind swung back to its earlier theme again, and he said out loud, hitting the road with his stick, "It shall *be* all right *this* term."

The school clock—he knew the sound so well that he often thought he heard it at home in Buckinghamshire—struck half-past three. He hastened his steps. His holidays had been good—better than usual; he had played golf well; the men at the Club had not been quite such idiots and fools as they usually were: they had listened to him quite patiently about Education—shall it be Greek or German? Public School Morality, and What a Mother can do for her Boy—all favorite subjects of his.

Perhaps this term was not going to be so bad—perhaps the new man would be an acquisition: he could not, at any rate, be *worse* than Searle of the preceding term. The new man was, Perrin had heard, only just down from the University—he would probably do what Perrin suggested.

No, this term was to be all right. He never liked the autumn term; but there were a great many new boys, his house was full, and then—he stopped once more and drew a deep breath—there was Miss Desart. He tried to twist the end of his mustache, but some hairs were longer than

others, and he never could obtain a combined movement. . . . Miss Desart. . . . He coughed.

He passed in through the black school gates, his shabby coat flapping
at his heels.

The distant Brown Wood, as it surrendered to the sun, flamed with
gold; the dark green hedges on the hill slowly caught the light.

II

The master's common room in the Lower School was a small square
room that was inclined in the summer to get very stuffy indeed. It stood,
moreover, exactly between the kitchen, where meals were prepared, and
the long dining-room, where meals were eaten, and there was therefore a
perpetual odor of food in the air. On a "mutton day"—there were three
"mutton" days a week—this odor hung in heavy, clammy folds about the
ceiling, and on those days there were always more boys kept in than on
the other days—on so small a thing may punishment hang.

To-day—this being the first day of the term—the room was exceedingly
tidy. On the right wall, touching the windows, were two rows of pigeon-
holes, and above each pigeon-hole was printed, on a white label, a name—
"Mr. Perrin," "Mr. Dormer," "Mr. Clinton," "Mr. Traill."

Each master had two pigeon-holes into which he might put his papers
and his letters; considerable friction had been caused by people putting
their papers into other people's pigeon-holes. On the opposite wall was an
enormous, shiny map of the world, with strange blue and red lines running across it. The third wall was filled with the fireplace, over which
were two stern and dusty photographs of the Parthenon, Athens, and St.
Peter's, Rome.

Although the air was sharp with the first early hint of autumn, the windows were open, and a little part of the garden could be seen—a gravel
path down which golden-brown leaves were fluttering, a round empty
flower-bed, a stone wall.

On the large table in the middle of the room tea was laid, one plate of
bread and butter, and a plate of rock buns. Dormer, a round, red-faced,
cheerful-looking person with white hair, aged about fifty, and Clinton, a
short, athletic youth, with close-cropped hair and a large mouth, were
drinking tea. Clinton had poured his into his saucer and was blowing at
it—a practice that Perrin greatly disliked.

However, this was the first day of term, and everyone was very friendly.
Perrin paused a moment in the doorway. "Ah! here we are again!" he said,
with easy jocularity.

Dormer gave him a hand, and said, "Glad to see you, Perrin; had good
holidays?"

Clinton took the last rock bun, and shouted with a kind of roar, "You
old nut!"

Perrin, as he moved to the table, thought that it was a little hard that all the things that irritated him most should happen just when he was most inclined to be easy and pleasant.

"Ha! no cake!" he said, with a surprised air.

"Oh! I say, I'm so sorry," said Clinton, with his mouth full, "I took the last. Ring the bell."

Perrin gulped down his annoyance, sat down, and poured out his tea. It was cold and leathery. Dormer was busily writing lists of names. The Lower School was divided into two houses—Dormer was house-master of one, and Perrin of the other. The other two junior men were under house-masters: Clinton belonged to Dormer; and Traill, the new man, to Perrin. Both houses were in the same building, but the sense of rival camps gave a pleasant spur of emulation and competition both to work and play.

"I say, Perrin, have you made out your bath-lists? Then there are locker-names—I want . . ." Perrin snapped at his bread and butter. "Ah, Dormer, please—my tea first."

"All right; only, it's getting on to four."

For some moments there was silence. Then there came timid raps on the door. Perrin, in his most stentorian voice, shouted, "Come in!"

The door slowly opened, and there might be seen dimly in the passage a misty cloud of white Eton collars and round, white faces. There was a shuffling of feet.

Perrin walked slowly to the door.

"Here we all are again! How pleasant! How extremely pleasant! All of us eager to come back, of course—um—yes. Well, you know you oughtn't to come now. Two minutes past four. I'll take your names then—another five minutes. It's up on the board. Well, Sexton? Hadn't you eyes? *Don't* you know that ten minutes past four *is* ten minutes past four and *not* four o'clock?"

"Yes, sir, please, sir—but, sir—"

Perrin closed the door, and walked slowly back to the fireplace.

"Ha, ha," he said, smiling reflectively; "had him there!"

Dormer was muttering to himself, "Wednesday, 9 o'clock, Bilto, Cummin; 10 o'clock, Sayer, Long. Thursday, 9 o'clock—"

The golden leaves blew with a whispering chatter down the path.

The door opened again, and someone came in—Traill, the new man. Perrin looked at him with curiosity and some excitement. The first impression of him, standing there in the doorway, was of someone very young and very eager to make friends. Someone young, by reason of his very dress—the dark brown Norfolk jacket, light gray flannel trousers, turned up and short, showing bright purple socks and brown brogues. His hair, parted in the middle and brushed back, was very light brown; his eyes were brown and his cheeks tanned. His figure was square, his back very broad, his legs rather short—he looked, beyond everything else, tremendously clean.

He stopped when he saw Perrin, and Dormer looked up and introduced them. Perrin was relieved that he was so young. Searle, last year, had been old enough to have an opinion of his own—several opinions of his own; he had contradicted Perrin on a great many points, and towards the end of the term they had scarcely been on speaking terms. Searle was a pig-headed ass. . . .

But Traill evidently wanted to "know"—was quite humble about it, and sat, pulling at his pipe, whilst Perrin enlarged about lists and dormitories and marks and discipline to his heart's content. "I must say as far as order goes I've never found any trouble. It's *in* a man if he's going to do it—I've always managed them all right—never any trouble—hum, ha! Yes, you'll find them the first few days just a little restive—seeing what you're made of, you know; drop on them, drop on them."

Traill asked about the holiday task.

"Oh, yes, Dormer set that. *Ivanhoe*—Scott, you know. Just got to read out the questions, and see they don't crib. Let them go when you hear the chapel bell."

Traill was profuse in his thanks.

"Not at all—anything you want to know."

Perrin smiled at him.

There was, once again, the timid knock at the door. The door was opened, and a crowd of tiny boys shuffled in, headed by a larger boy who had the bold look of one who has lost all terror of masters, their ways, and their common rooms.

"Well, Sexton?" Perrin cleared his throat.

"Please, sir, you told me to bring the new boys. These are all I could find, sir—Pippin Minor is crying in the matron's room, sir." Sexton backed out of the room.

Perrin stared at the agitated crowd for some moments without saying anything. The boys were herded together like cattle, and were staring at him with eyes that started from their round, close-cropped heads. Perrin took their names down. Then he talked to them for three minutes about discipline, decency, and decorum; then he reminded them of their mothers, and finally said a word about serving their country.

Then he passed on to the subject of pocket-money. "It will be safer for you to hand it over to me," he said slowly and impressively. "Then you shall have it when you want it."

A slight shiver of apprehension passed through the crowd; then slowly, one by one, they delivered up their shining silver. One tiny boy—he had apparently no neck and no legs; he was very chubby—had only two half-crowns. He clutched these in his hot palm until Perrin said, "Well, Rackets?"

Then, with eyes fixed devouringly upon them, the boy delivered them up.

"I don't like to see you so fond of money, Rackets." Perrin dropped the half-crowns slowly into his trouser pocket, one after the other. "I don't think you will ever see these half-crowns again." He smiled.

Rackets began to choke. His fist, which had closed again as though the money was still there, moved forward. A large, fat tear gathered slowly in his eye. He struggled to keep it back—he dug his fist into it, turned round, and fled from the room.

Perrin was amused. "Caught friend Rackets on the hip," he said.

Then suddenly, in the distance, an iron bell began to clang. The four men put on their gowns, gathered books together, and moved to the door. Traill hung back a little. "You take the big room with me, Traill," said Dormer. "I'll give you paper and blotting-paper."

They moved slowly out of the room, Perrin last. A door was opened. There was a sudden cessation of confused whispers—complete silence, and then Perrin's voice: "Question one. Who were Richard I., Gurth, Wamba, Brian-de-Bois-Guilbert? . . . B,r,i,a,n—hyphen . . ."

The door closed.

III

A few papers fluttered about the table. It was growing dark outside, and a silver moon showed above the dark mass of the garden wall.

The brown leaves, now invisible, passed rustling and whispering about the path. Into the room there stole softly, from the kitchen, the smell of onions. . . .

The Battle of the Umbrella

IT was Monday morning, and Monday morning is worse than any other day of the week.

There has been, in spite of many services and the reiteration of religious stories concerning which a shower of inconvenient questions are flung at the uncertain convictions of authority, a relief in the rest and repose of the preceding day.

Sunday was, at any rate, a day to look forward to in that it was different from the other six days of the week, and although it might not on its arrival show quite so pleasant a face as earlier hours had given it, nevertheless it was something—a landmark if nothing else.

And now on this dark and dreary Monday—with the first hour a tedious and bickering discussion on Divinity, and the second hour a universal and embittered Latin exercise—that early rising to the cold summoning of the bell was anything but pleasant.

Moreover, on this especial Monday the rain came thundering in furious torrents, and the row of trees opposite the Lower School wailed and cried with their dripping, naked boughs, and all the brown leaves on the paths were beaten and flattened into a miserable and hopeless pulp.

Monday was the only morning in the week on which Traill took early preparation at the Upper School, and he had noticed before that it nearly always rained on Mondays. He was in no very bright temper as he hurried down the cold stone passages, pulling on his gown and avoiding the bodies of numerous small boys who flung themselves against him as they rushed furiously downstairs in order to be in time for call-over.

He heard the rain beating against the window-panes and hurriedly selected the first umbrella that he saw in the stand and rushed to the Upper School.

That preparation hour was unpleasant. M. Pons, the French master, was in the room above him, and the ceiling shook with the delighted stamp of twenty boys blessed with a sense of humor and an opportunity of power. M. Pons could be figured with shaking hands in the middle of the room, appealing for quiet. And, as was ever the case, the spirit of rebellion passed down through the ceiling to the room beneath. Traill had his boys well under control; but whereas on ordinary occasions it was all done without effort and worked of its own accord, on this morning continual persistence was necessary, and he had to make examples of various offenders.

A preparation hour always invited the Seven Devils to dance across the two hundred of open books, and the tweaking of boys' bodies and the digging of pins into unsuspecting legs was the inevitable result. Traill rose at the end of the hour, cross, irritable, and already tired. He hurried down to the Lower School to breakfast and forgot the umbrella.

The rain was driving furiously against the window-panes of the Junior common room. The windows were tightly closed, and still the presence of yesterday's mutton was felt heavily, gloomily, about the ceiling. The brown and black oilcloth contained numberless little winds and draughts that leapt out from under it and crept here and there about the room.

A small fire was burning in the grate—a mountain of black coal and stray spirals of gray smoke, and little white edges of unburnt paper hanging from the black bars. Beyond the side door voices quarreling in the kitchen could be heard, and beyond the other door a hum of voices and a clatter of cups.

It was all so dingy that it struck even the heavy brain of Clinton, who was down first. Perrin was taking breakfast in the big dining-room, and Traill was not yet back from the Upper School.

Clinton seized the *Morning Post* and, with a grunt of dissatisfaction at the general appearance of things, sat down. He never thought very intently about anything, but, in a vague way, he did dislike Monday and rain and a smoking fire. He helped himself to more than his share of the breakfast, ate it in large, noisy mouthfuls, found the *Morning Post* dull, and relapsed on to the *Daily Mail*. The rain and the quarreling in the kitchen were very disturbing.

Then Traill came in and sat down with an air of relief. He had no very great opinion of Clinton, but they got on together quite agreeably, and he found that it was rather pleasanter to have an entirely negative person with one—it was not necessary to think about him.

"My word," said Clinton, his eyes glued to the *Daily Mail*, "the London Scottish fairly wiped the floor with the Harlequins yesterday—two goals and a try to a try—all that man Binton—extraordinary three-quarter—no flies on him! Have some sausages? Not bad. I wonder if they'll catch that chap Deakin?"

"Deakin?" said Traill rather drearily, looking up from his breakfast. How dismal it all was this morning! Oh, well—in a year's time!

"Yes, you know—the Hollins Road murder—the man who cut his wife and mother into little bits and mixed them up so that they couldn't tell which was which. There's a photograph of him here and his front door."

"I think," said Traill, shortly, "following up murder trials like that is perfectly beastly. It isn't civilized."

"All right!" said Clinton, helping himself to the remaining sausages. "Perrin's having breakfast in there, isn't he? He won't want any more."

"He sometimes does," said Traill, feeling that at the moment he hated Clinton's good-natured face more than anything in the whole world. "He's awfully sick if he comes in hungry and doesn't find anything."

Clinton smiled. "He's rather amusing when he's sick," he said. "He so often is. By the way, has the Head passed those exam. questions of yours yet?"

"No," said Traill, frowning. "He's made me do them five times now, and last time he crossed out a whole lot of questions that he himself had suggested the time before. I pointed that out to him, and he called me, politely and gently, but firmly, a liar. There's no question that he's got his knife into me now, and I've got friend Perrin to thank for it!"

"Yes," said Clinton, helping himself to marmalade, "Perrin doesn't love you—there's no question of that. Young Garden Minimus has been helping the feud."

"Garden? What's he got to do with it?"

"Well, you know that he was always Old Pompous' especial pet—well, Pompous has riled him, kept him in or something, so now he goes about telling everybody that he's transferred his allegiance to you. That makes Pompous sick as anything."

"I like the kid especially," Traill said. "He's rather a favorite of mine."

"Yes," said Clinton. "Well, look out for trouble, that's all. There'll be open war between you soon if you are not careful."

At that moment Perrin came in. He was continuing, as he entered, a conversation with some small boy whose head just appeared at the door for a moment and revealed Garden Minimus.

"Well, a hundred times," Perrin was saying, "and you don't go out till you've done it."

Garden displayed annoyance, and was heard to mutter under his breath. Perrin's face was gray; his hair appeared to be unbrushed, and there was a good deal of white chalk on the back of his sleeve.

"Really, it's too bad," he said to no one in particular and certainly not to Traill. "I don't know what's come over that boy—nothing but continuous impertinence. He shall go up to the Head if he isn't careful. Such a nice boy, too, before this term."

At this moment he saw that Traill was reading the *Morning Post* and Clinton the *Daily Mail.* He looked as though he were going to say something, then by a tremendous effort controlled himself. He stood in front of the dismal fire and looked at the other two, at the dreary window-panes and the driving rain, at the dusty pigeon-holes, the untidy heap of books, the torn lists hanging from the wall.

He had slept badly—had lain awake for hours thinking of Miss Desart, of his own miserable condition, of his poor mother—and then, slumbering at last, in an instant he had been pulled, dragged wide-awake by that thundering, clamoring bell.

He had been so tired that his eyes had refused to open, and he had sat stupidly on the edge of his bed with his head swaying and nodding. Then he had been late for preparation, and he knew that they had been "playing about" and had rubbed Somerset-Walpole's head in the ink and had stamped on his body, because, although it was so early, Somerset-Walpole's eyes were already red, his back a horrible confusion of dust and chalk, his hair and collar ink and disaster.

He was sorry for Somerset-Walpole, whose days were a perpetual tragedy; but as there was no other obvious victim, he selected him for the subject of his wrath, expatiated to the form on the necessity of getting up clean in the morning, and sent the large, blubbering creature up to the matron to be cleansed and scolded. Verily the delights of some people's school days have been vastly exaggerated!

Then Garden Minimus had been discovered sticking nibs into the fleshy portion of his neighbor, and, although he had vehemently denied the crime, had been heavily punished and had therefore sulked during the rest of the hour. At breakfast-time Perrin had called him up to him and had hinted that if he chose to be agreeable once again the punishment might be relaxed; but Garden did not please, and sulked and muttered under his breath, and Perrin thought he had caught the word "Pompous."

All these things may have been slight in themselves, but combined they amounted to a great deal—and all before half-past eight in the morning. Also he had had very little to eat.

He had been brought a small red tomato and a hard, rocky wedge of bacon with little white eyes in it, and an iron determination to hold out at all costs, whatever the consumer's appetite and determination. He smelt, when he came into the common room, sausages, and he saw, with a glance of the eye, that there were sausages no longer.

"I really think, Clinton," he said, "that a little less appetite on your part in the early morning would be better for everyone concerned."

Clinton was always perfectly good-tempered, and all he said now was, "All right, old chap—I always have an awful appetite in the morning. I always had."

Perrin drew himself to his full height and prepared to be dignified.

Clinton said, "I say, old man, you've got chalk all over your sleeve."

And Perrin, finding that it was indeed true, could say nothing and feebly tried to brush it off with his hand.

Traill had not spoken since Perrin had come in. He disliked intensely the atmosphere of restraint in the room. He had never before been on such bad terms with anyone, and now at every turn there were discomforts, difficulties, stiffnesses. At this moment he loathed the term and the place and the people as he had never loathed any of them before; he felt that he could not possibly last until the holidays.

Perrin was going to the Upper School for first hour. He was going to teach Divinity, the lesson that he loathed most of all. He gathered his books up and his gown, and went out into the hall to find his umbrella. The rain was falling more heavily than before, and lashed the panes as though it had some personal grievance against them.

Robert, the general factotum—a long, pale man with a spotty face and a wonderful capacity for dropping china—came in to collect the breakfast things. He passed, clattering about the table. Traill was still deep in the *Morning Post.*

Perrin came in with a clouded brow. "I can't find," he said, "my umbrella."

The rain beat upon the frames, Robert clashed the plates together, but there was no answer. Clinton's head was in his pigeon-hole, looking for papers.

"Robert, have you seen my umbrella?"

No, Robert had not seen any umbrella. He might have seen an umbrella last week, somewhere upstairs, in Miss Madder's room—an umbrella with lace, pink—Oh! of course, a parasol. There were three umbrellas in the stand by the hall door. Perhaps one of those was the one. No? Mr. Perrin had looked? Well, he didn't know of anywhere else. No—perhaps one of the young gentlemen. . . . There was nothing at all to be got out of Robert.

"Clinton!" No answer. "Clinton!"

At last Clinton turned round.

"Clinton, have you seen my umbrella?"

"No, old man—why should I? Isn't it outside?"

It was getting late, the rain was pelting down, and Perrin was quite determined that he would *not* under any circumstances use anyone else's umbrella.

He went out again and looked in the hall. He was beginning to get very angry. Was not this the last straw sent by the little gods to break his humble back? That it should be raining, that he should be late, and that there should be no umbrella! He stormed about the hall, he looked in impossible places, he shook the three umbrellas that were there; he began to mutter to himself—the little red and yellow china man was creeping down the stairs. He was shaking all over, and his hands were trembling like leaves.

He came into the common room again. "I can't think—" he said, with his trembling hand to his forehead. "I know I had it yesterday—last night. Clinton, you *must* have seen it."

"No," said Clinton in that abstract voice that is so profoundly irritating because it shows that the speaker's thoughts are far away. "No—I don't think I've seen it. What did I do with that Algebra? Oh! there it is. My word! isn't it raining!"

The Upper School bell began, far in the distance, its raucous clanging. Perrin was pacing up and down the room; every now and again he flung a furtive glance at Traill. Traill had paid, hitherto, no attention to the conversation. At last, hearing the Upper School bell, he looked up.

"What's the matter?" he said.

"Really, Robert," said Perrin, turning round to the factotum," you *must* have seen it somewhere. It's absurd! I want to go out."

"There are the other gentlemen's," said Robert, looking a little frightened of Perrin's twitching lips and white face.

It dawned upon Traill slowly that Perrin was looking for an umbrella. Then on that it followed that possibly the umbrella that he had taken that morning might be Perrin's umbrella. Of course it *must* be Perrin's umbrella. It was just the sort of umbrella, with its faded silk and stupid handle, that Perrin would be likely to have. However, it was really very awkward—most awkward.

He stood up and stayed with a hand nervously fingering the *Morning Post*.

Perrin rushed once more into the hall and then came furiously back. "I *must* have my umbrella," he said, storming at Robert. "I want to go to the Upper School."

He had left the door a little open.

"I am very sorry," Traill began; the paper crackling beneath his fingers. Perrin wheeled round and stared at him, his face very white.

"I'm very sorry," said Traill again, "but I'm afraid I must have taken it— my mistake. I wouldn't have taken it if I had dreamed—"

"You," said Perrin in a hoarse whisper.

"Yes," said Traill, "I'm afraid I took the first one I saw this morning. I'm afraid it must have been yours, as yours is missing. I assure you—"

He was smiling a little—really it was all too absurd. His smile drove Perrin into a trembling passion. He took a step forward.

"You dared to take my umbrella? he said, "without asking? I never heard such a piece of impertinence. But it's all of a piece—all of a piece!"

"But it's really too absurd," Traill broke in. "As though a man mightn't take another man's umbrella without all this disturbance. It's too absurd."

"Oh! is it?" said Perrin, his voice shaking. "That's all of a piece—that's exactly like the rest of your behavior here. You come here thinking that everything and everyone belongs to you. Oh, yes! we've all got to bow down to everything that your Highness chooses to say. We must give up everything to your Highness—our clothes, our possessions—you conceited —insufferable puppy!"

These words were gasped out. Perrin was now entirely beside himself with rage. He saw this man here before him as the originator of all his misfortunes, all his evils. He had put the other masters against him, he had put the boys against him, he had taken Garden away from him, he had been against him at every turn.

All control, all discipline, everything had fled from Mr. Perrin. He did not remember where he was, he did not remember that Robert was in the room, he did not remember that the door was open and that the boys could hear his shrill, excited voice. He only knew that here, in this smiling, supercilious, conceited young man, was his enemy, the man who would rob and ruin him.

"Really, this is too absurd," said Traill, stepping back a little, and conscious of the startled surprise on the face of Robert—he did not want to have a scene before a servant. "I am exceedingly sorry that I took your umbrella. I don't see that that gives you any reason to speak to me like that. We can discuss the matter afterwards—not here."

"Oh, yes!" screamed Perrin, moving still nearer his enemy. "Oh! of course to you it is nothing—nothing at all—it is all of a piece with the rest of your behavior. If you don't know how to behave like a gentleman, it's time someone taught you. Gentlemen don't steal other people's things. You can be put in prison for that sort of thing, you know."

"I didn't steal your beastly umbrella," said Traill, beginning in his anger to forget the ludicrousness of the situation. "I don't want your beastly things—keep them to yourself."

"I say"—this from Clinton—"chuck it, you two. Don't make such a row here—everyone can hear. Wait until later."

But Perrin heard nothing. He had stepped up to Traill now and was shaking his fist in Traill's face.

"It's beastly, is it?" he shouted. "I'll give you something for saying that— I'll let you know." And then, in a perfect scream, "Give me my umbrella! Give me my umbrella!"

"I haven't got your rotten umbrella," shouted Traill. "I left it somewhere. I've lost it. I'm jolly glad. You can jolly well go and look for it."

And at this moment, as Clinton afterwards described it, "the scrap began." Perrin suddenly flung himself upon Traill and beat his face with his fist. Traill clutched Perrin's arm and flung him back upon the breakfast-table. Perrin's head struck the coffee-pot, and as he rose he brought with him the tablecloth and all the things that Robert had left upon the table. With a fearful crash of crockery, with the odors of streaming coffee, with the cry of the terrified Robert, down everything came. Afterwards there was a pause whilst Perrin and Traill swayed together, then with another crash, they too came to the floor.

Clinton and Robert rushed forward. Two Upper School masters, Birkland and Comber, surveyed the scene from the doorway. There was an instant's absolute silence.

Then suddenly Traill and Perrin both rose from the floor. Traill's lip was cut and bleeding—coffee was on Perrin's color; their faces were very white.

For a moment they looked at each other in absolute silence, they then passed, without a spoken word, through the open door.

In such a way, and from such a cause, did this Battle of the Umbrella have its beginning.

Llanabba Castle

EVELYN WAUGH

EVELYN WAUGH, younger brother of the novelist Alec Waugh, was born in 1903. As a student at Lancing School he edited the school paper, won a prize for English verse, organized the Dilettantes' Society, and persuaded a master to act in his play Conversion, *which boldly satirized school life.*

At Herford College, Oxford, he was Senior History Scholar. Since his college days he has taught school, done newspaper work, and written both biography and fiction.

Decline and Fall, *the novel from which the following chapters are taken, is brilliant and witty satire of life in a boys' school.*

L
LANABBA CASTLE presents two quite different aspects, according as as you approach it from the Bangor or the coast road. From the back it looks very much like any other large country house, with a great many windows and a terrace, and a chain of glass houses and the roofs of innumerable nondescript kitchen buildings disappearing into the trees. But from the front—and that is how it is approached from Llanabba station—it is formidably feudal; one drives past at least a mile of machicolated wall before reaching the gates; these are towered and turreted and decorated with heraldic animals and a workable portcullis. Beyond them at the end of the avenue stands the Castle, a model of medieval impregnability.

The explanation of this rather striking contrast is simple enough. At the time of the cotton famine in the 'sixties Llanabba House was the property of a prosperous Lancashire mill-owner. His wife could not bear to think of their men starving; in fact, she and her daughters organised a little bazaar in their aid, though without any very substantial results. Her husband had read the Liberal economists and could not think of paying without due return. Accordingly "enlightened self-interest" found a way. An encampment of mill hands was settled in the park, and they were put to work walling the grounds and facing the house with great blocks of stone from a neighbouring quarry. At the end of the American war they returned to their mills, and Llanabba House became Llanabba Castle after a great deal of work had been done very cheaply.

Driving up from the station in a little closed taxi, Paul saw little of all this. It was almost dark in the avenue and quite dark inside the house.

"I am Mr. Pennyfeather," he said to the butler. "I have come here as a master."

"Yes," said the butler, "I know all about you. This way."

They went down a number of passages, unlit and smelling obscurely of all the ghastly smells of school, until they reached a brightly lighted door.

"In there. That's the Common Room." Without more ado, the butler made off into the darkness.

Paul looked round. It was not a very big room. Even he felt that, and all his life he had been accustomed to living in constricted spaces.

"I wonder how many people live here," he thought, and with a sick thrust of apprehension counted sixteen pipes in a rack at the side of the chimney-piece. Two gowns hung on a hook behind the door. In a corner were some golf clubs, a walking stick, an umbrella and two miniature rifles. Over the chimney-piece was a green baize notice-board covered with lists; there was a typewriter on the table. In a book-case were a number of very old text-books and some new exercise-books. There were also a bicycle-pump, two arm-chairs, a straight chair, half a bottle of invalid port, a boxing glove, a bowler hat, yesterday's *Daily News* and a packet of pipe-cleaners.

Paul sat down disconsolately on the straight chair.

Presently there was a knock at the door, and a small boy came in.

"Oh!" he said, looking at Paul intently.

"Hullo!" said Paul.

"I was looking for Captain Grimes," said the little boy.

"Oh!" said Paul.

The child continued to look at Paul with a penetrating, impersonal interest.

"I suppose you're the new master?" he said.

"Yes," said Paul. "I'm called Pennyfeather."

The little boy gave a shrill laugh. "I think that's terribly funny," he said, and went away.

Presently the door opened again, and two more boys looked in. They stood and giggled for a time and then made off.

In the course of the next half-hour six or seven boys appeared on various pretexts and stared at Paul.

Then a bell rang, and there was a terrific noise of whistling and scampering. The door opened, and a very short man of about thirty came into the Common Room. He had made a great deal of noise in coming because he had an artificial leg. He had a short red moustache, and was slightly bald.

"Hullo!" he said.

"Hullo!" said Paul.

"I'm Captain Grimes," said the new-comer, and "Come in, you," he added to someone outside.

Another boy came in.

"What do you mean," said Grimes, "by whistling when I told you to stop?"

"Everyone else was whistling," said the boy.

"What's that got to do with it?" said Grimes.

"I should think it had a lot to do with it," said the boy.

"Well, just you do a hundred lines, and next time, remember, I shall beat you with this," said Grimes, waving the walking stick.

"That wouldn't hurt much," said the boy, and went out.

"There's no discipline in the place," said Grimes, and then he went out too.

"I wonder whether I'm going to enjoy being a schoolmaster," thought Paul.

Quite soon another and older man came into the room.

"Hullo!" he said to Paul.

"Hullo!" said Paul.

"I'm Prendergast," said the new-comer. "Have some port?"

"Thank you, I'd love to."

"Well, there's only one glass."

"Oh, well, it doesn't matter, then."

"You might get your tooth-glass from your bedroom."

"I don't know where that is."

"Oh, well, never mind; we'll have some another night. I suppose you're the new master?"

"Yes."

"You'll hate it here. I know. I've been here ten years. Grimes only came this term. He hates it already. Have you seen Grimes?"

"Yes, I think so."

"He isn't a gentleman. Do you smoke?"

"Yes."

"A pipe, I mean."

"Yes."

"Those are my pipes. Remind me to show them to you after dinner."

At this moment the butler appeared with a message that Dr. Fagan wished to see Mr. Pennyfeather.

Dr. Fagan's part of the Castle was more palatial. He stood at the end of a long room with his back to a rococo marble chimney-piece; he wore a velvet dinner-jacket.

"Settling in?" he asked.

"Yes," said Paul.

Sitting before the fire, with a glass bottle of sweets in her lap, was a brightly dressed woman in early middle age.

"That," said Dr. Fagan with some disgust, "is my daughter."

"Pleased to meet you," said Miss Fagan. "Now what I always tell the young chaps as comes here is, 'Don't let the Dad overwork you.' He's a regular Tartar is Dad, but then you know what scholars are—inhuman. Ain't you," said Miss Fagan, turning on her father with sudden ferocity— "ain't you inhuman?"

"At times, my dear, I am grateful for what little detachment I have achieved. But here," he added, "is my other daughter."

Silently, except for a scarcely perceptible jingling of keys, another woman had entered the room. She was younger than her sister, but far less gay.

"How do you do?" she said. "I do hope you have brought some soap with you. I asked my father to tell you, but he so often forgets these things. Masters are not supplied with soap or with boot polish or with washing over two shillings and sixpence weekly. Do you take sugar in your tea?"

"Yes, usually."

"I will make a note of that and have two extra lumps put out for you. Don't let the boys get them, though."

"I have put you in charge of the fifth form for the rest of this term," said Dr. Fagan. "You will find them delightful boys, quite delightful. Clutterbuck wants watching, by the way, a very delicate little chap. I have also put you in charge of the games, the carpentering class and the fire drill. And I forget, do you teach music?"

"No, I'm afraid not."

"Unfortunate, most unfortunate. I understood from Mr. Levy that you did. I have arranged for you to take Beste-Chetwynde in organ lessons twice a week. Well, you must do the best you can. There goes the bell for dinner. I won't detain you. Oh, one other thing. Not a word to the boys, please, about the reasons for your leaving Oxford! We schoolmasters must temper discretion with deceit. There, I fancy I have said something for you to think about. Good night."

"Tootle-oo," said the elder Miss Fagan.

Captain Grimes

PAUL had very little difficulty in finding the dining-hall. He was guided there by the smell of cooking and the sound of voices. It was a large, panelled room, far from disagreeable, with fifty or sixty boys of ages ranging from ten to eighteen settled along four long tables. The smaller ones wore Eton suits, and elder ones dinner-jackets.

He was led to a place at the head of one of the tables. The boys on either side of him stood up very politely until he sat down. One of them was the boy who had whistled at Captain Grimes. Paul thought he rather liked him.

"I'm called Beste-Chetwynde," he said.

"I've got to teach you the organ, I believe."

"Yes, it's great fun: we play in the village church. Do you play terribly well?"

Paul felt this was not a moment for candour, and so, "tempering discretion with deceit," he said, "Yes, remarkably well."

"I say, do you really, or are you rotting?"

"Indeed, I'm not. I used to give lessons to the Master of Scone."

"Well, you won't be able to teach me much," said Beste-Chetwynde cheerfully. "I only do it to get off gym. I say, they haven't given you a napkin. These servants are too awful. Philbrick," he shouted to the butler, "why haven't you given Mr. Pennyfeather a napkin?"

"Forgot," said Philbrick, "and it's too late now because Miss Fagan's locked the linen up."

"Nonsense!" said Beste-Chetwynde; "go and get one at once. That man's all right, really," he added, "only he wants watching."

In a few minutes Philbrick returned with the napkin.

"It seems to me that you're a remarkably intelligent boy," said Paul.

"Captain Grimes doesn't think so. He says I'm half-witted. I'm glad you're not like Captain Grimes. He's so common, don't you think?"

"You mustn't talk about the other masters like that in front of me."

"Well, that's what we all think about him, anyway. What's more, he wears combinations. I saw it in his washing-book one day when I was fetching him his hat. I think combinations are rather awful, don't you?"

There was a commotion at the end of the hall.

"I expect that's Clutterbuck being sick," said Beste-Chetwynde. "He's usually sick when we have mutton."

The boy on Paul's other side now spoke for the first time.

"Mr. Prendergast wears a wig," he said, and then became very confused and subsided into a giggle.

"That's Briggs," said Beste-Chetwynde, "only everyone calls him Brolly, because of the shop, you know."

"They're silly rotters," said Briggs.

All this was a great deal easier than Paul had expected; it didn't seem so very hard to get on with boys, after all.

After a time they all stood up, and amid considerable noise Mr. Prendergast said grace. Someone called out "Prendy!" very loudly just by Paul's ear.

". . . *per Christum Dominum nostrum. Amen*," said Mr. Prendergast. "Beste-Chetwynde, was that you who made that noise?"

"Me, sir? No, sir."

"Pennyfeather, did Beste-Chetwynde make that noise?"

"No, I don't think so," said Paul, and Beste-Chetwynde gave him a friendly look, because, as a matter of fact, he had.

Captain Grimes linked arms with him outside the dining-hall.

"Filthy meal, isn't it, old boy?" he said.

"Pretty bad," said Paul.

"Prendy's on duty to-night. I'm off to the pub. How about you?"

"All right," said Paul.

"Prendy's not so bad in his way," said Grimes, "but he can't keep order. Of course, you know he wears a wig. Very hard for a man with a wig to keep order. I've got a false leg, but that's different. Boys respect that. Think I lost it in the war. Actually," said the Captain, "and strictly between ourselves, mind, I was run over by a tram in Stoke-on-Trent when I was one-over-the-eight. Still, it doesn't do to let that out to everyone. Funny thing, but I feel I can trust you. I think we're going to be pals."

"I hope so," said Paul.

"I've been feeling the need of a pal for some time. The bloke before you wasn't bad—a bit stand-offish, though. He had a motor-bike, you see. The daughters of the house didn't care for him. Have you met Miss Fagan?"

"I've met two."

"They're both bitches," said Grimes, and added moodily, "I'm engaged to be married to Flossie."

"Good God! Which is she?"

"The elder. The boys call them Flossie and Dingy. We haven't told the old boy yet. I'm waiting till I land in the soup again. Then I shall play that as my last card. I generally get into the soup sooner or later. Here's the pub. Not such a bad little place in its way. Clutterbuck's father makes all the beer round here. Not bad stuff, either. Two pints, please, Mrs. Roberts!"

In the further corner sat Philbrick, talking volubly in Welsh to a shady-looking old man.

"Damned cheek his coming in here!" said Grimes.

Mrs. Roberts brought them their beer. Grimes took a long draught and sighed happily.

"This looks like being the first end of term I've seen for two years," he said dreamily. "Funny thing, I can always get on all right for about six weeks, and then I land in the soup. I don't believe I was ever meant by Nature to be a schoolmaster. Temperament," said Grimes, with a far-away look in his eyes—"that's been my trouble, temperament and sex."

"Is it quite easy to get another job after—after you've been in the soup?" asked Paul.

"Not at first, it isn't, but there're ways. Besides, you see, I'm a public-school man. That means everything. There's a blessed equity in the English social system," said Grimes, "that ensures the public-school man against starvation. One goes through four or five years of perfect hell at an age when life is bound to be hell anyway, and after that the social system never lets one down.

"Not that I stood four or five years of it, mind; I got the push soon after my sixteenth birthday. But my house-master was a public-school man. He knew the system. 'Grimes,' he said, 'I can't keep you in the House after what has happened. I have the other boys to consider. But I don't want to be too hard on you. I want you to start again.' So he sat down there and then and wrote me a letter of recommendation to any future employer, a corking good letter, too. I've got it still. It's been very useful at one time or another. That's the public-school system all over. They may kick you out, but they never let you down.

"I subscribed a guinea to the War Memorial Fund. I felt I owed it to them. I was really sorry," said Grimes, "that that cheque never got through.

"After that I went into business. Uncle of mine had a brush factory at Edmonton. Doing pretty well before the war. That put the lid on the brush trade for me. You're too young to have been in the war, I suppose? Those were days, old boy. We shan't see the like of them again. I don't suppose I was really sober for more than a few hours for the whole of that war. Then I got into the soup again, pretty badly that time. Happened over in France. They said, 'Now, Grimes, you've got to behave like a gentleman. We don't want a court-martial in this regiment. We're going to leave you alone for half an hour. There's your revolver. You know what to do. Good-bye, old man,' they said quite affectionately.

"Well, I sat there for some time looking at that revolver. I put it up to my head twice, but each time I brought it down again. 'Public-school men don't end like this,' I said to myself. It was a long half-hour, but luckily they had left a decanter of whisky in there with me. They'd all had a few, I think. That's what made them all so solemn. There wasn't much whisky left when they came back, and, what with that and the strain of the situation, I could only laugh when they came in. Silly thing to do, but they looked so surprised, seeing me there alive and drunk.

" 'The man's a cad,' said the colonel, but even then I couldn't stop laughing, so they put me under arrest and called a court-martial.

"I must say I felt pretty low next day. A major came over from another battalion to try my case. He came to see me first, and bless me if it wasn't a cove I'd known at school!

" 'God bless my soul,' he said, 'if it isn't Grimes of Podger's! What's all this nonsense about a court-martial?' So I told him. 'H'm' he said, 'pretty bad. Still it's out of the question to shoot an old Harrovian. I'll see what I can do about it.' And next day I was sent to Ireland on a pretty cushy job connected with postal service. That saw me out as far as the war was concerned. You can't get into the soup in Ireland, do what you like. I don't know if all this bores you?"

"Not at all," said Paul. "I think it's most encouraging."

"I've been in the soup pretty often since then, but never quite so badly. Someone always turns up and says, 'I can't see a public-school man down and out. Let me put you on your feet again.' I should think," said Grimes, "I've been put on my feet more often than any living man."

Philbrick came across the bar parlour towards them.

"Feeling lonely?" he said. "I've been talking to the station-master here, and if either of you wants an introduction to a young lady——"

"Certainly not," said Paul.

"Oh, all right," said Philbrick, making off.

"Women are an enigma," said Grimes, "as far as Grimes is concerned."

Discipline

PRAYERS were held downstairs in the main hall of the Castle. The boys stood ranged along the panelled walls, each holding in his hands a little pile of books. Grimes sat on one of the chairs beside the baronial chimney-piece.

"Morning," he said to Paul; "only just down, I'm afraid. Do I smell of drink?"

"Yes," said Paul.

"Comes of missing breakfast. Prendy been telling you about his Doubts?"

"Yes," said Paul.

"Funny thing," said Grimes, "but I've never been worried in that way. I don't pretend to be a particularly pious sort of chap, but I've never had any Doubts. When you've been in the soup as often as I have, it gives you a sort of feeling that everything's for the best, really. You know, God's in His heaven; all's right with the world. I can't quite explain it, but I don't believe one can ever be unhappy for long provided one does just exactly what one wants to and when one wants to. The last chap who put me on my feet said I was 'singularly in harmony with the primitive promptings of humanity.' I've remembered that phrase because somehow it seemed to fit me. Here comes the old man. This is where we stand up."

As the bell stopped ringing Dr. Fagan swept into the hall, the robes of a Doctor of Philosophy swelling and billowing about him. He wore an orchid in his button-hole.

"Good morning, gentlemen," he said.

"Good morning, sir," chorused the boys.

The Doctor advanced to the table at the end of the room, picked up a Bible, and opening it at random, read a chapter of blood-curdling military history without any evident relish. From that he plunged into the Lord's Prayer, which the boys took up in a quiet chatter. Mr. Prendergast's voice led them in tones that testified to his ecclesiastical past.

Then the Doctor glanced at a sheet of notes he held in his hand. "Boys," he said, "I have some announcements to make. The Fagan cross-country running challenge cup will not be competed for this year on account of the floods."

"I expect the old boy has popped it," said Grimes in Paul's ear.

"Nor will the Llanabba Essay Prize."

"On account of the floods," said Grimes.

"I have received my account for the telephone," proceeded Dr. Fagan, "and I find that during the past quarter there have been no less than twenty-three trunk calls to London, none of which was sent by me or by members of my family. I look to the prefects to stop this, unless of course they are themselves responsible, in which case I must urge them in my own interests to make use of the village post-office, to which they have access.

"I think that is everything, isn't it, Mr. Prendergast?"

"*Cigars*," said Mr. Prendergast in a stage whisper.

"Ah, yes, cigars. Boys, I have been deeply distressed to learn that several cigar ends have been found—where have they been found?"

"*Boiler-room.*"

"In the boiler-room. I regard this as reprehensible. What boy has been smoking cigars in the boiler-room?"

There was a prolonged silence, during which the Doctor's eye travelled down the line of boys.

"I will give the culprit until luncheon to give himself up. If I do not hear from him by then the whole school will be heavily punished."

"Damn!" said Grimes. "I gave those cigars to Clutterbuck. I hope the little beast has the sense to keep quiet."

"Go to your classes," said the Doctor.

The boys filed out.

"I should think, by the look of them, they were exceedingly cheap cigars," added Mr. Prendergast sadly. "They were a pale yellow colour."

"That makes it worse," said the Doctor. "To think of any boy under my charge smoking pale yellow cigars in a boiler-room! It is *not* a gentlemanly fault."

The masters went upstairs.

"That's your little mob in there," said Grimes; "you let them out at eleven."

"But what am I to teach them?" said Paul in sudden panic.

"Oh, I shouldn't try to *teach* them anything, not just yet, anyway. Just keep them quiet."

"Now that's a thing I've never learned to do," sighed Mr. Prendergast.

Paul watched him amble into his class-room at the end of the passage, where a burst of applause greeted his arrival. Dumb with terror, he went into his own class-room.

Ten boys sat before him, their hands folded, their eyes bright with expectation.

"Good morning, sir," said the one nearest him.

"Good morning," said Paul.

"Good morning, sir," said the next.

"Good morning, said Paul.

"Good morning, sir," said the next.

"Oh, shut up," said Paul.

At this the boy took out a handkerchief and began to cry quietly.

"Oh, sir," came a chorus of reproach, "you've hurt his feelings. He's very sensitive; it's his Welsh blood, you know: it makes people very emotional. Say 'Good morning' to him, sir, or he won't be happy all day. After all, it is a good morning, isn't it, sir?"

"Silence!" shouted Paul above the uproar, and for a few moment things were quieter.

"Please, sir," said a small voice—Paul turned and saw a grave-looking youth holding up his hand—"please, sir, perhaps he's been smoking cigars and doesn't feel well."

"Silence!" said Paul again.

The ten boys stopped talking and sat perfectly still, staring at him. He felt himself getting hot and red under their scrutiny.

"I suppose the first thing I ought to do is to get your names clear. What is your name?" he asked, turning to the first boy.

"Tangent, sir."

"And yours?"

"Tangent, sir," said the next boy. Paul's heart sank.

"But you can't both be called Tangent."

"No, sir, *I'm* Tangent. He's just trying to be funny."

"I like that. *Me* trying to be funny! Please, sir, I'm Tangent, sir; really I am."

"If it comes to that," said Clutterbuck from the back of the room, "there is only one Tangent here, and that is me. Anyone else can jolly well go to blazes."

Paul felt desperate.

"Well, is there anyone who isn't Tangent?"

Four or five voices instantly arose.

"I'm not, sir; I'm not Tangent. I wouldn't be called Tangent, not on the end of a barge-pole."

In a few seconds the room had become divided into two parties: those who were Tangent and those who were not. Blows were already being exchanged, when the door opened and Grimes came in. There was a slight hush.

"I thought you might want this," he said, handing Paul a walking stick. "And if you take my advice, you'll set them something to do."

He went out; and Paul, firmly grasping the walking stick, faced his form.

"Listen," he said. "I don't care a damn what any of you are called, but if there's another word from anyone I shall keep you all in this afternoon."

"You can't keep me in," said Clutterbuck; "I'm going for a walk with Captain Grimes."

"Then I shall very nearly kill you with this stick. Meanwhile you will all write an essay on 'Self-indulgence.' There will be a prize of half a crown for the longest essay, irrespective of any possible merit."

From then onwards all was silence until break. Paul, still holding the stick, gazed despondently out of the window. Now and then there arose from below the shrill voices of the servants scolding each other in Welsh. By the time the bell rang Clutterbuck had covered sixteen pages, and was awarded the half-crown.

*   *   *

"Did you find those boys difficult to manage?" asked Mr. Prendergast, filling his pipe.

"Not at all," said Paul.

"Ah, you're lucky. I find all boys utterly intractable. I don't know why it is. Of course my wig has a lot to do with it. Have you noticed that I wear a wig?"

"No, no, of course not."

"Well, the boys did as soon as they saw it. It was a great mistake my ever getting one. I thought when I left Worthing that I looked too old to get a job easily. I was only forty-one. It was very expensive, even though I chose the cheapest quality. Perhaps that's why it looks so like a wig. I don't know. I knew from the first that it was a mistake, but once they had seen it, it was too late to go back. They make all sorts of jokes about it."

"I expect they'd laugh at something else if it wasn't that."

"Yes, no doubt they would. I dare say it's a good thing to localise their ridicule as far as possible. Oh dear! oh dear! If it wasn't for my pipes, I don't know how I should manage to keep on. What made you come here?"

"I was sent down from Scone for indecent behaviour."

"Oh, yes, like Grimes?"

"No," said Paul firmly, "not like Grimes."

"Oh, well, it's all much the same really. And there's the bell. Oh dear! oh dear! I believe that loathsome little man's taken my gown."

*   *   *

Two days later Beste-Chetwynde pulled out the *vox humana* and played *Pop goes the Weasel*.

"D'you know, sir, you've made rather a hit with the fifth form?"

He and Paul were seated in the organ-loft of the village church. It was their second music lesson.

"For goodness sake, leave the organ alone. How d'you mean 'hit'?"

"Well, Clutterbuck was in the matron's room this morning. He'd just got a tin of pine-apple chunks. Tangent said, 'Are you going to take that into Hall?' and he said, 'No, I'm going to eat them in Mr. Pennyfeather's hour.' 'Oh, no, you're not,' said Tangent. 'Sweets and biscuits are one thing, but pine-apple chunks are going too far. It's little stinkers like you,' he said, 'who turn decent masters savage.'"

"Do you think that's so very complimentary?"

"I think it's one of the most complimentary things I ever heard said about a master," said Beste-Chetwynde; "would you like me to try that hymn again?"

"No," said Paul decisively.

"Well, then, I'll tell you another thing," said Beste-Chetwynde. "You know that man Philbrick. Well, I think there's something odd about him."

"I've no doubt of it."

"It's not just that he's such a bad butler. The servants are always ghastly here. But I don't believe he's a butler at all."

"I don't quite see what else he *can* be."

"Well, have you ever known a butler with a diamond tie-pin?"

"No, I don't think I have."

"Well, Philbrick's got one and a diamond ring too. He showed them to Brolly. Colossal great diamonds, Brolly says. Philbrick said he used to have bushels of diamonds and emeralds before the war, and that he used to eat off gold plate. We believe that he's a Russian prince in exile."

"Generally speaking, Russians are not shy about using their titles, are they? Besides, he looks very English."

"Yes, we thought of that, but Brolly said lots of Russians came to school in England before the war. And now I *am* going to play the organ," said Beste-Chetwynde. "After all, my mother does pay five guineas a term extra for me to learn."

Conduct

SITTING over the Common Room fire that afternoon waiting for the bell for tea, Paul found himself reflecting that on the whole the last week had not been quite as awful as he had expected. As Beste-Chetwynde had told him, he was a distinct success with his form; after the first day an understanding had been established between them. It was tacitly agreed that when Paul wished to read or to write letters he was allowed to do so undisturbed while he left them to employ the time as they thought best; when Paul took it upon him to talk to them about their lessons they remained silent, and when he set them work to do some of it was done. It had rained steadily, so that there had been no games. No punishments, no reprisals, no exertion, and in the evenings the confessions of Grimes, any one of which would have glowed with outstanding shamelessness from the appendix to a treatise in psychoanalysis.

Mr. Prendergast came in with the post.

"A letter for you, two for Grimes, nothing for me," he said. "No one ever writes to me. There was a time when I used to get five or six letters a day, not counting circulars. My mother used to file them for me to answer

—one heap of charity appeals, another for personal letters, another for marriages and funerals, another for baptisms and churchings and another for anonymous abuse. I wonder why it is the clergy always get so many letters of that sort, sometimes from quite educated people. I remember my father had great trouble in that way once, and he was forced to call in the police because they became so threatening. And, do you know, it was the curate's wife who had sent them—such a quiet little woman. There's your letter. Grimes's look like bills. I can't think why shops give that man credit at all. I always pay cash, or at least I should if I ever bought anything. But d'you know that, except for my tobacco and the *Daily News* and occasionally a little port when it's very cold, I don't think I've bought anything for two years. The last thing I bought was that walking stick. I got it at Shanklin, and Grimes uses it for beating the boys with. I hadn't really meant to buy one, but I was there for the day—two years this August —and I went into the tobacconist's to buy some tobacco. He hadn't the sort I wanted, and I felt I couldn't go without getting something, so I bought that. It cost one and six," he added wistfully, "so I had no tea."

Paul took his letter. It had been forwarded from Onslow Square. On the flap were embossed the arms of Scone College. It was from one of his four friends.

Scone College, J.C.R.,
Oxford.

My Dear Pennyfeather (it ran),

"I need hardly tell you how distressed I was when I heard of your disastrous misfortune. It seems to me that a real injustice has been done to you. I have not heard the full facts of the case, but I was confirmed in my opinion by a very curious incident last evening. I was just going to bed when Digby-Vaine-Trumpington came into my rooms without knocking. He was smoking a cigar. I had never spoken to him before, as you know, and was very much surprised at his visit. He said: 'I'm told you are a friend of Pennyfeather's.' I said I was, and he said: 'Well, I gather I've rather got him into a mess.' I said: 'Yes,' and he said: 'Well, will you apologise to him for me when you write?' I said I would. Then he said: 'Look here, I'm told he's rather poor. I thought of sending him some money—£20 for sort of damages, you know. It's all I can spare at the moment. Wouldn't it be a useful thing to do?' I fairly let him have it, I can tell you, and told him just what I thought of him for making such an insulting suggestion. I asked him how he dared treat a gentleman like that just because he wasn't in his awful set. He seemed rather taken aback and said: 'Well, all *my* friends spend all their time trying to get money out of me,' and went off.

"I bicycled over to St. Magnus's at Little Beckley and took some rubbings of the brasses there. I wished you had been with me.

Yours,
Arthur Potts.

P.S.—I understand you are thinking of taking up educational work. It seems to me that the great problem of education is to train the moral perceptions, not merely to discipline the appetites. I cannot help thinking that it is in greater fastidiousness rather than in greater self-control that the future progress of the race lies. I shall be interested to hear what your experience has been over the matter. The chaplain does not agree with me in this. He says great sensibility usually leads to enervation of will. Let me know what you think."

"What do you think about that?" asked Paul, handing Mr. Prendergast the letter.

"Well," he said after studying it carefully, "I think your friend is wrong about sensibility. It doesn't do to rely on one's own feelings, does it, not in anything?"

"No, I mean about the money."

"Good gracious, Pennyfeather! I hope you are in no doubt about that. Accept it at once, of course."

"It's a temptation."

"My dear boy, it would be a sin to refuse. Twenty pounds! Why, it takes me half a term to earn that."

The bell rang for tea. In the dining-hall Paul gave the letter to Grimes.

"Shall I take that twenty pounds?" he asked.

"Take it? My God! I should think you would."

"Well, I'm not sure," said Paul.

He thought about it all through afternoon school, all the time he was dressing for dinner, and all through dinner. It was a severe struggle, but his early training was victorious.

"If I take that money," he said to himself, "I shall never know whether I have acted rightly or not. It would always be on my mind. If I refuse, I shall be sure of having done right. I shall look back upon my self-denial with exquisite self-approval. By refusing I can convince myself that, in spite of the unbelievable things that have been happening to me during the last ten days, I am still the same Paul Pennyfeather I have respected so long. It is a test-case of the durability of my ideals."

He tried to explain something of what he felt to Grimes as they sat in Mrs. Roberts's bar parlour that evening.

"I'm afraid you'll find my attitude rather difficult to understand," he said. "I suppose it's largely a matter of upbringing. There is every reason why I should take this money. Digby-Vaine-Trumpington is exceedingly rich; and if he keeps it, it will undoubtedly be spent on betting or on some deplorable debauch. Owing to his party I have suffered irreparable harm. My whole future is shattered, and I have directly lost one hundred and twenty pounds a year in scholarships and two hundred and fifty pounds a year allowance from my guardian. By any ordinary process of thought, the money is justly mine. But," said Paul Pennyfeather, "there is my honour.

For generations the British bourgeoisie have spoken of themselves as gentlemen, and by that they have meant, among other things, a self-respecting scorn of irregular perquisites. It is the quality that distinguishes the gentleman from both the artist and the aristocrat. Now I am a gentleman. I can't help it: it's born in me. I just can't take that money."

"Well, I'm a gentleman too, old boy," said Grimes, "and I was afraid you might feel like that, so I did my best for you and saved you from yourself."

"What d'you mean by that?"

"Dear old boy, don't be angry, but immediately after tea I sent off a wire to your friend Potts: *Tell Trumpington send money quick,* and signed it '*Pennyfeather.*' I don't mind lending you the bob till it comes, either."

"Grimes, you wretch!" said Paul, but, in spite of himself, he felt a great wave of satisfaction surge up within him. "We must have another drink on that."

"Good for you," said Grimes, "and it's on me this round."

"To the durability of ideals!" said Paul as he got his pint.

"My word, what a mouthful!" said Grimes; "I can't say that. Cheerioh!"

      ❋   ❋   ❋

Two days later came another letter from Arthur Potts:

DEAR PENNYFEATHER,

I enclose Trumpington's cheque for £20. I am glad that my dealings with him are at an end. I cannot pretend to understand your attitude in this matter, but no doubt you are the best judge.

Stiggins is reading a paper to the O.S.C.U. on "Sex Repression and Religious Experience." Everyone expects rather a row, because you know how keen Walton is on the mystical element, which I think Stiggins is inclined to discount.

Yours,

ARTHUR POTTS.

P.S.—There is a most interesting article in the *Educational Review* on the new methods that are being tried at the Innesborough High School to induce co-ordination of the senses. They put small objects into the children's mouths and make them draw the shapes in red chalk. Have you tried this with your boys? I must say I envy you your opportunities. Are your colleagues enlightened?

"This same Potts," said Grimes as he read the letter, "would appear to be something of a stinker. Still, we've got the doings. How about a binge?"

"Yes," said Paul, "I think we ought to do something about one. I should like to ask Prendy too."

"Why, of course. It's just what Prendy needs. He's been looking awfully down in the mouth lately. Why shouldn't we all go over to the Metropole at Cwmpryddyg for dinner one night? We shall have to wait until the old boy goes away, otherwise he'll notice that there's no one on duty."

Later in the day Paul suggested the plan to Mr. Prendergast.

"Really, Pennyfeather," he said, "I think that's uncommonly kind of you. I hardly know what to say. Of course, I should love it. I can't remember when I dined at an hotel last. Certainly not since the War. It *will* be a treat. My dear boy, I'm quite overcome."

And, much to Paul's embarrassment, a tear welled up in each of Mr. Prendergast's eyes, and coursed down his cheeks.

The Duties of a Schoolmaster

QUINTILIAN

*MARCUS FABIUS QUINTILIANUS was born about 35 A.D. at Cala-
gurris. His father was a rhetorician who practised at Rome, and so young
Quintilian was sent to Rome for his education. On completing his education, he returned to his native city to teach rhetoric. In 68 A.D. he was
again in Rome having success as a teacher. He was the first rhetorician to
set up a public school and to receive a salary from the state. He continued
to teach for twenty years and had among his pupils Pliny the Younger. He
died about the year 100 A.D., full of honor and holding the title of consul.*

*The Duties of a Schoolmaster is from the Institutio Oratoria, a book of
lasting interest for its precepts on education.*

Let him (the teacher) therefore adopt a parental attitude to his pupils,
and regard himself as the representative of those who have committed their children to his charge. Let him be free from vice himself and
refuse to tolerate it in others. Let him be strict but not austere, genial but
not too familiar: for austerity will make him unpopular, while familiarity
breeds contempt. Let his discourse continually turn on what is good and
honorable; the more he admonishes, the less he will have to punish. He
must control his temper without, however, shutting his eyes to faults requiring correction: his instruction must be free from affectation, his industry great, his demands on his class continuous, but not extravagant.
He must be ready to answer questions and to put them unasked to those
who sit silent. In praising the recitations of his pupils he must be neither
grudging nor over-generous: the former quality will give them a distaste
for work, while the latter will produce a complacent self-satisfaction. In
correcting faults he must avoid sarcasm and above all abuse: for teachers
whose rebukes seem to imply positive dislike discourage industry. He
should declaim daily himself and, what is more, without stint, that his
class may take his utterances home with them. For however many models
for imitation he may give them from the authors they are reading, it will
still be found that fuller nourishment is provided by the living voice, as
we call it, more especially when it proceeds from the teacher himself, who,
if his pupils are rightly instructed, should be the object of their affection
and respect. And it is scarcely possible to say how much more readily we
imitate those whom we like.

"The Duties of a Schoolmaster" is reprinted by permission of The Harvard University Press from Loeb Classical Library Editions of *Quintilian,* Volume I, Book II,
Chapter II, translated by H. E. Butler.

An Old Man's Thought of School

WALT WHITMAN

IN July, 1855, a small book of ninety-five pages containing a ten-page preface and twelve untitled poems was issued by a Brooklyn press. Printed in gold letters on the cover and on the backstrip were the words Leaves of Grass. There was no author's name on the title page, but facing the title page was the photograph of a bearded man in his thirties with his collar open and without a tie. The copyright had been entered "by Walter Whitman."

WALT WHITMAN (1819-1892), author of Leaves of Grass, poet of Democracy, champion of the common man, was an original and vital force in American literature. His was the first voice in American literature to speak for the manifold expressions of the Industrial Revolution in America.

He was born on Long Island, lived in Brooklyn, and in Camden, New Jersey, where he spent the last twenty years of his life, a semi-invalid and in poverty.

The poem which follows was written for the inauguration of a public school in Camden, in 1874.

An old man's thought of school,
   An old man gathering youthful memories and blooms that youth
      itself cannot.

Now only do I know you,
O fair auroral skies—O morning dew upon the grass!

And these I see, these sparkling eyes,
These stores of mystic meaning, these young lives,
Building, equipping like a fleet of ships, immortal ships,
Soon to sail out over the measureless seas,
On the soul's voyage.

Only a lot of boys and girls?
Only the tiresome spelling, writing, ciphering classes?
Only a public school?

Ah more, infinitely more;
(As George Fox rais'd his warning cry, "Is it this pile of brick and mortar,
    these dead floors, windows, rails, you call the church?
Why this is not the church at all—the church is living, ever living souls.")
And you America,
Cast you the real reckoning for your present?
The lights and shadows of your future, good or evil?
To girlhood, boyhood look, the teacher and the school.

What Is a College For?

WOODROW WILSON

WOODROW WILSON (1856-1924), twenty-eighth President of the United States, was born at Staunton, Virginia, the son of a Presbyterian minister. He was graduated from Princeton in 1879, studied law at the University of Virginia, and received a Ph.D. from The Johns Hopkins University in 1886. He became a college teacher and taught at Bryn Mawr, Wesleyan, and Princeton, becoming president of the latter in 1902. While president of Princeton, he introduced many social and educational reforms. He left teaching in 1910, became subsequently Governor of New Jersey, and President of the United States.

WHAT should a lad go to college for,—for work, for the realization of a definite aim, for discipline and a severe training of his faculties, or for relaxation, for the release and exercise of his social powers, for the broadening effects of life in a sort of miniature world in which study is only one among many interests? That is not the only alternative suggested by recent discussions. They also suggest a sharp alternative with regard to the character of the study the college student should undertake. Should he seek at college a general discipline of his faculties, a general awakening to the issues and interests of the modern world, or should he, rather seek specially and definitely to prepare himself for the work he expects to do after he leaves college, for his support and advancement in the world? The two alternatives are very different. The one asks whether the lad does not get as good a preparation for modern life by being manager of a football team with a complicated programme of intercollegiate games and trips away from home as by becoming proficient in mathematics or in history and mastering the abstract tasks of the mind; the other asks whether he is not better prepared by being given the special skill and training of a particular calling or profession, an immediate drill in the work he is to do after he graduates, than by being made a master of his own mind in the more general fields of knowledge to which his subsequent calling will be related, in all probability, only as every undertaking is related to the general thought and experience of the world.

"Learning" is not involved. No one has ever dreamed of imparting learning to undergraduates. It cannot be done in four years. To become a man

"What Is College For?" is from *The Public Papers of Woodrow Wilson* and is reprinted by permission of Mrs. Woodrow Wilson.

of learning is the enterprise of a lifetime. The issue does not rise to that high ground. The question is merely this: do we wish college to be, first of all and chiefly, a place of mental discipline or only a school of general experience; and, if we wish it to be a place of mental discipline, of what sort do we wish the discipline to be,—a general awakening and release of the faculties, or a preliminary initiation into the drill of a particular vocation?

These are questions which go to the root of the matter. They admit of no simple and confident answer. Their roots spring out of life and all its varied sources. To reply to them, therefore, involves an examination of modern life and an assessment of the part an educated man ought to play in it,—an analysis which no man may attempt with perfect self-confidence. The life of our day is a very complex thing which no man can pretend to comprehend in its entirety.

But some things are obvious enough concerning it. There is an uncommon challenge to effort in the modern world, and all the achievements to which it challenges are uncommonly difficult. Individuals are yoked together in modern enterprise by a harness which is both new and inelastic. The man who understands only some single process, some single piece of work which he has been set to do, will never do anything else, and is apt to be deprived at almost any moment of the opportunity to do even that, because processes change, industry undergoes instant revolutions. New inventions, fresh discoveries, alterations in the markets of the world throw accustomed methods and the men who are accustomed to them out of date and use without pause or pity. The man of special skill may be changed into an unskilled laborer overnight. Moreover, it is a day in which no enterprise stands alone or independent, but is related to every other and feels changes in all parts of the globe. The men with mere skill, with mere technical knowledge, will be mere servants perpetually, and may at any time become useless servants, their skill gone out of use and fashion. The particular thing they do may become unnecessary or may be so changed that they cannot comprehend or adjust themselves to the change.

These, then, are the things the modern world must have in its trained men, and I do not know where else it is to get them if not from its educated men and the occasional self-developed genius of an exceptional man here and there. It needs, at the top, not a few, but many men with the power to organize and guide. The college is meant to stimulate in a considerable number of men what would be stimulated in only a few if we were to depend entirely upon nature and circumstance. Below the ranks of generalship and guidance, the modern world needs for the execution of its varied and difficult business a very much larger number of men with great capacity and readiness for the rapid and concentrated exertion of a whole series of faculties: planning faculties as well as technical skill, the ability to handle men as well as to handle tools and correct processes, faculties of adjustment and adaptation as well as of precise execution,—men of resource as well as knowledge. These are the athletes, the athletes of faculty, of which our generation most stands in need. All through its ranks, besides, it needs masterful men who can acquire a working knowledge of many things readily, quickly, intelligently, and with exactness,—things they had not foreseen or prepared themselves for beforehand, and for which they could not have prepared themselves beforehand. Quick apprehension, quick comprehension, quick action are what modern life puts a premium upon,—a readiness to turn this way or that and not lose force or momentum.

To me, then, the question seems to be, Shall the lad who goes to college go there for the purpose of getting ready to be a servant merely, a servant who will be nobody and who may become useless, or shall he go there for the purpose of getting ready to be a master adventurer in the field of modern opportunity?

We must expect hewers of wood and drawers of water to come out of the colleges in their due proportion, of course, but I take it for granted that even the least gifted of them did not go to college with the ambition to be nothing more. And yet one has hardly made the statement before he begins to doubt whether he can safely take anything for granted. Part of the very question we are discussing is the ambition with which young men now go to college. It is a day when a college course has become fashionable,—but not for the purpose of learning, not for the purpose of obtaining a definite preparation for anything,—no such purpose could become *fashionable*. The clientage of our colleges has greatly changed since the time when most of the young men who resorted to them did so with a view to entering one or other of the learned professions. Young men who expect to go into business of one kind or another now outnumber among our under-graduates those who expect to make some sort of learning the basis of their work throughout life; and I dare say that they generally go to college without having made any very definite analysis of their aim and purpose in going. Their parents seem to have made as little.

The enormous increase of wealth in the country in recent years, too, has had its effect upon the colleges,—not in the way that might have been expected,—not, as yet, by changing the standard of life to any very noticeable extent or introducing luxury and extravagance and vicious indulgence. College undergraduates have usually the freshness of youth about them, out of which there springs a wholesome simplicity, and it is not easy to spoil them or to destroy their natural democracy. They make a life of their own and insist upon the maintenance of its standards. But the increase of wealth has brought into the colleges, in rapidly augmenting numbers, the sons of very rich men, and lads who expect to inherit wealth are not as easily stimulated to effort, are not as apt to form definite and serious purposes, as those who know that they must whet their wits for the struggle of life.

There was a time when the mere possession of wealth conferred distinction; and when wealth confers distinction it is apt to breed a sort of consciousness of opportunity and responsibility in those who possess it and incline them to seek serious achievement. But that time is long past in America. Wealth is common. And, by the same token, the position of the lad who is to inherit it is a peculiarly disadvantageous one, if the standard of success is to rise above mediocrity. Wealth removes the necessity for effort, and yet effort is necessary for the attainment of distinction, and very great effort at that, in the modern world, as I have already pointed out. It would look as if the ordinary lad with expectations were fore-doomed to obscurity; for the ordinary lad will not exert himself unless he must.

We live in an age in which no achievement is to be cheaply had. All the cheap achievements, open to amateurs, are exhausted and have become commonplace. Adventure, for example, is no longer extraordinary: which is another way of saying that it is commonplace. Any amateur may seek and find adventure; but it has been sought and had in all its kinds. Rest-less men, idle men, chivalrous men, men drawn on by mere curiosity and men drawn on by love of the knowledge that lies outside books and laboratories, have crossed the whole face of the habitable globe in search of it, ferreting it out in corners even, following its bypaths and beating its coverts, and it is nowhere any longer a novelty or distinction to have dis-covered and enjoyed it. The whole round of pleasure, moreover, has been exhausted time out of mind, and most of it discredited as not pleasure after all, but just an expensive counterfeit; so that many rich people have been driven to devote themselves to expense regardless of pleasure. No new pleasure, I am credibly informed, has been invented within the mem-ory of man. For every genuine thrill and satisfaction, therefore, we are ap-parently, in this sophisticated world, shut in to work, to modifying and quickening the life of the age. If college be one of the highways to life and achievement, it must be one of the highways to work.

The man who comes out of college into the modern world must, there-fore, have got out of it, if he has not wasted four vitally significant years of his life, a quickening and a training which will make him in some degree a master among men. If he has got less, college was not worth his while. To have made it worth his while he must have got such a prepara-tion and development of his faculties as will give him movement as well as mere mechanical efficiency in affairs complex, difficult, and subject to change. The word efficiency has in our day the power to think at the centre of it, the power of independent movement and initiative. It is not merely the suitability to be a good tool, it is the power to wield tools, and among the tools are men and circumstances and changing processes of industry, changing phases of life itself. There should be technical schools a great many and the technical schools of America should be among the best in the world. The men they train are indispensable. The modern world needs more tools than managers, more workmen than master workmen. But even the technical schools must have some thought of mastery and adaptability in their processes; and the colleges, which are not technical schools, should think of that chiefly. We must distinguish what the college is for, without disparaging any other school, of any other kind. It is for the training of the men who are to rise above the ranks.

That is what a college is for. What it does, what it requires of its undergraduates and of its teachers, should be adjusted to that conception. The very statement of the object, which must be plain to all who make any distinction at all between a college and a technical school, makes it evident that the college must subject its men to a general intellectual training which will be narrowed to no one point of view, to no one vocation or calling. It must release and quicken as many faculties of the mind as possible,—and not only release and quicken them but discipline and strengthen them also by putting them to the test of systematic labor. Work, definite, exacting, long continued, but not narrow or petty or merely rule of thumb, must be its law of life for those who would pass its gates and go out with its authentication.

By a general training I do not mean vague spaces of study, miscellaneous fields of reading, a varied smattering of a score of subjects and the thorough digestion of none. The field of modern knowledge is extremely wide and varied. After a certain number of really fundamental subjects have been studied in the schools, the college undergraduate must be offered a choice of the route he will travel in carrying his studies further. He cannot be shown the whole body of knowledge within a single curriculum. There is no longer any single highway of learning. The roads that traverse its vast and crowded spaces are not even parallel, and four years is too short a time in which to search them all out. But there is a general programme still possible by which the college student can be made acquainted with the field of modern learning by sample, by which he can be subjected to the several kinds of mental discipline,—in philosophy, in some one of the great sciences, in some one of the great languages which carry the thought of the world, in history and in politics, which is its framework,—which will give him valid naturalization as a citizen of the world of thought, the world of educated men,—and no smatterer merely, able barely to spell its constitution out, but a man who has really comprehended and made use of its chief intellectual processes and is ready to lay his mind alongside its tasks with some confidence that he can master them and can understand why and how they are to be performed. This is the general training which should be characteristic of the college, and the men who undergo it ought to be made to undergo it with deep seriousness and diligent labour; not as soft amateurs with whom learning and its thorough tasks are side interests merely, but as those who approach life with the intention of becoming professionals in its fields of achievement.

Just now, where this is attempted, it seems to fail of success. College men, it is said, and often said with truth, come out undisciplined, untrained, unfitted for what they are about to undertake. It is argued, therefore, that what they should have been given was special vocational instruction; that if they had had that they would have been interested in their work while they were undergraduates, would have taken it more seriously, and would have come out of college ready to be used, as they now cannot be. No doubt that is to be preferred to a scattered and aimless choice of studies, and no doubt what the colleges offer is miscellaneous and aimless enough in many cases; but, at best, these are very hopeful assumptions on the part of those who would convert our colleges into vocational schools. They are generally put forward by persons who do not know how college life and work are now organized and conducted. I do not wonder that they know little of what has happened. The whole thing is of very recent development, at any rate in its elaborate complexity. It is a growth, as we now see it, of the last ten or twelve years; and even recent graduates of our colleges would rub their eyes incredulously to see it if they were to stand again on the inside and look at it intimately.

What has happened is, in general terms, this: that the work of the college, the work of its classrooms and laboratories, has become the merely formal and compulsory side of its life, and that a score of other things, lumped under the term "undergraduate activities," have become the vital, spontaneous, absorbing realities for nine out of every ten men who go to college. These activities embrace social, athletic, dramatic, musical, literary, religious, and professional organizations of every kind, besides many organized for mere amusement and some, of great use and dignity, which seek to exercise a general oversight and sensible direction of college ways and customs. Those which consume the most time are, of course, the athletic, dramatic, and musical clubs, whose practices, rehearsals, games, and performances fill the term time and the brief vacations alike. But it is the social organizations into which the thought, the energy, the initiative, the enthusiasm of the largest number of men go, and go in lavish measure.

The chief of these social organizations are residential families,—fraternities, clubs, groups of house-mates of one kind or another,—in which, naturally enough, all the undergraduate interests, all the undergraduate activities of the college have their vital centre. The natural history of their origin and development is very interesting. They grew up very normally. They were necessary because of what the college did not do.

Every college in America, at any rate every college outside a city, has tried to provide living rooms for its undergraduates, dormitories in which they can live and sleep and do their work outside the classroom and the laboratory. Very few colleges whose numbers have grown rapidly have been able to supply dormitories enough for all their students, and some have deliberately abandoned the attempt, but in many of them a very considerable proportion of the undergraduates live on the campus, in college buildings. It is a very wholesome thing that they should live thus under the direct influence of the daily life of such a place and, at least in legal theory, under the authority of the university of which the college forms a principal part. But the connection between the dormitory life and the real life of the university, its intellectual tasks and disciplines, its outlook upon the greater world of thought and action which lies beyond, far beyond, the boundaries of campus and classroom, is very meagre and shadowy indeed. It is hardly more than atmospheric, and the atmosphere is very attenuated, perceptible only by the most sensitive.

Formerly, in more primitive, and I must say less desirable, days than these in which we have learned the full vigour of freedom, college tutors and proctors lived in the dormitories and exercised a precarious authority. The men were looked after in their rooms and made to keep hours and observe rules. But those days are happily gone by. The system failed of its object. The lads were mischievous and recalcitrant, those placed in authority over them generally young and unwise; and the rules were odious to those whom they were meant to restrain. There was the atmosphere of the boarding-school about the buildings, and of a boarding-school whose pupils had outgrown it. Life in college dormitories is much pleasanter now and much more orderly, because it is free and governed only by college opinion, which is a real, not a nominal, master. The men come and go as they please and have little consciousness of any connection with authority or with the governing influences of the university in their rooms, except that the university is their landlord and makes rules such as a landlord may make.

Formerly, in more primitive and less pleasant days, the college provided a refectory or "commons" where all undergraduates had their meals, a noisy family. It was part of the boarding-school life; and the average undergraduate had outgrown it as consciously as he had outgrown the futile discipline of the dormitory. Now nothing of the kind is attempted. Here and there, in connection with some large college which has found that the boarding-houses and restaurants of the town have been furnishing poor food at outrageous prices to those of its undergraduates who could not otherwise provide for themselves, will be found a great "commons," at which hundreds of men take their meals, amid the hurly-burly of numbers, without elegance or much comfort, but nevertheless at a well-spread table where the food is good and the prices moderate. The undergraduate may use it or not as he pleases. It is merely a great cooperative boarding-place, bearing not even a family resemblance to the antique "commons." It is one of the conveniences of the place. It has been provided by the university authorities, but it might have been provided in some other way and have been quite independent of them; and it is usually under undergraduate management.

Those who do not like the associations or the fare of such a place provide for themselves elsewhere, in clubs or otherwise,—generally in fraternity houses. At most colleges there is no such common boarding-place, and all must shift for themselves. It is this necessity in the one case and desire in the other that has created the chief complexity now observable in college life and which has been chiefly instrumental in bringing about that dissociation of undergraduate life from the deeper and more permanent influences of the university which has of recent years become so marked and so significant.

Fraternity chapters were once—and that not so very long ago—merely groups of undergraduates who had bound themselves together by the vows of various secret societies which had spread their branches among the colleges. They had their fraternity rooms, their places of meeting; they were distinguished by well-known badges and formed little coteries distinguishable enough from the general body of undergraduates, as they wished to be; but in all ordinary matters they shared the common life of the place. The daily experiences of the college life they shared with their fellows of all kinds and all connections, in an easy democracy; their contacts were the common contacts of the classroom and the laboratory not only, but also of the boarding-house table and of all the usual undergraduate resorts. Members of the same fraternity were naturally enough inclined to associate chiefly with one another, and were often, much too often, inclined, in matters of college "politics," to act as a unit and in their own interest; but they did not live separately. They did not hold aloof or constitute themselves separate families, living apart in their own houses, in privacy. Now all that is changed. Every fraternity has its own house, equipped as a complete home. The fraternity houses will often be the most interesting and the most beautiful buildings a visitor will be shown when he visits the college. In them members take all their meals, in them they spend their leisure hours and often do their reading,—for each house has its library—and in them many of the members, as many as can be accommodated, have their sleeping rooms and live, because the college has not dormitories enough to lodge them or because they prefer lodging outside the dormitories. In colleges where there are no fraternities, clubs of one sort or another take their places, build homes of their own, enjoy a similar privacy and separateness, and constitute the centre of all that is most comfortable and interesting and attractive in undergraduate life.

I am pointing out this interesting and very important development, not for the purpose of criticising it, but merely to explain its natural history and the far-reaching results it has brought about. The college having determined, wisely enough, some generation or two ago, not to be any longer a boarding-school, has resolved itself into a mere teaching machine, with the necessary lecture rooms and laboratories attached and sometimes a few dormitories, which it regards as desirable but not indispensable, and has resigned into the hands of the undergraduates themselves the whole management of their life outside the classroom; and not only its management but also the setting up of all its machinery of every kind,—as much as they please,—and the constitution of its whole environment, so that teachers and pupils are not members of one university body but constitute two bodies sharply distinguished,—and the undergraduate body the more highly organized and independent of the two. They parley with one another, but they do not live with one another, and it is much easier for the influence of the highly organized and very self-conscious undergraduate body to penetrate the faculty than it is for the influence of the faculty to permeate the undergraduates.

It was inevitable it should turn out so in the circumstances. I do not wonder that the consequences were not foreseen and that the whole development has crept upon us almost unawares. But the consequences have been very important and very far-reaching. It is easy now to see that if you leave undergraduates entirely to themselves, to organize their own lives while in college as they please,—and organize it in some way they must if thus cast adrift,—that life, and not the deeper interests of the university, will presently dominate their thoughts, their imaginations, their favourite purposes. And not only that. The work of administering this complex life, with all its organizations and independent interests, successfully absorbs the energies, the initiative, the planning and originating powers of the best men among the undergraduates. It is no small task. It would tax and absorb older men; and only the finer, more spirited, more attractive, more original and effective men are fitted for it or equal to it, where leadership goes by gifts of personality as well as by ability. The very men the teacher most desires to get hold of and to enlist in some enterprise of the mind, the very men it would most reward him to instruct and whose training would count for most in leadership outside of college, in the country at large, and for the promotion of every interest the nation has, the natural leaders and doers, are drawn off and monopolized by these necessary and engaging undergraduate undertakings. The born leaders and managers and originators are drafted off to "run the college" (it is in fact nothing less), and the classroom, the laboratory, the studious conference with instructors get only the residuum of their attention, only what can be spared of their energy—are secondary matters where they ought to come first. It is the organization that is at fault, not the persons who enter into it and are moulded by it. It cannot turn out otherwise in the circumstances. The side shows are so numerous, so diverting,—so important, if you will—that they have swallowed up the circus, and those who perform in the main tent must often whistle for their audiences, discouraged and humiliated.

Such is college life nowadays, and such its relation to college work and the all-important intellectual interests which the colleges are endowed and maintained to foster. I need not stop to argue that the main purposes of education cannot be successfully realized under such conditions. I need not stop to urge that the college was not and can never be intended for the uses it is now being put to. A young man can learn to become the manager of a football team or of a residential club, the leader of an orchestra or a glee club, the star of amateur theatricals, on oarsman or a chessplayer without putting himself to the trouble or his parents to the expense of four years at a college. These are innocent enough things for him to do and to learn, though hardly very important in the long run; they may, for all I know, make for efficiency in some of the simpler kinds of business; and no wise man who knows college lads would propose to shut them off from them or wish to discourage their interest in them. All work and no play makes Jack a dull boy, not only, but may make him a vicious boy as well. Amusement, athletic games, the zest of contest and competition, the challenge there is in most college activities to the instinct of initiative and the gifts of leadership and achievement,—all these are wholesome means of stimulation, which keep young men from going stale and turning to things that demoralize. But they should not assume the front of the stage where more serious and lasting interests are to be served. Men cannot be prepared by them for modern life.

The college is meant for a severer, more definite discipline than this: a discipline which will fit men for the contests and achievements of an age whose every task is conditioned upon some intelligent and effective use of the mind, upon some substantial knowledge, some special insight, some trained capacity, some penetration which comes from study, not from natural readiness or mere practical experience.

The side shows need not be abolished. They need not be cast out or even discredited. But they must be subordinated. They must be put in their natural place as diversions, and ousted from their present dignity and preëminence as occupations.

And this can be done without making of the college again a boarding-school. The characteristic of the boarding-school is that its pupils are in all things in tutelage, are under masters at every turn of their life, must do as they are bidden, not in the performance of their set tasks only, but also in all their comings and goings. It is this characteristic that made it impossible and undesirable to continue the life of the boarding-school into the college, where it is necessary that the pupil should begin to show his manhood and make his own career. No one who knows what wholesome and regulated freedom can do for young men ought ever to wish to hail them back to the days of childish discipline and restraint of which the college of our grandfathers was typical. But a new discipline is desirable, is absolutely necessary, if the college is to be recalled to its proper purpose, its bounden duty. It cannot perform its duty as it is now organized.

The fundamental thing to be accomplished in the new organization is, that, instead of being the heterogeneous congeries of petty organizations it now is, instead of being allowed to go to pieces in a score of fractions free to cast off from the whole as they please, it should be drawn together again into a single university family of which the teachers shall be as natural and as intimate members as the undergraduates. The "life" of the college should not be separated from its chief purposes and most essential objects, should not be contrasted with its duties and in rivalry with them. The two should be but two sides of one and the same thing; the association of men, young and old, for serious mental endeavour and also, in the intervals of work for every wholesome sport and diversion. Undergraduate life should not be in rivalry and contrast with undergraduate duties: undergraduates should not be merely in attendance upon the college, but parts of it on every side of its life, very conscious and active parts. They should consciously live its whole life,—not under masters, as in school, and yet associated in some intimate daily fashion with their masters in learning: so that learning may not seem one thing and life another. The organizations whose objects lie outside study should be but parts of the whole, not set against it, but included within it.

All this can be accomplished by a comparatively simple change of organization which will make master and pupil members of the same free, self-governed family, upon natural terms of intimacy. But how it can be done is not our present interest. That is another story. It is our present purpose merely to be clear what a college is for. That, perhaps, I have now pointed out with sufficient explicitness. I have shown the incompatibility of the present social organization of our colleges with the realization of that purpose only to add emphasis to the statement of what that purpose is. Once get that clearly established in the mind of the country, and the means of realizing it will readily and quickly be found. The object of the college is intellectual discipline and moral enlightenment, and it is the immediate task of those who administer the colleges of the country to find the means and the organization by which that object can be attained. Education is a process and, like all other processes, has its proper means and machinery. It does not consist in courses of study. It consists of the vital assimilation of knowledge, and the mode of life, for the college as for the individual, is nine parts of the digestion.

Education of Young Women in the United States

ALEXIS de TOCQUEVILLE

ALEXIS de TOCQUEVILLE (1805-1859) was born in Paris and educated at home until his fifteenth year, when he went to the Lycée at Metz. At eighteen he returned to Paris to study law and at twenty-one began his career in the law. Early given to liberal views, he developed an interest in democracy and sought an opportunity to observe democracy in action in America. He petitioned the French Government for a leave of absence to study the prison system in America. The petition was granted, and in 1831 de Tocqueville arrived in this country. He soon completed his official mission and was free to accomplish his real object—the analysis of democracy as a working principle of society and government. He traveled widely in the United States, observed closely, wrote daily notes, and on his return to France set about the task of writing Democracy in America. *This work, first published in an American edition in 1838, presents the whole panorama of American life as de Tocqueville saw it.*

The following excerpts on education are from this book.

No free communities ever existed without morals, and as I observed in the former part of this work, morals are the work of woman. Consequently, whatever affects the condition of women, their habits and their opinions, has great political importance in my eyes.

Among almost all Protestant nations young women are far more the mistresses of their own actions than they are in Catholic countries. This independence is still greater in Protestant countries like England, which have retained or acquired the right of self-government; freedom is then infused into the domestic circle by political habits and by religious opinions. In the United States the doctrines of Protestantism are combined with great political liberty and a most democratic state of society, and nowhere are young women surrendered so early or so completely to their own guidance.

Long before an American girl arrives at the marriageable age, her emancipation from maternal control begins: she has scarcely ceased to be a child when she already thinks for herself, speaks with freedom, and acts on her own impulse. The great scene of the world is constantly open to her view; far from seeking to conceal it from her, it is every day disclosed more completely and she is taught to survey it with a firm and calm gaze. Thus the vices and dangers of society are early revealed to her; as she sees them clearly, she views them without illusion and braves them without fear, for she is full of reliance on her own strength, and her confidence seems to be shared by all around her.

An American girl scarcely ever displays that virginal softness in the midst of young desires or that innocent and ingenuous grace which usually attend the European woman in the transition from girlhood to youth. It is rare that an American woman, at any age, displays childish timidity or ignorance. Like the young women of Europe she seeks to please, but she knows precisely the cost of pleasing. If she does not abandon herself to evil, at least she knows that it exists; and she is remarkable rather for purity of manners than for chastity of mind.

I have been frequently surprised and almost frightened at the singular address and happy boldness with which young women in America contrive to manage their thoughts and their language amid all the difficulties of free conversation; a philosopher would have stumbled at every step along the narrow path which they trod without accident and without effort. It is easy, indeed, to perceive that even amid the independence of early youth an American woman is always mistress of herself; she indulges in all permitted pleasures without yielding herself up to any of them, and her reason never allows the reins of self-guidance to drop, though it often seems to hold them loosely.

In France, where traditions of every age are still so strangely mingled in the opinions and tastes of the people, women commonly receive a reserved, retired, and almost conventual education, as they did in aristocratic times; and then they are suddenly abandoned without a guide and without assistance in the midst of all the irregularities inseparable from democratic society.

The Americans are more consistent. They have found out that in a democracy the independence of individuals cannot fail to be very great, youth premature, tastes ill-restrained, customs fleeting, public opinion often unsettled and powerless, paternal authority weak, and marital authority contested. Under these circumstances, believing that they had little chance of repressing in woman the most vehement passions of the human heart, they held that the surer way was to teach her the art of combating those passions for herself. As they could not prevent her virtue from being exposed to frequent danger, they determined that she should know how best to defend it, and more reliance was placed on the free vigor of her will than on safeguards which have been shaken or overthrown. Instead, then, of inculcating mistrust of herself, they constantly seek to enhance her confidence in her own strength of character. As it is neither possible nor desirable to keep a young woman in perpetual and complete ignorance, they hasten to give her a precocious knowledge on all subjects. Far from hiding the corruptions of the world from her, they prefer that she should see them at once and train herself to shun them, and they hold it of more importance to protect her conduct than to be over-scrupulous of the innocence of her thoughts.

Although the Americans are a very religious people, they do not rely on religion alone to defend the virtue of woman; they seek to arm her reason also. In this respect they have followed the same method as in several others: they first make vigorous efforts to cause individual independence to control itself, and they do not call in the aid of religion until they have reached the utmost limits of human strength.

I am aware that an education of this kind is not without danger; I am sensible that it tends to invigorate the judgment at the expense of the imagination and to make cold and virtuous women instead of affectionate wives and agreeable companions to man. Society may be more tranquil and better regulated, but domestic life has often fewer charms. These, however, are secondary evils, which may be braved for the sake of higher interests. At the stage at which we are now arrived, the choice is no longer left to us; a democratic education is indispensable to protect women from the dangers with which democratic institutions and manners surround them.

The Study of Greek and Latin Literature

WHAT was called the People in the most democratic republics of antiquity was very unlike what we designate by that term. In Athens all the citizens took part in public affairs; but there were only twenty thousand citizens to more than three hundred and fifty thousand inhabitants. All the rest were slaves, and discharged the greater part of those duties which belong at the present day to the lower or even to the middle classes. Athens, then, with her universal suffrage, was, after all, merely an aristocratic republic, in which all the nobles had an equal right to the government.

The struggle between the patricians and plebeians of Rome must be considered in the same light: it was simply an internal feud between the elder and younger branches of the same family. All belonged to the aristocracy and all had the aristocratic spirit.

It is to be remarked, moreover, that, among the ancients books were always scarce and dear, and that very great difficulties impeded their publication and circulation. These circumstances concentrated literary tastes and habits among a small number of men, who formed a small literary aristocracy out of the choicer spirits of the great political aristocracy.

Accordingly, nothing goes to prove that literature was ever treated as a trade among the Greeks and Romans.

These communities, which were not only aristocracies, but very polished and free nations, of course imparted to their literary productions the special defects and merits that characterize the literature of aristocratic times. And indeed a very superficial survey of the works of ancient authors will suffice to convince us that if those writers were sometimes deficient in variety and fertility in their subjects, or in boldness, vivacity, and power of generalization in their thoughts, they always displayed exquisite care and skill in their details. Nothing in their works seems to be done hastily or at random; every line is written for the eye of the connoisseur and is shaped after some conception of ideal beauty. No literature places those fine qualities in which the writers of democracies are naturally deficient in bolder relief than that of the ancients; no literature, therefore, ought to be more studied in democratic times. This study is better suited than any other to combat the literary defects inherent in those times; as for their natural literary qualities, these will spring up of their own accord without its being necessary to learn to acquire them.

It is important that this point should be clearly understood. A particular study may be useful to the literature of a people without being appropriate to its social and political wants. If men were to persist in teaching nothing but the literature of the dead languages in a community where everyone is habitually led to make vehement exertions to augment or to maintain his fortune, the result would be a very polished, but a very dangerous set of citizens. For as their social and political condition would give them every day a sense of wants, which their education would never teach them to supply, they would perturb the state, in the name of the Greeks and Romans, instead of enriching it by their productive industry.

It is evident that in democratic communities the interest of individuals as well as the security of the commonwealth demands that the education of the greater number should be scientific, commercial, and industrial rather than literary. Greek and Latin should not be taught in all the schools; but it is important that those who, by their natural disposition or their fortune, are destined to cultivate letters or prepared to relish them should find schools where a complete knowledge of ancient literature may be acquired and where the true scholar may be formed. A few excellent universities would do more towards the attainment of this object than a multitude of bad grammar-schools, where superfluous matters, badly learned, stand in the way of sound instruction in necessary studies.

All who aspire to literary excellence in democratic nations ought frequently to refresh themselves at the springs of ancient literature; there is no more wholesome medicine for the mind. Not that I hold the literary productions of the ancients to be irreproachable, but I think that they have some special merits, admirably calculated to counterbalance our peculiar defects. They are a prop on the side on which we are in most danger of falling.

The Good Schoolmaster

THOMAS FULLER

THOMAS FULLER (1608-1661) entered Queens' College, Cambridge, at the age of thirteen. Among his college contemporaries were three distinguished men—John Milton, George Herbert, and Jeremy Taylor. He left Cambridge in 1628 and entered the church. For a time he was rector of a country parish and later a popular preacher in London. He fell into disfavor with the king, left London, but returned after the war, and continued to preach until his death in 1661.

He was a man of broad tolerance and sympathy who looked on life with wide-open but kindly eyes. In 1642 he published The Holy State and the Profane State, *a series of character studies of the Theophrastian type. These essays are quaint and humorous and contain abundant wisdom and sound common sense.*

THERE is scarce any profession in the commonwealth more necessary, which is so slightly performed. The reasons whereof I conceive to be these: First, young scholars make this calling their refuge, yea, perchance, before they have taken any degree in the university, commence schoolmasters in the country, as if nothing else were required to set up this profession but only a rod and a ferula. Secondly, others who are able, use it only as a passage to better preferment, to patch the rents in their present fortune, till they can provide a new one, and betake themselves to some more gainful calling. Thirdly, they are disheartened from doing their best with the miserable reward which in some places they receive, being masters to the children and slaves to their parents. Fourthly, being grown rich, they grow negligent, and scorn to touch the school, but by the proxy of an usher. But see how well our schoolmaster behaves himself.

1. *His genius inclines him with delight to his profession.* Some men had as lief be schoolboys as schoolmasters, to be tied to the school as Cooper's Dictionary and Scapula's Lexicon are chained to the desk therein; and though great scholars, and skilful in other arts, are bunglers in this: but God of his goodness hath fitted several men for several callings, that the necessity of church and state, in all conditions, may be provided for. So that he who beholds the fabric thereof may say, God hewed out this stone, and appointed it to lie in this very place, for it would fit none other so well, and here it doth most excellent. And thus God mouldeth some for

229

this

a schoolmaster's life, undertaking it with desire and delight, and discharging it with dexterity and happy success.

2. *He studies his scholars' natures as carefully as they their books;* and ranks their dispositions into several forms. And though it may seem difficult for him in a great school to descend to all particulars, yet experienced schoolmasters may quickly make a grammar of boys' natures, and reduce them all, saving some few exceptions, to these general rules:

(a) Those that are ingenious and industrious. The conjunction of two such planets in a youth presage much good unto him. To such a lad a frown may be a whipping, and a whipping a death; yea, where their master whips them once, shame whips them all the week after. Such natures he useth with all gentleness.

(b) Those that are ingenious and idle. These think, with the hare in the fable, that, running with snails (so they count the rest of their schoolfellows), they shall come soon enough to the post, though sleeping a good while before their starting. Oh, a good rod would finely take them napping!

(c) Those that are dull and diligent. Wines, the stronger they be, the more lees they have when they are new. Many boys are muddy-headed till they be clarified with age, and such afterwards prove the best. Bristol diamonds are both bright, and squared and pointed by nature, and yet are soft and worthless; whereas orient ones in India are rough and rugged naturally. Hard, rugged, and dull natures of youth acquit themselves afterwards the jewels of the country, and therefore their dullness at first is to be borne with, if they be diligent. That schoolmaster deserves to be beaten himself, who beats nature in a boy for a fault. And I question whether all the whipping in the world can make their parts, which are naturally sluggish, rise one minute before the hour nature hath appointed.

(d) Those that are invincibly dull and negligent also. Correction may reform the latter, not amend the former. All the whetting in the world can never set a razor's edge on that which hath no steel in it. Such boys he consigneth over to other professions. Shipwrights and boatmakers will choose those crooked pieces of timber which other carpenters refuse. Those may make excellent merchants and mechanics who will not serve for scholars.

3. *He is able, diligent, and methodical in his teaching;* not leading them rather in a circle than forwards. He minces his precepts for children to swallow, hanging clogs on the nimbleness of his own soul, that his scholars may go along with him.

4. *He is and will be known to be an absolute monarch in his school.* If cockering mothers proffer him money to purchase their sons an exemption from his rod (to live as it were in a peculiar, out of their master's jurisdiction), with disdain he refuseth it, and scorns the late custom, in some places, of commuting whipping into money, and ransoming boys from the rod at a set price. If he hath a stubborn youth, correction-proof, he

debaseth not his authority by contesting with him, but fairly, if he can, puts him away before his obstinacy hath infected others.

5. *He is moderate in inflicting deserved correction.* Many a schoolmaster better answereth the name paidotribes than paidogogos, rather tearing his scholars' flesh with whipping, than giving them good education. No wonder if his scholars hate the muses, being presented unto them in the shapes of fiends and furies. Junius complains *de insolenti carnificina* [1] of his schoolmaster, by whom *conscindebatur flagris septies aut octies in dies singulos.* [2] Yea, hear the lamentable verses of poor Tusser, in his own Life:

> From Paul's I went, to Eton sent,
> To learn straightways the Latin phrase,
> Where fifty-three stripes given to me
>   At once I had.
> For fault but small, or none at all,
> It came to pass thus beat I was;
> See, Udal, see the mercy of thee
>   To me, poor lad.

Such an Orbilius mars more scholars than he makes: their tyranny hath caused many tongues to stammer, which spake plain by nature, and whose stuttering at first was nothing else but fears quavering on their speech at their master's presence; and whose mauling them about their heads hath dulled those who in quickness exceeded their master.

6. *He makes his school free to him who sues to him in forma pauperis.* And surely learning is the greatest alms that can be given. But he is a beast who, because the poor scholar cannot pay him wages, pays the scholar in his whipping. Rather are diligent lads to be encouraged with all excitements to learning. This minds me of what I have heard concerning Mr. Bust, the worthy late schoolmaster of Eton, who would never suffer any wandering begging scholar, such as justly the statute hath ranked in the forefront of rogues, to come into his school, but would thrust him out with earnestness (however privately charitable unto him) lest his schoolboys should be disheartened from their books, by seeing some scholars, after their studying in the university, preferred to beggary.

7. *He spoils not a good school to make thereof a bad college,* therein to teach his scholars logic. For besides that logic may have an action of trespass against grammar for encroaching on her liberties, syllogisms are solecisms taught in the school, and oftentimes they are forced afterwards in the university to unlearn the fumbling skill they had before.

8. *Out of his school he is no whit pedantical in carriage or discourse;* contenting himself to be rich in Latin, though he doth not jingle with it in every company wherein he comes.

[1] Harsh brutality.
[2] He was scourged seven or eight times a day.

To conclude, let this amongst other motives make schoolmasters careful in their place, that the eminencies of their scholars have commended the memories of their schoolmasters to posterity, who otherwise in obscurity had altogether been forgotten. Who had ever heard of R. Bond in Lancashire, but for the breeding of learned Ascham his scholar; or of Hartgrave in Brundley school, in the same country, but because he was the first did teach worthy Dr. Whitaker? Nor do I honor the memory of Mulcaster for anything so much as for his scholar, that gulf of learning, Bishop Andrews. This made the Athenians, the day before the great feast of Theseus their founder, to sacrifice a ram to the memory of Conidas his schoolmaster that first instructed him.

The Bonds of Discipline

IAN HAY

IAN HAY (SIR JOHN HAY BEITH) was born in 1876 and educated at St. John's College, Cambridge. His first novel Pip *was written while he was a science master in a boys' school. He had become well known as a novelist by 1915, when he published* The First Hundred Thousand, *a war story written during the First World War while he was serving as Captain in the British Expeditionary Force.*

He has written twenty-seven novels and when not writing is busy defending his title as one of the three finest bow-shots in England. In The Lighter Side of School Life *and in* Housemaster *he writes of school life with delightful humor.*

THE power to impress one's fellow-creatures is one of the most elusive of human mysteries. Some people are born with it: they have only to walk on to a platform or a barrack-square, or into a classroom, and the meeting comes to order automatically. It has nothing to do with a man's personal appearance: some of the most insignificant creatures that ever breathed have been able to twist a crowd round their little fingers before now. Some of them are doing it to-day, with nations.

Few that are not born with the power ever achieve it. It can be done, of course, like everything else, by laborious persistence and an infinity of backbone: take Demosthenes, for instance. But in the main, no. You may be earnest, eloquent, shrewd, humorous—but the Thing, unless you are born with it, is not for you, and never will be.

The most effective, because the most effortless disciplinarian at Marbledown was the Headmaster himself—the Headpiece, as Mr. Beamish, in unconscious homage, had christened him. He was the most effective teacher too, though Mr. Donkin ran him a close second. But their methods differed as widely as rapier from bludgeon. The Head was all cold dignity, and clear, flawless exposition. Since his arrival at Marbledown he had organised the Sixth Form into a perfectly functioning machine for the acquisition of Open Scholarships.

Mr. Donkin's methods were less ornate.

"Keep boys in order," he said. "Kick them in the stomach if necessary.

"The Bonds of Discipline" is from *Housemaster* and is reprinted by permission of Houghton Mifflin Company.

Don't let them play the fool or go to sleep, and they'll be so bored at doing nothing that they'll work like beavers to pass the time!"

That was what Mr. Donkin. said. But there was more to his methods than that, as the Fifth Form could have told you—and as Mr. Ovington realised when Mr. Donkin's boys were promoted to the Sixth.

Other efficient disciplinarians on the Staff were Mr. Kent, who handled the Army Class like a well-ordered platoon—which was not altogether surprising, for he was an ex-Regular soldier; Mr. Beamish, whose Double Blue rendered homage among his small subjects of the First Form completely automatic; and that acid critic of other people's methods, Frank Hastings.

At the other end of the scale came the gentleman whom Master Bimbo had described as resembling a fourpenny rabbit—Philip de Pourville, the Junior Stinks Beak.

Mr. Ovington's predecessor, Dr. Adams, a ripe scholar and a deep but somewhat garrulous thinker, had once lamented at a Masters' Meeting the impossibility of procuring a Science master who was a gentleman. This *obiter dictum* had not gone too well with the scientists present, but it did express an undoubted truth—namely, that it is difficult to obtain a Science master anywhere who has been educated in the classical tradition; and to old-fashioned pedagogues of the Adams type a man with a mere Science degree, however superlative, can never attain to the same social plane as the public-school product who has scraped a Second or Third in Classical Moderations or Tripos.

And therefore when Philip de Pourville applied for the post of Junior Science Master of Marbledown, Dr. Adams appointed him on the spot, despite the claims of several highly qualified rivals, whose cardinal fault was that they had been educated at schools of which Dr. Adams had never heard. He had heard of de Pourville's school, however; in fact, he had once been a boy there himself. So de Pourville got the appointment over the heads of everybody else. It is not suggested that the appointment was in itself a bad one: de Pourville was the possessor of a perfectly adequate degree, and being an old public-school boy himself could fairly be expected to be familiar with the workings of that complex mystery known as public-school tradition.

For all that, he was Dr. Adams' last appointment; for not long afterwards the Governing Body, for reasons already stated, relegated that venerable diehard to a rural deanery, and installed Mr. Ovington in his stead.

Philip de Pourville had been at Marbledown for nearly two years now, and was gradually getting used to the place—as it is said that eels gradually get used to skinning. From which the acute reader will gather that he was not entirely enjoying his duties as Junior Science Master. And yet he could have enjoyed every moment of them if things had been just a little different. He knew his job, he was a natural teacher, and he was not afraid of drudgery. He had resigned his post as Assistant Demonstrator in his own College laboratory at Cambridge because he had not enough to do; because he felt himself a little too closely confined by the narrow, formal, and monastic life of a don. He wanted a wider horizon—a place where there was youth, movement, *joie de vivre*. He found all three at Marbledown.

The attitude of an English public-school boy to education is peculiar —you might call it paradoxical—but it is perfectly consistent. He says to his instructors, in effect:

"As a busily growing animal I am scatter-brained and entirely lacking in mental application. Having no desire at present to expend my precious energies upon the pursuit of knowledge, I shall not make the slightest attempt to assist you in your attempts to impart it. If you can capture my unwilling attention and goad me by stern measures into the requisite activity, I shall dislike you intensely, but I shall respect you. If you fail, I shall regard you with the contempt you deserve, and probably do my best, in a jolly, high-spirited way, to make your life a hell upon earth. And what could be fairer than that?" What indeed?

Unfortunately Philip de Pourville did not know this—or rather, he did not remember it as he should. He had been a studious boy in his own schooldays—an incorrigible "groise," to employ the technical expression— with a passionate interest in Natural Science, of which in the classical strongholds of this country little is known either by boys or masters, except that you can take it as an alternative to Latin Verse.

But Philip honestly worshipped this despised branch of learning, and desired earnestly to raise its status and improve its teaching in the great schools of England. The next age was going to be the Age of Science; the Classics were dying on their feet; and unless the public schools were awakened to the fact, they would soon be dying on their feet too. So you can imagine something of the raptness and the vision which Philip took with him on this, his great Crusade. (Button had not been far out.)

And then, at the very dawn of battle, on the very threshold of adventure, he discovered that he had overlooked something—a liability—a hundred-per-cent. liability.

He could not keep boys in order.

II

The middle hour of morning school normally ended at noon, but the School clock still wanted ten minutes to the hour when Philip de Pourville left the Laboratory Block at the double, preceded by a yelling horde of light-hearted young scientists, and pursued by the fumes of the three smelliest gases known to inorganic chemistry.

His flock on this occasion were the Senior Moderns—as tough a collection of scholastic lambs as ever broke the heart of a young and apolo-

getic shepherd—who had been undergoing nominally an hour's instruction in practical chemistry. The reason of their premature disbandment
will appear later.

Their appointed task on this particular morning had been a fairly
simple problem in qualitative analysis. De Pourville had issued each boy
with a small quantity of sodium sulphate, and had bidden him, by the
exercise of his wits and what chemical learning he possessed, to find
out what it was.

But practical chemistry is a difficult subject to supervise, even if the
practical chemists take their task seriously, which the Senior Moderns
were very far from doing. To be just, a laboratory offers infinite distrac-
tions from the path of rectitude. The class are scattered over a considerable area, and it is quite impossible to watch them all at once.
They are surrounded by bottles containing liquids, and jars containing
solids which, if surreptitiously mixed together in a beaker or test-tube
and submitted to the influence of a Bunsen burner, can frequently be
stimulated into some interesting reaction, of an odoriferous or, with luck,
explosive character. Against such attractions as these routine tests of
the constituents of a solution of sodium sulphate have little chance.

Moreover, it is almost impossible to prevent conversation, usually of
an entirely untechnical character. In other words, the laboratory
hummed with cheerful chat, punctuated by minor explosions and con-
flagrations.

However, Philip started conscientiously upon his round.

Having frustrated, with mild reproof, two of his younger disciples
in an attempt to prepare a sample of nitroglycerine—by the simple
expedient of shaking up some glycerine and nitric acid together, like
a cocktail, in a test-tube—he came round the corner of a bench just in
time to detect one Pop Ogilvie in the act of pouring mercury from the
laboratory jar into a small bottle, apparently Pop's own private property.
Uncomfortably accepting the explanation that Pop required the mercury
for the construction of a home-made barometer, to be set up in his House
study, Philip passed on, and presently arrived at the remotest and least
supervisable end of the laboratory, popularly known as Bolshie Corner.
Here were gathered Goat Hicks, of the Red House, already mentioned in
this narrative, and his two particular cronies, Oily Boyd, a sycophant, and
Mug Pollard, a humorist. The trio might without disrespect or inaccuracy
have been labelled Public Enemies Number One, Two, and Three, of
anything in the shape of ordered progress in the Senior Moderns.

Philip bade them a nervous good morning.

"Morning," replied Goat. "What's this muck that you've served out to
us this time?" Goat was in the habit of addressing Mr. de Pourville in exactly the same terms as he employed toward Sam, the unkempt youth
who cleaned up the laboratory: it all expressed his impartial contempt for
Science in general.

"That is for you to find out, Hicks."

"How am I supposed to start?"

"Swallow it, and see if it poisons you," suggested Mug Pollard, the humorist. "Give it a chance, anyhow."

There was laughter at this, in which de Pourville feebly joined. He enjoyed a joke as well as anybody, he told himself. Then he replied:

"Ascertain if it is soluble in water. Test it with litmus for an acid reaction. Bubble some sulphuretted hydrogen through. You will find an apparatus in the draught-cupboard."

"Is that the stuff that stinks like rotten eggs?"

"That is the characteristic odour."

"The bigger the Egg the bigger the stink, I suppose," said Pollard—and Oily Boyd sniggered offensively. De Pourville grasped the obvious allusion, but decided to ignore it. Schoolboys cherish the curious belief, he assured himself, that masters never know their own nicknames, or one another's.

"What's the stuff with the rotten-cabbage smell?" continued Hicks.

"I expect you mean carbon disulphide."

"I expect so too. How do you make it?"

"In various ways. For purposes of simple demonstration I should heat some fragments of charcoal to redness, and pass sulphur vapour over them. Now you had better be getting on with your present experiment."

He turned to go, but Pollard nudged Hicks and winked at Boyd.

"Isn't there a worse stink still, sir?" asked Hicks, in what was clearly meant to be a conciliatory voice. "It's fearfully interesting to hear these things from you. You make them so clear."

De Pourville, a little taken aback by this unexpected testimonial, replied that Mr. Pollard was probably referring to phosphoretted hydrogen, which was released when fragments of phosphorus were boiled in a concentrated solution of caustic potash. It had a characteristic odour of decaying fish.

"Now I really must get on," he said, and passed down the other side of the bench. Here he encountered a tall, fair-haired boy, mainly distinguished by a good-tempered smile and a lazy drawl. He was engaged in wiping down his next-door neighbour's face with his pocket-handkerchief.

"First aid for a too-adventurous research student, sir," he explained. "No harm done, except to the features, and they have been beyond hope since birth."

De Pourville liked this boy, one Nightingale. He could hardly be regarded as an earnest seeker after knowledge, but he never gave trouble, and his easy familiarity was entirely devoid of offence.

"Thank you, Nightingale," he said. "What have you been doing to yourself, Walpole?" he asked the recipient of first aid.

"I was trying a test, sir, and the thing blew up in my——"

"The premature ebullition," Nightingale explained, "of the contents of a test-tube. Due to childish inability to distinguish between the respective properties of dilute and concentrated HCl," he added. "Isn't the atmosphere in here getting a bit oppressive, sir?"

He hastily transferred his handkerchief from Walpole's features to his own nose.

De Pourville's more expert organ analysed the situation in a moment. He turned instinctively in the direction of Bolshie Corner; but before he could speak or move the air was rent by coughings and chokings from all sides, accompanied by imprecations as pungent as the combined odours of rotten eggs, rotten cabbage, and rotten fish which now assailed his senses.

Next moment there was a general stampede, headed by the authors of the outrage. The Junior Science Master, like Xenophon, "accompanied the rear-guard."

"I suppose we needn't go back, sir?" demanded his pupils, thronging round him in the quadrangle outside. "I mean to say—without gas-masks —well——!"

Philip glanced up towards the School clock, on its tower. It marked ten minutes to twelve.

"Very well," he said. "Go to your Houses, and make as little noise as possible. We don't want to disturb the—others, do we?"

The Senior Modern promptly dispersed in joyous disorder. Philip, who was not due in school again until afternoon, sighed, took a nervous glance in the direction of the adjacent Sixth Form windows, mounted his bicycle, and pedalled off down the hill in the direction of the stone bridge and Marbledown Market Place, where his lodgings were situated. As already noted, he was, thanks to the successful collaboration of Messrs. Hicks, Pollard, and Boyd, some ten minutes before his normal time.

In all this that unpleasant trio were the instruments of an inscrutable Providence, as you shall see.

The Arts of Teaching and Being Taught

MARK VAN DOREN

*MARK VAN DOREN was born in Illinois in 1894. In 1914 he was gradu-
ated from the University of Illinois, and after taking an M. A. at the same
university, left the midwest to study at Columbia. In 1920 he received his
Ph.D. from Columbia and became a member of the English Department
there. Since then through his writing and through his participation in the
radio program* Invitation to Learning *he has exercised a wide influence
upon American thinking.*

*Van Doren is a versatile writer. Well known as a novelist, he is also a
poet and critic. He has written critical studies of Thoreau, Dryden, and
Shakespeare. His* Collected Poems *won the Pulitzer Prize in 1940.*

THE Liberal arts have been said by Mortimer Adler to be "nothing
but the arts of teaching and being taught." If teaching and studying
are imagined on their highest level, and if it is understood that great books
as well as men may qualify as teachers, the definition is not oversimplified.
The great books are necessary. So, however, are the men; and it is always
important that men should think it honorable to be teachers. When the
profession is apologetic, society is not sound. "Whom the gods hate they
make schoolmasters," said Lucian. But that is true only if the gods hate
men. For the gods know, even if we do not, that man is in a special sense
the teachable animal. When dogs and monkeys are taught, the aim is to
make them resemble another species, usually man. But men must be
taught to resemble themselves. Only by education can they be said to
become the kind of animal they are.

The responsibility of the teacher is so great that a full vision of it can
be crushing. He has persons in his charge. The fact should sober him; but
he hears in addition that he is responsible for the entire society which
these persons represent. The size of the assignment suggests that only
madmen would dare to accept it, and that such is the meaning of Lucian's sentence. But it is not as serious as all that. The teacher needs only
to remember that he is neither deity nor engine; he is a man, and in proportion as he succeeds at his calling he will be surrounded by more men.
He and they are society.

The liberal education that has been described in the foregoing pages, and not only described but recommended for all, needs more good teachers than now exist. The requisite number must exist, even if it takes a thousand years to produce them—that is, to educate them. They will need to have better habits than most teachers today even pretend to have. But that will never be unless some teachers in our time consent to change their own habits; the race to come must have its ancestors.

The first habit to be changed is that of assuming that all one needs to know is one's own subject. In any college a given teacher will be biased toward some form of knowledge that agrees with his nature; indeed, unless he loves particular truths he cannot make his students love truth at all. But in a good college he will unite this love with a sense of what every student is there for: the common understanding which men need. He will try to know his colleagues as well as himself; and he will believe as they do in the single, central task of the institution. This is to produce a world whose citizens know the same things, and the indispensable things; and this without the regimentation which the anarchy of our present system threatens.

Good teachers have always been and will always be, and there are good teachers now. The necessity henceforth is that fewer of them be accidents. The area of accident is reduced when there is a design which includes the education of teachers. Not the training—a contemporary term that suggests lubricating oil and precision parts, not to say reflexes and responses. The design is less for institutions that turn out teachers than for a whole view of education that sees them as being naturally made when they teach themselves, with the help of one another and their students.

"It makes no difference to me," said Comenius, "whether I teach or am taught." If Socrates was the perfect teacher, the reason is that he was the perfect student. His suspicion of the Sophists was based upon the fact that their primary desire was not to learn. They preferred to lecture, and their capital was catchwords which they used over and over again, with no warning to the listener that the meanings had shifted. The teacher learns by teaching, which is the highest form of study. The more wisdom he shares, the more he keeps; for wisdom is shared when we ask real questions, and when we want answers no matter what the source, be it ourselves or others, be it old or young, be it one in authority or the most insignificant subordinate.

Such a teacher creates in a sense his own school. "Happy the natural college," says Emerson, "thus self-instituted around every natural teacher." There is no substitute for the natural teacher, and no formula whereby he may be made. But his kind is more numerous in certain situations than in others, and the best hope for education is a landscape of learning in which he will belong. When men seriously want to be educated, says Newman "when they aim at something precise, something refined, something really luminous, something really large, something choice, they avail themselves, in some shape or other, of the ancient method of oral instruction, of present communication between man and man, of teachers instead of teaching, of the personal influence of a master, and the humble initiation of a disciple. . . . If we wish to become exact and fully furnished in any subject of teaching which is diversified and complicated, we must consult the living man and listen to his living voice. . . . The general principles of any study you may learn by books at home; but the detail, the color, the time, the air, the life which makes it live in us, you must catch all these from those in whom it lives already."

This is the right doctrine, despite the fact that indolent and eccentric men have taken advantage of it. Unique individual charm is not the final virtue of a teacher. The charm should be personal, meaning that the thought behind it should be better than other thought, not merely different. The most personal thing about Socrates was not his nose or his voice but his love of wisdom. "He who thinks," the friend of Phaedrus said under the plane tree, "that only in principles of justice and the goodness and nobility taught and communicated orally for the sake of instruction and graven in the soul is there clearness and perfection and seriousness—this is the right sort of man." The desire of the true teacher is not to triumph but to teach, and in teaching to learn. The teacher without charm is negligible, but the teacher without anything else is contemptible; and he is most contemptible when he courts applause. The good college is the natural college in so far as it is a place where the personal wisdom of older men, grounded deeply enough in the great tradition to be free wisdom, modifies younger men. But the art of education can assist nature here, as art always assists nature, by providing more opportunity than exists for colleges to be what they can.

The good teacher is a man whose conversation is never finished, partly because it is about real things and so cannot be finished, but partly because there is always a new audience, which itself takes part. The student in learning teaches himself and his teacher. How he learns remains something of a mystery, for there is an artist in him, the teachable man, who has his own devices and proceeds to his own conclusions. The art of being taught is the art of letting the nature of learning take its course. It is a course which the teacher can free from many obstacles, and to which he can give formal aid; but he does not invent it any more than the student does. The student does not decide to have the mind with which he educates himself. He uses the one he has, both for the things that can be taught him and for those he must possess through his own effort, or according to his own desire; for just as the good teacher loves some particular knowledge more than any other, so the good student will range beyond the prescriptions of the curriculum, reading what his genius pleases in addition to what his nature requires.

The teacher will encourage these excursions. "Who is so stupidly curious as to send his son to school in order that he may learn what the teacher thinks?" This question of St. Augustine's will be remembered by a good teacher whenever he is tempted to suppress some novelty in a student's thought. It may or may not lead to knowledge, but if it is the student's own discovery it has a present importance which had better not be doubted. There is a skill in instruction, but St. Thomas Aquinas has pointed out that there is also a skill in discovery, and it is our own discoveries that best persuade us. The art of being taught is the art of discovery, as the art of teaching is the art of assisting discovery to take place.

Discovery can take place only if the relation between the teacher and the student is one of mutual respect. It is especially important that the teacher should respect the student, and it will be easy for him to do so if he assumes that the student is someone from who he may learn. Then it will be the discovery that is mutual, though courtesy in the teacher will exaggerate this. The teacher is courteous because he is respectful, and because that is the way in which courtesy is taught. But his respect is for the subject too, which means that although he loves the student he is sometimes obligated to be severe. The teacher is kind, but to someone he is training to forget him. "My son is coming to do without me," wrote Emerson in his Journal. "And I am coming to do without Plato." The good teacher disappears out of the student's life as Virgil and Beatrice disappear out of *The Divine Comedy*. They are remembered as persons, and so is every good teacher remembered; but when the student has found his own way in the world he cannot recall how much of his wisdom he owes to another. It is his now, and that is what his teacher had intended.

The teacher who desires evidence that his students are interested should also ask for evidence that they are disinterested—that they understand what he is saying. For if they understand him they are sharing with him the experience of thought, which is not an individual experience. The true teacher is singularly innocent of ambition to be praised, loved, or remembered. He is, in fact, the best secular image of the innocent man. And the student respects no other man, least of all one who is crafty or worldly. He will see plenty of worldly men in his time, and their craft will surpass that of any mistaken teacher. It is only in the long run that the innocent man turns out to have been right. The last things learned will agree with him, and then perhaps he will be remembered. But across the "labyrinth of the world," as Comenius puts it, the student and the teacher will share in silence that "paradise of the heart" where agreement is more than a matter of debit and credit.

The teacher, of course, must have authority over the student before he can be respected in the way the student wants to respect him. But authority comes naturally with knowledge that is lucid as the liberal arts make knowledge lucid. The teacher who is not a liberal artist may indoctrinate or charm, but he will not teach. Indoctrination makes the teacher's thought prevail, but teaching is less a matter of what either the teacher or the student thinks than of what the mind itself, the third person, decides and says. The teacher will conceal none of his authority, for he is democrat enough to know that its purpose is to strengthen the student against the time when he will have to choose between accepting and rejecting it. Authority exists only to be denied by better authority; its best act is to destroy itself. The teacher is successful at the moment when his student becomes original. He must be "a kind of fate to his pupil," says Lane Cooper, "and at the same time must bestow upon him the supreme good gift of free will. . . . The original sin of the individual must be scourged and purged away; his original goodness must be cherished and encouraged." If this imputes a kind of divinity to the teacher, that is precisely what some students do. They are wrong, and every teacher knows it; but the good teacher is able to interpret and forgive the blasphemy, meanwhile letting the shadow it casts upon him measure the depth of his duty.

The education of teachers is an education in the liberal arts. When this education is good, and falls on the right ground, it produces persons with usable intellects and imaginations who know both what and why they are teaching. A teacher who can answer neither of those questions is no teacher, for thus he proves himself incapable of the one pleasure reserved for him among the pleasures possible to man: the pleasure of being intelligible. Human communication, so difficult and so rare, is his professed assignment, and at the moment in his students' lives when such success as is achieved will count forever. It will count in their understanding, and so in their happiness. It will also count, by making them more communicative themselves, in the happiness of mankind.

One kind of contemporary teacher lacks the courage of his authority, which he misconceives as authority is commonly misconceived. He thinks it is power. But power has no authority in the region of intellect and morals. Authority there is excellence in knowledge and art; and excellence in such things has indeed a special power which only the initiated know. The special power of the teacher is revealed in the competence of his search for the fundamental questions to be asked—questions fundamental enough to engage all men, so that argument can be reventilated and revived.

The search for such questions, when it does go on today, is often mistaken for its opposite. The search is itself an argument, but it is accused of a desire to stop argument forever. Curiosity about initial questions is confused with propaganda for final answers. The tolerance we practice in matters of opinion is the tolerance not of hope but of despair, as a recent distinction has it. We do not trust argument unless it is aimless—without, in other words, the background of an agreement that the purpose of it is the discovery of truth. We do not trust truth, which we identify only with those who have told lies in its name. Truth is remote, but not to care how remote it is puts one in Dante's dark circle of those who lived without blame and without praise, but were for themselves; who from cowardice made the great refusal; who lost the good of the intellect, and so were never alive.

"To be indifferent which of two opinions is true," says John Locke in language very different from Dante's, "is the right temper of the mind that preserves it from being imposed on, and disposes it to examine with that indifferency till it has done its best to find the truth. But to be indifferent whether we embrace falsehood or truth is the great road to error." All opinions are to be tolerated for what they are worth, but the person today who endeavors to compare opinions by applying a scale of worth is seldom tolerated. His scale may be wrong, but that is not why he is criticized. There is no common search for a right scale that would make such criticism possible. The open mind is one which has begun to think, but we act as if it were one which had stopped doing so because thought can be serious and dangerous, and because it is hard work. We do not doubt well. The good doubter doubts something; we dismiss everything. One sign of this is that we think it beneath our dignity to agree—the typical professor takes no position, either his own or any other's. He calls this tolerance, and does not seem to mind that it is tolerance of bad thinking as well as good. Perhaps Locke has explained why there is so much of it today. Cynicism paralyzes argument.

The last generation of students may never forgive its teachers who taught contempt and fear of truth. The distinction they made was the one between fact and opinion, not the one between opinion and truth. The difference itself is a fact, to be ignorant of which is neither to be armed against opinion nor to have one's own. The immediate danger is that we shall have a riot of ill-considered slogans. "Respect for the truth is an acquired taste," and the recovery of it may take a long time, for it involves an understanding that freedom has its own compulsions, and it requires a discipline in the adjustment of thought to thought which only the liberal arts can teach. To say that truth is better than falsehood is not to speak vaguely. It is more powerful, it is more interesting, and it is less lonely. "There is but one world in common for those who are awake," said Heraclitus, "but when men are asleep each turns away into a world of his own." It is the love of truth that makes men free in the common light of day.

The Education of a Saint

ST. AUGUSTINE

ST. AUGUSTINE, one of the great Fathers of the Latin Church, was born in 354 of a pagan father and a Christian mother. In spite of his mother's training, the boy grew up without an interest in Christian principles. His youth was wayward. Early in life he formed an irregular union and became the father of a son. Yet in spite of youthful aberrations, Augustine was an earnest student and set out to prepare himself for the career of a rhetorician. His study of Greek and Latin led him to a search for truth. This quest resulted first in his becoming a Manichaean, but later he fell under the influence of Ambrose, Bishop of Milan, and was converted to Christianity. In the course of time he became Bishop of Hippo and from then until his death in 430 spent his time in ecclesiastical labors.

His principal writings are the City of God *and his* Confessions.

Concerning the Hatred of Learning, the Love of Play, and the Fear of Being Whipped Noticeable in Boys: and of the Folly of Our Elders and Masters.

O MY God! what miseries and mockeries did I then experience, when obedience to my teachers was set before me as proper to my boyhood, that I might flourish in this world, and distinguish myself in the science of speech, which should get me honour amongst men, and deceitful riches! After that I was put to school to get learning of which I (worthless as I was) knew not what use there was; and yet, if slow to learn, I was flogged! For this was deemed praiseworthy by our forefathers; and many before us passing the same course, had appointed beforehand for us these troublesome ways by which we were compelled to pass, multiplying labour and sorrow upon the sons of Adam. But we found, O Lord, men praying to Thee, and we learned from them to conceive of Thee, according to our ability, to be some Great One, who was able (though not visible to our senses) to hear and help us. For as a boy I began to pray to Thee, my "help" and my "refuge," and in invoking Thee broke the bands of my tongue, and entreated Thee though little, with no little earnestness, that I might not be beaten at school. And when Thou heardest me not, giving me not over to folly thereby, my elders, yea, and my own parents too, who wished me no ill, laughed at my stripes, my then great and grievous ill.

Is there any one, Lord, with so high a spirit, cleaving to Thee with so strong an affection—for even a kind of obtuseness may do that much—but is there, I say, any one who, by cleaving devoutly to Thee, is endowed with so great a courage that he can esteem lightly those racks and hooks, and varied tortures of the same sort, against which, throughout the whole world, men supplicate Thee with great fear, deriding those who most bitterly fear them, just as our parents derided the torments with which our masters punished us when we were boys? For we were no less afraid of our pains, nor did we pray less to Thee to avoid them; and yet we sinned, in writing, or reading, or reflecting upon our lessons less than was required of us. For we wanted not, O Lord, memory or capacity,—of which, by Thy will, we possessed enough for our age,—but we delighted only in play; and we were punished for this by those who were doing the same things themselves. But the idleness of our elders they call business, whilst boys who do the like are punished by those same elders, and yet neither boys nor men find any pity. For will any one of good sense approve of my being whipped because, as a boy, I played ball, and so was hindered from learning quickly those lessons by means of which, as a man, I should play more unbecomingly? And did he by whom I was beaten do other than this, who, when he was overcome in any little controversy with a co-tutor, was more tormented by anger and envy than I when beaten by a playfellow in a match at ball?

Through a Love of Ball-playing and Shows, He Neglects His Studies and the Injunctions of His Parents.

And yet I erred, O Lord God, the Creator and Disposer of all things in Nature,—but of sin the Disposer only,—I erred, O Lord my God, in doing contrary to the wishes of my parents and of those masters; for this learning which they (no matter for what motive) wished me to acquire, I might have put to good account afterwards. For I disobeyed them not because I had chosen a better way, but from a fondness for play, loving the honour of victory in the matches and to have my ears tickled with lying fables, in order that they might itch the more furiously—the same curiosity beaming more and more in my eyes for the shows and sports of my elders. Yet those who give these entertainments are held in such high repute, that almost all desire the same for their children, whom they are still willing should be beaten, if so be these same games keep them from the studies by which they desire them to arrive at being the givers of them. Look down upon these things, O Lord, with compassion, and deliver us who now call upon Thee; deliver those also who do not call upon Thee, that they may call upon Thee, and that Thou mayest deliver them.

Being Compelled, He Gave His Attention to Learning, But Fully
Acknowledges That This Was the Work of God.

But in this my childhood (which was far less dreaded for me than
youth) I had no love of learning, and hated to be forced to it, yet was I
forced to it notwithstanding; and this was well done towards me, but I
did not well, for I would not have learned had I not been compelled. For
no man doth well against his will, even if that which he doth be well.
Neither did they who forced me do well, but the good that was done to
me came from Thee, my God. For they considered not in what way I
should employ what they forced me to learn, unless to satisfy the inordinate desires of a rich beggary and a shameful glory. But Thou, by whom
the very hairs of our heads are numbered, didst use for my good the error
of all who pressed me to learn; and my own error in willing not to learn,
didst Thou make use of for my punishment—of which I, being so small a
boy and so great a sinner, was not unworthy. Thus by the instrumentality
of those who did not well didst Thou well for me; and by my own sin
didst Thou justly punish me. For it is even as Thou has appointed, that
every inordinate affection should bring its own punishment.

He Delighted in Latin Studies, and the Empty Fables of the Poets,
But Hated the Elements of Literature and the Greek Language.

But what was the cause of my dislike of Greek literature, which I
studied from my boyhood, I cannot even now understand. For the Latin I
loved exceedingly—not what our first masters, but what the grammarians
teach; for those primary lessons of reading, writing, and ciphering, I considered no less of a burden and a punishment than Greek. Yet whence was
this unless from the sin and vanity of this life? for I was "but flesh, a wind
that passeth away and cometh not again." For those primary lessons were
better, assuredly, because more certain; seeing that by their agency I
acquired, and still retain, the power of reading what I find written, and
writing myself what I will; whilst in the others I was compelled to learn
about the wanderings of a certain Aeneas, oblivious of my own, and to
weep for Dido dead, because she slew herself for love; while at the same
time I brooked with dry eyes my wretched self dying far from Thee, in
the midst of those things, O God, my life.

For what can be more wretched than the wretch who pities not himself
shedding tears over the death of Dido for love of Aeneas, but shedding no
tears over his own death in not loving Thee, O God, light of my heart, and
bread of the inner mouth of my soul, and the power that weddest my
mind with my innermost thoughts? I did not love Thee, and committed
fornication against Thee; and those around me thus sinning cried, "Well
done! Well done!" For the friendship of this world is fornication against

Thee; and "Well done! Well done!" is cried until one feels ashamed not to be such a man. And for this I shed no tears, though I wept for Dido, who sought death at the sword's point, myself the while seeking the lowest of Thy creatures—having forsaken Thee—earth tending to the earth; and if forbidden to read these things, how grieved would I feel that I was not permitted to read what grieved me. This sort of madness is considered a more honourable and more fruitful learning than that by which I learned to read and write.

But now, O my God, cry unto my soul; and let Thy Truth say unto me, "It is not so, it is not so; better much was that first teaching." For behold, I would rather forget the wanderings of Aeneas, and all such things, than how to write and read. But it is true that over the entrance of the grammar school there hangs a veil; but this is not so much a sign of the majesty of the mystery, as of a covering for error. Let not them exclaim against me of whom I am no longer in fear, whilst I confess to Thee, my God, that which my soul desires, and acquiesce in reprehending my evil ways, that I may love Thy good ways. Neither let those cry out against me who buy or sell grammar-learnings. For if I ask them whether it be true, as the poet says, that Aeneas once came to Carthage, the unlearned will reply that they do not know, the learned will deny it to be true. But if I ask with what letters the name Aeneas is written, all who have learnt this will answer truly, in accordance with the conventional understanding men have arrived at as to these signs. Again, if I should ask which, if forgotten, would cause the greatest inconvenience in our life, reading and writing, or these poetical fictions, who does not see what every one would answer who had not entirely forgotten himself? I erred, then, when as a boy I preferred those vain studies to those more profitable ones, or rather loved the one and hated the other. "One and one are two, two and two are four," this was then in truth a hateful song to me; while the wooden horse full of armed men, and the burning of Troy, and the "spectral image" of Creusa were a most pleasant spectacle of vanity.

Why He Despised Greek Literature, and Easily Learned Latin.

But why, then, did I dislike Greek learning, which was full of like tales? For Homer also was skilled in inventing similar stories, and is most sweetly vain, yet was he disagreeable to me as a boy. I believe Virgil, indeed, would be the same to Grecian children, if compelled to learn him, as I was Homer. The difficulty, in truth, the difficulty of learning a foreign language mingled as it were with gall all the sweetness of those fabulous Grecian stories. For not a single word of it did I understand, and to make me do so, they vehemently urged me with cruel threatenings and punishments. There was a time also when (as an infant) I knew no Latin; but this I acquired without any fear or tormenting, by merely taking notice, amid the blandishments of my nurses, the jests of those who smiled on me, and the sportiveness of those who toyed with me. I learnt all this, indeed, without being urged by any pressure of punishment, for my own heart urged me to bring forth its own conceptions, which I could not do unless by learning words, not of those who taught me, but of those who talked to me; into whose ears, also, I brought forth whatever I discerned. From this it is sufficiently clear that a free curiosity hath more influence in our learning these things than a necessity full of fear. But this last restrains the overflowings of that freedom, through Thy laws, O God,— Thy laws, from the ferule of the schoolmaster to the trials of the martyr, being effective to mingle for us a salutary bitter, calling us back to Thyself from the pernicious delights which allure us from Thee.

He Continues on the Unhappy Method of Training Youth in Literary Subjects.

Bear with me, my God, while I speak a little of those talents Thou has bestowed upon me, and on what follies I wasted them. For a lesson sufficiently disquieting to my soul was given me, in hope of praise, and fear of shame or stripes, to speak the words of Juno, as she raged and sorrowed that she could not

> "Latium bar
> From all approaches of the Dardan king,"

which I had heard Juno never uttered. Yet were we compelled to stray in the footsteps of these poetic fictions, and to turn that into prose which the poet had said in verse. And his speaking was most applauded in whom, according to the reputation of the persons delineated, the passions of anger and sorrow were most strikingly reproduced, and clothed in the most suitable language. But what is it to me, O my true Life, my God, that my declaiming was applauded above that of many who were my contemporaries and fellow-students? Behold is not all this smoke and wind? Was there nothing else, too, on which I could exercise my wit and tongue? Thy praise, Lord, Thy praises might have supported the tendrils of my heart by Thy Scriptures; so had it not been dragged away by these empty trifles, a shameful prey of the fowls of the air. For there is more than one way in which men sacrifice to the fallen angels.

Dante Meets the Spirit of Virgil, His Guide and Teacher

DANTE ALIGHIERI

DANTE ALIGHIERI (1265-1321), Italian poet, was born probably at Florence. Though the details of his life are obscure, we know that he joined the party of the Bianchi, attained the municipal office of prior, and incurred the displeasure of the Pope. He fled from Florence in 1301, was for a time in Paris, and died in Ravenna.

The Divina Commedia, *his greatest work, comprises the* Inferno, *the* Purgatorio, *and the* Paradiso. *The following selection from the* Inferno *is in the translation of Henry W. Longfellow.*

Mɪᴅᴡᴀʏ upon the journey of our life
    I found myself within a forest dark,
    For the straightforward pathway had been lost.
Ah me! how hard a thing it is to say
    What was this forest savage, rough, and stern,
    Which in the very thought renews the fear.
So bitter is it, death is little more;
    But of the good to treat, which there I found,
    Speak will I of the other things I saw there.
I cannot well repeat how there I entered,
    So full was I of slumber at the moment
    In which I had abandoned the true way.
But after I had reached a mountain's foot,
    At that point where the valley terminated,
    Which had with consternation pierced my heart,
Upward I looked, and I beheld its shoulders,
    Vested already with that planet's rays
    Which leadeth others right by every road.
Then was the fear a little quieted
    That in my heart's lake had endured throughout
    The night, which I had passed so piteously.
And even as he, who, with distressful breath,
    Forth issued from the sea upon the shore,
    Turns to the water perilous and gazes;

So did my soul, that still was fleeing onward,
    Turn itself back to re-behold the pass
    Which never yet a living person left.
After my weary body I had rested,
    The way resumed I on the desert slope,
    So that the firm foot ever was the lower.
And lo! almost where the ascent began,
    A panther light and swift exceedingly,
    Which with a spotted skin was covered o'er!
And never moved she from before my face,
    Nay, rather did impede so much my way,
    That many times I to return had turned.
The time was the beginning of the morning,
    And up the sun was mounting with those stars
    That with him were, what time the Love Divine
At first in motion set those beauteous things;
    So were to me occasion of good hope,
    The variegated skin of that wild beast,
The hour of time, and the delicious season;
    But not so much, that did not give me fear
    A lion's aspect which appeared to me.
He seemed as if against me he were coming
    With head uplifted, and with ravenous hunger,
    So that it seemed the air was afraid of him;
And a she-wolf, that with all hungerings
    Seemed to be laden in her meagreness,
    And many folk has caused to live forlorn!
She brought upon me so much heaviness,
    With the affright that from her aspect came,
    That I the hope relinquished of the height.
And as he is who willingly acquires,
    And the time comes that causes him to lose,
    Who weeps in all his thoughts and is despondent,
E'en such made me that beast withouten peace,
    Which, coming on against me by degrees
    Thrust me back thither where the sun is silent.
While I was rushing downward to the lowland,
    Before mine eyes did one present himself,
    Who seemed from long-continued silence hoarse.
When I beheld him in the desert vast,
    "Have pity on me," unto him I cried,
    "Whiche'er thou art, or shade or real man!"
He answered me: "Not man; man once I was,
    And both my parents were of Lombardy,
    And Mantuans by country both of them.

Sub Julio was I born, though it was late,
 And lived at Rome under the good Augustus,
 During the time of false and lying gods.
A poet was I, and I sang that just
 Son of Anchises, who came forth from Troy,
 After that Ilion the superb was burned.
But thou, why goest thou back to such annoyance?
 Why climb'st thou not the Mount Delectable,
 Which is the source and cause of every joy?"
"Now, art thou that Virgilius and that fountain
 Which spreads abroad so wide a river of speech?"
 I made response to him with bashful forehead.
"O, of the other poets honour and light,
 Avail me the long study and great love
 That have impelled me to explore thy volume!
Thou art my master, and my author thou,
 Thou art alone the one from whom I took
 The beautiful style that has done honour to me.
Behold the beast, for which I have turned back;
 Do thou protect me from her, famous Sage,
 For she doth make my veins and pulses tremble."
"Thee it behoves to take another road,"
 Responded he, when he beheld me weeping,
 "If from this savage place thou wouldst escape;
Because this beast, at which thou criest out,
 Suffers not any one to pass her way,
 But so doth harass him, that she destroys him;
And has a nature so malign and ruthless,
 That never doth she glut her greedy will,
 And after food is hungrier than before.

   .   .   .

Therefore I think and judge it for thy best
 Thou follow me, and I will be thy guide,
 And lead thee hence through the eternal place,
Where thou shalt hear the desperate lamentations,
 Shalt see the ancient spirits disconsolate,
 Who cry out each one for the second death;
And thou shalt see those who contented are
 Within the fire, because they hope to come,
 Whene'er it may be, to the blessed people;
To whom, then, if thou wishest to ascend,
 A soul shall be for that than I more worthy;
 With her at my departure I will leave thee;

Because that Emperor, who reigns above,
  In that I was rebellious to his law,
  Wills that through me none come into his city.
He governs everywhere, and there he reigns;
  There is his city and his lofty throne;
  O happy he whom thereto he elects!"
And I to him: "Poet, I thee entreat,
  By that same God whom thou didst never know,
  So that I may escape this woe and worse,
Thou wouldst conduct me there where thou hast said,
  That I may see the portal of Saint Peter,
  And those thou makest so disconsolate."
Then he moved on, and I behind him followed.

Site of a University

JOHN HENRY NEWMAN

JOHN HENRY NEWMAN (1801-1890), received his B. A. degree from Trinity College, Oxford, in 1820. Two years later he was elected fellow of Oriel College along with Edward Pusey, who later became with Newman a leader of the Oxford Movement. Following his ordination in 1824, Newman became curate of St. Clement's Church, Oxford. In 1826 he became tutor of Oriel College, a position which he held until 1832, when increasing disagreement with the provost forced him to resign his tutorship. In the same year he traveled in the south of Europe, visiting Naples and Rome. It was during his European travel while crossing from Palermo to Marseilles that he wrote his best-known verses, "Lead, kindly light." On his return to England he began writing Tracts for the Times. *These tracts and his four o'clock sermons at St. Mary's, Oxford, were in large measure responsible for the Oxford Movement.*

Gradually Newman became aware of his profound dissatisfaction with the Anglican Church. This dissatisfaction led him in 1843 to resign the living of St. Mary's and in 1845 to join the Church of Rome. In the following year he was ordained priest in the Roman Church, and in 1879 he was created cardinal.

The Site of a University *is taken from the* Rise and Progress of Universities, *a series of papers published in Dublin in 1854 while Newman was rector of the new Catholic University of that city.*

The two other selections are found in The Idea of a University Defined. *Newman believed that the chief function of a university is instruction rather than research. He firmly believed that a liberal education is essential to fit men for the best kind of life.*

IF we would know what a University is, considered in its elementary idea, we must betake ourselves to the first and most celebrated home of European literature and source of European civilization, to the bright and beautiful Athens,—Athens, whose schools drew to her bosom, and then sent back again to the business of life, the youth of the Western World for a long thousand years. Seated on the verge of the continent, the city seemed hardly suited for the duties of a central metropolis of knowledge; yet, what it lost in convenience of approach, it gained in its neighbourhood to the traditions of the mysterious East, and in the loveliness of the region in which it lay. Hither, then, as to a sort of ideal land, where all archetypes of the great and the fair were found in substantial being, and all departments of truth explored, and all diversities of intellectual power exhibited, where taste and philosophy were majestically enthroned as in a royal court, where there was no sovereignty but that of mind, and no nobility but that of genius, where professors were rulers, and princes did homage, hither flocked continually from the very corners of the *orbis terrarum*, the many-tongued generation, just rising, or just risen into manhood, in order to gain wisdom.

Pisistratus had in an early age discovered and nursed the infant genius of his people, and Cimon, after the Persian war, had given it a home. That war had established the naval supremacy of Athens; she had become an imperial state; and the Ionians, bound to her by the double chain of kindred and of subjection, were importing into her both their merchandise and their civilization. The arts and philosophy of the Asiatic coast were easily carried across the sea, and there was Cimon, as I have said, with his ample fortune, ready to receive them with due honours. Not content with patronizing their professors, he built the first of those noble porticos, of which we hear so much in Athens, and he formed the groves, which in process of time became the celebrated Academy. Planting is one of the most graceful, as in Athens it was one of the most beneficent, of employments. Cimon took in hand the wild wood, pruned and dressed it, and laid it out with handsome walks and welcome fountains. Nor, while hospitable to the authors of the city's civilization, was he ungrateful to the instruments of her prosperity. His trees extended their cool, umbrageous branches over the merchants, who assembled in the Agora, for many generations.

Those merchants certainly had deserved that act of bounty; for all the while their ships had been carrying forth the intellectual fame of Athens to the western world. Then commenced what may be called her University existence. Pericles, who succeeded Cimon both in the government and in the patronage of art, is said by Plutarch to have entertained the idea of making Athens the Capital of federated Greece: in this he failed, but his encouragement of such men as Phidias and Anaxagoras led the way to her acquiring a far more lasting sovereignty over a far wider empire. Little understanding the sources of her own greatness, Athens would go to war: peace is the interest of a seat of commerce and the arts; but to war she went; yet to her, whether peace or war, it mattered not. The political power of Athens waned and disappeared; kingdoms rose and fell; centuries rolled away,—they did but bring fresh triumphs to the city of the poet and the sage. There at length the swarthy Moor and Spaniard were seen to meet the blue-eyed Gaul; and the Cappadocian, late subject of Mithridates, gazed without alarm at the haughty conquering Roman. Revolution after revolution passed over the face of Europe, as well as of

Greece, but still she was there,—Athens, the city of mind,—as radiant, as splendid, as delicate, as young, as ever she had been.

Many a more fruitful coast or isle is washed by the blue Aegean, many a spot is there more beautiful or sublime to see, many a territory more ample; but there was one charm in Attica, which, in the same perfection, was nowhere else. The deep pastures of Arcadia, the plain, Argos, the Thessalian vale, these had not the gift; Boeotia, which lay to its immediate north, was notorious for its very want of it. The heavy atmosphere of that Boeotia might be good for vegetation, but it was associated in popular belief with the dulness of the Boeotian intellect: on the contrary, the special purity, elasticity, clearness, and salubrity of the air of Attica, fit concomitant and emblem of its genius, did that for it which earth did not:— it brought out every bright hue and tender shade of the landscape over which it was spread, and would have illuminated the face of even a more bare and rugged country.

A confined triangle, perhaps fifty miles its greatest length, and thirty its greatest breadth; two elevated rocky barriers, meeting at an angle; three prominent mountains, commanding the plain,—Parnes, Pentelicus, and Hymettus; an unsatisfactory soil; some streams, not always full;—such is about the report which the agent of a London company would have made of Attica. He would report that the climate was mild; the hills were limestone; there was plenty of good marble; more pasture land than at first survey might have been expected, sufficient certainly for sheep and goats; fisheries productive; silver mines once, but long since worked out; figs fair; oil first-rate; olives in profusion. But what he would not think of noting down, was, that that olive tree was so choice in nature and so noble in shape that it excited a religious veneration; and that it took so kindly to the light soil, as to expand into woods upon the open plain, and to climb up and fringe the hills. He would not think of writing word to his employers, how that clear air, of which I have spoken, brought out, yet blended and subdued, the colours on the marble, till they had a softness and harmony, for all their richness, which in a picture looks exaggerated, yet is after all within the truth. He would not tell, how that same delicate and brilliant atmosphere freshened up the pale olive, till the olive forgot its monotony, and its cheek glowed like the arbutus or beech of the Umbrian hills. He would say nothing of the thyme and the thousand fragrant herbs which carpeted Hymettus; he would hear nothing of the hum of its bees; nor take much account of the rare flavour of its honey, since Gozo and Minorca were sufficient for the English demand. He would look over the Aegean from the height he had ascended; he would follow with his eye the chain of islands, which, starting from the Sunian headland, seemed to offer the fabled divinities of Attica, when they would visit their Ionian cousins, a sort of viaduct thereto across the sea: but that fancy would not occur to him, nor any admiration of the dark violent billows with their white edges down below; nor of those graceful, fan-like jets of silver upon the rocks, which slowly rise aloft like water spirits from the deep, then shiver, and break, and spread, and shroud themselves, and disappear in a soft mist of foam; nor of the gentle, incessant heaving and panting of the whole liquid plain; nor of the long waves, keeping steady time, like a line of soldiery as they resound upon the hollow shore,—he would not deign to notice that restless living element at all except to bless his stars that he was not upon it. Nor the distinct details, nor the refined colouring, nor the graceful outline and roseate golden hue of the jutting crags, nor the bold shadows cast from Otus or Lauprium by the declining sun;—our agent of a mercantile firm would not value these matters even at a low figure. Rather we must turn for the sympathy we seek to yon pilgrim student, come from a semi-barbarous land to that small corner of the earth, as to a shrine, where he might take his fill of gazing on those emblems and coruscations of invisible unoriginate perfection. It was the stranger from a remote province, from Britain or from Mauritania, who in a scene so different from that of his chilly, woody swamps, or of his fiery, choking sands, learned at once what a real University must be, by coming to understand the sort of country which was its suitable home.

Nor was this all that a University required, and found in Athens. No one, even there, could live on poetry. If the students at that famous place had nothing better than bright hues and soothing sounds, they would not have been able or disposed to turn their residence there to much account. Of course they must have the means of living, nay, in a certain sense, of enjoyment, if Athens was to be an Alma Mater at the time, or to remain afterwards a pleasant thought in their memory. And so they had: be it recollected Athens was a port, and a mart of trade, perhaps the first in Greece; and this was very much to the point, when a number of strangers were ever flocking to it, whose combat was to be with intellectual, not physical difficulties, and who claimed to have their bodily wants supplied, that they might be at leisure to set about furnishing their minds. Now, barren as was the soil of Attica, and bare the face of the country, yet it had only too many resources for an elegant, nay, luxurious abode there. So abundant were the imports of the place, that it was a common saying, that the productions, which were found singly elsewhere, were brought all together in Athens. Corn and wine, the staple of subsistence in such a climate, came from the isles of the Aegean; fine wool and carpeting from Asia Minor; slaves, as now, from the Euxine, and timber too; and iron and brass from the coasts of the Mediterranean. The Athenian did not condescend to manufactures himself, but encouraged them in others; and a population of foreigners caught at the lucrative occupation both for home consumption and for exportation. Their cloth, and other textures for dress and furniture, and their hardware—for instance, armour—were in great request. Labour was cheap; stone and marble in plenty; and the taste and skill, which at first were devoted to public buildings, as temples and porticos, were in the course of time applied to the mansions of public men. If nature did much for Athens, it is undeniable that art did much more.

Here some one will interrupt me with the remark: "by the by, where are we, and whither are we going?—what has all this to do with a University? at least what has it to do with education? It is instructive doubtless; but still how much has it to do with your subject?" Now I beg to assure the reader that I am most conscientiously employed upon my subject; and I should have thought every one would have seen this: however, since the objection is made, I may be allowed to pause awhile, and show distinctly the drift of what I have been saying, before I go farther. *What has this to do with my subject!* why, the question of the *site* is the very first that comes into consideration, when a *Studium Generale* is contemplated; for that site should be a liberal and noble one; who will deny it? All authorities agree in this, and very little reflection will be sufficient to make it clear. I recollect a conversation I once had on this very subject with a very eminent man. I was a youth of eighteen, and was leaving my University for the Long Vacation, when I found myself in company in a public conveyance with a middle-aged person, whose face was strange to me. However, it was the great academical luminary of the day, whom afterwards I knew very well. Luckily for me, I did not suspect it; and luckily too, it was a fancy of his, as his friends knew, to make himself on easy terms especially with stage-coach companions. So, what with my flippancy and his condescension, I managed to hear many things which were novel to me at the time; and one point which he was strong upon, and was evidently fond of urging, was the material pomp and circumstance which should environ a great seat of learning. He considered it was worth the consideration of the government, whether Oxford should not stand in a domain of its own. An ample range, say four miles in diameter, should be turned into wood and meadow, and the University should be approached on all sides by a magnificent park, with fine trees in groups and groves and avenues, and with glimpses and views of the fair city, as the traveller drew near it. There is nothing surely absurd in the idea, though it would cost a round sum to realize it. What has a better claim to the purest and fairest possessions of nature, than the seat of wisdom? So thought my coach companion; and he did but express the tradition of ages and the instinct of mankind.

For instance, take the great University of Paris. That famous school engrossed as its territory the whole south bank of the Seine, and occupied one half, and that the pleasanter half, of the city. King Louis had the island pretty well as his own,—it was scarcely more than a fortification; and the north of the river was given over to the nobles and citizens to do what they could with its marshes; but the eligible south, rising from the stream, which swept around its base, to the fair summit of St. Genevieve, with its broad meadows, its vineyards and its gardens, and with the sacred elevation of Montmartre confronting it, all this was the inheritance of the

University. There was that pleasant Pratum, stretching along the river's bank, in which the students for centuries took their recreation, which Alcuin seems to mention in his farewell verses to Paris, and which has given a name to the great Abbey of St. Germain-des-Prés. For long years it was devoted to the purposes of innocent and healthy enjoyment; but evil times came on the University; disorder arose within its precincts, and the fair meadow became the scene of party brawls; heresy stalked through Europe, and Germany and England no longer sending their contingent of students, a heavy debt was the consequence to the academical body. To let their land was the only resource left to them: buildings rose upon it, and spread along the green sod, and the country at length became town. Great was the grief and indignation of the doctors and masters, when this catastrophe occurred. "A wretched sight," said the Proctor of the German nation, "a wretched sight, to witness the sale of that ancient manor, whither the Muses were wont to wander for retirement and pleasure. Whither shall the youthful student now betake himself, what relief will he find for his eyes, wearied with intense reading, now that the pleasant stream is taken from him?" Two centuries and more have passed since this complaint was uttered; and time has shown that the outward calamity, which it recorded, was but the emblem of the great moral revolution, which was to follow; till the institution itself has followed its green meadows, into the region of things which once were and now are not.

The Aim of a University Course

IF then a practical end must be assigned to a University course, I say it is that of training good members of society. Its art is the art of social life, and its end is fitness for the world. It neither confines its views to particular professions on the one hand, nor creates heroes or inspires genius on the other. Works indeed of genius fall under no art; heroic minds come under no rule; a University is not a birthplace of poets or of immortal authors, of founders of schools, leaders of colonies, or conquerors of nations. It does not promise a generation of Aristotles or Newtons, of Napoleons or Washingtons, of Raphaels or Shakespeares, though such miracles of nature it has before now contained within its precincts. Nor is it content on the other hand with forming the critic or the experimentalist, the economist or the engineer, though such too it includes within its scope. But a University training is the great ordinary means to a great but ordinary end; it aims at raising the intellectual tone of society, at cultivating the public mind, at purifying the national taste, at supplying true principles to popular enthusiasm and fixed aims to popular aspiration, at giving enlargement and sobriety to the ideas of the age, at facilitating the exercise of political power, and refining the intercourse of private life. It is the education which gives a man a clear conscious view of his own opinions and judgments, a truth in developing them, an eloquence in expressing them and a force in urging them. It teaches him to see things as they are, to go right to the point, to disentangle a skein of thought, to detect what is sophistical, and to discard what is irrelevant. It prepares him to fill any post with credit, and to master any subject with facility. It shows him how to accommodate himself to others, how to throw himself into their state of mind, how to bring before them his own, how to influence them how to come to an understanding with them, how to bear with them. He is at home in any society, he has common ground with every class; he knows when to speak and when to be silent; he is able to converse, he is able to listen; he can ask a question pertinently, and gain a lesson seasonably, when he has nothing to impart himself; he is ever ready, yet never in the way; he is a pleasant companion, and a comrade you can depend upon; he knows when to be serious and when to trifle, and he has a sure tact which enables him to trifle with gracefulness and to be serious with effect. He has the repose of a mind which lives in itself, while it lives in the world, and which has resources for its happiness at home when it cannot go abroad. He has a gift which serves him in public, and supports him in retirement, without which good fortune is but vulgar, and with which failure and disappointment have a charm. The art which tends to make a man all this, is in the object which it pursues as useful as the art of wealth or the art of health, though it is less susceptible of method, and less tangible, less certain, less complete, in its result.

The Man of the World

PRIDE, under such training, instead of running to waste in the education of the mind, is turned to account; it gets a new name; it is called self-respect; and ceases to be the disagreeable, uncompanionable quality which it is in itself. Though it be the motive principle of the soul, it seldom comes to view; and when it shows itself, then delicacy and gentleness are its attire, and good sense and sense of honour direct its motions. It is no longer a restless agent, without definite aim; it has a large field of exertion assigned to it, and it subserves those social interests which it would naturally trouble. It is directed into the channel of industry, frugality, honesty, and obedience; and it becomes the very staple of religion and morality held in honour in a day like our own. It becomes the safeguard of chastity, the guarantee of veracity, in high and low; it is the very household god of society, as at present constituted, inspiring neatness and decency in the servant girl, propriety of carriage and refined manners in her mistress, uprightness, manliness, and generosity in the head of the family. It diffuses a light over town and country; it covers the soil with handsome edifices and smiling gardens; it tills the field, it stocks and embellishes the shop. It is the stimulating principle of providence on the one hand, and of free expenditure on the other; of an honourable ambition, and of elegant enjoyment. It breathes upon the face of the community, and the hollow sepulchre is forthwith beautiful to look upon.

Refined by the civilization which has brought it into activity, this self-respect infuses into the mind an intense horror of exposure, and a keen sensitiveness of notoriety and ridicule. It becomes the enemy of extravagances of any kind; it shrinks from what are called scenes; it has no mercy on the mock-heroic, on pretence or egotism, on verbosity in language, or what is called prosiness in conversation. It detests gross adulation; not that it tends at all to the eradication of the appetite to which the flatterer ministers, but it sees the absurdity of indulging it, it understands the annoyance thereby given to others, and if a tribute must be paid to the wealthy or the powerful, it demands greater subtlety and art in the preparation. Thus vanity is changed into a more dangerous self-conceit, as being checked in its natural eruption. It teaches men to suppress their feelings, and to control their tempers, and to mitigate both the severity and the tone of their judgments. As Lord Shaftesbury would desire, it prefers playful wit and satire in putting down what is objectionable, as a more refined and good-natured, as well as a more effectual method, than the expedient which is natural to uneducated minds. It is from this impatience of the tragic and the bombastic that it is now quietly but energetically opposing itself to the unchristian practice of duelling, which it brands as simply out of taste, and as the remnant of a barbarous age; and certainly it seems likely to effect what Religion has aimed at abolishing in vain.

. . . it is almost a definition of a gentleman to say he is one who never inflicts pain. This description is both refined and, as far as it goes, accurate. He is mainly occupied in merely removing the obstacles which hinder the free and unembarrassed action of those about him; and he concurs with their movements rather than takes the initiative himself. His benefits may be considered as parallel to what are called comforts or conveniences in arrangements of a personal nature: like an easy-chair or a good fire, which do their part in dispelling cold and fatigue, though nature provides both means of rest and animal heat without them. The true gentleman in like manner carefully avoids whatever may cause a jar or a jolt in the minds of those with whom he is cast;—all clashing of opinion, or collision of feeling, all restraint, or suspicion, or gloom, or resentment; his great concern being to make every one at their ease and at home. He has his eyes on all his company; he is tender towards the bashful, gentle towards the distant, and merciful towards the absurd; he can recollect to whom he is speaking; he guards against unseasonable allusions, or topics which may irritate; he is seldom prominent in conversation, and never wearisome. He makes light of favours while he does them, and seems to be receiving when he is conferring. He never speaks of himself except when compelled, never defends himself by a mere retort, he has no ears for slander or gossip, is scrupulous in imputing motives to those who interfere with him, and interprets every thing for the best. He is never mean or little in his disputes, never takes unfair advantage, never mistakes personalities or sharp sayings for arguments, or insinuates evil which he dare not say out. From a long-sighted prudence, he observes the maxim of the ancient sage, that we should ever conduct ourselves towards our enemy as if he were one day to be our friend. He has too much good sense to be affronted at insults, he is too well employed to remember injuries, and too indolent to bear malice. He is patient, forbearing, and resigned, on philosophical principles; he submits to pain, because it is inevitable, to bereavement, because it is irreparable, and to death, because it is his destiny. If he engages in controversy of any kind, his disciplined intellect preserves him from the blundering discourtesy of better, perhaps, but less educated minds; who, like blunt weapons, tear and hack instead of cutting clean, who mistake the point in argument, waste their strength on trifles, misconceive their adversary, and leave the question more involved than they find it. He may be right or wrong in his opinion, but he is too clear-headed to be unjust; he is as simple as he is forcible, and as brief as he is decisive. Nowhere shall we find greater candour, consideration, indulgence: he throws himself into the minds of his opponents, he accounts for their mistakes. He knows the weakness of human reason as well as its strength, its province and its limits. If he be an unbeliever, he will be too profound and large-minded to ridicule religion or to act against it; he is too wise to be a dogmatist or fanatic in his infidelity. He respects piety and devotion; he even supports institutions as venerable, beautiful, or useful, to which he does not assent; he honours the ministers of religion, and it contents him to decline its mysteries without assailing or denouncing them. He is a friend of religious toleration, and that, not only because his philosophy has taught him to look on all forms of faith with an impartial eye, but also from the gentleness and effeminacy of feeling, which is the attendant on civilization.

Not that he may not hold a religion too, in his own way, even when he is not a Christian. In that case his religion is one of imagination and sentiment; it is the embodiment of those ideas of the sublime, majestic, and beautiful, without which there can be no large philosophy. Sometimes he acknowledges the being of God, sometimes he invests an unknown principle or quality with the attributes of perfection. And this deduction of his reason, or creation of his fancy, he makes the occasion of such excellent thoughts, and the starting-point of so varied and systematic a teaching, that he even seems like a disciple of Christianity itself. From the very accuracy and steadiness of his logical powers, he is able to see what sentiments are consistent in those who hold any religious doctrine at all, and he appears to others to feel and to hold a whole circle of theological truths, which exist in his mind no otherwise than as a number of deductions.

Stephen Breaks His Glasses

JAMES JOYCE

JAMES JOYCE, author of the controversial novel Ulysses, *was born in Dublin in 1882 and educated at Jesuit schools. A precocious and sensitive boy, he early excelled in essay writing, and as a schoolboy won a prize for an essay on* Ulysses *called* My Favourite Hero. *During his student days Joyce read widely, wrote poetry, translated from the Latin, and learned to speak four languages. From 1898 to 1902 he attended University College (Jesuit) and on his graduation left Dublin for Paris. There he studied medicine, but soon gave up this study and for ten years taught languages at Trieste and in Switzerland. He returned to Paris and spent the rest of his life in a long struggle to find publishers for the prose and verse which he wrote. Joyce died in 1941, one of the most controversial and most influential figures in contemporary literature.*

The following selection is from the first chapter of A Portrait of the Artist as a Young Man, *an autobiographical novel depicting Joyce's schooldays and his groping toward an aesthetic ideal.*

FATHER ARNALL came in and the Latin lesson began and he remained still leaning on the desk with his arms folded. Father Arnall gave out the theme-books and he said that they were scandalous and that they were all to be written out again with the corrections at once. But the worst of all was Fleming's theme because the pages were stuck together by a blot: and Father Arnall held it up by a corner and said it was an insult to any master to send him up such a theme. Then he asked Jack Lawton to decline the noun *mare* and Jack Lawton stopped at the ablative singular and could not go on with the plural.

—You should be ashamed of yourself, said Father Arnall sternly. You, the leader of the class!

Then he asked the next boy and the next and the next. Nobody knew. Father Arnall became very quiet, more and more quiet as each boy tried to answer it and could not. But his face was black looking and his eyes were staring though his voice was so quiet. Then he asked Fleming and Fleming said that that word had no plural. Father Arnall suddenly shut the book and shouted at him:

—Kneel out there in the middle of the class. You are one of the idlest boys I ever met. Copy out your themes again the rest of you.

Fleming moved heavily out of his place and knelt between the two last benches. The other boys bent over their theme-books and began to write. A silence filled the classroom and Stephen, glancing timidly at Father Arnall's dark face, saw that it was a little red from the wax he was in.

Was that a sin for Father Arnall to be in a wax or was he allowed to get into a wax when the boys were idle because that made them study better or was he only letting on to be in a wax? It was because he was allowed because a priest would know what a sin was and would not do it. But if he did it one time by mistake what would he do to go to confession? Perhaps he would go to confession to the minister. And if the minister did it he would go to the rector: and the rector to the provincial: and the provincial to the general of the jesuits. That was called the order: and he had heard his father say that they were all clever men. They could all have become high-up people in the world if they had not become jesuits. And he wondered what Father Arnall and Paddy Barrett would have become and what Mr McGlade and Mr Gleeson would have become if they had not become jesuits. It was hard to think what because you would have to think of them in a different way with different coloured coats and trousers and with beards and moustaches and different kinds of hats.

The door opened quietly and closed. A quick whisper ran through the class: the prefect of studies. There was an instant of dead silence and then the loud crack of a pandybat on the last desk. Stephen's heart leapt up in fear.

—Any boys want flogging here, Father Arnall? cried the prefect of studies. Any lazy idle loafers that want flogging in this class?

He came to the middle of the class and saw Fleming on his knees.

—Hoho! he cried. Who is this boy? Why is he on his knees? What is your name, boy?

—Fleming, sir.

—Hoho, Fleming! An idler of course. I can see it in your eye. Why is he on his knees, Father Arnall?

—He wrote a bad Latin theme, Father Arnall said, and he missed all the questions in grammar.

—Of course he did! cried the prefect of studies, of course he did! A born idler! I can see it in the corner of his eye.

He banged his pandybat down on the desk and cried:

—Up, Fleming! Up, my boy!

Fleming stood up slowly.

—Hold out! cried the prefect of studies.

Fleming held out his hand. The pandybat came down on it with a loud smacking sound: one, two, three, four, five, six.

—Other hand!

The pandybat came down again in six loud quick smacks.

—Kneel down! cried the prefect of studies.

Fleming knelt down squeezing his hands under his armpits, his face contorted with pain, but Stephen knew how hard his hands were because Fleming was always rubbing rosin into them. But perhaps he was in great pain for the noise of the pandybat was terrible. Stephen's heart was beating and fluttering.

—At your work, all of you! shouted the prefect of studies. We want no lazy idle loafers here, lazy idle little schemers. At your work, I tell you. Father Dolan will be in to see you every day. Father Dolan will be in tomorrow.

He poked one of the boys in the side with the pandybat, saying:

—You, boy! When will Father Dolan be in again?

—Tomorrow, sir, said Tom Furlong's voice.

—Tomorrow and tomorrow and tomorrow, said the prefect of studies. Make up your minds for that. Every day Father Dolan. Write away. You, boy, who are you?

Stephen's heart jumped suddenly.

—Dedalus, sir.

—Why are you not writing like the others?

—I . . . my . . .

He could not speak with fright.

—Why is he not writing, Father Arnall?

—He broke his glasses, said Father Arnall, and I exempted him from work.

—Broke? What is this I hear? What is this? Your name is? said the prefect of studies.

—Dedalus, sir.

—Out here, Dedalus. Lazy little schemer. I see schemer in your face. Where did you break your glasses?

Stephen stumbled into the middle of the class, blinded by fear and haste.

—Where did you break your glasses? repeated the prefect of studies.

—The cinderpath, sir.

—Hoho! The cinderpath! cried the prefect of studies. I know that trick.

Stephen lifted his eyes in wonder and saw for a moment Father Dolan's whitegrey not young face, his baldy whitegrey head with fluff at the sides of it, the steel rims of his spectacles and his no-coloured eyes looking through the glasses. Why did he say he knew that trick?

—Lazy idle little loafer! cried the prefect of studies. Broke my glasses! An old schoolboy trick! Out with your hand this moment!

Stephen closed his eyes and held out in the air his trembling hand with the palm upwards. He felt the prefect of studies touch it for a moment at the fingers to straighten it and then the swish of the sleeve of the soutane as the pandybat was lifted to strike. A hot burning stinging tingling blow like the loud crack of a broken stick made his trembling hand crumple together like a leaf in the fire: and at the sound and the pain scalding tears were driven into his eyes. His whole body was shaking with fright, his arm was shaking and his crumpled burning livid hand shook like a loose leaf in the air. A cry sprang to his lips, a prayer to be let off. But though the tears scalded his eyes and his limbs quivered with pain and fright he held back the hot tears and the cry that scalded his throat.

—Other hand! shouted the prefect of studies.

Stephen drew back his maimed and quivering right arm and held out his left hand. The soutane sleeve swished again as the pandybat was lifted and a loud crashing sound and a fierce maddening tingling burning pain made his hand shrink together with the palms and fingers in a livid quivering mass. The scalding water burst forth from his eyes and, burning with shame and agony and fear, he drew back his shaking arm in terror and burst out into a whine of pain. His body shook with a palsy of fright and in shame and rage he felt the scalding cry come from his throat and the scalding tears falling out of his eyes and down his flaming cheeks.

—Kneel down! cried the prefect of studies.

Stephen knelt down quickly pressing his beaten hands to his sides. To think of them beaten and swollen with pain all in a moment made him feel so sorry for them as if they were not his own but someone else's that he felt sorry for. And as he knelt, calming the last sobs in his throat and feeling the burning tingling pain pressed in to his sides, he thought of the hands which he had held out in the air with the palms up and of the firm touch of the prefect of studies when he had steadied the shaking fingers and of the beaten swollen reddened mass of palm and fingers that shook helplessly in the air.

—Get at your work, all of you, cried the prefect of studies from the door. Father Dolan will be in every day to see if any boy, any lazy idle little loafer wants flogging. Every day. Every day.

The door closed behind him.

The hushed class continued to copy out the themes. Father Arnall rose from his seat and went among them, helping the boys with gentle words and telling them the mistakes they had made. His voice was very gentle and soft. Then he returned to his seat and said to Fleming and Stephen:

—You may return to your places, you two.

Fleming and Stephen rose and, walking to their seats, sat down. Stephen, scarlet with shame, opened a book quickly with one weak hand and bent down upon it, his face close to the page.

It was unfair and cruel because the doctor had told him not to read without glasses and he had written home to his father that morning to send him a new pair. And Father Arnall had said that he need not study till the new glasses came. Then to be called a schemer before the class and to be pandied when he always got the card for first or second and was the leader of the Yorkists! How could the prefect of studies know that it was a trick? He felt the touch of the prefect's fingers as they had steadied his hand and at first he had thought he was going to shake hands with him because the fingers were soft and firm: but then in an instant he had heard the swish of the soutane sleeve and the crash. It was cruel and unfair to make him kneel in the middle of the class then: and Father Arnall had told them both that they might return to their places without making any difference between them. He listened to Father Arnall's low and gentle voice as he corrected the themes. Perhaps he was sorry now and wanted to be decent. But it was unfair and cruel. The prefect of studies was a priest but that was cruel and unfair. And his whitegrey face and the no-coloured eyes behind the steel rimmed spectacles were cruel looking because he had steadied the hand first with his firm soft fingers and that was to hit it better and louder.

—It's a stinking mean thing, that's what it is, said Fleming in the corridor as the classes were passing out in file to the refectory, to pandy a fellow for what is not his fault.

—You really broke your glasses by accident, didn't you? Nasty Roche asked.

Stephen felt his heart filled by Fleming's words and did not answer.

—Of course he did! said Fleming. I wouldn't stand it. I'd go up and tell the rector on him.

—Yes, said Cecil Thunder eagerly, and I saw him lift the pandybat over his shoulder and he's not allowed to do that.

—Did they hurt much? Nasty Roche asked.

—Very much, Stephen said.

—I wouldn't stand it, Fleming repeated, from Baldyhead or any other Baldyhead. It's a stinking mean low trick, that's what it is. I'd go straight up to the rector and tell him about it after dinner.

—Yes, do. Yes, do, said Cecil Thunder.

—Yes, do. Yes, go up and tell the rector on him, Dedalus, said Nasty Roche, because he said that he'd come in tomorrow again and pandy you.

—Yes, yes. Tell the rector, all said.

And there were some fellows out of second of grammar listening and one of them said:

—The senate and the Roman people declared that Dedalus had been wrongly punished.

It was wrong; it was unfair and cruel: and, as he sat in the refectory, he suffered time after time in memory the same humiliation until he began to wonder whether it might not really be that there was something in his face which made him look like a schemer and he wished he had a little mirror to see. But there could not be; and it was unjust and cruel and unfair.

He could not eat the blackish fish fritters they got on Wednesdays in Lent and one of his potatoes had the mark of the spade in it. Yes, he would do what the fellows had told him. He would go up and tell the rector that he had been wrongly punished. A thing like that had been done before by somebody in history, by some great person whose head was in the books of history. And the rector would declare that he had been wrongly punished because the senate and the Roman people always declared that the men who did that had been wrongly punished. Those were the great men whose names were in Richmal Magnall's Questions. History was all about those men and what they did and that was what Peter Parley's Tales about Greece and Rome were all about. Peter Parley himself was on the first page in a picture. There was a road over a heath with grass at the side and little bushes: and Peter Parley had a broad hat like a protestant minister and a big stick and he was walking fast along the road to Greece and Rome.

It was easy what he had to do. All he had to do was when the dinner was over and he came out in his turn to go on walking but not out to the corridor but up the staircase on the right that led to the castle. He had nothing to do but that; to turn to the right and walk fast up the staircase and in half a minute he would be in the low dark narrow corridor that led through the castle to the rector's room. And every fellow had said that it was unfair, even the fellow out of second of grammar who had said that about the senate and the Roman people.

What would happen? He heard the fellows of the higher line stand up at the top of the refectory and heard their steps as they came down the matting: Paddy Rath and Jimmy Magee and the Spaniard and the Portuguese and the fifth was big Corrigan who was going to be flogged by Mr Gleeson. That was why the prefect of studies had called him a schemer and pandied him for nothing: and, straining his weak eyes, tired with the tears, he watched big Corrigan's broad shoulders and big hanging black head passing in the file. But he had done something and besides Mr Gleeson would not flog him hard: and he remembered how big Corrigan looked in the bath. He had skin the same colour as the turf-coloured bogwater in the shallow end of the bath and when he walked along the side his feet slapped loudly on the wet tiles and at every step his thighs shook a little because he was fat.

The refectory was half empty and the fellows were still passing out in file. He could go up the staircase because there was never a priest or a prefect outside the refectory door. But he could not go. The rector would side with the prefect of studies and think it was a schoolboy trick and then the prefect of studies would come in every day the same, only it would be worse because he would be dreadfully waxy at any fellow going up to the rector about him. The fellows had told him to go but they would not go themselves. They had forgotten all about it. No, it was best to forget all about it and perhaps the prefect of studies had only said he would come in. No, it was best to hide out of the way because when you were small and young you could often escape that way.

The fellows at his table stood up. He stood up and passed out among them in the file. He had to decide. He was coming near the door. If he went on with the fellows he could never go up to the rector because he could not leave the playground for that. And if he went and was pandied all the same all the fellows would make fun and talk about young Dedalus going up to the rector to tell on the prefect of studies.

He was walking down along the matting and he saw the door before him. It was impossible: he could not. He thought of the baldy head of the prefect of studies with the cruel no-coloured eyes looking at him and he heard the voice of the prefect of studies asking him twice what his name was. Why could he not remember the name when he was told the first time? Was he not listening the first time or was it to make fun out of the name? The great men in the history had names like that and nobody made fun of them. It was his own name that he should have made fun of if he wanted to make fun. Dolan: it was like the name of a woman who washed clothes.

He had reached the door and, turning quickly up to the right, walked up the stairs; and, before he could make up his mind to come back, he had entered the low dark narrow corridor that led to the castle. And as he crossed the threshold of the door of the corridor he saw, without turning his head to look, that all the fellows were looking after him as they went filing by.

He passed along the narrow dark corridor, passing little doors that were the doors of the rooms of the community. He peered in front of him and right and left through the gloom and thought that those must be portraits. It was dark and silent and his eyes were weak and tired with tears so that he could not see. But he thought they were the portraits of the saints and great men of the order who were looking down on him silently as he passed: Saint Ignatius Loyola holding an open book and pointing to the word *Ad Majorem Dei Gloriam* in it, saint Francis Xavier pointing to his chest, Lorenzo Ricci with his berretta on his head like one of the prefects of the lines, the three patrons of holy youth, saint Stanislaus Kostka, saint Aloysius Gonzaga and Blessed John Berchmans, all with young faces because they died when they were young, and Father Peter Kenny sitting in a chair wrapped in a big cloak.

He came out on the landing above the entrance hall and looked about him. That was where Hamilton Rowan had passed and the marks of the soldiers' slugs were there. And it was there that the old servants had seen the ghost in the white cloak of a marshal.

An old servant was sweeping at the end of the landing. He asked him where was the rector's room and the old servant pointed to the door at the far end and looked after him as he went on to it and knocked.

There was no answer. He knocked again more loudly and his heart jumped when he heard a muffled voice say:

—Come in!

He turned the handle and opened the door and fumbled for the handle of the green baize door inside. He found it and pushed it open and went in.

He saw the rector sitting at a desk writing. There was a skull on the desk and a strange solemn smell in the room like the old leather of chairs.

His heart was beating fast on account of the solemn place he was in and the silence of the room: and he looked at the skull and at the rector's kind-looking face.

—Well, my little man, said the rector, what is it?

Stephen swallowed down the thing in his throat and said:

—I broke my glasses, sir.

The rector opened his mouth and said:

—O!

Then he smiled and said:

—Well, if we broke our glasses we must write home for a new pair.

—I wrote home, sir, said Stephen, and Father Arnall said I am not to study till they come.

—Quite right! said the rector.

Stephen swallowed down the thing again and tried to keep his legs and his voice from shaking.

—But, sir . . .

—Yes?

—Father Dolan came in today and pandied me because I was not writing my theme.

The rector looked at him in silence and he could feel the blood rising to his face and the tears about to rise to his eyes.

The rector said:

—Your name is Dedalus, isn't it?

—Yes, sir.

—And where did you break your glasses?

—On the cinderpath, sir. A fellow was coming out of the bicycle house and I fell and they got broken. I don't know the fellow's name.

The rector looked at him again in silence. Then he smiled and said:

—O, well, it was a mistake, I am sure Father Dolan did not know.

—But I told him I broke them, sir, and he pandied me.

—Did you tell him that you had written home for a new pair? the rector asked.

—No, sir.

—O well then, said the rector, Father Dolan did not understand. You can say that I excuse you from your lessons for a few days.

Stephen said quickly for fear his trembling would prevent him:

—Yes, sir, but Father Dolan said he will come in tomorrow to pandy me again for it.

—Very well, the rector said, it is a mistake and I shall speak to Father Dolan myself. Will that do now?

Stephen felt the tears wetting his eyes and murmured:

—O yes sir, thanks.

The rector held his hand across the side of the desk where the skull was and Stephen, placing his hand in it for a moment, felt a cool moist palm.

—Good day now, said the rector, withdrawing his hand and bowing.

—Good day, sir, said Stephen.

He bowed and walked quietly out of the room, closing the doors carefully and slowly.

But when he had passed the old servant on the landing and was again in the low narrow dark corridor he began to walk faster and faster. Faster and faster he hurried on through the gloom excitedly. He bumped his elbow against the door at the end and, hurrying down the staircase, walked quickly through the two corridors and out into the air.

He could hear the cries of the fellows on the playgrounds. He broke into a run and, running quicker and quicker, ran across the cinderpath and reached the third line playground, panting.

The fellows had seen him running. They closed round him in a ring, pushing one against another to hear.

—Tell us! Tell us!

—What did he say?

—Did you go in?

—What did he say?

—Tell us! Tell us!

He told them what he had said and what the rector had said and, when he had told them, all the fellows flung their caps spinning up into the air and cried:

—Hurroo!

They caught their caps and sent them up again spinning skyhigh and cried again:

—Hurroo! Hurroo!

They made a cradle of their locked hands and hoisted him up among them and carried him along till he struggled to get free. And when he had escaped from them they broke away in all directions, flinging their caps again into the air and whistling as they went spinning up and crying:

—Hurroo!

And they gave three groans for Baldyhead Dolan and three cheers for Conmee and they said he was the decentest rector that was ever in Clongowes.

The cheers died away in the soft grey air. He was alone. He was happy and free: but he would not be anyway proud with Father Dolan. He would be very quiet and obedient: and he wished that he could do something kind for him to show him that he was not proud.

The air was soft and grey and mild and evening was coming. There was the smell of evening in the air, the smell of the fields in the country where they digged up turnips to peel them and eat them when they went out for a walk to Major Barton's, the smell there was in the little wood beyond the pavilion where the gallnuts were.

The fellows were practising long shies and bowling lobs and slow twisters. In the soft grey silence he could hear the bump of the balls: and from here and from there through the quiet air the sound of the cricket bats: pick, pack, pock, puck: like drops of water in a fountain falling softly in the brimming bowl.

In School Hours

H. C. BUNNER

H. C. BUNNER (1855-1896) has the distinction of having been editor-in-chief for eighteen years of Puck, *the first humorous magazine in America. In the early issues of the magazine it was his pen which wrote most of the humor.*

At his home in Nutley, New Jersey, and in New York, he was the moving spirit of a brilliant social group. He was witty and urbane, broad in his interests, positive in his enthusiasms and antipathies. His best work, both in verse and prose, is characterized by adroit craftsmanship and superb parody. Though his wit is keen and penetrating, it is never caustic. His humor is always kindly, sweet-tempered, frequently ebullient.

You remember the moments that come
   In a school-day afternoon:
When the illegitimate hum
   Subsides to a drowsy swoon?
When the smell of ink and slates
   Grows oppressively *warm* and thick;
Sleep opens her tempting gates;
   And the clock has a drowsy tick?

Forgetful of watch and rule,
   The teacher has time to think
Of a "recess" in life's long school;
   Of a time to "go out and drink"
At the spring where the Muse has sipped,
   And laurel and bay-leaf bloom—
And a contraband note is slipped,
   Meanwhile, across the room.

From a trembling hand it flies
   Like a little white dove of peace;
And away on its mission it hies
   In an "Atlas of Ancient Greece."

And the sender hides her face;
    For her eyes have a watery shine,
And saline deposits trace
    The recent tear-drop's line.

From the dovecote side it goes
    Across to the ruder half—
Where a large majority shows
    A suppressed desire to laugh.
But the boy that they dare not tease
    Receives the crumpled twist—
And the little hunchback who sees
    Only shakes an impotent fist.

The boy with a fair-curled head
    Smiles with a masculine scorn.
When the sad small note is read,
    With its straggling script forlorn:
"Charley, wy is it you wont
    Forgiv me laughfing at you?
I wil kill my self if you dont
    Honest I will for true!"

He responds: He is pleased to find
    She is wiser, at any rate.
He'll be happy to ride behind
    The hearse. May he ask the date?
She reads—with a glittering eye,
    And the look of an angered queen.
This was tragic at thirty. Why
    Is it trivial at thirteen?

Trivial! what shall eclipse
    The pain of our childish woes?
The rose-bud pales its lips
    When a very small zephyr blows.
You smile, O Dian, bland,
    If Endymion's glance is cold:
But Despair seems close at hand
    To that hapless thirteen-year-old.

❊ ❊ ❊ ❊ ❊ ❊ ❊ ❊ ❊ ❊

To the teacher's ears like a dream
    The school-room noises float—
Then a sudden bustle—a scream
    From a girl—"She has cut her throat!"

And the poor little hunchbacked chap
    From his corner leaps like a flash—
Has her death-like head in his lap—
    And his fingers upon the gash.

'T is not deep. An "eraser" blade
    Was the chosen weapon of death;
And the face on the boy's knee laid
    Is alive with a fluttering breath.
But faint from the shock and fright,
    She lies, too weak to be stirred,
Blood-stained, inky and white,
    Pathetic, small, absurd.

The cruel Adonis stands
    Much scared and woe-begone now;
Smoothing with nervous hands
    The damp hair off her brow.
He is penitent, through and through;
    And she—she is satisfied.
Knowing my sex as I do,
    I wish I could add: She died.

Former Students

IRWIN EDMAN

IRWIN EDMAN was born in 1896, grew up in New York City, was graduated from Columbia in 1917, and received a Ph.D. from the same university in 1920. He has taught philosophy at Columbia since 1918. A distinguished teacher and scholar, he is also a popular essayist and writer of light verse, his witty poems appearing from time to time in The New Yorker. *To radio audiences he is well known as chairman of the philosophy section of the program* Invitation to Learning.

Former Students *is Chap. XI of* Philosopher's Holiday, *a series of autobiographical essays full of wisdom for teachers.*

ONCE at a gathering in New York various people were mentioned who in diverse ways had begun to make their young presence felt in the world. One had written a play; another had become a psycho-analyst; still another a distinguished literary critic; one a radical editor; still another a foreign correspondent; and one even "the Iron Man" of big-league baseball. Every once in a while I found myself murmuring with not greatly concealed pride: "He is a former student of mine." Finally, a rather bored young lady looked at me pointedly. "Tell me," she asked, "was Chaliapin a former student of yours?"

I have since tried, not very successfully, to refrain from muttering proudly when the brighter young minds among contemporaries are mentioned: "Former student of mine!" For I cannot pretend to have taught any of them their present accomplishments. They did not learn playwriting, psychiatry, literary criticism, foreign correspondence, or baseball from me. And if I were honest, I should have to claim as former students of mine the hundreds of boring and unpleasant people, the failure and the complacent, successful nonentities, the rakes and the time-servers, whom I had the opportunity once to lecture to and whose quiz papers I once read. There are ten thousand former students of mine, I have calculated, roaming about the world. That does not include half a dozen, including some of the best, I have outlived. It does include hundreds I have forgotten and doubtless hundreds who have forgotten me. I met one of the latter once. It was at a club in New York. He was a little drunk, and he

looked at me vaguely. He seemed to recall that he had seen me somewhere.
A light dawned.

"I greatly enjoyed that course of yours in—in history."

"Mathematics," I corrected him gently.

"That's it," he said, "mathematics. You made calculus interesting, I must say."

"No," I said, "it was the theory of functions." I thought I might as well be credited with something even more majestic that I new nothing about.

I must admit former students generally do better than that, and they greet a former teacher with a touching sense that once long ago they did get something from him. Sometimes it is nothing more than a joke, used to illustrate something they have completely forgotten. But the joke remains, and probably the theory it was meant to illustrate is dated by now, anyway. Sometimes they surprise you by remembering a quite incidental remark. Occasionally it is good enough for you to wish you could be sure you *had* said it and they had not heard it from some other professor—a professor of calculus, for instance. Or they remember some trick of gesture you had, or the way you suddenly, for emphasis, write a single word on the blackboard, or the mordant things you try to say to listeners, cruelties invariably regarded as merely gently whimsical. Or they even remember ideas that, being the first time they had heard them, made a great impression. They are ideas, often, about which by this time you have changed your mind, or lost faith in. One former student told me he had still the notebook he kept in the first year I taught anybody. He promises not to use it for blackmail against me. He insists that I misspelt Malebranche on the blackboard and, as a result, he has misspelt it almost automatically ever since.

Among the students one does remember, there is a tendency to remember them as they were, as, with notebooks before them, they sat as young men of nineteen or twenty in your classroom, or talked with you in your office. I find it hard to realize that time passes, or to realize that though freshmen and sophomores always look the same each year, they don't look the same (though they often are) ten years or fifteen years later. Meeting some of them after a lapse of years, one wonders what has happened to them, or whether one could ever have taught them anything, or where they can have learned all they seem to have found out about books and life, or how they could, who had once been so eager and bright, be so stodgy now.

I have had them look at me, too, in obvious wonder that they could ever have believed I could teach them anything and, once or twice, frankly express resentment at what they had learned.

I often wonder what students remember of a "former teacher," and can judge of their memories only by my own. But I wonder, too, what it is that one teaches them; how much difference a teacher can make. The psycho-analysts assure us these days that the great damage we call education is done largely in the first six years of a child's life, and that a teacher can do less and less fundamentally to the mind and character of a pupil after that as he passes from grade school to college. I hope that is so. It appears to relieve many of us of great responsibilities. The freshman comes with a kind of fatal predestination; he is what he is, and a course of a seminar cannot make any very great difference. I realize how momentary a tangent any teaching is upon a student's psyche, or his mental equipment.

Yet it is something, and something for which students, doubtless with justice, are not grateful.

"Teaching," Santayana writes in *Character and Opinion in the United States,* "is a delightful paternal art, and especially teaching intelligent and warm-hearted youngsters, as most American collegians are; but it is an art like acting, where the performance, often rehearsed, must be adapted to an audience hearing it only once. The speaker must make concessions to their impatience, their taste, their capacity, their prejudices, their ultimate good; he must neither bore nor perplex nor demoralize them. His thoughts must be such as can flow daily, and be set down in notes; they must come when the bell rings and stop appropriately when the bell rings a second time. The best that is in him, as Mephistopheles says in *Faust,* he dare not tell them; and as the substance of this possession is spiritual, to withhold is often to lose it."

What boredom, perplexity, and demoralization do one's students remember! I once caught a glimpse of what it was. I ran into a former student at a week-end in the country. I had known him fairly well and, even before I knew him, had noticed, as had some colleagues, the sharp, critical eye which he fixed upon one during a lecture. There are always half a dozen students in a class in whose presence one would not willingly be boring or stupid or inaccurate. When one is so unwillingly, one sees the immediate register of disappointment (or is it fulfilled expectation?) in their eyes. S—— had been one of those.

The conversation had been general and desultory. At the end of the evening he came into my room. He sat down on a chair and looked at me sharply. He seemed older than I remembered him, but he had always seemed grown up. He had, I had heard, various reasons for discouragement, both personal and professional, since he had left college. At one point some years ago he had suddenly turned up and asked if I couldn't think of a good reason for his not committing suicide, since he was about to do so. My reasons were not too good, but they seemed good enough. He was here still, not much happier apparently.

"Look here," he said, "I have been wanting to tell you for some years that your former students have a lot to hold against you, especially the good ones, those who got what you gave them."

"What harm did I do?" I asked, weakly. "I am in a worse case than Socrates. At least he could boast at his trial that none of his former students—those whom he was supposed to have corrupted—had appeared to testify against him. But here you come yourself, saying I have done you irreparable damage. Really, a course in the Philosophy of Art can't do that much harm to anyone, not even to those who get an A."

"Yes it can, and did," he insisted, "and I'm not the only one who was damaged, and you're not the only one who did the damage, though you did a good deal. You taught me and a good many others to think that contemplation, detachment, eternal things, that Truth, Goodness, and Beauty, were the proper preoccupations for a young man in this world. Well, that isn't the kind of world we are living in, and you gave us a profound sense of unreality. It's taken me years to get over it and I'm not quite over it yet. But Freud and Marx have helped me, and I wish I had found out about them sooner. I must admit I first heard about them from you, but you didn't sound as if you thought them as important as Plato or Santayana. You made me live beyond my intellectual income; you made me set store by a lot of things that had no more relation to the moving things in the world and to the lives of men than backgammon or Venetian brocades. I admit you woke me up to a few beautiful things and moving ideas, but it was a fool's Paradise. I've reversed the usual order and gone through Purgatory since."

"Well, you've found a new Paradise of your own—the revolution—haven't you?"

"Call it that, but it's one of the forces going on in the world; it isn't the lost causes of sweetness and light."

I tried to say something about the lost causes being the only enduring ones; but S—— suddenly softened a little. "It was a pleasant enough trance while it lasted," he said.

"I'm sorry the coming to was so bad," I said.

Former students are not often so bitter, I must admit. They are frequently almost embarrassing in their assertion that you awakened them to think, or to think clearly, or to feel qualities in things and ideas and people they had never perceived before. They can be incredibly kind, even or especially when they think they are being objective and just. For it is difficult to distinguish the persons from the things they communicate, and many a teacher gets a certain glamour in a student's memory because the teacher is associated with that student's first encounter with Plato or Shakespeare, Bach or Phidias. A teacher dealing with great things cannot help sometimes seeming—if only to the undistinguishing young—to be their voice or their oracle; and to a very young mind, if only for a short time, the teacher is confused with the things taught. This may, indeed, be very bad for the teacher, who, in the mirror of his student's generosity, makes something like the same identification, too. His colleagues will correct him, and many of his unbemused students would, too, given the opportunity. For even the luckiest teacher dealing with students avid for ideas will have a good many who look at him as if they dared him to teach them anything. I met one of that category once. He looked at me curiously. "I never could understand," he said, "why you thought philosophy interesting. And yet you seemed to do so. I was quite struck with that fact. That's the only thing I remember from the course."

It should really be a most discouraging fact (I am convinced it is a fact, in any case) that there is nothing much one does for the good student, and nothing very much that one can do for the poor one. In the case of the brilliant successes among former students of mine, I am convinced they were in essence as sophomores what they are now. If they are now learned men, they were already on the road to learning in their sophomore year. One of my former pupils can lay claim now to an erudition that I shall never have. But he was an erudite sophomore, and a little disturbing to an instructor in his first year of teaching. Another, though he is wiser about the world now, was wiser then than I shall ever be about it, and wrote almost as clearly and well then as he does now. The campus politicians are now real politicians, some of them, and not only in the field of politics. Sometimes there are apparent changes: the æsthetes become hard-boiled or disillusioned; the sentimentalists, cynics. But even in those cases the change is not always a real one.

Now that I have been teaching more than twenty years and have thus seen five generations—a college generation being four years—of college students, former students seem to return. I do not mean that they come back in the flesh as one did recently with his ten-year-old child to the campus; I mean one recognizes in the sophomore or junior there in the first row a replica of some predecessor not so very different of classes long ago. If I had known fewer students I should have been readier to predict what will become of them. It is easy enough with the run of the mill, though even with them, so rapidly is our world changing, it is not so easy as it used to be. There are not so many fathers' businesses to go into; the typical pre-lawyer may not find an office to be a lawyer in; the young snob and richling may find the world in which he can be both of those things vanishing under his feet. It is not easy even with the "originals," who also, for a teacher long in harness, fall into types. How was I to guess —how would anyone have guessed—that the editor of the best college humorous magazine in ten years, neatly ironic, merrily sceptical, and amusedly disillusioned, would turn into an uncompromising revolutionary, the Washington correspondent of the *Daily Worker?* How was one to suspect that the playboy whose life was bounded by fraternities and dances and drinking would be sobered by something or other into becoming a diligent professional classical scholar—a pedantic one at that? How could I have dreamed (though I might have done so) that the withering cynic of his class, whose god was Swift, should have become a mystical and fanatical rabbi?

I suspect that in each of these cases, had I been wiser or known my student better, I should not have had much occasion for surprise. There is much one does not find out about students, since it is natural that a teacher does rather more of the talking. And there is a lot one would never find out from the way in which students talk to a teacher.

There is only one thing by which I continue, with a foolish and persistent naïveté, to be surprised. I expect, somehow, that a student ten years after college will still have the brightness and enthusiasm, the disinterested love of ideas, and the impersonal passion for them that some develop during their undergraduate days. Time and again I have run into them, and wondered what the world has done to them that that passionate detachment should have gone. I know some of the things, brutal or familiar enough to the point almost of banality: a family, the struggle for a living, a disillusion with the status of contemplation in the nightmare of a violent world. But it is not revolution or disillusion that surprises me; both are intelligible. It is the death-in-life that assails the spirits of young men who had been alive when I knew them in college. A fierce hate, a transcendent revolutionary contempt for ideas, especially traditional ones, a revolt against the academy; all these things are not dismaying. They are symptoms that life is not dead and that spirit lives in some form, however tortured or fantastic or unprecedented. It is when spirit is utterly dead, when the one-time eager youth becomes precociously middle-aged, that one feels above all that education is a failure. One awakened something for a short time. But did one? Perhaps I have, like a good many teachers, flattered myself. It was not we who awakened them; it was the season of their lives, and the things and ideas which, despite us, for a moment—if only for a moment—stirred them. There are times when, if one thought about former students too much, one could not go on teaching. For the teacher meeting his former students is reminded of the fact that Plato long ago pointed out in the *Republic*. It is not what the teacher but what the world teaches them that will in the long run count, and what they can learn from the latter comes from habits fixed soon after birth and temperaments fixed long before it. There are just a few things a teacher can do, and that only for the sensitive and the spirited. He can initiate enthusiasms, clear paths, and inculcate discipline. He can communicate a passion and a method; no more. His most serious triumph as a teacher is the paradoxical one of having his students, while he is teaching them and perhaps afterwards, forget him in the absorption of the tradition or the inquiry of which he is the transient voice. Lucky for him if later his students feel his voice was just. As in the playing of music, it is the music, not the musician, that is ultimate. And in the art of teaching, it is what is taught that counts, not the teacher. It is a great tribute to an artist to say that he plays Beethoven or Bach, and puts nothing between them and his audience. But in so doing he becomes one with both the composer and the listener. In the listener's memory he anonymously shares the composer's immortality. The teacher, too, is best remembered who is thus forgotten.

He lives in what has happened to the minds of his students, and in what they remember of things infinitely greater than themselves or than himself. They will remember, perhaps, that once in a way, in the midst of the routine of the classroom, it was something not himself that spoke, something not themselves that listened. The teacher may well be content to be otherwise forgotten, or to live in something grown to ripeness in his students that he, however minutely, helped bring to birth. There are many students thus come to fruition whom I should be proud to have say: "He was my teacher." There is no other immortality a teacher can have.

America Was Schoolmasters

ROBERT P. TRISTRAM COFFIN

ROBERT P. TRISTRAM COFFIN, was born in Brunswick, Maine, in 1892, and grew up on a Maine salt-water farm. His early education he received at a rural red-brick schoolhouse. He was graduated from Bowdoin College in 1915. In 1921 he went to Oxford as Rhodes Scholar from Maine. On his return to this country he became Professor of English at Wells College and a few years later Professor of English at Bowdoin.

He has been a prolific writer of both prose and verse. In 1936 he was awarded the Pulitzer Prize for poetry. He is well known for his pastoral poetry of Maine life and for his historical narratives of the Maine coast.

AMERICA was forests,
America was grain,
Wheat from dawn to sunset,
And rainbows trailing rain.

America was beavers,
Buffalo in seas,
Cornsilk and the johnnycake,
Song of scythes and bees.

America was brown men
With eyes full of the sun,
But America was schoolmasters,
Tall one by lonely one.

They hewed oak, carried water,
Their hands were knuckle-boned,
They piled on loads of syntax
Till the small boys groaned.

They taught the girls such manners
As stiffened them for life,
But made many a fine speller,
Good mother and good wife.

They took small wiry children,
Wild as panther-cats,
And turned them into reasoning
Sunny democrats.

They caught a nation eager,
They caught a nation young,
They taught the nation fairness,
Thrift, and the golden tongue.

They started at the bottom
And built up strong and sweet,
They shaped our minds and morals
With switches on the seat!

The Human Boy

JACQUES BARZUN

BORN in France in 1907 of a family devoted to scholarship, Jacques Barzun passed his youth in a stimulating intellectual environment. He came to this country soon after the close of World War I, entered Columbia University, and was graduated in 1927. He became an American citizen in 1932. He now teaches at Columbia, lectures widely, contributes to periodicals.

"The Human Boy" is Chapter 16 of Teacher in America, *a book which analyzes objectives and misconceptions of the teaching function at both school and college level.*

Lᴇᴛ me say bluntly, as I do not hesitate to do when my students broach the subject, that friendship between an instructor and a student is impossible. This does not mean that the two should remain strangers; there can exist cordial, easy relations, tinged perhaps with a certain kind of affection; but friendship, not. For friendship has strict prerequisites, among them, freedom of choice and equality of status. Neither of these can exist in the teacher-student relation. The absence of equality may horrify the sentimental but it is a fact nevertheless. Consider only a few of the things a teacher must do—he must judge work done, decide passing or failing, order tasks, reprove mistakes, discipline conduct, and *deal impartially with all similar cases.* These, I submit, are not the acts of a friend, even if—as equality would demand—the student were allowed reciprocal privileges.

I shall go further and say that it is not good for a teacher to associate steadily with students. Real reciprocity is here again out of the question; differences of age, temperament, purpose and background, are so many hidden reefs over which even conversation founders. This does not mean that it is not delightful once in a while to accept a dinner invitation from a group of students who are friends among themselves, or to join "the gang" in a sandwich and glass of beer after a seminar. And the talk over the beer need not be in the least stiff or scholastic. Simple manners go farthest, provided they are genuine, and they best protect the very delicate adjustment between student and teacher on which the latter's efficacy depends.

Even in the most promising of instances, which are few and far between, students are interesting only as students—I would say "as cases," were it not that medical usage has led the laity to attach to the word a false notion of detachment and pure science. This is not so: the "case" is defined as the state of the patient. Hence it is an absorbing, ever-changing human problem and not merely a mechanical puzzle. Depending on circumstance, the problem takes in more or less of the patient's social background, more or less of his unique personality, and this excludes only what does not bear on improving him. The same is true in teaching—and the comparison, by the way, explains why it is equally bad to teach and to doctor in the bosom of the family. Too many irrelevant feelings and incompatible relations enter in. To be sure, some persons are less aware of these crisscrossings than others, else one would not see so many love affairs developing between men teachers and their women students, but in spite of the success and frequency of these involvements, I cannot look upon them as belonging to the ideal relation of teacher and taught. Not to mention that it is bad for love-making to combine it with a desire to improve and be improved.

For improvement in some form is surely the goal of associating young minds with trained ones in what the Navy Department calls "regular contact hours." Self-improvement is certainly the motive for the student's hunting down of his instructor. The boy wants to draw the older man out on subjects that necessarily beset youth at college—politics, sex, career, family. Or he wants a sympathetic listener for his own peculiar story; he wants good advice from someone other than a parent or a friend. The family physician sometimes serves, but more rarely than before the days of busy specialization; and the father confessor is available to only a few. So the teacher hears it all—the quarrels with contemporaries, the disappointments and injustices in campus affairs, the girls that charm but leave insatiate, and most persistently, the vision of the good life clearly seen but lying inaccessible on a pathless height.

There is no use pretending that all this does not go straight to one's heart. If ever another's life palpitates visibly before one's eyes, it is at this time, when the consciousness of what living means has just dawned and no thick shell has yet grown over it to protect or suppress it. The spectacle is in itself so touching, its details often so moving, that sentimentalists and cynics among adults take advantage of it to indulge their vices of mind. The sentimentalist eggs on the flow of feeling to wallow in it helplessly; the cynic—equally upset—dismisses the manifestation as "a stage" and the trouble as "adolescent."

Meanwhile, the "stage" is a reality and adolescence remains one of the four seasons of life. It is the season of storms and its shipwrecks are genuine calamities. Unless the causes are foreseen and dealt with, both firmly and tenderly, the disasters are wept over in vain, too late. It is at college, among boys who are barely young men, that the first winnowing by the unseen hand occurs. It is at this time that they feel ignorance and the desire to know, despair and the desire to act—all with a vividness and an urgency unbelievably powerful and explosive. It is just because these forces are as yet raw and unchanneled that young men can be taught; and for the same reason, that with bad luck or bad handling the same forces destroy from within: boys take to drink, commit suicide and murder, plot wild schemes to recoup money or other losses, burn inwardly with shame, injustice, or contempt, stare dishonor in the face, or feverishly nurse mad, hopeless, and sometimes meaningless ambitions.

Not unnaturally, the teacher who has these glimpses of the demonic in the confidences that are brought to him may be unnerved. Often he is the youngest man on the staff. He inspires trust by the recentness of his student days and the fact that he has crossed the bar and been stamped with the professional seal of guarantee. Yet inexperienced himself, how is he to deal with so many chaotic revelations? What advice can he give, with what assurance, and how far can he engage his responsibility? Perhaps he should have thought of that before becoming a teacher. As every mariner must expect that his first voyage as captain will be signalized by a typhoon, so with a teacher *in loco parentis*. That is the normal risk. Besides, he can apply to older friends, though taking care to maintain professional secrecy; and he can regain poise by reminding himself of certain truths. In the first place, he cannot act for another, or even feel. He can only think, and convey calm and comfort. What any boy needs most to be told is that he is not alone in his distress; that cases similar to his are known to history, and that the victims have lived to tell the tale. You would suppose that college men would help one another by just this kind of talk. But they do not. Boys may live and play together and yet remain like a handful of small shot in a bowl—hard, round, impenetrable—and, if shot could feel, lonely. Since in real trouble the family is "no use," the teacher is the only man who can be counted on to reassert that we are members one of another; and since this belief depends on a subtle sympathy which cannot be commanded, it is best to let college men freely follow their affinities and take as advisers men they trust.

In a Classroom

JOHN HOLMES

JOHN HOLMES was born in Somerville, Massachusetts, in 1904. In 1929 he was graduated from Tufts College, where he is now Assistant Professor. For a number of years he was poetry critic for the Boston Evening Tran- script. *He has been a frequent contributor to magazines and has published several volumes of poems.*

ALL the time I am talking, I am talking to you
Trying to make it true.
I am trying to say, Be sure.
Endure. It will be the way you want it.
I am remembering when I was wild, too.
Secret. Rich. Unknown
Except to one friend. Even then alone.
I am asking you what you want to be,
Asking you what you want of me.
Telling you there is nothing in yourself
Ever to fear.
And wondering if you hear.

Keate's Way

ANDRÉ MAUROIS

ANDRÉ MAUROIS, French biographer and novelist, was born in 1885. He received his education at various lycées and at Rouen and Caen. After completing his formal education, he worked in his father's factory until the outbreak of World War I in 1914. He then entered the army and with his knowledge of English was soon attached to the British army as a liaison officer. Out of his army experience came his first book, Les Silences du Colonel Bramble, *published in 1918. The success of this book led Maurois to seek a career as a writer. Today he is a distinguished biographer.*

IN the year 1809 George III appointed as Headmaster of Eton, Dr. Keate, a terrible little man who considered the flogging-block a necessary station on the road to perfection, and who ended a sermon on the Sixth Beatitude by saying, "Now, boys, be pure in heart! For if not, I'll flog you until you are!"

The country gentlemen and merchant princes who put their sons under his care were not displeased by such a specimen of pious ferocity, nor could they think lightly of the man who had birched half the ministers, bishops, generals, and dukes in the kingdom.

In those days the severest discipline found favour with the best people. The recent French Revolution had proved the dangers of liberalism when it affects the governing classes. Official England, which was the soul of the Holy Alliance, believed that in combating Napoleon she was combating liberalism in the purple. She required from her public schools a generation of smooth-tongued hypocrites.

In order to crush out any possible republican ardour in the young aristocrats of Eton, their studies were organized on conventional and frivolous lines. At the end of five years the pupil had read Homer twice through, almost all Virgil and an expurgated Horace; he could turn out passable Latin epigrams on Wellington and Nelson. The taste for Latin quotations was then so pronounced, that Pitt in the House of Commons being interrupted in a quotation from the *Æneid,* the whole House, Whigs and Tories alike, rose as one man to supply the end. Certainly a fine example of homogeneous culture.

The study of science, being optional, was naturally neglected, but dancing was obligatory. On the subject of religion Keate held doubt to be a crime, but that otherwise it wasn't worth talking about. He feared mysticism more than indifference, permitted laughing in chapel and wasn't strict about keeping the Sabbath.

Here, in order to make the reader understand the—perhaps unconscious —Machiavellism of this celebrated trainer of youth, we may note that he did not mind being told a few lies: "A sign of respect," he would say.

Barbarous customs reigned amongst the boys themselves. The little boys were the slaves or "fags" of the big boys. The fag made his master's bed, fetched from the pump outside and carried up his water in the morning, brushed his clothes, and cleaned his shoes. Disobedience was punished by torments to fit the crime. A boy writing home, not to complain, but to describe his life, says: "Rolls, whose fag I am, put on spurs to force me to jump a ditch which was too wide for me. Each time I funked it he dug them into me, and of course my legs are bleeding, my 'Greek Poets' reduced to pulp, and my new clothes torn to tatters."

The glorious "art of self-defence" was in high honour. At the conclusion of one strenuous bout, a boy was left dead upon the floor. Keate, coming to look at the corpse, said simply: "This is regrettable, of course, but I desire above all things that an Eton boy should be ready to return a blow for a blow."

The real, but hidden, aim of the system was to form "hard-faced men," all run in the same mould. In action you might be independent, but any originality of thought, of dress, or of language was the most heinous of crimes. To betray the smallest interest in ideas or books was a bit of disgusting affection to be forcibly pulled up by the roots.

Such a life as this seemed to the majority of English boys quite right. The pride they felt in carrying on the traditions of a school like Eton founded by a king, and under the protection of and near neighbour to all the succeeding kings, was balm of Gilead to their woes.

Only a few sensitive souls suffered terribly and suffered long.

One of these, for example, the young Percy Bysshe Shelley, son of a rich Sussex landowner and grandson to Sir Bysshe Shelley, Bart., did not seem able to acclimatize himself at all.

This boy, who was exceptionally beautiful, with brilliant blue eyes, dark curling hair, and a delicate complexion, displayed a sensitiveness of conscience most unusual in one of his class, as well as an incredible tendency to question the Rules of the Game.

When first he appeared in the school, the Sixth Form captains, seeing his slender build and girlish air, imagined they would have little need to enforce their authority over him. But they soon discovered that the smallest threat threw him into a passion of resistance. An unbreakable will, with a lack of the necessary physical strength to carry out its decrees, forefated him to rebellion. His eyes, dreamy when at peace, acquired, under the influence of enthusiasm or indignation, a light that was almost wild; his voice, usually soft and low, became agonized and shrill.

His love of books, his contempt for games, his long hair floating in the wind, his collar opened on a girlish throat, everything about him scandalized those self-charged to maintain in the little world of Eton the brutal spirit of which it was so proud.

But Shelley, from his first day there, having decided that fagging was an outrage to human dignity, had refused obedience to the orders of his fag-master, and in consequence was proclaimed an outlaw.

He was called "Mad Shelley." The strongest of his tormentors undertook to save his soul as by fire, although they gave up attacking him in single combat, when they found he would stop at nothing. Scratching and slapping, he fought with open hands like a girl.

An organized "Shelley-bait" became one of the favourite amusements. Some scout would discover the strange lad reading poetry by the riverside, and at once give the "view hallo!" Shelley, with his hair streaming on the wind, would take flight across the meadows, through the college cloister, the Eton streets. Finally, surrounded like a stag at bay, he would utter a prolonged and piercing shriek, while his tormentors would "nail" him to the wall with balls slimey with mud.

A voice would cry "Shelley!" And "Shelley!" another voice would take it up. The old walls would re-echo to yells of "Shelley!" in every key. A lickspittle fag would pluck at the victim's jacket; another would pinch him; a third would kick away the books he squeezed convulsively under his arm. Then, every finger would be pointed towards him, while fresh cries of "Shelley!" "Shelley!" "Shelley!" finally shattered his nerves.

The crisis was reached for which his tormentors waited—an outburst of mad rage, in which the boy's eyes flashed fire, his cheeks grew white, his whole body trembled and shook.

Tired at length of a spectacle that was always the same, the school went back to its games.

Shelley picked up his mud-stained books and, lost in thought, wandered away through the meadows that border the Thames and, flinging himself down on the sun-flecked grass, watched the river glide past him. Running water, like music, has the power to change misery into melancholy. Both, through their smooth, unceasing flow, pour over the soul the anodyne of forgetfulness and peace. The massive towers of Windsor and Eton typified to the young rebel a hostile and unchanging world, but the reflection of the willow-trees trembling in the water soothed him by its tenuous fragility.

He returned to his books, to Diderot, to Voltaire, to the system of M. d'Holbach. To love these Frenchmen, so hated by his masters, seemed an act of defiance worthy of his courage. An English work condensed them all. Godwin's *Political Justice*. It was his favourite reading.

Godwin made all things seem simple. Had men studied him the world would have attained to a state of idyllic happiness. Had they listened to the voice of reason, that is of Godwin, two hours' work a day would have been sufficient for all their needs. Free love would have replaced the stupid conventions of marriage, and philosophy have banished the terrors of superstition.

Unfortunately, "prejudices" still shut men's minds to truth.

Shelley closed his book, stretched himself out upon the sunny, flower-starred grass, and meditated on the misery of man. From the school buildings behind him a confused murmur of stupid voices floated out over the exquisite landscape of wood and stream, but here at least no mocking eye could spy upon him. The boy's tears ran down, and pressing his hands together, he made this vow: "I swear to be just and wise and free, if such power in me lies. I swear never to become an accomplice, even by my silence, of the selfish and the powerful. I swear to dedicate my whole life to the worship of beauty."

Had Dr. Keate been witness to an outburst of religious ardour so deplorable in any well-regulated school, he would certainly have treated the case in his favourite way.

The Spires of Oxford

WINIFRED M. LETTS

WINIFRED M. LETTS is an Irish writer who was born in 1887. She was educated at Alexandra College, Dublin, the city in which she now lives. Best known in the United States as a poet, Winifred Letts is better known in the British Isles as a dramatist and writer of children's books. Two of her plays have been performed at the Abbey Theatre. Many of her poems reflect the humor and pathos of the simple Irish people among whom she lived in western Ireland. Her experiences as a volunteer nurse in World War I found expression in her volume Poems of the War.

The Spires of Oxford, written at the beginning of World War I, is, perhaps, her best-known lyric poem.

I SAW the spires of Oxford
   As I was passing by,
The gray spires of Oxford
   Against a pearl-gray sky.
My heart was with the Oxford men
   Who went abroad to die.

The years go fast in Oxford,
   The golden years and gay,
The hoary Colleges look down
   On careless boys at play.
But when the bugles sounded war
   They put their games away.

They left the peaceful river,
   The cricket-field, the quad,
The shaven lawns of Oxford
   To seek a bloody sod—
They gave their merry youth away
   For country and for God.

God rest you, happy gentlemen;
   Who laid your good lives down,

Who took the khaki and the gun
Instead of cap and gown.
God bring you to a fairer place
Than even Oxford town.

Ichabod Crane

WASHINGTON IRVING

WASHINGTON IRVING (1783-1859) was born in New York of British parents. Interested in writing from childhood, he published his first essays in the New York Morning Chronicle *in 1802 under the name of Jonathan Oldstyle, Gent. Soon after his return from a leisurely journey abroad in 1806 he was admitted to the practice of law, but writing was more to his taste. The* Salmagundi *papers, Addisonian essays lampooning local society and politics, appeared in the following year. With the publication in 1809 of* A History of New York, *by Diedrich Knickerbocker, his literary reputation was established.*

From 1815-1832 Irving lived in England. When in 1818 the family cutlery business failed, he turned to writing as a means of livelihood. The Sketch Book of Geoffrey Crayon, Gent., *published in the following year, won him financial competence and literary recognition both at home and abroad.*

From 1829-1831 he was secretary of the American Legation in London, and from 1842-1846, Minister to Spain. He died at Sunnyside on the Hudson on November 28, 1859, the first American writer of belles-lettres.

Ichabod Crane is the well-known schoolmaster in The Legend of Sleepy Hollow.

IN this by-place of nature, there abode, in a remote period of American history, that is to say, some thirty years since, a worthy wight of the name of Ichabod Crane; who sojourned, or, as he expressed it, "tarried," in Sleepy Hollow, for the purpose of instructing the children of the vicinity. He was a native of Connecticut, a State which supplies the Union with pioneers for the mind as well as for the forest, and sends forth yearly its legions of frontier woodsmen and country schoolmasters. The cognomen of Crane was not inapplicable to his person. He was tall, but exceedingly lank, with narrow shoulders, long arms and legs, hands that dangled a mile out of his sleeves, feet that might have served for shovels, and his whole frame most loosely hung together. His head was small, and flat at top, with huge ears, large green glassy eyes, and a long snipe nose, so that it looked like a weathercock perched upon his spindle neck, to tell which way the wind blew. To see him striding along the profile of a hill on a windy day, with his clothes bagging and fluttering about him, one might have mistaken him for the genius of famine descending upon the earth, or some scarecrow eloped from a cornfield.

His school-house was a low building of one large room, rudely constructed of logs; the windows partly glazed, and partly patched with leaves of old copy-books. It was most ingeniously secured at vacant hours by a withe twisted in the handle of the door, and stakes set against the window-shutters; so that, though a thief might get in with perfect ease, he would find some embarrassment in getting out: an idea most probably borrowed by the architect, Yost Van Houten, from the mystery of an eel-pot. The school-house stood in a rather lonely but pleasant situation, just at the foot of a woody hill, with a brook running close by, and a formidable birch-tree growing at one end of it. From hence the low murmur of his pupils' voices, conning over their lessons, might be heard in a drowsy summer's day, like the hum of a bee-hive; interrupted now and then by the authoritative voice of the master, in the tone of menace or command; or, peradventure, by the appalling sound of the birch, as he urged some tardy loiterer along the flowery path of knowledge. Truth to say, he was a conscientious man, and ever bore in mind the golden maxim, "Spare the rod and spoil the child."—Ichabod Crane's scholars certainly were not spoiled.

I would not have it imagined, however, that he was one of those cruel potentates of the school, who joy in the smart of their subjects; on the contrary, he administered justice with discrimination rather than severity, taking the burden off the backs of the weak, and laying it on those of the strong. Your mere puny stripling, that winced at the least flourish of the rod, was passed by with indulgence; but the claims of justice were satisfied by inflicting a double portion on some little, tough, wrong-headed, broad-skirted Dutch urchin, who sulked and swelled and grew dogged and sullen beneath the birch. All this he called "doing his duty" by their parents; and he never inflicted a chastisement without following it by the assurance, so consolatory to the smarting urchin, that "he would remember it, and thank him for it the longest day he had to live."

When school-hours were over, he was even the companion and playmate of the larger boys; and on holiday afternoons would convoy some of the smaller ones home, who happened to have pretty sisters, or good housewives for mothers, noted for the comforts of the cupboard. Indeed it behooved him to keep on good terms with his pupils. The revenue arising from his school was small, and would have been scarcely sufficient to furnish him with daily bread, for he was a huge feeder, and, though lank, had the dilating powers of an anaconda; but to help out his maintenance, he was, according to country custom in those parts, boarded and lodged at the houses of the farmers, whose children he instructed. With these he lived successively a week at a time; thus going the rounds of the neighborhood, with all his worldly effects tied up in a cotton handkerchief.

That all this might not be too onerous on the purses of his rustic patrons, who are apt to consider the costs of schooling a grievous burden, and schoolmasters as mere drones, he had various ways of rendering himself both useful and agreeable. He assisted the farmers occasionally in the lighter labors of their farms; helped to make hay; mended the fences; took the horses to water; drove the cows from pasture; and cut wood for the winter fire. He laid aside, too, all the dominant dignity and absolute sway with which he lorded it in his little empire, the school, and became wonderfully gentle and ingratiating. He found favor in the eyes of the mothers, by petting the children, particularly the youngest; and like the lion bold, which whilom so magnanimously the lamb did hold, he would sit with a child on one knee, and rock a cradle with his foot for whole hours together.

In addition to his other vocations, he was the singing-master of the neighborhood, and picked up many bright shillings by instructing the young folks in psalmody. It was a matter of no little vanity to him, on Sundays, to take his station in front of the church-gallery, with a band of chosen singers; where, in his own mind, he completely carried away the palm from the parson. Certain it is, his voice resounded far above all the rest of the congregation; and there are peculiar quavers still to be heard in that church, and which may even be heard half a mile off, quite to the opposite side of the mill-pond, on a still Sunday morning, which are said to be legitimately descended from the nose of Ichabod Crane. Thus, by divers little makeshifts in that ingenious way which is commonly denominated "by hook and by crook," the worthy pedagogue got on tolerably enough, and was thought, by all who understood nothing of the labor of headwork to have a wonderfully easy life of it.

Quincy

HENRY ADAMS

OF distinguished ancestry, Henry Adams (1838-1918) was born on Beacon Hill, Boston. The account of his education and the development of his intellectual life is set forth in his autobiography, The Education of Henry Adams, *from which the selections which follow are taken. In this book Adams contends that his early education was defective. Even Harvard failed to give him what he needed, though the hours spent in the study of James Russell Lowell he always recalled with gratitude. During his college years he did some writing but made little effort to achieve scholastic distinction.*

In 1858 Adams went abroad to study law, but he returned after two years with little knowledge of law, having spent his time chiefly in travel. During the Civil War years he served as his father's secretary in Washington and in London, reading assiduously in his leisure time and occasionally writing an article for magazine publication. He returned to Washington from London in 1868 and continued to write for periodicals. In 1870 he accepted the invitation of President Eliot to teach history at Harvard. Of his work as a teacher he did not think highly. Feeling that nine out of ten students are not interested in learning, he deliberately sought to cultivate the tenth. After seven years of teaching, Adams resigned his position at Harvard, took up residence in Washington, and devoted his time to writing. In following years he traveled widely, visiting Europe and the Orient and returning to Washington from time to time.

The Education of Henry Adams was privately printed in 1907 and published in 1918 after the author's death. Though this work is generally regarded as autobiography, Adams himself regarded his book as "a study of twentieth-century multiplicity." The following selections from the book deal with Adams's Harvard experiences both as student and as teacher.

UNDER the shadow of Boston State House, turning its back on the house of John Hancock, the little passage called Hancock Avenue runs, or ran, from Beacon Street, skirting the State House grounds, to

"Boston," "Harvard College," and "Quincy" are from *The Education of Henry Adams, an Autobiography,* by Henry Adams; copyright, 1918, by the Massachusetts Historical Society; reprinted by permission of Houghton Mifflin Company.

Mount Vernon Street, on the summit of Beacon Hill; and there, in the third house below Mount Vernon Place, February 16, 1838, a child was born, and christened later by his uncle, the minister of the First Church after the tenets of Boston Unitarianism, as Henry Brooks Adams.

———

This problem of education, started in 1838, went on for three years, while the baby grew, like other babies, unconsciously, as a vegetable, the outside world working as it never had worked before, to get his new universe ready for him. Often in old age he puzzled over the question whether, on the doctrine of chances, he was at liberty to accept himself or his world as an accident. No such accident had ever happened before in human experience. For him, alone, the old universe was thrown into the ash-heap and a new one created. He and his eighteenth-century, troglodytic Boston were suddenly cut apart—separated forever—in act if not in sentiment, by the opening of the Boston and Albany Railroad; the appearance of the first Cunard steamers in the bay; and the telegraphic messages which carried from Baltimore to Washington the news that Henry Clay and James K. Polk were nominated for the Presidency. This was in May, 1844; he was six years old; his new world was ready for use, and only fragments of the old met his eyes.

Of all this that was being done to complicate his education, he knew only the color of yellow. He first found himself sitting on a yellow kitchen floor in strong sunlight. He was three years old when he took this earliest step in education; a lesson of color. The second followed soon; a lesson of taste. On December 3, 1841, he developed scarlet fever. For several days he was as good as dead, reviving only under the careful nursing of his family. When he began to recover strength, about January 1, 1842, his hunger must have been stronger than any other pleasure or pain, for while in after life he retained not the faintest recollection of his illness, he remembered quite clearly his aunt entering the sickroom bearing in her hand a saucer with a baked apple.

The order of impressions retained by memory might naturally be that of color and taste, although one would rather suppose that the sense of pain would be first to educate. In fact, the third recollection of the child was that of discomfort. The moment he could be removed, he was bundled up in blankets and carried from the little house in Hancock Avenue to a larger one which his parents were to occupy for the rest of their lives in the neighboring Mount Vernon Street. The season was midwinter, January 10, 1842, and he never forgot his acute distress for want of air under his blankets, or the noises of moving furniture.

As a means of variation from a normal type, sickness in childhood ought to have a certain value not to be classed under any fitness or unfitness of natural selection; and especially scarlet fever affected boys seriously, both physically and in character, though they might through life puzzle themselves to decide whether it had fitted or unfitted them for success;

but this fever of Henry Adams took greater and greater importance in his eyes, from the point of view of education, the longer he lived. At first, the effect was physical. He fell behind his brothers two or three inches in height, and proportionally in bone and weight. His character and processes of mind seemed to share in this fining-down process of scale. He was not good in a fight, and his nerves were more delicate than boys' nerves ought to be. He exaggerated these weaknesses as he grew older. The habit of doubt; of distrusting his own judgment and of totally rejecting the judgment of the world; the tendency to regard every question as open; the hesitation to act except as a choice of evils; the shirking of responsibility; the love of line, form, quality; the horror of ennui; the passion for companionship and the antipathy to society—all these are well-known qualities of New England character in no way peculiar to individuals but in this instance they seemed to be stimulated by the fever, and Henry Adams could never make up his mind whether, on the whole, the change of character was morbid or healthy, good or bad for his purpose. His brothers were the type; he was the variation.

As far as the boy knew, the sickness did not affect him at all, and he grew up in excellent health, bodily and mental, taking life as it was given; accepting its local standards without a difficulty, and enjoying much of it as keenly as any other boy of his age. He seemed to himself quite normal, and his companions seemed always to think him so. Whatever was peculiar about him was education, not character, and came to him, directly and indirectly, as the result of that eighteenth-century inheritance which he took with his name.

The atmosphere of education in which he lived was colonial, revolutionary, almost Cromwellian, as though he were steeped, from his greatest grandmother's birth, in the odor of political crime. Resistance to something was the law of New England nature; the boy looked out on the world with the instinct of resistance; for numberless generations his predecessors had viewed the world chiefly as a thing to be reformed, filled with evil forces to be abolished, and they saw no reason to suppose that they had wholly succeeded in the abolition; the duty was unchanged. That duty implied not only resistance to evil, but hatred of it. Boys naturally look on all force as an enemy, and generally find it so, but the New Englander, whether boy or man, in his long struggle with a stingy or hostile universe, had learned also to love the pleasure of hating; his joys were few.

———

Boys are wild animals, rich in the treasures of sense, but the New England boy had a wider range of emotions than boys of more equable climates. He felt his nature crudely, as it was meant. To the boy Henry Adams, summer was drunken. Among senses, smell was the strongest— smell of hot pine-woods and sweet-fern in the scorching summer noon; of new-mown hay; of ploughed earth; of box hedges; of peaches, lilacs, syringas; of stables, barns, cowyards; of salt water and low tide on the marshes; nothing came amiss. Next to smell came taste, and the children knew the taste of everything they saw or touched, from pennyroyal and flagroot to the shell of a pignut and the letters of a spelling-book—the taste of A-B, AB, suddenly revived on the boy's tongue sixty years afterwards. Light, line, and color as sensual pleasures, came later and were as crude as the rest. The New England light is glare, and the atmosphere harshens color. The boy was a full man before he ever knew what was meant by atmosphere; his idea of pleasure in light was the blaze of a New England sun. His idea of color was a peony, with the dew of early morning on its petals. The intense blue of the sea, as he saw it a mile or two away, from the Quincy hills; the cumuli in a June afternoon sky; the strong reds and greens and purples of colored prints and children's picture-books, as the American colors then ran; these were ideals. The opposites or antipathies, were the cold grays of November evenings, and the thick, muddy thaws of Boston winter. With such standards, the Bostonian could not but develop a double nature. Life was a double thing. After a January blizzard, the boy who could look with pleasure into the violent snow-glare of the cold white sunshine, with its intense light and shade, scarcely knew what was meant by tone. He could reach it only by education.

Winter and summer, then, were two hostile lives, and bred two separate natures. Winter was always the effort to live; summer was tropical license. Whether the children rolled in the grass, or waded in the brook, or swam in the salt ocean, or sailed in the bay, or fished for smelts in the creeks, or netted minnows in the salt-marshes, or took to the pine-woods and the granite quarries, or chased muskrats and hunted snapping-turtles in the swamps, or mushrooms or nuts on the autumn hills, summer and country were always sensual living, while winter was always compulsory learning. Summer was the multiplicity of nature; winter was school.

Boston

IN any and all its forms, the boy detested school, and the prejudice became deeper with years. He always reckoned his schooldays, from ten to sixteen years old, as time thrown away. Perhaps his needs turned out to be exceptional, but his existence was exceptional. Between 1850 and 1900 nearly every one's existence was exceptional. For success in the life imposed on him he needed, as afterwards appeared, the facile use of only four tools: Mathematics, French, German, and Spanish. With these, he could master in very short time any special branch of inquiry, and feel at home in any society. Latin and Greek, he could, with the help of the modern languages, learn more completely by the intelligent work of six weeks than in the six years he spent on them at school. These four tools were necessary to his success in life, but he never controlled any one of them.

Thus, at the outset, he was condemned to failure more or less complete in the life awaiting him, but not more so than his companions. Indeed, had his father kept the boy at home, and given him half an hour's direction every day, he would have done more for him than school ever could do for them. Of course, school-taught men and boys looked down on home-bred boys, and rather prided themselves on their own ignorance, but the man of sixty can generally see what he needed in life, and in Henry Adams's opinion it was not school.

Most school experience was bad. Boy associations at fifteen were worse than none. Boston at that time offered few healthy resources for boys or men. The bar-room and billiard-room were more familiar than parents knew. As a rule boys could skate and swim and were sent to dancing-school; they played a rudimentary game of baseball, football, and hockey; a few could sail a boat; still fewer had been out with a gun to shoot yellow-legs or a stray wild duck; one or two may have learned something about natural history if they came from the neighborhood of Concord; none could ride across country, or knew what shooting with dogs meant. Sport as a pursuit was unknown. Boat-racing came after 1850. For horse-racing, only the trotting-course existed. Of all pleasures, winter sleighing was still the gayest and most popular. From none of these amusements could the boy learn anything likely to be of use to him in the world. Books remained as in the eighteenth century, the source of life, and as they came out—Thackeray, Dickens, Bulwer, Tennyson, Macaulay, Carlyle, and the rest—they were devoured; but as far as happiness went, the happiest hours of the boy's education were passed in summer lying on a musty heap of Congressional Documents in the old farmhouse at Quincy, reading "Quentin Durward," "Ivanhoe," and "The Talisman," and raiding the garden at intervals for peaches and pears. On the whole he learned most then.

Harvard College

ONE day in June, 1854, young Adams walked for the last time down the steps of Mr. Dixwell's school in Boylston Place, and felt no sensation but one of unqualified joy that this experience was ended. Never before or afterwards in his life did he close a period so long as four years without some sensation of loss—some sentiment of habit—but school was what in after life he commonly heard his friends denounce as an intolerable bore. He was born too old for it. The same thing could be said of most New

England boys. Mentally they never were boys. Their education as men
should have begun at ten years old. They were fully five years more mature than the English or European boy for whom schools were made. For
the purposes of future advancement, as afterwards appeared, these first
six years of a possible education were wasted in doing imperfectly what
might have been done perfectly in one, and in any case would have had
small value. The next regular step was Harvard College. He was more
than glad to go. For generation after generation, Adamses and Brookses
and Boylstons and Gorhams had gone to Harvard College, and although
none of them, as far as known, had ever done any good there, or thought
himself the better for it, custom, social ties, convenience, and, above all,
economy, kept each generation in the track. Any other education would
have required a serious effort, but no one took Harvard College seriously.
All went there because their friends went there, and the College was their
ideal of social self-respect.

Harvard College, as far as it educated at all, was a mild and liberal
school, which sent young men into the world with all they needed to
make respectable citizens, and something of what they wanted to make
useful ones. Leaders of men it never tried to make. Its ideals were altogether different. The Unitarian clergy had given to the College a character
of moderation, balance, judgment, restraint, what the French called
mesure: excellent traits, which the College attained with singular success,
so that its graduates could commonly be recognized by the stamp, but
such a type of character rarely lent itself to autobiography. In effect, the
school created a type but not a will. Four years of Harvard College, if
successful, resulted in an autobiographical blank, a mind on which only
a water-mark had been stamped.

The stamp, as such things went, was a good one. The chief wonder of
education is that it does not ruin everybody concerned in it, teachers
and taught. Sometimes in after life, Adams debated whether in fact it had
not ruined him and most of his companions, but, disappointment apart,
Harvard College was probably less hurtful than any other university then
in existence. It taught little, and that little ill, but it left the mind open,
free from bias, ignorant of facts, but docile. The graduate had few strong
prejudices. He knew little, but his mind remained supple, ready to receive
knowledge.

———

If the student got little from his mates, he got little more from his masters. The four years passed at college were, for his purpose, wasted. Harvard College was a good school, but at bottom what the boy disliked most
was any school at all. He did not want to be one in a hundred—one per
cent of an education. He regarded himself as the only person for whom
his education had value, and he wanted the whole of it. He got barely
half of an average. Long afterwards, when the devious path of life led him
back to teach in his turn what no student naturally cared or needed to

know, he diverted some dreary hours of faculty-meetings by looking up his record in the class-lists, and found himself graded precisely in the middle. In the one branch he most needed—mathematics—barring the few first scholars, failure was so nearly universal that no attempt at grading could have had value, and whether he stood fortieth or ninetieth must have been the accident or the personal favor of the professor. Here his education failed lamentably. At best he could never have been a mathematician; at worst he would never have cared to be one; but he needed to read mathematics, like any other universal language, and he never reached the alphabet.

Beyond two or three Greek plays, the student got nothing from the ancient languages. Beyond some incoherent theories of free-trade and protection, he got little from Political Economy. He could not afterwards remember to have heard the name of Karl Marx mentioned, or the title of "Capital." He was equally ignorant of Auguste Comte. These were the two writers of his time who most influenced his thought. The bit of practical teaching he afterwards reviewed with most curiosity was the course in Chemistry, which taught him a number of theories that befogged his mind for a lifetime. The only teaching that appealed to his imagination was a course of lectures by Louis Agassiz on the Glacial Period and Palaeontology, which had more influence on his curiosity than the rest of the college instruction altogether. The entire work of the four years could have been easily put into the work of any four months in after life.

Harvard College was a negative force, and negative forces have value. Slowly it weakened the violent political bias of childhood, not by putting interests in its place, but by mental habits which had no bias at all. It would also have weakened the literary bias, if Adams had been capable of finding other amusement, but the climate kept him steady to desultory and useless reading, till he had run through libraries of volumes which he forgot even to their title-pages. Rather by instinct than by guidance, he turned to writing, and his professors or tutors occasionally gave his English composition a hesitating approval; but in that branch, as in all the rest, even when he made a long struggle for recognition, he never convinced his teachers that his abilities, at their best, warranted placing him on the rank-list, among the first third of his class. Instructors generally reach a fairly accurate gauge of their scholars' powers. Henry Adams himself held the opinion that his instructors were very nearly right, and when he became a professor in his turn, and made mortifying mistakes in ranking his scholars, he still obstinately insisted that on the whole, he was not far wrong. Student or professor, he accepted the negative standard because it was the standard of the school.

Master and Pupil

O. M.

(To J. F. R.)

Two years ago I taught him Greek,
  And used to give him hints on bowling;
His classics were a trifle weak;
  His 'action' needed some controlling.
Convinced of my superior *nous*
  I thought him crude, and I was rather
Inclined, as master of his House,
  To treat him like a heavy father.

I wrote the usual reports
  Upon his 'lack of concentration';
Though certainly at winter Sports
  He did not earn this condemnation.
I took him out San Moritz way
  One Christmas, and our *rôles* inverted,
For in the land of ski and sleigh
  His mastery was soon asserted.

I thought him just a normal lad,
  Well-mannered, wholesome, unaffected;
The makings of a Galahad
  In him I had not yet detected;
And when I strove to mend his style,
  Blue-penciling his exercises,
I little guessed that all the while
  His soul was ripe for high emprises.

Two years ago! and here I am,
  Rejected as unfit; still trying
(As Verrall taught me on the Cam)
  To make Greek Plays electrifying.
And he who, till he was eighteen,
  Found life one long excuse for laughing,
For eighteen solid months has been
  Continuously 'strafed' or 'strafing.'

He writes me letters from the front
　　Which prove, although he doesn't know it,
That though his words are plain and blunt,
　　He has the vision of a poet;
And lately, on his eight days' rest,
　　After long months of hard campaigning,
He came, and lo! an angel guest
　　I was aware of entertaining.

About himself he seldom spoke,
　　But often of his widowed mother,
And how she nobly bore the stroke
　　That robbed them of his sailor brother.
And still, from loyalty or whim,
　　He would defer to my opinion,
Unconscious how I envied him
　　His hard-earned gift of self-dominion.

For he had faced the awful King
　　Of Shadows in the darksome Valley,
And scorned the terrors of his sting
　　In many a perilous storm and sally.
Firm in the faith that never tires
　　Or thinks that man is God-forsaken,
From war's fierce seven-times-heated fires
　　He had emerged unseared, unshaken.

There are, alas! no sons of mine
　　To serve their country in her trial,
Embattled in the cause divine
　　Of sacrifice and self-denial;
But if there were, I could not pray
　　That God might shield them from disaster
More strongly than I plead to-day
　　For this my pupil and my master.

Lupton Chapel Service

ARTHUR MACHEN

ARTHUR MACHEN, Welsh novelist and essayist, was born in 1863, in Gwent, the son of a Welsh clergyman. As a child he was dreamy and introspective; as a man he is a solitary and a mystic. At eighteen he went to London, worked as a clerk in a publishing house, and, to ease his misery, wrote poetry.

In the course of his life he has been a teacher, a free-lance writer, a Shakesperian actor, and a journalist. His novels have been caviar to the general, savored by the few.

MEANWHILE the Lupton Sunday went on after its customary fashion. At eleven o'clock the Chapel was full of boys. There were nearly six hundred of them there, the big ones in frock-coats, with high, pointed collars, which made them look like youthful Gladstones. The younger boys wore broad, turn-down collars and had short, square jackets made somewhat in the Basque fashion. Young and old had their hair cut close to the scalp, and this gave them all a brisk but bullety appearance. The masters, in cassock, gown and hood, occupied the choir stalls. Mr. Horbury, the High Usher, clothed in a flowing surplice, was taking Morning Prayer, and the Head occupied a kind of throne by the altar.

The Chapel was not an inspiring building. It was the fourteenth century, certainly, but the fourteenth century translated by 1840, and, it is to be feared, sadly betrayed by the translators. The tracery of the windows was poor and shallow; the mouldings of the piers and arches faulty to a degree; the chancel was absurdly out of proportion, and the pitch-pine benches and stalls had a sticky look. There was a stained-glass window in memory of the Old Luptonians who fell in the Crimea. One wondered what the Woman of Samaria by the Well had to do either with Lupton or the Crimea. And the colouring was like that used in very common, cheap sweets.

The service went with a rush. The prayers, versicles and responses, and psalms were said, the officiant and the congregation rather pressing than pausing—often, indeed, coming so swiftly to cues that two or three words

"Lupton Chapel Service," from *The Secret Glory*, by Arthur Machen, is reprinted by permission of Martin Secker & Warburg Ltd.

at the end of one verse and two or three at the beginning of the next would be lost in a confused noise of contending voices. But *Venite* and *Te Deum* and *Benedictus* were rattled off to frisky Anglicans with great spirit; sometimes the organ tooted, sometimes it bleated gently, like a flock of sheep; now one might have sworn that the music of penny whistles stole on the ear, and again, as the organist coupled up the full organ, using suddenly all the battery of his stops, a gas explosion and a Salvation Army band seemed to strive against one another. A well-known nobleman who had been to Chapel at Lupton was heard to say, with reference to this experience: "I am no Ritualist, heaven knows—but I confess I like a hearty service."

But it was, above all, the sermon that has made the Chapel a place of many memories. The Old Boys say—and one supposes that they are in earnest—that the tall, dignified figure of the Doctor, standing high above them all, his scarlet hood making a brilliant splash of colour against the dingy, bilious paint of the pale green walls, has been an inspiration to them in all quarters of the globe, in all manner of difficulties and temptations.

One man writes that in the midst of a complicated and dangerous deal on the Stock Exchange he remembered a sermon of Dr. Chesson's, called in the printed volume, "Fighting the Good Fight."

"You have a phrase amongst you which I often hear," said the Head. "That phrase is 'Play the game,' and I wish to say that, though you know it not; though, it may be, the words are often spoken half in jest; still they are but your modern, boyish rendering of the old, stirring message which I have just read to you.

" 'Fight the Good Fight.' 'Play the Game.' Remember the words in the storm and struggle, the anxiety and stress that may be—nay, must be—before you—etc., etc., etc."

"After the crisis was over," wrote the Stock Exchange man, "I was thankful that I *had* remembered those words."

"That voice sounding like a trumpet on the battle-field, bidding us all remember that Success was the prize of Effort and Endurance——" So writes a well-known journalist.

"I remembered what the Doctor said to us once about 'running the race,' " says a young soldier, recounting a narrow escape from a fierce enemy, "so I stuck to my orders."

Ambrose, on that Sunday morning, sat in his place, relishing acutely all the savours of the scene, consumed with inward mirth at the thought that this also professed to be a rite of religion. There was an aimless and flighty merriment about the chant to the *Te Deum* that made it difficult for him to control his laughter; and when he joined in the hymn "Pleasant are Thy courts above," there was an odd choke in his voice that made the boy next to him shuffle uneasily.

But the sermon!

It will be found on page 125 of the *Lupton Sermons*. It dealt with the Parable of the Talents, and showed the boys in what the sin of the man who concealed his Talent really consisted.

"I daresay," said the Head, "that many of the older amongst you have wondered what this man's sin really was. You may have read your Greek Testaments carefully, and then have tried to form in your minds some analogy to the circumstances of the parable—and it would not surprise me if you were to tell me that you had failed.

" 'What manner of man was this?' I can imagine your saying one to another. I shall not be astonished if you confess that, for you at least, the question seems unanswerable.

"Yes! Unanswerable to you. For you are English boys, the sons of English gentlemen, to whom the atmosphere of casuistry, of concealment, of subtlety, is unknown; by whom such an atmosphere would be rejected with scorn. You come from homes where there is no shadow, no dark corner which must not be pried into. Your relations and your friends are not of those who hide their gifts from the light of day. Some of you, perhaps, have had the privilege of listening to the talk of one or other of the great statesmen who guide the doctrines of this vast Empire. You will have observed, I am sure, that in the world of politics there is no vain simulation of modesty, no feigned reluctance to speak of worthy achievement. All of you are members of this great community, of which each one of us is so proud, which we think of as the great inspiration and motive force of our lives. Here, you will say, there are no Hidden Talents, for the note of the English Public School (thank God for it!) is openness, frankness, healthy emulation; each endeavouring to do his best for the good of all. In our studies and in our games each desires to excel, to carry off the prize. We strive for a corruptible crown, thinking that this, after all, is the surest discipline for the crown that is incorruptible. If a man say that he loveth God whom he hath not seen, and love not his brother whom he hath seen! Let your light *shine* before men. Be sure that we shall never win Heaven by despising earth.

"Yet that man hid his Talent in a napkin. What does the story mean? What message has it for us to-day?

"I will tell you.   .

"Some years ago during our summer holidays I was on a walking tour in a mountainous district in the north of England. The sky was of a most brilliant blue, the sun poured, as it were, a gospel of gladness on the earth. Towards the close of the day I was entering a peaceful and beautiful valley amongst the hills, when three sullen notes of a bell came down the breeze towards me. There was a pause. Again the three strokes, and for a third time this dismal summons struck on my ears. I walked on in the direction of the sound, wondering whence it came and what it signified; and soon I saw before me a great pile of buildings, surrounded by a gloomy and lofty wall.

"It was a Roman Catholic monastery. The bell was ringing the Angelus, as it is called.

"I obtained admittance to this place and spoke to some of the unhappy monks. I should astonish you if I mentioned the names of some of the deluded men who had immured themselves in this prison-house. It is sufficient to say that among them were a soldier who had won distinction on the battle-field, an artist, a statesman and a physician of no mean repute.

"Now do you understand? Ah! a day will come—you know, I think, what that day is called—when these poor men will have to answer the question: 'Where is the Talent that was given to you?'

" 'Where was your sword in the hour of your country's danger?'

" 'Where was your picture, your consecration of your art to the service of morality and humanity, when the doors of the great Exhibition were thrown open?'

" 'Where was your silver eloquence, your voice of persuasion, when the strife of party was at its fiercest?'

" 'Where was your God-given skill in healing when One of Royal Blood lay fainting on the bed of dire—almost mortal—sickness?'

"And the answer? 'I laid it up in a napkin.' And now, etc., etc."

Then the whole six hundred boys sang "O Paradise! O Paradise!" with a fervour and sincerity that were irresistible. The organ thundered till the bad glass shivered and rattled, and the service was over.

The Ideal Student:
Rules for Behaviour at the University

HENRY PEACHAM

HENRY PEACHAM (1576?-1643?), writer and schoolmaster, was edu-
cated at Trinity College, Cambridge. Soon after his graduation he became
master of a school. His talents and accomplishments were numerous: he
wrote competent Latin and English verses; he was a student of botany, a
composer of music, a mathematician, and a student of heraldry. Further-
more, he could paint and draw and engrave. Perhaps he felt that so rich an
array of talent was wasted on schoolboys, for he soon took a hearty dislike
to his profession, though he continued to be interested in his pupils. He
gave up his school and spent a year in foreign travel, returning in 1614 to
settle in London and write the work by which he is best known, The Compleat Gentleman. *This book was written for William Howard, Lord Arun-*
del's youngest son, a boy of eight, to whom Peacham dedicated the work.
The book endeavors to encourage young men to devote themselves both to
the arts and to athletic exercises. Three editions attest its popularity. It was
the third edition, containing notes on heraldry, which Dr. Johnson used
when he was composing heraldic definitions for his dictionary.

It will be obvious to teachers that the maxims found in the following
excerpts from The Compleat Gentleman *are still sound and useful.*

SINCE the University whereunto you are embodied is not untruly called
the Light and Eye of the Land, in regard from hence, as from the centre
of the sun, the glorious beams of knowledge disperse themselves over all,
without which a chaos of blindness would repossess us again; think that
you are in public view, and *nucibus relictis*,[1] with your gown you have
put on the man, that from hence the reputation of your whole life taketh
her first growth and beginning. For as no glory crowneth with more
abundant praise than that which is here won by diligence and wit, so
there is no infamy abaseth the value and esteem of a gentleman all his
life after more than that procured by sloth and error in the Universities;
yea, though in those years whose innocency have ever pleaded their pardon; whereat I have not a little marvelled, considering the freedom and
privilege of greater places.

---

[1] "Having put away childish things."

But as in a delicate garden kept by a cunning hand, and overlooked with a curious eye, the least disorder or rankness of any one flower putteth a beautiful bed or well-contrived knot out of square, when rudeness and deformity is born withal in rough and undressed places: so believe it, in this Paradise of the Muses, the least neglect and impression of error's foot is so much the more apparent and censured, by how much the sacred Arts have greater interest in the culture of the mind, and correction of manners.

Wherefore your first care, even with the pulling off your boots, let be the choice of your acquaintance and company. For as infection in cities in a time of sickness is taken by concourse and negligent running abroad, when those that keep within and are wary of themselves escape with more safety, so it falleth out here in the University; for this eye hath also her diseases as well as any other part of the body, (I will not say with the physicians, more) with those, whose private houses and studies being not able to contain them, are so cheap of themselves, and so pliable to good fellowship abroad, that in mind and manners (the tokens plainly appearing) they are past recovery ere any friend could hear they were sick.

Entertain therefore the acquaintance of men of the soundest reputation for religion, life and learning, whose conference and company may be unto you a living and a moving library. "For conference and converse was the first mother of all arts and science," as being the greatest discovery of our ignorance and increaser of knowledge, teaching and making us wise by the judgments and examples of many: and you must learn herein of Plato, that is, "To be a lover of knowledge; desirous to hear much, and lastly, to inquire and ask often."

For the companions of your recreation, comfort yourself with gentlemen of your own rank and quality, for that friendship is best contenting and lasting. To be over free and familiar with inferiors, argues a baseness of spirit, and begetteth contempt; for as one shall here at the first prize himself, so let him look at the same rate for ever after to be valued of others.

Carry yourself even and fairly, *Tanquam in statera,*[1] with that moderation in your speech and action (that you seem with Ulysses, to have Minerva always at your elbow:) which, should they be weighed by Envy herself, she might pass them for current; that you be thought rather leaving the University, than lately come thither. But hereto the regard of your worth, the dignity of the place, and abundance of so many fair precedents, will be sufficient motive to stir you up.

Husband your time to the best, for, "The greedy desire of gaining Time is a covetousness only honest." And if you follow the advice of Erasmus, and the practice of Plinius secundus, *Diem in operas partiri,* to divide the day into several tasks of study, you shall find a great ease and furtherance hereby; remembering ever to refer your most serious and important studies

---

[1] "As if on a balance."

unto the morning, "which finisheth alone" (say the learned) "three parts of the work." Julius Caesar having spent the whole day in the field about his military affairs, divided the night also, for three several uses: one part for his sleep, a second for the commonwealth and public business, the third for his book and studies. So careful and thrifty were they then of this precious treasure which we as prodigally lavish out, either vainly or viciously, by whole months and years, until we be called to an account by our great Creditor, who will not abate us the vain expense of a minute.

A Plan for General Education

THOMAS JEFFERSON

THOMAS JEFFERSON (1743-1826) was one of the most versatile of the early statesmen of our country. Congressman, diplomat, and third President of the United States, he found time in the midst of heavy responsibilities to continue his interest in the classics, in music, architecture, poetry, science, agriculture, and education. He was a philosopher and lawyer, interested in both the abstract and the legal rights of man.

Jefferson studied at William and Mary College, practiced law, and in 1769 entered the House of Burgesses. From that time until his retirement from the presidency he was almost constantly in the service of his state and nation.

Realizing the importance of education in the agricultural democracy which he envisioned, he favored a state-supported educational system rather than one under private control. He felt that his founding of the University of Virginia in 1819 was one of the most important acts of his life.

Notes on Virginia, from which the following selection is taken, is Jefferson's reply to a series of questions regarding his native state asked by the Secretary of the French Legation at Philadelphia in 1781.

ANOTHER object of the revisal is, to diffuse knowledge more generally through the mass of the people. This bill proposes to lay off every country into small districts of five or six miles square, called hundreds and in each of them to establish a school for teaching, reading, writing, and arithmetic. The tutor to be supported by the hundred, and every person in it entitled to send their children three years gratis, and as much longer as they please, paying for it. These schools to be under a visitor who is annually to chuse the boy of best genius in the school, of those whose parents are too poor to give them further education, and to send him forward to one of the grammar schools, of which twenty are proposed to be erected in different parts of the country, for teaching Greek, Latin, geography, and the higher branches of numerical arithmetic. Of the boys thus sent in any one year, trial is to be made at the grammar schools one or two years, and the best genius of the whole selected, and continued six

"A Plan for General Education" is from *The Writings of Thomas Jefferson;* reprinted by permission of G. P. Putnam's Sons.

years, and the residue dismissed. By this means twenty of the best geniuses will be raked from the rubbish annually, and be instructed, at the public expense, so far as the grammar schools go. At the end of six years instruction, one half are to be discontinued (from among whom the grammar schools will probably be supplied with future masters); and the other half, who are to be chosen for the superiority of their parts and disposition, are to be sent and continued three years in the study of such science as they shall chuse, at William and Mary college, the plan of which is proposed to be enlarged, as will be hereafter explained, and extended to all the useful sciences. The ultimate result of the whole scheme of education would be the teaching all the children of the State reading, writing, and common arithmetic; turning out ten annually, of superior genius, well taught in Greek, Latin, geography, and the higher branches of arithmetic; turning out ten others annually, of still superior parts, who, to those branches of learning, shall have added such of the sciences as their genius shall have led them to; the furnishing to the wealthier part of the people convenient schools at which their children may be educated at their own expense.— The general objects of this law are to provide an education adapted to the years, to the capacity, and the condition of every one, and directed to their freedom and happiness. Specific details were not proper for the law. These must be the business of the visitors entrusted with its execution. The first stage of this education being the schools of the hundreds, wherein the great mass of the people will receive their instruction, the principal foundations of future order will be laid here. Instead, therefore, of putting the Bible and Testament into the hands of the children at an age when their judgments are not sufficiently matured for religious inquiries, their memories may here be stored with the most useful facts from Grecian, Roman, European, and American history. The first elements of morality too may be instilled into their minds; such as, when further developed as their judgments advance in strength, may teach them how to work out their own greatest happiness, by shewing them that it does not depend on the condition of life in which chance has placed them, but is always the result of a good conscience, good health, occupation, and freedom in all just pursuits.—Those whom either the wealth of their parents or the adoption of the state shall destine to higher degrees of learning, will go on to the grammar schools, which constitute the next stage, there to be instructed in the languages. The learning Greek and Latin, I am told, is going into disuse in Europe. I know not what their manners and occupations may call for: but it would be very ill-judged in us to follow their example in this instance. There is a certain period of life, say from eight to fifteen or sixteen years of age, when the mind like the body is not yet firm enough for laborious and close operations. If applied to such, it falls an early victim of premature exertion; exhibiting, indeed, at first, in these young and tender subjects, the flattering appearance of their being men while they are yet children, but ending in reducing them to be children when they should be men. The memory is then most susceptible and tenacious of impressions; and the learning of languages being chiefly a work of memory, it seems precisely fitted to the powers of this period, which is long enough too for acquiring the most useful languages, antient and modern. I do not pretend that language is science. It is only an instrument for the attainment of science. But that time is not lost which is employed in providing tools for future operation: more especially as in this case the books put into the hands of the youth for this purpose may be such as will at the same time impress their minds with useful facts and good principles. If this period be suffered to pass in idleness, the mind becomes lethargic and impotent, as would the body it inhabits if unexercised during the same time. The sympathy between body and mind during their rise, progress and decline, is too strict and obvious to endanger our being misled while we reason from the one to the other.—As soon as they are of sufficient age, it is supposed they will be sent on from the grammar schools to the university, which constitutes our third and last stage, there to study those sciences which may be adapted to their views.— By that part of our plan which prescribes the selection of the youths of genius from among the classes of the poor, we hope to avail the state of those talents which nature has sown as liberally among the poor as the rich, but which perish without use, if not sought for and cultivated.—But of all the views of this law none is more important, none more legitimate, than that of rendering the people the safe, as they are the ultimate, guardians of their own liberty. For this purpose the reading in the first stage, where *they* will receive their whole education, is proposed, as has been said, to be chiefly historical. History, by apprising them of the past, will enable them to judge of the future; it will avail them of the experience of other times and other nations; it will enable them to know ambition under every disguise it may assume; and knowing it, to defeat its views. In every government on earth is some trace of human weakness, some germ of corruption and degeneracy, which cunning will discover, and wickedness insensibly open, cultivate and improve. Every government degenerates when trusted to the rulers of the people alone. The people themselves therefore are its only safe depositories. And to render even them safe, their minds must be improved to a certain degree. This indeed is not all that is necessary, though it be essentially necessary. An amendment of our constitution must here come in aid of the public education. The influence over government must be shared among all the people. If every individual which composes their mass participates of the ultimate authority, the government will be safe; because the corrupting the whole mass will exceed any private resources of wealth; and public ones cannot be provided but by levies on the people. In this case every man would have to pay his own price. The government of Great Britain has been corrupted, because but one man in ten has a right to vote for members of parliament. The sellers of the government, therefore, get nine-tenths of their price clear.

It has been thought that corruption is restrained by confining the right of suffrage to a few of the wealthier of the people: but it would be more effectually restrained by an extension of that right to such numbers as would bid defiance to the means of corruption.

School Days at Hammersmith

W. B. YEATS

THOUGH born in Dublin, W. B. Yeats (1865-1939), Irish poet and dramatist, spent most of his childhood in London, where he attended the Godolphin School, Hammersmith. At fifteen he returned to Dublin and continued his schooling there. For a few years he studied painting, but he soon discovered that his major interest was in poetry.

The greatest influence on his early writing was exerted by Lady Gregory. Together they founded the Irish Academy and the Abbey Theatre, for which Yeats wrote plays. Soon he was recognized as the real leader of the Irish literary renaissance. Though Yeats is a distinguished dramatist, he is best known as a great lyric poet. It is an interesting fact that much of his best poetry was written in his old age. When he died at the age of seventy-three, the New Republic said that "he died like Shelley at the height of his powers and with half his work unwritten."

THE only lessons I had ever learned were those my father taught me, for he terrified me by descriptions of my moral degradation and he humiliated me by my likeness to disagreeable people; but presently I was sent to school at Hammersmith. It was a Gothic building of yellow brick: a large hall full of desks, some small class-rooms and a separate house for boarders, all built perhaps in 1860 or 1870. I thought it an ancient building and that it had belonged to the founder of the school, Lord Godolphin, who was romantic to me because there was a novel about him. I never read the novel, but I thought only romantic people were put in books. On one side, there was a piano factory of yellow brick, upon two sides half-finished rows of little shops and villas all yellow brick, and on the fourth side, outside the wall of our playing field, a brick-field of cinders and piles of half-burned yellow bricks. All the names and faces of my school-fellows have faded from me except one name without a face and the face and name of one friend, mainly no doubt because it was all so long ago, but partly because I only seem to remember things dramatic in themselves or that are somehow associated with unforgettable places.

For some days as I walked homeward along the Hammersmith Road, I told myself that whatever I most cared for had been taken away. I had found a small, green-covered book given to my father by a Dublin man of science; it gave an account of the strange sea creatures the man of science had discovered among the rocks at Howth or dredged out of Dublin Bay. It had long been my favourite book; and when I read it I believed that I was growing very wise, but now I should have no time for it nor for my own thoughts. Every moment would be taken up learning or saying lessons, or in walking between school and home four times a day for I came home in the middle of the day for dinner. But presently I forgot my trouble, absorbed in two things I had never known, companionship and enmity. After my first day's lesson, a circle of boys had got around me in a playing field and asked me questions, "Who's your father?" "What does he do?" "How much money has he?" Presently a boy said something insulting. I had never struck anybody or been struck, and now all in a minute, without any intention upon my side, but as if I had been a doll moved by a string, I was hitting at the boys within reach and being hit. After that I was called names for being Irish, and had many fights and never, for years, got the better in any one of them; for I was delicate and had no muscles. Sometimes, however, I found means of retaliation, even of aggression. There was a boy with a big stride, much feared by little boys, and finding him alone in the playing field, I went up to him and said, "Rise upon Sugaun and sink upon Gad." "What does that mean?" he said. "Rise upon hay-leg and sink upon straw," I answered and told him that in Ireland the sergeant tied straw and hay to the ankles of a stupid recruit to show him the difference between his legs. My ears were boxed, and when I complained to my friends, they said I had brought it upon myself, and that I deserved all I got. I probably dared myself to other feats of a like sort, for I did not think English people intelligent or well-behaved unless they were artists. Every one I knew well in Sligo despised Nationalists and Catholics, but all disliked England with a prejudice that had come down perhaps from the days of the Irish Parliament. I knew stories to the discredit of England, and took them all seriously. My mother had met some English woman who did not like Dublin because the legs of the men were too straight, and at Sligo, as everybody knew, an Englishman had once said to a car-driver, "If you people were not so lazy, you would pull down the mountain and spread it out over the sand and that would give you acres of good fields." At Sligo there is a wide river mouth and at ebb tide most of it is dry sand, but all Sligo knew that in some way I cannot remember it was the spreading of the tide over the sand that left the narrow channel fit for shipping. At any rate the carman had gone chuckling all over Sligo with his tale. People would tell it to prove that Englishmen were always grumbling. "They grumble about their dinners and everything—there was an Englishman who wanted to pull down Knock-na-Rea" and so on. My mother had shown them to me kissing at railway stations, and taught me to feel disgust at their lack of reserve, and my father told how my grandfather, William-Yeats, who had died before I was born, when he came home to his Rectory in County Down from an English visit, spoke of some man he had met on a coach road who "Englishman-like" told him all his affairs. My father explained that an Englishman generally believed that his private affairs did him credit, while an Irishman, being poor and probably in debt, had no such confidence. I, however, did not believe in this explanation. My Sligo nurses, who had in all likelihood the Irish Catholic political hatred, had never spoken well of any Englishman. Once when walking in the town of Sligo I had turned to look after an English man and woman whose clothes attracted me. The man I remember had grey clothes and knee-breeches and the woman a grey dress, and my nurse had said contemptuously, "Tow-rows"—perhaps before my time, there had been some English song with the burden "tow row row"—and everybody had told me that English people ate skates and even dog-fish, and I myself had only just arrived in England when I saw an old man put marmalade in his porridge.

I was divided from all those boys, not merely by the anecdotes that are everywhere perhaps a chief expression of the distrust of races, but because our mental images were different. I read their boys' books and they excited me, but if I read of some English victory, I did not believe that I read of my own people. They thought of Cressy and Agincourt and the Union Jack and were all very patriotic, and I, without those memories of Limerick and the Yellow Ford that would have strengthened an Irish Catholic, thought of mountain and lake, of my grandfather and of ships. Anti-Irish feeling was running high, for the Land League had been founded and landlords had been shot, and I, who had no politics, was yet full of pride, for it is romantic to live in a dangerous country.

I daresay I thought the rough manners of a cheap school, as my grandfather Yeats had those of a chance companion, typical of all England. At any rate I had a harassed life and got many a black eye and had many outbursts of grief and rage. Once a boy, the son of a great Bohemian glass-maker, who was older than the rest of us, and had been sent out of his country because of a love affair, beat a boy for me because we were "both foreigners". And a boy, who grew to be the school athlete and my chief friend, beat a great many. His are the face and name that I remember— his name was of Huguenot origin and his face like his gaunt and lithe body had something of the American Indian in colour and lineament.

I was very much afraid of the other boys, and that made me doubt myself for the first time. When I had gathered pieces of wood in the corner for my great ship, I was confident that I could keep calm among the storms and die fighting when the great battle came. But now I was ashamed of my lack of courage; for I wanted to be like my grandfather who thought so little of danger that he had jumped overboard in the Bay of Biscay after an old hat. I was very much afraid of physical pain, and one day when I had made some noise in class, my friend the athlete was accused and I allowed him to get two strokes of the cane before I gave myself up. He had held out his hands without flinching and had not rubbed them on his sides afterwards. I was not caned, but was made to stand up for the rest of the lesson. I suffered very much afterwards when the thought came to me, but he did not reproach me.

I had been some years at school before I had my last fight. My friend, the athlete, had given me many months of peace, but at last refused to beat any more and said I must learn to box, and not go near the other boys till I knew how. I went home with him every day and boxed in his room, and the bouts had always the same ending. My excitability gave me an advantage at first and I would drive him across the room, and then he would drive me across and it would end very commonly with my nose bleeding. One day his father, an elderly banker, brought us out into the garden and tried to make us box in a cold-blooded, courteous way, but it was no use. At last he said I might go near the boys again and I was no sooner inside the gate of the playing field than a boy flung a handful of mud and cried out, "Mad Irishman". I hit him several times on the face without being hit, till the boys round said we should make friends. I held out my hand in fear; for I knew if we went on I should be beaten, and he took it sullenly. I had so poor a reputation as a fighter that it was a great disgrace to him, and even the masters made fun of his swollen face; and though some little boys came in a deputation to ask me to lick a boy they named, I had never another fight with a school-fellow. We had a great many fights with the street boys and the boys of a neighbouring charity school. We had always the better because we were not allowed to fling stones, and that compelled us to close or do our best to close. The monitors had been told to report any boy who fought in the street, but they only reported those who flung stones. I always ran at the athlete's heels, but I never hit any one. My father considered these fights absurd, and even that they were an English absurdity, and so I could not get angry enough to like hitting and being hit; and then too my friend drove the enemy before him. He had no doubts or speculations to lighten his fist upon an enemy, that, being of low behaviour, should be beaten as often as possible, and there were real wrongs to avenge: one of our boys had been killed by the blow of a stone hid in a snowball. Sometimes we on our side got into trouble with the parents of boys. There was a quarrel between the athlete and an old German who had a barber's shop we passed every day on our way home, and one day he spat through the window and hit the German on his bald head—the monitors had not forbidden spitting. The German ran after us, but when the athlete squared up he went away. Now, though I knew it was not right to spit at people, my admiration for my friend arose to a great height. I spread his fame over the school, and next day there was a fine stir when somebody saw the old German going up the gravel walk to the head-master's room. Presently there was such a noise in the passage that even the master had to listen. It was the head-master's red-haired brother turning the old German out and shouting to the man-servant, "See that he doesn't steal the top-coats." We heard afterwards that he had asked the names of the two boys who passed his window every day and been told the names of the two head boys who passed also but were notoriously gentlemanly in their manners. Yet my friend was timid also and that restored my confidence in myself. He would often ask me to buy the sweets or the ginger-beer because he was afraid sometimes when speaking to a stranger.

I had one reputation that I valued. At first when I went to the Hammersmith swimming-baths with the other boys, I was afraid to plunge in until I had gone so far down the ladder that the water came up to my thighs; but one day when I was alone I fell from the spring-board which was five or six feet above the water. After that I would dive from a greater height than the others and I practised swimming under water and pretending not to be out of breath when I came up. And then, if I ran a race, I took care not to pant or show any sign of strain. And in this I had an advantage even over the athlete, for though he could run faster and was harder to tire than anybody else he grew very pale; and I was often paid compliments. I used to run with my friend when he was training to keep him in company. He would give me a long start and soon overtake me.

I followed the career of a certain professional runner for months, buying papers that would tell me if he had won or lost. I had seen him described as "the bright particular star of American athletics", and the wonderful phrase had thrown enchantment over him. Had he been called the particular bright star, I should have cared nothing for him. I did not understand the symptom for years after. I was nursing my own dream, my form of the common schoolboy dream though I was no longer gathering the little pieces of broken and rotting wood. Often instead of learning my lesson, I covered the white squares of the chessboard on my little table with pen and ink pictures of myself, doing all kinds of courageous things. One day my father said, "There was a man in Nelson's ship at the battle of Trafalgar, a ship's purser, whose hair turned white; what a sensitive temperament; that man should have achieved something!" I was vexed and bewildered, and am still bewildered and still vexed, finding it a poor and crazy thing that we who have imagined so many noble persons cannot bring our flesh to heel.

.   .   .   .   .

The head-master was a clergyman, a good-humoured, easy-going man, as temperate, one had no doubt in his religious life as in all else, and if he ever lost sleep on our account, it was from a very proper anxiety as to our gentility. I was in disgrace once because I went to school in some brilliant blue homespun serge my mother had bought in Devonshire, and I was told I must never wear it again. He had tried several times, though he must have known it was hopeless, to persuade our parents to put us into Eton clothes, and on certain days we were compelled to wear gloves.

After my first year, we were forbidden to play marbles because it was a form of gambling and was played by nasty little boys, and a few months later told not to cross our legs in class. It was a school for the sons of professional men who had failed or were at the outset of their career, and the boys held an indignation meeting when they discovered that a new boy was an apothecary's son (I think at first I was his only friend), and we all pretended that our parents were richer than they were. I told a little boy who had often seen my mother knitting or mending my clothes that she only mended or knitted because she liked it, though I knew it was necessity.

It was like, I suppose, most schools of its type, an obscene, bullying place, where a big boy would hit a small boy in the wind to see him double up, and where certain boys, too young for any emotion of sex, would sing the dirty songs of the street, but I daresay it suited me better than a better school. I have heard the head-master say, "How has so-and-so done in his Greek?" and the class-master reply, "Very badly, but he is doing well in his cricket," and the head-master reply to that, "Oh, leave him alone." I was unfitted for school work, and though I would often work well for weeks together, I had to give the whole evening to one lesson if I was to know it. My thoughts were a great excitement, but when I tried to do anything with them, it was like trying to pack a balloon into a shed in a high wind. I was always near the bottom of my class, and always making excuses that but added to my timidity; but no master was rough with me. I was known to collect moths and butterflies and to get into no worse mischief than hiding now and again an old tailless white rat in my coat-pocket or my desk.

There was but one interruption of our quiet habits, the brief engagement of an Irish master, a fine Greek scholar and vehement teacher, but of fantastic speech. He would open the class by saying, "There he goes, there he goes", or some like words as the head-master passed by at the end of the hall. "Of course this school is no good. How could it be with a clergyman for head-master?" And then perhaps his eye would light on me, and he would make me stand up and tell me it was a scandal I was so idle when all the world knew that any Irish boy was cleverer than a whole class-room of English boys, a description I had to pay for afterwards. Sometimes he would call up a little boy who had a girl's face and kiss him upon both cheeks and talk of taking him to Greece in the holidays, and presently we heard he had written to the boy's parents about it, but long before the holidays he was dismissed.

Among School Children

I

I WALK through the long schoolroom questioning;
A kind old nun in a white hood replies;
The children learn to cipher and to sing,
To study reading-books and history,
To cut and sew, be neat in everything
In the best modern way—the children's eyes
In momentary wonder stare upon
A sixty-year-old smiling public man.

II

I dream of a Ledaean body, bent
Above a sinking fire, a tale that she
Told of a harsh reproof, or trivial event
That changed some childish day to tragedy—
Told, and it seemed that our two natures blent
Into a sphere from youthful sympathy,
Or else, to alter Plato's parable,
Into the yolk and white of the one shell.

III

And thinking of that fit of grief or rage
I look upon one child or t'other there
And wonder if she stood so at that age—
For even daughters of the swan can share
Something of every paddler's heritage—
And had that colour upon cheek or hair,
And thereupon my heart is driven wild:
She stands before me as a living child.

IV

Her present image floats into the mind—
Did Quattrocento finger fashion it
Hollow of cheek as though it drank the wind
And took a mess of shadows for its meat?
And I though never of Ledaean kind
Had pretty plumage once—enough of that,

Better to smile on all that smile, and show
There is a comfortable kind of old scarecrow.

V

What youthful mother, a shape upon her lap
Honey of generation had betrayed,
And that must sleep, shriek, struggle to escape
As recollection or the drug decide,
Would think her son, did she but see that shape
With sixty or more winters on its head,
A compensation for the pang of his birth,
Or the uncertainty of his setting forth?

VI

Plato thought nature but a spume that plays
Upon a ghostly paradigm of things;
Solider Aristotle played the taws
Upon the bottom of a king of kings;
World-famous golden-thighed Pythagoras
Fingered upon a fiddle-stick or strings
What a star sang and careless Muses heard:
Old clothes upon old sticks to scare a bird.

VII

Both nuns and mothers worship images,
But those the candles light are not as those
That animate a mother's reveries,
But keep a marble or a bronze repose.
And yet they too break hearts—O Presences
That passion, piety or affection knows,
And that all heavenly glory symbolise—
O self-born mockers of man's enterprise;

VIII

Labour is blossoming or dancing where
The body is not bruised to pleasure soul,
Nor beauty born out of its own despair,
Nor blear-eyed wisdom out of midnight oil.
O chestnut tree, great rooted blossomer,
Are you the leaf, the blossom or the bole?
O body swayed to music, O brightening glance,
How can we know the dancer from the dance?

Finis

THOMAS HUGHES

KNOWN *chiefly as the author of* Tom Brown's School Days, *Thomas Hughes (1822-1896) attended Rugby while the famous Dr. Thomas Arnold, father of Matthew Arnold, was headmaster. From Rugby, Hughes went to Oxford. After receiving his degree in 1845, he studied law, and three years later was admitted to the bar.*

Early in his life he became a proponent of Christian socialism. This interest led him to support social reforms in England and to found in America, in the mountains of Tennessee, a cooperative colony which he called Rugby.

The selection given here is from Hughes' best-known novel, Tom Brown's School Days, *called by Kingsley "the jolliest book ever written."*

> Strange friend, past, present, and to be;
> Loved deeplier, darklier understood;
> Behold I dream a dream of good,
> And mingle all the world with thee.
>
> —TENNYSON

IN the summer of 1842, our hero stopped once again at the well-known station; and leaving his bag and fishing-rod with a porter, walked slowly and sadly up toward the town. It was now July. He had rushed away from Oxford the moment that term was over, for a fishing ramble in Scotland with two college friends, and had been for three weeks living on oatcake, mutton-hams, and whisky, in the wildest parts of Skye. They had descended one sultry evening on the little inn at Kyle Rhea ferry; and while Tom and another of the party put their tackle together and began exploring the stream for a sea-trout for supper, the third strolled into the house to arrange for their entertainment. Presently he came out in a loose blouse and slippers, a short pipe in his mouth, and an old newspaper in his hand, and threw himself on the heathery scrub which met the shingle, within easy hail of the fishermen. There he lay, the picture of free-and-easy, loafing, hand-to-mouth young England, "improving his mind," as he shouted to them, by the perusal of the fortnight-old weekly paper, soiled with the marks of toddy-glasses and tobacco-ashes, the legacy of the last traveler, which he had hunted out from the kitchen of the little hostelry, and, being

327

a youth of a communicative turn of mind, began imparting the contents
to the fishermen as he went on.

"What a bother they are making about these wretched corn-laws!
Here's three or four columns full of nothing but sliding scales and fixed
duties. Hang this tobacco, it's always going out! Ah, here's something
better—a splendid match between Kent and England, Brown, Kent winning by three wickets. Felix fifty-six runs without a chance, and not out!"

Tom, intent on a fish which had risen at him twice, answered only with
a grunt.

"Anything about the Goodwood?" called out the third man.

"Rory O'More drawn. Butterfly colt amiss," shouted the student.

"Just my luck," grumbled the inquirer, jerking his flies off the water,
and throwing again with a heavy, sullen splash, and frightening Tom's
fish.

"I say, can't you throw lighter over there? We ain't fishing for gram-
puses," shouted Tom across the stream.

"Hullo, Brown! here's something for you," called out the reading man
next moment. "Why, your old master, Arnold of Rugby, is dead."

Tom's hand stopped half-way in his cast, and his line and flies went all
tangling round and round his rod; you might have knocked him over with
a feather. Neither of his companions took any notice of him, luckily; and
with a violent effort he set to work mechanically to disentangle his line.
He felt completely carried off his moral and intellectual legs, as if he had
lost his standing-point in the invisible world. Besides which, the deep,
loving loyalty which he felt for his old leader made the shock intensely
painful. It was the first great wrench of his life, the first gap which the
angel Death had made in his circle, and he felt numbed, and beaten down,
and spiritless. Well, well! I believe it was good for him and for many
others in like case, who had to learn by that loss that the soul of man
cannot stand or lean upon any human prop, however strong, and wise, and
good; but that He upon whom alone it can stand and lean will knock away
all such props in His own wise and merciful way, until there is no ground
or stay left but Himself, the Rock of Ages, upon whom alone a sure
foundation for every soul of man is laid.

As he wearily labored at his line, the thought struck him, "It may be all
false—a mere newspaper lie." And he strode up to the recumbent smoker.

"Let me look at the paper," said he.

"Nothing else in it," answered the other, handing it up to him listlessly.
"Hullo, Brown! what's the matter, old fellow? Ain't you well?"

"Where is it?" said Tom, turning over the leaves, his hands trembling,
and his eyes swimming, so that he could not read.

"What? What are you looking for?" said his friend, jumping up and
looking over his shoulder.

"That—about Arnold," said Tom.

"Oh, here," said the other, putting his finger on the paragraph. Tom read

.it over and over again. There could be no mistake of identity, though the account was short enough.

"Thank you," said he at last, dropping the paper. "I shall go for a walk. Don't you and Herbert wait supper for me." And away he strode, up over the moor at the back of the house, to be alone, and master his grief if possible.

His friend looked after him, sympathizing and wondering, and, knocking the ashes out of his pipe, walked over to Herbert. After a short parley they walked together up to the house.

"I'm afraid that confounded newspaper has spoiled Brown's fun for this trip."

"How odd that he should be so fond of his old master," said Herbert. Yet they also were both public-school men.

The two, however, notwithstanding Tom's prohibition, waited supper for him, and had everything ready when he came back some half an hour afterward. But he could not join in their cheerful talk, and the party was soon silent, notwithstanding the efforts of all three. One thing only had Tom resolved, and that was, that he couldn't stay in Scotland any longer: he felt an irresistible longing to get to Rugby, and then home, and soon broke it to the others, who had too much tact to oppose.

So by daylight the next morning he was marching through Ross-shire, and in the evening hit the Caledonian Canal, took the next steamer, and traveled as fast as boat and railway could carry him to the Rugby station.

As he walked up to the town, he felt shy and afraid of being seen, and took the back streets—why, he didn't know, but he followed his instinct. At the School-gates he made a dead pause; there was not a soul in the quadrangle—all was lonely, and silent, and sad. So with another effort he strode through the quadrangle, and into the School-house offices.

He found the little matron in her room in deep mourning; shook her hand, tried to talk, and moved nervously about. She was evidently thinking of the same subject as he, but he couldn't begin talking.

"Where shall I find Thomas?" said he at last, getting desperate.

"In the servants' hall, I think, sir. But won't you take anything?" said the matron, looking rather disappointed.

"No, thank you," said he, and strode off again to find the old verger, who was sitting in his little den, as of old, puzzling over hieroglyphics.

He looked up through his spectacles as Tom seized his hand and wrung it.

"Ah! you've heard all about it, sir, I see," said he.

Tom nodded, and then sat down on the shoe-board, while the old man told his tale, and wiped his spectacles and fairly flowed over with quaint, homely, honest sorrow.

By the time he had done Tom felt much better.

"Where is he buried, Thomas?" said he at last.

"Under the altar in the chapel, sir," answered Thomas. "You'd like to have the key, I dare say?"

"Thank you, Thomas—yes, I should, very much." And the old man fumbled among his bunch, and then got up, as though he would go with him; but after a few steps stopped short, and said, "Perhaps you'd like to go by yourself, sir?"

Tom nodded, and the bunch of keys were handed to him, with an injunction to be sure and lock the door after him, and bring them back before eight o'clock.

He walked quickly through the quadrangle and out into the close. The longing which had been upon him and driven him thus far, like the gad-fly in the Greek legends, giving him no rest in mind or body, seemed all of a sudden not to be satisfied, but to shrivel up and pall. "Why should I go on? It's no use," he thought, and threw himself at full length on the turf, and looked vaguely and listlessly at all the well-known objects. There were a few of the town boys playing cricket, their wicket pitched on the best piece in the middle of the big-side ground—a sin about equal to sacrilege in the eyes of a captain of the eleven. He was very nearly getting up to go and send them off. "Pshaw! they won't remember me. They've more right there than I," he muttered. And the thought that his scepter had departed, and his mark was wearing out, came home to him for the first time, and bitterly enough. He was lying on the very spot where the fights came off—where he himself had fought six years ago his first and last battle. He conjured up the scene till he could almost hear the shouts of the ring, and East's whisper in his ear; and looking across the close to the Doctor's private door, half expected to see it open, and the tall figure in cap and gown come striding under the elm-trees toward him.

No, no; that sight could never be seen again. There was no flag flying on the round tower; the School-house windows were all shuttered up; and when the flag went up again, and the shutters came down, it would be to welcome a stranger. All that was left on earth of him whom he had honored was lying cold and still under the chapel floor. He would go in and see the place once more, and then leave it once for all. New men and new methods might do for other people; let those who would, worship the rising star; he, at least, would be faithful to the sun which had set. And so he got up, and walked to the chapel door, and unlocked it, fancying himself the only mourner in all the broad land, and feeding on his own selfish sorrow.

He passed through the vestibule, and then paused for a moment to glance over the empty benches. His heart was still proud and high, and he walked up to the seat which he had last occupied as a sixth-form boy, and sat himself down there to collect his thoughts.

And, truth to tell, they needed collecting and setting in order not a little. The memories of eight years were all dancing through his brain, and carrying him about whither they would, while, beneath them all, his heart was throbbing with the dull sense of a loss that could never be made up to him. The rays of the evening sun came solemnly through the painted windows above his head, and fell in gorgeous colors on the opposite wall, and the perfect stillness soothed his spirit by little and little. And he turned to the pulpit, and looked at it, and then, leaning forward with his head on his hands, groaned aloud. If he could only have seen the Doctor again for five minutes—have told him all that was in his heart, what he owed to him, how he loved and reverenced him, and would by God's help, follow his steps in life and death—he could have borne it all without a murmur. But that he should have gone away for ever without knowing it all, was too much to bear. "But am I sure that he does not know it all?" The thought made him start. "May he not even now be near me, in this very chapel? If he be, am I sorrowing as he would have me sorrow, as I should wish to have sorrowed when I shall meet him again?"

He raised himself up and looked round, and after a minute rose and walked humbly down to the lowest bench, and sat down on the very seat which he had occupied on his first Sunday at Rugby. And then the old memories rushed back again, but softened and subdued, and soothing him as he let himself be carried away by them. And he looked up at the great painted window above the altar, and remembered how, when a little boy, he used to try not to look through it at the elm-trees and the rooks, before the painted glass came; and the subscription for the painted glass, and the letter he wrote home for money to give to it. And there, down below, was the very name of the boy who sat on his right hand on that first day, scratched rudely in the oak paneling.

And then came the thought of his old school-fellows; and form after form of boys nobler, and braver, and purer than he rose up and seemed to rebuke him. Could he not think of them, and what they had felt and were feeling—they who had honored and loved from the first the man whom he had taken years to know and love? Could he not think of those yet dearer to him who was gone, who bore his name and shared his blood, and were now without a husband or a father? Then the grief which he began to share with others became gentle and holy, and he rose up once more, and walked up the steps to the altar, and while the tears flowed freely down his cheeks, knelt down humbly and hopefully, to lay down there his share of a burden which had proved itself too heavy for him to bear in his own strength.

Here let us leave him. Where better could we leave him than at the altar before which he had first caught a glimpse of the glory of his birth-right, and felt the drawing of the bond which links all living souls to-gether in one brotherhood—at the grave beneath the altar of him who had opened his eyes to see that glory, and softened his heart till he could feel that bond?

And let us not be hard on him, if at that moment his soul is fuller of the tomb and him who lies there than of the altar and Him of whom it speaks.

Such stages have to be gone through, I believe, by all young and brave souls, who must win their way through hero-worship to the worship of Him who is the King and Lord of heroes. For it is only through our mysterious human relationships—through the love and tenderness and purity of mothers and sisters and wives, through the strength and courage and wisdom of fathers and brothers and teachers—that we can come to the knowledge of Him in whom alone the love, and the tenderness, and the purity, and the strength, and the courage, and the wisdom of all these dwell for ever and ever in perfect fullness.

Rugby Chapel

MATTHEW ARNOLD

MATTHEW ARNOLD (1822-1888), poet and critic, was the son of Dr. Thomas Arnold, the famous headmaster of Rugby. Educated at Winchester, Rugby, and Oxford, Arnold became in 1851 an inspector of schools, a position which he held until 1883, when Gladstone conferred on him a pension. For ten years he held the professorship of poetry at Oxford.

Most of his poetry was written in the earlier part of his life. As he grew older, he turned to literary criticism and lecturing in the hope of bringing "sweetness and light" to the British middle class. Throughout his life he published educational reports and exerted an influence for the improvement of education, particularly secondary education, in England.

The elegy, Rugby Chapel, *was written in 1857 in memory of Arnold's father.*

COLDLY, sadly descends
The autumn evening. The field
Strewn with its dank yellow drifts
Of wither'd leaves, and the elms,
Fade into dimness apace,
Silent:—hardly a shout
From a few boys late at their play!
The lights come out in the street,
In the school-room windows; but cold,
Solemn, unlighted, austere,
Through the gathering darkness, arise
The chapel-walls, in whose bound
Thou, my father! art laid.

There thou dost lie, in the gloom
Of the autumn evening. But ah!
That word, *gloom,* to my mind
Brings thee back in the light
Of thy radiant vigour again!
In the gloom of November we pass'd
Days not dark at thy side;

Seasons impair'd not the ray
Of thine even cheerfulness clear.
Such thou wast! and I stand
In the autumn evening, and think
Of bygone autumns with thee.

Fifteen years have gone round
Since thou arosest to tread,
In the summer morning, the road
Of death, at a call unforeseen,
Sudden. For fifteen years,
We who till then in thy shade
Rested as under the boughs
Of a mighty oak, have endured
Sunshine and rain as we might,
Bare, unshaded, alone,
Lacking the shelter of thee.

O strong soul, by what shore
Tarriest thou now? For that force,
Surely, has not been left vain!
Somewhere, surely, afar,
In the sounding labour-house vast
Of being, is practised that strength,
Zealous, beneficent, firm!

Yes, in some far-shining sphere,
Conscious or not of the past,
Still thou performest the word
Of the Spirit in whom thou dost live,
Prompt, unwearied, as here!
Still thou upraisest with zeal
The humble good from the ground,
Sternly repressest the bad!
Still, like a trumpet, dost rouse
Those who with half-open eyes
Tread the border-land dim
'Twixt vice and virtue; reviv'st,
Succourest!—this was thy work,
This was thy life upon earth.

What is the course of the life
Of mortal men on the earth?
Most men eddy about
Here and there—eat and drink,

Chatter and love and hate,
Gather and squander, are raised
Aloft, are hurl'd in the dust,
Striving blindly, achieving
Nothing; and then they die—
Perish; and no one asks
Who or what they have been,
More than he asks what waves
In the moonlit solitudes mild
Of the midmost Ocean, have swell'd,
Foam'd for a moment, and gone.

And there are some, whom a thirst
Ardent, unquenchable, fires,
Not with the crowd to be spent,
Not without aim to go round
In an eddy of purposeless dust
Effort unmeaning and vain.
Ah yes! some of us strive
Not without action to die
Fruitless, but something to snatch
From dull oblivion, nor all
Glut the devouring grave!
We, we have chosen our path—
Path to a clear-purposed goal,
Path of advance!—but it leads
A long, steep journey, through sunk
Gorges, o'er mountains in snow.
Cheerful, with friends, we set forth;
Then, on the height, comes the storm.
Thunder crashes from rock
To rock; the cataracts reply;
Lightnings dazzle our eyes;
Roaring torrents have breach'd
The track; the stream-bed descends
In the place where the wayfarer once
Planted his footstep; the spray
Boils o'er its borders; aloft,
The unseen snow-beds dislodge
Their hanging ruin. Alas,
Havoc is made in our train!
Friends who set forth at our side
Falter, are lost in the storm!
We, we only, are left!
With frowning foreheads, with lips

Sternly compress'd, we strain on,
On—and at nightfall, at last,
Come to the end of our way,
To the lonely inn 'mid the rocks;
Where the gaunt and taciturn host
Stands on the threshold, the wind
Shaking his thin white hairs—
Holds his lantern to scan
Our storm-beat figures, and asks:
Whom in our party we bring?
Whom we have left in the snow?
Sadly we answer: We bring
Only ourselves; we lost
Sight of the rest in the storm.
Hardly ourselves we fought through,
Stripp'd, without friends, as we are.
Friends, companions, and train
The avalanche swept from our side.

But thou would'st not *alone*
Be saved, my father! *alone*
Conquer and come to thy goal,
Leaving the rest in the wild.
We were weary, and we
Fearful, and we, in our march,
Fain to drop down and to die.
Still thou turnedst, and still
Beckonedst the trembler, and still
Gavest the weary thy hand.
If, in the paths of the world,
Stones might have wounded thy feet,
Toil or dejection have tried
Thy spirit, of that we saw
Nothing!—to us thou wert still
Cheerful, and helpful, and firm!
Therefore to thee it was given
Many to save with thyself;
And at the end of thy day,
O faithful shepherd! to come,
Bringing thy sheep in thy hand.

And through thee I believe
In the noble and great who are gone;
Pure souls honour'd and blest
By former ages, who else—

Such, so soulless, so poor,
Is the race of men whom I see—
Seem'd but a dream of the heart,
Seem'd but a cry of desire.
Yes! I believe that there lived
Others like thee in the past,
Not like the men of the crowd
Who all round me to-day
Bluster or cringe, and make life
Hideous, and arid, and vile;
But souls temper'd with fire,
Fervent, heroic, and good,
Helpers and friends of mankind.

Servants of God!—or sons
Shall I not call you? because
Not as servants ye knew
Your Father's innermost mind,
His, who unwillingly sees
One of his little ones lost—
Yours is the praise, if mankind
Hath not as yet in its march
Fainted, and fallen, and died!

See! In the rocks of the world
Marches the host of mankind,
A feeble, wavering line.
Where are they tending?—A God
Marshall'd them, gave them their goal.
Ah, but the way is so long!
Years they have been in the wild!
Sore thirst plagues them; the rocks,
Rising all round, overawe;
Factions divide them; their host
Threatens to break, to dissolve.
Ah, keep, keep them combined!
Else, of the myriads who fill
That army, not one shall arrive;
Sole they shall stray; in the rocks
Labour for ever in vain,
Die one by one in the waste.

Then, in such hour of need
Of your fainting, dispirited race,
Ye, like angels, appear,

Radiant with ardour divine.
Beacons of hope, ye appear!
Languor is not in your heart,
Weakness is not in your word,
Weariness not on your brow.
Ye alight in our van; at your voice,
Panic, despair, flee away.
Ye move through the ranks, recall
The stragglers, refresh the outworn,
Praise, reinspire the brave.
Order, courage, return.
Eyes rekindling, and prayers,
Follow your steps as ye go.
Ye fill up the gaps in our files,
Strengthen the wavering line,
Stablish, continue our march,
On, to the bound of the waste,
On, to the City of God.

Of the Education of Youth

JOHN LYLY

JOHN LYLY (1554?-1606), dramatist and author of Euphues, *was edu-cated both at Oxford and at Cambridge. On completing his studies, he went to London and attempted literary work. In 1579 on the publication of the first part of* Euphues, the Anatomy of Wit, *he leaped into fame. The second part,* Euphues and His England, *he published in 1580.*

Euphues is a prose romance relating the adventures and conversations of a young gentleman of Athens, Euphues, and his friend, Philautus, a native of Naples. The story is almost entirely a discussion of education, religion, love, and the proper conduct of life. The selection which follows is taken from a section on education called Euphues and his Ephoebus. *The book is interesting not only for its ideas but also for its prose style, which is characterized chiefly by antithesis and epigram. The novelty of the style has earned for it the name Euphuism.*

Young and tender age is easely framed to manners, and hardly are those things mollyfied which are hard. For as the steele is imprinted in the soft waxe, so learning is engraven in ye minde of an young Impe. *Plato* that divine Philosopher admonished all nursses and weaners of youth, that they should not be too busie to tell them fonde fables or filthy tales, least at theyr entraunce into the worlde they shoulde bee contami-nated with unseemely behaviour, unto the which *Phocilides* the Poet doth pithely allude, saying: Whilest that the childe is young, let him be in-structed in vertue and lytterature.

Moreover they are to be trayned up in the language of their country, to pronounce aptly and distinctly without stammering every word and sil-lable of their native speach, and to be kept from barbarous talke, as the ship from rockes: least being affected with their barbarisme, they be infected also with their uncleane conversation.

It is an olde Proverbe that if one dwell the next doore to a cre[e]ple he will learne to hault, if one bee conversant with an hipocrit, he wil soone endevour to dissemble. When this young infant shall grow in yeares and be of that ripenesse that he can conceive learning, insomuch that he is to be committed to the tuityon of some tutour, all dillygence is to be had to search such a one as shall neither be unlearned, neither ill lyved, neither a lyght person.

A gentleman that hath honest and discreet servants dysposeth them to the encrease of his Segnioryes, one he appointeth stewarde of his courtes, an other overseer of his landes, one his factor in far countries for his merchaundize, an other purvayour for his cates at home. But if among all his servaunts he shal espy one, either filthy in his talke or foolish in his behaviour, either without wit or voyde of honestye, either an unthrift or a wittall, him he sets not as a survayour and overseer of his manors, but a supervisour of hys childrens conditions and manners, to him he committeth ye guiding and tuition of his sons, which is by his proper nature a slave a knave by condition, a beast in behaviour. And sooner will they bestow an hundreth crownes to have a horse well broken, then a childe well taught, wherein I cannot but marvell to see them so carefull to encrease their possessions, when they be so carelesse to have them wise that should inherite them.

A good and discreete schoolemaster should be such an one as *Phœnix* was the instructor of *Achilles,* whom *Pelleus* (as *Homer* reporteth) appoynted to that ende that he should be unto *Achilles* not onely a teacher of learning, but an ensample of good lyving. But that is most principally to be looked for, and most diligently to be foreseene, that such tutors be sought out for the education of a young childe, whose lyfe hath never bene stayned with dishonestie, whose good name hath never bene called unto question, whose manners hath ben irreprehensible before the world. As husbandmen hedge in their trees, so should good schoolemasters with good manners hedge in the wit and disposition of the scholler, whereby the blossomes of learning may the sooner encrease to a budde.

Many parents are in this to be mislyked, which having neither tryal of his honestie, nor experience of his learning to whome they commit the childe to be taught, without any deepe or due consideration put them to one either ignoraunt or obstinate, the which if they themselves shall doe of ignoraunce the folly cannot be excused, if of obstinacie, their lewdnesse is to bee abhorred.

Some fathers are overcome with ye flatterie of those fooles which professe outwardly great knowledge, and shew a certeine kinde of dissembling sinceritie in their lyfe, others at the entreating of their familiar friends are content to commit their sonnes to one, without either substaunce of honestie or shadow of learning. By which their undiscreet dealing, they are like those sicke men which reject the expert and cunning Phisition, and at the request of their friendes admitte the heedelesse practiser, which daungereth the patient, and bringeth the bodye to his bane: Or not unlyke unto those, which at the instaunt and importunate sute of their acquaintaunce refuse a cunning Pilot, and chuse an unskilfull Marriner, which hazardeth the ship and themselves in the calmest Sea.

The Ideal Teacher

CONFUCIUS

CONFUCIUS (550 or 551-478 B. C.), the great sage of China, after a youth of poverty established in his twenty-second year a school of young and enquiring spirits who wished to be instructed in the principles of right conduct and government. He rejected no disciple who could pay even the smallest fee, and he retained no disciple who did not show earnestness and capacity. In his fifty-second year he was made chief magistrate of the city of Chung-tu. In this position he was so influential that he fell afoul of a powerful ruler, and soon his influence waned. In his fifty-sixth year he began a weary period of wandering among various states hoping to find a prince who would accept him as counselor and institute reforms in government. Though several princes were willing to entertain Confucius, no prince was willing to follow his teachings. Confucius returned to his home and spent his last years teaching his disciples concerning literature, human conduct, and honesty in social relationships.

The translation of Confucius which follows is by Lin Yutang. Born in China in 1895, Lin Yutang has studied at Harvard, Jena, and Leipzig Universities. For a time he taught English at Peking National University. He now makes his home in New York.

T HE principles of college education are as follows: First, prevention, or preventing bad habits before they arise. Secondly, timeliness, or giving the students things when they are ready for them. Thirdly, order, or teaching the different subjects in proper sequence. Fourthly, mutual stimulation (literally "friction"), or letting the students admire the excellence of other students. These four things ensure the success of education.

On the other hand, to forbid them after they have already acquired bad habits would seem to make everything go against their grain and efforts at correction would be without success. To teach them after the young age is past would make their learning difficult and futile. To fail to teach the different subjects in their proper order would bring about chaos in their studies, without good results. To study a subject all alone without friends would make a student too narrow in scope, lacking in general knowledge.

"The Ideal Teacher" and "The Process of Learning" are from *The Wisdom of Confucius*, translated by Lin Yutang; copyright, 1938, by Random House, Inc.; reprinted by permission of the publishers.

Bad company would encourage them to go against their teachers and bad pastimes would cause them to neglect their studies. These six things cause the breakdown of a college education.

With the knowledge of the reasons for success in education and the causes of its failure, the superior man is then qualified to be a teacher.

Therefore in his teaching the superior man guides his students but does not pull them along; he urges them to go forward and does not suppress them; he opens the way, but does not take them to the place. Guiding without pulling makes the process of learning gentle; urging without suppressing makes the process of learning easy; and opening the way without leading the students to the place makes them think for themselves. Now if the process of learning is made gentle and easy and the students are encouraged to think for themselves, we may call the man a good teacher.

There are four common errors in education which the teacher must beware of. Some students try to learn too much or too many subjects, some learn too little or too few subjects, some learn things too easily and some are too easily discouraged. These four things show that individuals differ in their mental endowments, and only through a knowledge of the different mental endowments can the teacher correct their mistakes. A teacher is but a man who tried to bring out the good and remedy the weaknesses of his students.

A good singer makes others follow his tune, and a good educator makes others follow his ideal. His words are concise but expressive, casual but full of hidden meaning, and he is good at drawing ingenious examples to make people understand him. In this way, he may be said to be a good man to make others follow his ideal.

The superior man knows what is difficult and what is easy, what is excellent and what is deplorable in the things to be learned, and then he is good at drawing examples. Being good at drawing examples, he then knows how to be a teacher. Knowing how to be a teacher, he then knows how to be an elder. And knowing how to be an elder, he then knows how to be a ruler of men. Therefore, the art of being a teacher is the art of learning to be a ruler of men. Therefore one cannot be too careful in selecting one's teacher. That is the meaning of the passage in the *Ancient Records* which says, "The Three Kings and the Four Dynasties (Yu, Hsia, Shang and Chou) laid the greatest emphasis upon the selection of teachers."

In this matter of education, the most difficult thing is to establish a respect for the teacher. When the teacher is respected, then people respect what he teaches, and when people respect what he teaches, then they respect learning or scholarship. Therefore there are only two classes of persons that the king dare not regard as his subjects: his teacher and the *shih* (child representing the spirit of the deceased at a sacrifice). According to the customs of the college, a teacher doesn't have to stand facing north even when receiving an edict from the king, which shows the great respect for the teacher.

The Process of Learning

WITH a good student, the teacher doesn't have much to do and the results are double, besides getting the student's respect. With a bad student, the teacher has to work hard and the results are only half of what is to be expected, besides getting hated by the student. A good questioner proceeds like a man chopping wood—he begins at the easier end, attacking the knots last, and after a time the teacher and student come to understand the point with a sense of pleasure. A bad questioner does just exactly the opposite. One who knows how to answer questions is like a group of bells. When you strike the big bell, the big one rings, and when you strike the small bell, the small one rings. It is important, however, to allow time for its tone gradually to die out. One who does not know how to answer questions is exactly the reverse of this. These are all suggestions for the process of teaching and learning.

That type of scholarship which is bent on remembering things in order to answer questions does not qualify one to be a teacher. A good teacher should observe the students' conversations. When he sees a student is doing his best but is lost, then he explains it to him, and if after the explanation, the student still does not understand, he may as well leave the matter alone.

The son of a tinker naturally learns how to mend fur coats, and the son of a good maker of bows naturally learns how to make a bamboo *chi* (shallow pan made of woven sliced bamboo for holding grain), and a man breaking in a horse first puts the horse behind the carriage. A gentleman can learn from these three things the proper method of education. The scholars of ancient times learned the truth about things from analogies.

The drum itself does not come under any of the five modes of music, and yet the five modes cannot succeed in harmony without the drum. Water itself does not belong to any of the five colors, and yet (in painting) the five colors would lack brightness without the use of water. Learning itself does not come under any of the five senses, and yet the five senses cannot be properly trained without learning. The teacher does not come under the five degrees of clan kinship, and yet the five degrees of clan kinship would not love one another without the teacher.

The gentleman says, "A great personality does not (necessarily) fit one for any particular office. A great character does not (necessarily) qualify one for any particular service. Great honesty does not (necessarily) make a man keep his word. Great regard for time does not (necessarily) make one punctual." To know these four things is to know the really fundamental things in life.

In offering sacrifices to the river gods, the ancient kings always began with worshipping the gods of the rivers before worshipping the gods of the seas. A distinction was made between the source and the outlet, and to know this distinction is to know how to attend to the essentials.

Those Two Boys

FRANKLIN P. ADAMS

F. P. ADAMS, *better known as F. P. A., conductor of the newspaper col-*
umn The Conning Tower, *expert on the radio program* Information,
Please, *was born in Chicago in 1881. After his graduation from the Armour*
Scientific Academy in 1899, he spent a year at the University of Michigan.
He entered journalism in 1903 and is today one of this country's best-
known newspaper columnists.

WHEN Bill was a lad he was terribly bad.
　　He worried his parents a lot;
He'd lie and he'd swear and pull little girls' hair;
　　His boyhood was naught but a blot.

At play and in school he would fracture each rule—
　　In mischief from autumn to spring;
And the villagers knew when to manhood he grew
　　He would never amount to a thing.

When Jim was a child he was not very wild;
　　He was known as a good little boy;
He was honest and bright and the teacher's delight—
　　To his mother and father a joy.

All the neighbours were sure that his virtue'd endure,
　　That his life would be free of a spot;
They were certain that Jim had a great head on him
　　And that Jim would amount to a lot.

And Jim grew to manhood and honour and fame
　　And bears a good name;
While Bill is shut up in a dark prison cell—
　　You never can tell.

Pedagogy

THOMAS CARLYLE

THOMAS CARLYLE (1795-1881), essayist and historian, was born at Ecclefechan, in Dumfriesshire, Scotland, of peasant stock. His early school experiences at Annan Grammar School were unhappy. His father, seeing the boy's ability, sent him at the age of fifteen to Edinburgh University to study for the ministry. When in 1814 a career in the church lost its appeal, Carlyle became a schoolmaster, but his reserve, his irritability, and his sarcasm were hardly ideal qualities for success in teaching. In 1819 he gave up teaching and returned to Edinburgh to study law, but his health was bad; he suffered from insomnia and dyspepsia, and the law ceased to interest him. At this time he experienced an intellectual and spiritual crisis: he abandoned his orthodox religious views and came to believe that the results of modern inquiry could be combined with a reverent and religious conception of the universe.

From 1822-1824 Carlyle supported himself by acting as tutor to Charles Buller. On the termination of his tutoring, he decided definitely upon a literary career.

In 1826 Carlyle married Jane Baillie Welsh and settled in Edinburgh. During the next few years he contributed essays to the Edinburgh Review *and wrote* Sartor Resartus. *In 1834 he moved to London, and there he made his home for the remaining years of his life.*

The following selection is taken from Sartor Resartus. *This book consists of two parts: (1) a discourse on the philosophy of clothes based on the speculations of an imaginary Professor Teufelsdröckh and leading to the conclusion that all symbols, forms, and human institutions are properly clothes; and (2) a biography of Teufelsdröckh, which is in some measure, Carlyle's autobiography.*

'My Teachers,' says he, 'were hide-bound Pedants, without knowledge of man's nature, or of boy's; or of aught save their lexicons and quarterly account-books. Innumerable dead Vocables (no dead Language, for they themselves knew no Language) they crammed into us, and called it fostering the growth of mind. How can an inanimate, mechanical Gerund-grinder, the like of whom will, in a subsequent century, be manufactured at Nürnberg out of wood and leather, foster the growth of anything; much more of Mind, which grows, not like a vegetable (by having its roots littered with etymological compost), but like a spirit, by mysterious contact of Spirit; Thought kindling itself at the fire of living Thought? How shall *he* give kindling, in whose own inward man there is no live coal, but all is burnt-out to a dead grammatical cinder? The Hinterschlag Professors knew syntax enough; and of the human soul thus much: that it had a faculty called Memory, and could be acted-on through the muscular integument by appliance of birch-rods.

'Alas, so is it everywhere, so will it ever be; till the Hodman is discharged, or reduced to hodbearing, and an Architect is hired, and on all hands fitly encouraged: till communities and individuals discover, not without surprise, that fashioning the souls of a generation by Knowledge can rank on a level with blowing their bodies to pieces by Gunpowder; that with Generals and Fieldmarshals for killing, there should be world-honoured Dignitaries, and were it possible, true God-ordained Priests, for teaching. But as yet, though the Soldier wears openly, and even parades, his butchering-tool, nowhere, far as I have travelled, did the Schoolmaster make show of his instructing-tool: nay, were he to walk abroad with birch girt on thigh, as if he therefrom expected honour, would there not, among the idler class, perhaps a certain levity be excited?'

. . . 'The University where I was educated still stands vivid enough in my remembrance, and I know its name well; which name, however, I, from tenderness to existing interests and persons, shall in nowise divulge. It is my painful duty to say that, out of England and Spain, ours was the worst of all hitherto discovered Universities. This is indeed a time when right Education is, as nearly as may be, impossible: however, in degrees of wrongness there is no limit: nay, I can conceive a worse system than that of the Nameless itself; as poisoned victual may be worse than absolute hunger.

'It is written, When the blind lead the blind, both shall fall into the ditch: wherefore, in such circumstances, may it not sometimes be safer, if both leader and led simply—sit still? Had you, anywhere in Crim Tartary; walled-in a square enclosure; furnished it with a small, ill-chosen Library; and then turned loose into it eleven-hundred Christian striplings, to tumble about as they listed, from three to seven years: certain persons, under the title of Professors, being stationed at the gates, to declare aloud that it was a University, and exact considerable admission-fees,—you had, not indeed in mechanical structure, yet in spirit and result, some imperfect resemblance of our High Seminary. I say, imperfect; for if our mechanical structure was quite other, so neither was our result altogether the same: unhappily, we were not in Crim Tartary, but in a corrupt European city, full of smoke and sin: moreover, in the middle of a Public, which, without far costlier apparatus than that of the Square Enclosure, and Declaration aloud, you could not be sure of gulling.

'Gullible, however, by fit apparatus, all Publics are; and gulled, with the most surprising profit. Towards anything like a *Statistics of Imposture*, indeed, little as yet has been done: with a strange indifference, our Economists, nigh buried under Tables for minor Branches of Industry, have altogether overlooked the grand all-overtopping Hypocrisy Branch; as if our whole arts of Puffery, of Quackery, Priestcraft, Kingcraft, and the innumerable other crafts and mysteries of that genus, had not ranked in Productive Industry at all! Can any one, for example, so much as say, What moneys, in Literature and Shoeblacking, are realised by actual Instruction and actual jet Polish; what by fictitious-persuasive Proclamation of such; specifying, in distinct items, the distributions, circulations, disbursements, incomings of said moneys, with the smallest approach to accuracy? But to ask, How far, in all the several infinitely-complected departments of social business, in government, education, in manual, commercial, intellectual fabrication of every sort, man's Want is supplied by true Ware; how far by the mere Appearance of true Ware:—in other words, To what extent, by what methods, with what effects, in various times and countries, Deception takes the place of wages of Performance: here truly is an Inquiry big with results for the future time, but to which hitherto only the vaguest answer can be given. If for the present, in our Europe, we estimate the ratio of Ware to Appearance of Ware so high even as at One to a Hundred (which, considering the Wages of a Pope, Russian Autocrat, or English Game-Preserver, is probably not far from the mark),—what almost prodigious saving may there not be anticipated, as the *Statistics of Imposture* advances, and so the manufacturing of Shams (that of Realities rising into clearer and clearer distinction therefrom) gradually declines, and at length becomes all but wholly unnecessary!

'This for the coming golden ages. What I had to remark, for the present brazen one, is, that in several provinces, as in Education, Polity, Religion, where so much is wanted and indispensable, and so little can as yet be furnished, probably Imposture is of sanative, anodyne nature, and man's Gullibility not his worst blessing. Suppose your sinews of war quite broken; I mean your military chest insolvent, forage all but exhausted; and that the whole army is about to mutiny, disband, and cut your and each other's throat,—then were it not well could you, as if by miracle, pay them in any sort of fairy-money, feed them on coagulated water, or mere imagination of meat; whereby, till the real supply came up, they might be kept together and quiet? Such perhaps was the aim of Nature, who does nothing without aim, in furnishing her favourite, Man, with this his so omnipotent or rather omnipatient Talent of being Gulled.

'How beautifully it works, with a little mechanism; nay, almost makes mechanism for itself! These Professors in the Nameless lived with ease, with safety, by a mere Reputation, constructed in past times, and then too with no great effort, by quite another class of persons. Which Reputation, like a strong, brisk-going undershot wheel, sunk into the general current, bade fair, with only a little annual repainting on their part, to hold long together, and of its own accord assiduously grind for them. Happy that it was so, for the Millers! They themselves needed not to work; their attempts at working, at what they called Educating, now when I look back on it, filled me with a certain mute admiration.

'Besides all this, we boasted ourselves a Rational University; in the highest degree hostile to Mysticism; thus was the young vacant mind furnished with much talk about Progress of the Species, Dark Ages, Prejudice, and the like; so that all were quickly enough blown out into a state of windy argumentativeness; whereby the better sort had soon to end in sick, impotent Scepticism; the worser sort explode (*crepiren*) in finished Self-conceit, and to all spiritual intents become dead.—But this too is portion of mankind's lot. If our era is the Era of Unbelief, why murmur under it; is there not a better coming, nay come? As in long-drawn Systole and long-drawn Diastole, must the period of Faith alternate with the period of Denial; must the vernal growth, the summer luxuriance of all Opinions, Spiritual Representations and Creations, be followed by, and again follow, the autumnal decay, the winter dissolution. For man lives in Time, has his whole earthly being, endeavour and destiny shaped for him by Time: only in the transitory Time-Symbol is the ever-motionless Eternity we stand on made manifest. And yet, in such winter-seasons of Denial, it is for the nobler-minded perhaps a comparative misery to have been born, and to be awake and work; and for the duller a felicity, if, like hibernating animals, safe-lodged in some Salamanca University, or Sybaris City, or other superstitious or voluptuous Castle of Indolence, they can slumber-through, in stupid dreams, and only awaken when the loud-roaring hailstorms have all done their work, and to our prayers and martyrdoms the new Spring has been vouchsafed.'

That in the environment, here mysteriously enough shadowed forth, Teufelsdröckh must have felt ill at ease, cannot be doubtful. 'The hungry young,' he says, 'looked up to their spiritual Nurses; and, for food, were bidden eat the east-wind. What vain jargon of controversial Metaphysic, Etymology, and mechanical Manipulation falsely named Science, was current there, I indeed learned, better perhaps than the most. Among eleven-hundred Christian youths, there will not be wanting some eleven eager to learn. By collision with such, a certain warmth, a certain polish was communicated; by instinct and happy accident, I took less to rioting (*renommiren*), than to thinking and reading, which latter also I was free to do. Nay from the chaos of that Library, I succeeded in fishing-up more books perhaps than had been known to the very keepers thereof. The foundation of a Literary Life was hereby laid: I learned, on my own strength, to read fluently in almost all cultivated languages, on almost all subjects and sciences; farther, as man is ever the prime object to man, already it was my favourite employment to read character in speculation, and from the Writing to construe the Writer. A certain groundplan of Human Nature and Life began to fashion itself in me; wondrous enough, now when I look back on it; for my whole Universe, physical and spiritual, was as yet a Machine! However, such a conscious, recognised groundplan, the truest I had, *was* beginning to be there, and by additional experiments might be corrected and indefinitely extended.'

Education

ARTHUR GUITERMAN

ARTHUR GUITERMAN (1871-1943), poet, playwright, and lecturer, was born in Austria, educated in the public schools of New York City and at the College of the City of New York, from which he was graduated in 1891. He is widely known as a writer of light verse.

MARK HOPKINS sat on one end of a log
    And a farm boy sat on the other.
Mark Hopkins came as a pedagogue
    And taught as an elder brother.
I don't care what Mark Hopkins taught,
If his Latin was small and his Greek was naught,
For the farmer boy he thought, thought he,
    All through lecture time and quiz,
"The kind of a man I mean to be
    Is the kind of a man Mark Hopkins is."

Theology, languages, medicine, law,
Are peacock feathers to deck a daw
If the boys who come from your splendid schools
Are well-trained sharpers or flippant fools.
You may boast of your age and your ivied walls,
Your great endowments, your marble halls
    And all your modern features,
Your vast curriculum's scope and reach
And the multifarious *things* you teach—
    But how about your teachers?
Are they men who can stand in a father's place,
Who are paid, best paid, by the ardent face
When boyhood gives, as boyhood can,
Its love and faith to a fine, true man?

No printed word nor spoken plea
Can teach young hearts what men should be,

Not all the books on all the shelves,
But what the teachers are, themselves.
For Education is, Making Men;
So is it now, so was it when
Mark Hopkins sat on one end of a log
  And James Garfield sat on the other.

Of School Discipline

JOHN AMOS COMENIUS

JOHN AMOS COMENIUS (1592-1671) was born in Moravia. As a member of the Moravian church, he suffered greatly in the Catholic-Protestant warfare which raged over his native land during the period of the Thirty Years' War. His home was plundered, his books were burned, his wife and children were murdered, and he himself was driven into exile. During his exile he took charge of a school in Poland, where he worked out in practice the great work on method which he later published. So advanced were his views on education that he was invited to join a commission appointed by the English Parliament to undertake the reform of English education, but because of the unsettled state of the times the commission never met, and so Comenius went to Sweden, where he reorganized Swedish schools. It is interesting to know that in 1654 he was consulted with reference to the presidency of Harvard College. The last years of his life were spent in Amsterdam, where he died, an exile, at the age of seventy-nine.

The Great Didactic was written in Czech but first published in Latin at Amsterdam in 1657. The first English edition appeared in 1896. In this work Comenius formulated and explained his two fundamental ideas, one, that all instruction must be carefully graded and arranged to proceed from the easy to the difficult, the near to the remote, the known to the unknown; and two, that in imparting knowledge to children, the teacher must make constant appeal through sense-perception to the understanding of the child.

Comenius occupies a position of commanding importance in the history of education. He introduced the whole modern conception of the educational process.

T HERE is a proverb in Bohemia, "A school without discipline is like a mill without water," and this is very true. For, if you withdraw the water from a mill, it stops, and, in the same way, if you deprive a school of discipline, you take away from it its motive power. A field also, if it be never ploughed, produces nothing but weeds; and trees, if not continually pruned, revert to their wild state and bear no fruit. It must not be thought, however, that we wish our schools to resound with shrieks and with blows.

"Of School Discipline" is from *The Great Didactic*, by John Amos Comenius; reprinted by permission of The Macmillan Company.

What we demand is vigilance and attention on the part of the master and of the pupils. For discipline is nothing but an unfailing method by which we may make our scholars, scholars in reality.

As regards discipline, therefore, it is advisable that the educator of youth know its object, its subject-matter, and the various forms which it may assume, since he will then know why, when, and how, systematised severity is to be used.

We may start with the incontestable proposition that punishment should be employed towards those who err. But it is not because they have erred that they should be punished (for what has been done cannot be undone), but in order that they may not err again in the future. Discipline should therefore be free from personal elements, such as anger or dislike, and should be exercised with such frankness and sincerity of purpose, that even the pupils may feel that the action taken is for their good, and that those set over them are but exercising paternal authority. They will thus regard it in the same light as a bitter draught prescribed for them by the doctor.

Now no discipline of a severe kind should be exercised in connection with studies or literary exercises, but only where questions of morality are at stake. For, as we have already shown, studies, if they are properly organised, form in themselves a sufficient attraction, and entice all (with the exception of monstrosities) by their inherent pleasantness. If this be not the case, the fault lies, not with the pupil, but with the master, and, if our skill is unable to make an impression on the understanding, our blows will have no effect. Indeed, by any application of force we are far more likely to produce a distaste for letters than a love for them. Whenever, therefore, we see that a mind is diseased and dislikes study, we should try to remove its indisposition by gentle remedies, but should on no account employ violent ones. The very sun in the heavens gives us a lesson on this point. In early spring, when plants are young and tender, he does not scorch them, but warms and invigorates them by slow degrees, not putting forth his full heat until they are full-grown and bring forth fruit and seeds. The gardener proceeds on the same principle, and does not apply the pruning-knife to plants that are immature. In the same way a musician does not strike his lyre a blow with his fist or with a stick, nor does he throw it against the wall, because it produces a discordant sound; but, setting to work on scientific principles, he tunes it and gets it into order. Just such a skillful and sympathetic treatment is necessary to instil a love of learning into the minds of our pupils, and any other procedure will only convert their idleness into antipathy and their lack of interest into downright stupidity.

If, however, some stimulus be found necessary, better means than blows can be found. Sometimes a few severe words or a reprimand before the whole class is very efficacious, while sometimes a little praise bestowed on the others has great effect. "See how well so-and-so attends! See how quickly he sees each point! While you sit there like a stone!" It is often of use to laugh at the backward ones. "You silly fellow, can't you understand such a simple matter?" Weekly, or at any rate monthly, contests for the first place in class may also be introduced, as we have shown elsewhere. Great care, however, should be taken that these experiments do not degenerate into a mere amusement, and thus lose their force; since, if they are to act as a stimulus to industry, they must be backed on the part of the pupil by a love of praise and a dislike of blame or of losing his place in class. It is therefore absolutely essential that the master be always in the room, that he throw a good deal of energy into his work, and that he scold the idlers and praise the hard-working boys before the whole class.

Only in the case of moral delinquencies may a severer discipline be used: (1) as, for instance, in the case of impiety of any kind, such as blasphemy, obscenity, or any other open offence against God's law. (2) In the case of stubbornness and premeditated misbehaviour, such as disobeying the master's orders, or the conscious neglect of duty. (3) In the case of pride and disdain, or even of envy and idleness; as, for example, if a boy refuse to give a schoolfellow assistance when asked to do so.

For offences of the first kind are an insult to God's majesty. Those of the second kind undermine the foundation of all virtue, namely, humility and obedience. While those of the third kind prevent any rapid progress in studies. An offence against God is a crime, and should be expiated by an extremely severe punishment. An offence against man is iniquitous, and such a tendency should be promptly and sternly corrected. But an offence against Priscian is a stain that may be wiped out by the sponge of blame. In a word, the object of discipline should be to stir us up to revere God, to assist our neighbours, and to perform the labours and duties of life with alacrity.

The sun in the heavens teaches us the best form of discipline, since to all things that grow it ministers (1) light and heat, continuously; (2) rain and wind, frequently; (3) lightning and thunder, but seldom; although these latter are not wholly without their use.

It is by imitating this that the master should try to keep his pupils up to their work.

(1) He should give them frequent examples of the conduct that they should try to imitate, and should point to himself as a living example. Unless he does this, all his work will be in vain.

(2) He may employ advice, exhortation, and sometimes blame, but should take great care to make his motive clear and to show unmistakably that his actions are based on paternal affection, and are destined to build up the characters of his pupils and not to crush them. Unless the pupil understands this and is fully persuaded of it, he will despise all discipline and will deliberately resist it.

(3) Finally, if some characters are unaffected by gentle methods, re-

course must be had to more violent ones, and every means should be tried before any pupil is pronounced impossible to teach. Without doubt there are many to whom the proverb, "Beating is the only thing that improves a Phrygian," applies with great force. And it is certain that, even if such measures do not produce any great effect on the boy who is punished, they act as a great stimulus to the others by inspiring them with fear. We should take great care, however, not to use these extreme measures too readily, or too zealously, as, if we do, we may exhaust all our resources before the extreme case of insubordination which they were intended to meet, arises.

In short, the object of discipline should be to confirm those who are being trained up for God and for the Church, in that disposition which God demands in His sons, the pupils in the school of Christ, so that they may rejoice with trembling (Psalm ii. 11), and looking to their own salvation may rejoice always in the Lord (Phil. ii. 4 and 10), that is to say, that they may love and reverence their masters, and not merely allow themselves to be led in the right direction, but actually tend towards it of their own accord.

This training of the character can only be accomplished in the above-mentioned ways: by good example, by gentle words, and by continually taking a sincere and undisguised interest in the pupil. Sudden bursts of anger should only be used in exceptional circumstances, and then with the intention that renewed good feeling shall be the result.

For (to give one more example) did any one ever see a goldsmith produce a work of art by the use of the hammer alone? Never. It is easier to cast such things than to beat them out, and, if any excrescence have to be removed, it is not by violent blows that the artificer gets rid of it, but by a series of gentle taps, or by means of a file or a pair of forceps; while he completes the operation by polishing and smoothing his work. And do we believe that irrational force will enable us to produce intelligent beings, images of the living God?

A fisherman, too, who catches fish in deep waters with a drag-net, not only fastens on pieces of lead to sink it, but also attaches corks to the other end of it, that it may rise to the surface of the water. In the same way whoever wishes to ensnare the young in the nets of virtue, must, on the one hand, humble and abase them by severity, and, on the other, exalt them by gentleness and affection. Happy are the masters who can combine these two extremes! Happy are the boys who find such masters!

Here we may quote the opinion which that great man, Eilhard Lubinus, doctor of theology, has expressed on the reform of schools in the preface to his edition of the New Testament in Greek, Latin, and German—

"The second point is this: the young should never be compelled to do anything, but their tasks should be of such a kind and should be set them in such a way that they will do them of their own accord, and take pleasure in them. I am therefore of opinion that rods and blows, those weapons of slavery, are quite unsuitable to freemen, and should never be used in schools, but should be reserved for boys of an abnormal and servile disposition. Such boys are easily recognised and must be removed from the school at once, on account both of the sluggishness of their disposition and of the depravity that is generally found in conjunction with it. Besides, any knowledge that they may acquire will be employed for wicked purposes, and will be like a sword in the hands of a madman. There are, however, other kinds of punishment suitable for boys who are free-born and of normal disposition, and these we may employ."

The Teaching of English

MARY ELLEN CHASE

MARY ELLEN CHASE, writer and teacher, was born in Blue Hill, Maine, in 1887. She was educated at Blue Hill Academy; the University of Maine, and the University of Minnesota, from which she received a Ph.D. degree in 1922. Her first teaching experience was in a Maine district school. Since 1926 she has taught English at Smith College.

Miss Chase began to write during her student days at the University of Maine. Her first published work was a football story which appeared in the American Boy. *She is now the author of several novels, a great many short stories, essays, and reviews.*

MY grandmother, who died at eighty-seven, was as she grew older more and more perplexed over the meaning and significance of my profession in life. Whenever I returned home for summer vacations, she always cornered me and asked exactly what the teaching of English meant. Since no such pedagogical term was used in her day and generation, she added to her bewilderment a kind of uneasy suspicion lest this strange subject to which I gave my time and strength was in some way inferior to those more obvious subjects such as Latin or mathematics. Upon each return we used to have disturbing colloquies of this nature:

"Just what do you do when you teach English? Do you mean that you teach your students to read?"

"Yes, and a great many more things."

"What things?"

"Well, I try to teach them to write as well as to read."

"What do you mean—to write?"

"To say what they think in good English."

"Do you mean *grammar?*"

"Yes, partly. But there is a lot more to it than grammar."

"What, exactly?"

"Well, I try to teach them to write good sentences that mean something."

"Do you mean you teach them to be writers?"

"No. I can't teach them to be writers. But I try to teach them to say what they think."

"Do people nowadays have to be taught to say what they think?"

"Yes, and they have to be taught to think straight."

"To think straight about what?"

"Well, about the things they do think about, and the things they read."

"What things do they read?"

"Oh, poetry and essays and novels."

"Can't they read those things by themselves?"

"Well, I try to show them what poetry and prose mean, not just what they say in so many words."

"You mean you read things like Shakespeare and Dickens in your classes?"

"Yes, and many other things, too."

"It can't be so hard just to read things and talk about them as to teach, say, Latin or arithmetic, is it?"

"Yes. I think it's a great deal harder."

"Well, maybe. But it doesn't seem so to me. . . . Do you like teaching English?"

"Yes, I like it better than anything else in the world."

After such a conversation as this with my grandmother I always felt a kind of odd insecurity assailing me. I wondered if the teaching of English was as vague an exercise and occupation as my own answers to her questions. I felt, in fact, sure only about two of my answers: first, that the teaching of English is at once the hardest teaching in the world to do and, second, that it is more fun to do than anything else in the world.

2

After twenty-two years spent in the teaching of college English I still believe true the first of my contentions to my puzzled grandmother: that English is the most difficult of all subjects to teach. Unlike others more tidy because more clearly defined, English has no *terminus ab quo*, no *terminus ad quem*. More closely related to life than any other study, even than the sciences, it embraces literally everything within its invisible and illimitable boundaries. And yet, on the other hand, in itself it baffles definition. It is a language, yet, because of the very necessity of its use, it lacks in most imaginations the dignity and the charm of an ancient or even a modern foreign tongue. It is an art, yet again the familiar and the necessary, the daily and the commonplace, dim its aesthetic qualities and possibilities. It seems the hand-maiden to other subjects rather than the mistress of them all, simply because no other subject can be understood without it. Thus the teacher of English is hampered at the start by misconceptions so natural and inevitable that they are doubly hard to put to rout.

Of all the excellent teachers of college English whom I have known I have never discovered one who knew precisely what he was doing. Therein have lain their power and their charm. I have come, indeed, to think that a firm hold upon definite objectives and methods by the teacher of English is likely to mark him as mediocre or even as poor at his job. Our objectives are as nebulous and intangible as are our methods, for the simple reason that we are dependent for the efficacy of both upon the multifarious imaginations of our students. The success of our teaching like the nature of it is forevermore conditioned by the capacities of the minds with which we work, by the wealth or poverty of perception, by the presence or absence of humor, by the possession or lack of understanding and vision. The meaning and value of any piece of literature are rarely the same to any two persons; the arrangement of words in a sentence may mean everything, something, or nothing both to those who read them and to those who labor to write them. *Man proposes, but God disposes* is a truth to be learned as quickly as possible by all teachers of English! And it is through the extreme flexibility of his mind, through the recognition that he is but a variable means to a most variable end, that the teacher of English reaps his variable reward.

Once at Hillside I was endeavoring to teach a stupid and somewhat sullen boy of thirteen the fundamentals of English grammar. We were dealing one morning with adverbs of manner, those sprightly parts of speech which add life and action to their verbs. Seeing the necessity for extreme simplicity in my explanations, I made the insecure announcement that most adverbs of manner end in *ly*. I wrote various of these on the blackboard: quick*ly*, slow*ly*, gent*ly*, noisi*ly*, smooth*ly*, stern*ly*, silent*ly*. Then I turned to the boy and said:

"I want you to think quietly for a few minutes and then give me some adverbs of manner of your own."

"I don't need to think," he said instantly. "*July*."

Since that day I have had many such doors so summarily slammed upon my objectives that I have learned to look upon them merely as my own loosely defined and pleasant possessions, which may never become, indeed, often *can* never become, the property of those whom I teach. I have learned that for one student who sees reality and excitement in an adverb, there are many who will never see a part of speech other than a part of speech. I have learned that for one student who comes to college with a sense of the dignity and the delicacy in words, there are many, even from the best of schools, to whom the writing of English is stupid and useless and the careful and thoughtful reading of it only a bit less so. I have learned that my methods must be as different and varied as the different and varied personalities of my students, who from the start are governed by forces over which I have small control. I have learned that to know precisely what I am doing in any given class at any given moment is a state of mind as intolerably dull for my students as for myself and as arid as the proverbial Valley of Baca.

It is, then, this very necessity for elasticity of mind on the part of the teacher, for quick and intelligent changes in approach, which makes the teaching of English such a difficult job. We deal with the most personal and most fortified of possessions, with thoughts and feelings, suggestions and impressions, notions, fancies, predilections, ideas. We learn, if we are any good at our work, to welcome opposition, opinions different from our own, heresies, heterodoxies, iconoclasms. Our delight lies in the activity of awakened minds to any end at all. For we deal not with ends but with means. If Karl Marx dictates the criticism of certain of our students, we keep our heads; if James Joyce rather than Wordsworth proves the bread of life to others, we rejoice in this form of nourishment, strange though it may be to us; if Pater's style stirs someone to rebellion, we turn to Hemingway until the rebellion is quelled, if it ever is. We learn that we can be firm toward our own loyalties and yet not immovable toward others. Our one aim is to intensify the powers of thinking and of feeling in those whom we teach; and the only method we have of doing this is to open, through countless ways, every possible avenue to thought, emotion and expression and to keep ourselves alive while we are doing so.

3

I feel sure that all honest teachers of English admit from the start that their job, difficult as it may be, is, first of all, a self-indulgence. For I still believe true the second of my contentions to my grandmother that the teaching of English is more fun to do than anything else in the world. The best of us have come into the profession because we have been unable to keep out of it. In one way or another we fell in love with books early in life, with their words and phrases, their music and rhythm, their people and their events, their meaning and their thought; and to attempt to convey to others our own passion has been the simplest means open to us of continuing therein ourselves.

Most college professors of English like, as they reach what is known as the "top," to stick to their own fields of study and enthusiasm. This becomes their own particular form of self-indulgence. If they are mad about Chaucer or Shakespeare or the Seventeenth Century, they like to teach within their own boundaries. They are not eager to meet the incoming hordes of college freshmen, who, for better or for worse, write themes which must be read, and read badly the books assigned to them. They prefer to deal with students who have gone through the mill of Freshman English and who have, presumably, come out refined and ready for more delicate and costly nourishment. But, unlike the majority, I am one who, even after twenty-two years of trying to teach

English to freshmen, still find its ways ways of pleasantness if not always paths of peace.

Too many young teachers of freshmen bring an unfortunate residue of the graduate schools into their class-rooms. Coming into college teaching fresh (or perhaps not so fresh) from the doctorate, they need some time, at the expense of their students, to realize that a fund of knowledge is the worst possible capital with which to begin their work and that the emulation of their graduate professors is the worst possible way to teach freshmen. In this teaching, resiliency and humor, liveliness and enthusiasm, informality and companionship, count for far more than knowledge. I have found from long experience that the teacher of freshmen who has had past experience in secondary schools is far more likely to succeed in college teaching, with or without the doctorate, than one who has gone directly from the bachelor's degree to further study.

I have spent some of the most pleasant hours of my life with college freshmen. I have found that succeeding years do not much alter the crop in spite of increasingly excellent teaching in many of the schools. Perhaps the average seventeen- or eighteen-year-old mind is subject to certain well-defined boundaries, which await for their extension the freedom and independence of college. At all events, with relatively few exceptions, my freshmen exhibit the same mental habits and characteristics, different as they are in temperament and personality. To many of them the use of words is a tolerable exercise but often quite unconnected with thought. It is fun to snap them out of sloppy thinking or to bring them up sharply from the abyss of no thinking at all; to make them conscious of the interdependence of words and thoughts; to make them see that a paragraph is a logical procession of sentences and thoughts which march along together, each depending upon the other; to make them see words with their eyes; to teach them that ears alone are the most dangerous of senses.

It is, indeed, this dependence upon ears, this multiplying of words without knoweldge, this *inanis verborum torrens* scorned by Quintilian, which, to me, forms the first task of the teacher of Freshman English. This it is, as we all know, which lends to the reading of early themes the zest of a treasure-hunt. Even in Smith College, where entering students have been exceptionally well trained in the best of schools, this dependence upon hearing alone can give birth to such a sentence as this which recently began a freshman theme:

I have long since refused to accept those age-old traditions of life, death, and God.

Or to this moving bit of portraiture:

Over the mantel hung a portrait of my grandfather. He had never married, never loved, and never deviated from the paths of respectability.

The writing of English has, I believe, never been sufficiently respected as a means to mental discipline; yet surely the power to visualize as well as to hear the words which one places upon paper is the first "objective" of the teacher. To use English fluently and well can never be taught. All writing, says Emerson in one of his essays, comes by the Grace of God, a truth recognized early by all wise teachers of freshmen. But straight thinking, even although it is destined to remain within narrow limits, can be taught by patience, energy, and humor; and this training in the careful, rather than the skillful, use of words seems to me the chief reason for the continued existence of English composition in our colleges.

I like to teach my freshmen to read, and I have ample opportunity to do so since at least fifty percent of them come to college without really knowing how. They are not, of course, so bad at narrative or even at certain forms of poetry, but an essay leaves them wandering in labyrinthine mazes. The meaning of what they read is lost in a succession of words; the personality of single words means little if anything. I understand that there are now specialists in the exercise of reading whose business it is to remedy defects by all sorts of tests and methods. My own manner of remedy will doubtless seem unsound to them; yet it has not been without effect. I like to teach my students to see a word in terms of light and color, whether it is clear and shining, heavy and dark, black or white or yellow; to show them that any page of any given book has a character of its own through mere letters even before the words themselves are seen as words. I have discovered in my own teaching that once single words are grasped in their appearance, their sound, their meaning, and in the countless suggestions and associations which each holds within itself, the power to read more difficult prose comes as though by magic.

I have found that the most minute detail sometimes stirs the imagination. I have always been sensitive to the drama in punctuation although to most of my students the mastery of its use is drudgery and its existence at best only a matter of convenience. I like to convince them that in itself it is an art and that the skillful employment of it, as Charles Lamb so well knew, can add personality and suggestion to their themes. I like to awaken them to the vivacity of a comma, the dignity and silence of a semi-colon, the suspense and quickening latent in a question mark, the redundancy and danger in an exclamation point.

I have always felt sorry that figures of speech, which used to be taught thirty years ago when the science of Rhetoric was still in good and honorable estate, have now become honorable points of ignorance to many teachers and matters of inattention to most students. I still find similes the most provoking of subjects for study and appreciation. My freshmen and I take delight in them and in the imagination which prompts them. I like to try to show what is behind the desire, instinctive in us all, to compare one thing with another; how comparisons arise from one's background, nature, and experience; how the range and wealth of imagination differ in the individual. I like to show how a simile gives a double picture, how it at the same time heightens, clarifies, and intensifies one's feeling, thought, or image.

As the mountains are roundabout Jerusalem, so the Lord is roundabout His people, henceforth and even forever.

The mail-coach it was that distributed over the face of the land, like the opening of apocalyptic vials, the heart-shaking news of Trafalgar, of Salamanca, of Vittoria, of Waterloo.

We go on a still hunt for similes in my class in anything which we happen to be reading. Sometimes I am sufficiently mad or sanguine to propose that we try our minds and hands at them. One of my freshmen, whom God disposed of early, writes:

The sun was sinking below the western horizon like a new penny dropped into a slot machine in order to bring out the night.

Another, through whom He is still working, says:

When I was very young, the fields stretching on and on before our farmhouse door meant nothing to me but land; when I was happy, as a place to play upon, when I was sad, as a place where no one ever came. Now as I look upon them they are wide and long like the thoughts of quiet people, like the wish to know more and more of things that cannot be seen.

The first makes me wholesomely conscious of the limitations imposed upon all teachers of English composition; the second makes me want to stick to my job if only for my own sake.

Now that terms as terms have passed from class vocabularies, now that *unity, coherence,* and *emphasis* have gone, never, we hope, to return, now that mere text-books have lost their old significance and become uneasy means to a questionable end, the teacher of English becomes not so much a task-master as the companion of his students. What we are after is an awakened consciousness, differing in each individual, an excitement in thinking, reading, and writing for their own sake, new discoveries, new enthusiasms, the casting off, or the retention with better understanding, of the old. What we want is to stimulate the love of mental adventure and of constructive doubt, to create emotional satisfaction in the things of the mind, to reveal through books the variety and the wonder of human experience.

How we do these things matters not at all. The numberless ways of their accomplishment reside in the numberless personalities of those of us who teach. The one thing that does matter is that we shall be awake and alive, alert and eager, flexible and unperturbed, likable and exciting. Once we are these things, we can cast away all the aphorisms and methods conceived and issued by the teachers' colleges as so much useless baggage, for we are vastly better off without them.

4

Like all teachers of English I indulge myself by communicating to my students my own enthusiasms in literature. Perhaps this practice is after all not so much a self-indulgence as it is a necessity; for no teacher is at his best in dealing with something which does not satisfy himself. My freshmen each year read a Greek play with me simply because *Medea* or *The Trojan Women, Electra* or *The Trachiniae* have delighted and nourished me through many years. To most of them new doors are opened; to the few who never enter in, Euripides and Sophocles, even in a good translation surely need make no apology to college freshmen! From the ancients we move to the moderns to realize that art has no boundaries in time or in space. One of my students discovered last year that Homer in the *Odyssey* and Willa Cather in *My Antonia* held ideas as well as principles of literature in common, a discovery which for her and for us all brought the old and the new suddenly together.

I have found this companionship in literature very much the same whether I share it with freshmen or with my older college students, who study with me the fiction of the eighteenth and nineteenth centuries. With both, my desires are the same. I want to make both see that mere pleasurable excitement in any given piece of literature is not a sufficient end in itself but rather a spring-board toward something better than itself. I want to make both conscious of the manifold ways by which an author has caused this pleasurable excitement, to make both understand how the product of an artist's mind can be made even more beautiful in the light of a reader's intelligence. I want to make both realize that all art is thus creative, that one mind creates in another perhaps even a greater abundance than was in its own, and that in this sense the reader becomes an artist together with the writer.

The analysis of books which is necessary in order to gain this understanding is irksome to some students, since the taste of many readers, in college and out, is but a vague sense of likes and dislikes from which they do not wish to be dislodged. And yet a standard of literary appreciation is the one aim of the teacher of literature, for from its sure foundation a critical sense is added to the mere enjoyment of reading. The vision of the artist can never be re-created in the reader without a knowledge of his work, his ways and means; and this knowledge is dependent upon seeing the whole only through the sum of all its parts.

I have found analysis to be the most exciting of literary occupations; and I hope I have managed to convey a measure of excitement to those who break down and rebuild with me. The sharpened powers which analysis gives extend far beyond the novel or poem analyzed. Not only is the whole seen in all its truth, but the parts take on each its own value. The words and sentences, motifs and music, images and figures, characters and situations, a memorable phrase, lines of description or of thought— each exists for itself as well as for the whole; and each in the mind of the reader becomes linked with numberless suggestions and associations from out his own experience. The analysis of novels turns mere events into ideas, which, according to Santayana, is the function of literature; the analysis of poems transfigures words into emotion; the analysis of essays gives form and body to ideas and reflections.

There is a figure in a fragment of Sappho, which, regardless of the unknown thought of the poet, always suggests to me this necessity of breaking up a whole in order to endow it with the breath of life.

Like the hyacinth which the shepherd tramples underfoot upon the mountain, but which yet blooms purple on the ground.

"The literature that is of lasting value is an accident," writes a recent essayist. "It is something that happens to one." It is this accident, this sudden happening in the minds of our students, which is our goal as teachers of literature whatever our "methods" may be. It is this accident which turns readers into artists through their sudden understanding that the values of art and life are one and the same. It is this accident for which we work and wait, knowing always that the capacity for intelligent appreciation of literature among a people means far more to the life of that people than any works of art it may produce.

5

I have often wondered whether my grandmother's mind in some future state has been clarified as to what the teaching of English really means. My own remains as delightfully vague as my answers to her questions many years ago or as this incomplete and uncertain description of my pleasant days with students. And since any immortality which there may be may find no room for books or even for enlightenment upon their richest use, I seize upon the nearer immortality granted to those whose life is in literature, knowing that this life, too, in the words of Ovid is identical with the power of his heaven, *Immensa est finemque non habet.*

The School Boy Reads His Iliad

DAVID MORTON

DAVID MORTON, *poet and teacher, was born in Kentucky in 1886. He was graduated from Vanderbilt University in 1909. For several years following he was a newspaper reporter and editorial writer. He began to teach in 1915 and since then has taught both in school and college. He became Professor of English at Amherst in 1926.*

THE sounding battles leave him nodding still:
    The din of javelins at the distant wall
Is far too faint to wake that weary will
    That all but sleeps for cities where they fall.
He cares not if this Helen's face were fair,
    Nor if the thousand ships shall go or stay;
In vain the rumbling chariots throng the air
    With sounds the centuries shall not hush away.

Beyond the window where the Spring is new,
    Are marbles in a square, and tops again,
And floating voices tell him what they do,
    Luring his thought from these long-warring men—
And though the camp be visited with gods,
    He dreams of marbles and of tops, and nods.

The Apology

PLATO

PLATO was born in 431(?) B.C.; he died in 351(?) B.C. He came of a
distinguished family and in his youth received instruction in grammar,
music, and gymnastics. At about the age of twenty he became a follower
of Socrates, for whom he held deep affection. After the death of Socrates
Plato withdrew from Athens to Megara and subsequently traveled in Italy,
Cyrene, Sicily, and Egypt. After his return to Athens he began to teach in
the Academy, a form of early university and school of research. He made
two voyages to Sicily: one in an attempt to educate the young Dionysius
of Syracuse in philosophy, the other to reconcile the disputes which had
broken out between Dionysius and Dion. Both voyages failed of their purpose. Plato returned to Athens and spent the remaining years of his life
teaching at the Academy.

We are indebted to Plato for almost all we know about Socrates. The
dialogues are largely a tribute by Plato to the great teacher who first turned
his thought to philosophy. Though the portrait of Socrates in the dialogues is a dramatic creation, there is no reason to doubt that in the
Apology we have a very lifelike representation. We see him as a man of
invincible moral courage, a man who would die rather than violate what
he believed to be right. Throughout his life his chief concern was to examine men and reveal the extent of their ignorance. Unlike the Sophists he was
not a professional teacher. He simply sought those public places where
he would meet men and have an opportunity to cross-examine their beliefs
on politics and morality. Much that passed for thought and morality was
to Socrates a mass of error and conventionality and unexamined common-
places. Against this body of confused and inconsistent popular beliefs
Socrates waged unceasing war. He was convinced that what passed for
knowledge was ignorance. He attempted to reconstruct human thought
and action on a basis of "reasoned truth." He cross-examined men to test
their knowledge and to teach them the importance of virtue. But this re-
lentless exposure of the hollowness of what passed for knowledge brought
Socrates into unpopularity. In 399 B.C. he was accused by his fellow
Athenians of denying the gods and of corrupting young men. He was
brought to trial, convicted, and condemned to death. On the appointed
day he drank the hemlock and died.

"The Apology" is from The Trial and Death of Socrates, by Plato, translated by
F. J. Church; reprinted by permission of The Macmillan Company.

SOCRATES. I cannot tell what impression my accusers have made upon you, Athenians: for my own part, I know that they nearly made me forget who I was, so plausible were they; and yet they have scarcely uttered one single word of truth. But of all their many falsehoods, the one which astonished me most, was when they said that I was a clever speaker, and that you must be careful not to let me mislead you. I thought that it was most impudent of them not to be ashamed to talk in that way; for as soon as I open my mouth the lie will be exposed, and I shall prove that I am not a clever speaker in any way at all: unless, indeed, by a clever speaker they mean a man who speaks the truth. If that is their meaning, I agree with them that I am a much greater orator than they. My accusers, then I repeat, have said little or nothing that is true; but from me you shall hear the whole truth. Certainly you will not hear an elaborate speech, Athenians, drest up, like theirs, with words and phrases. I will say to you what I have to say, without preparation, and in the words which come first, for I believe that my cause is just; so let none of you expect anything else. Indeed, my friends, it would hardly be seemly for me, at my age, to come before you like a young man with his specious falsehoods. But there is one thing, Athenians, which I do most earnestly beg and entreat of you. Do not be surprised and do not interrupt, if in my defence I speak in the same way that I am accustomed to speak in the market-place, at the tables of the money-changers, where many of you have heard me, and elsewhere. The truth is this. I am more than seventy years old, and this is the first time that I have ever come before a Court of Law; so your manner of speech here is quite strange to me. If I had been really a stranger, you would have forgiven me for speaking in the language and the fashion of my native country: and so now I ask you to grant me what I think I have a right to claim. Never mind the style of my speech—it may be better or it may be worse—give your whole attention to the question, Is what I say just, or is it not? That is what makes a good judge, as speaking the truth makes a good advocate.

I have to defend myself, Athenians, first against the old false charges of my old accusers, and then against the later ones of my present accusers. For many men have been accusing me to you, and for very many years, who have not uttered a word of truth: and I fear them more than I fear Anytus and his companions, formidable as they are. But, my friends, those others are still more formidable; for they got hold of most of you when you were children, and they have been more persistent in accusing me with lies, and in trying to persuade you that there is one Socrates, a wise man, who speculates about the heavens, and who examines into all things that are beneath the earth, and who can 'make the worse appear the better reason.' These men, Athenians, who spread abroad this report, are the accusers whom I fear; for their hearers think that persons who pursue such inquiries never believe in the gods. And then they are many, and their attacks have been going on for a long time: and they spoke to you when you were at the age most readily to believe them: for you were all young, and many of you were children: and there was no one to answer them when they attacked me. And the most unreasonable thing of all is that commonly I do not even know their names: I cannot tell you who they are, except in the case of the comic poets. But all the rest who have been trying to prejudice you against me, from motives of spite and jealousy, and sometimes, it may be, from conviction, are the enemies whom it is hardest to meet. For I cannot call any one of them forward in Court, to cross-examine him: I have, as it were, simply to fight with shadows in my defence, and to put questions which there is no one to answer. I ask you, therefore, to believe that, as I say, I have been attacked by two classes of accusers—first by Meletus and his friends, and then by those older ones of whom I have spoken. And, with your leave, I will defend myself first against my old enemies; for you heard their accusations first, and they were much more persistent than my present accusers are.

Well, I must make my defence, Athenians, and try in the short time allowed me to remove the prejudice which you have had against me for a long time. I hope that I may manage to do this, if it be good for you and for me, and that my defence may be successful; but I am quite aware of the nature of my task, and I know that it is a difficult one. Be the issue, however, as God wills, I must obey the law, and make my defence.

Let us begin again, then, and see what is the charge which has given rise to the prejudice against me, which was what Meletus relied on when he drew his indictment. What is the calumny which my enemies have been spreading about me? I must assume that they are formally accusing me, and read their indictment. It would run somewhat in this fashion: "Socrates is an evil-doer, who meddles with inquiries into things beneath the earth, and in heaven, and who 'makes the worse appear the better reason,' and who teaches others these same things." That is what they say; and in the Comedy of Aristophanes you yourselves saw a man called Socrates swinging round in a basket, and saying that he walked the air, and talking a great deal of nonsense about matters of which I understand nothing, either more or less. I do not mean to disparage that kind of knowledge, if there is any man who possesses it. I trust Meletus may never be able to prosecute me for that. But, the truth is, Athenians, I have nothing to do with these matters, and almost all of you are yourselves my witnesses of this. I beg all of you who have ever heard me converse, and they are many, to inform your neighbours and tell them if any of you have ever heard me conversing about such matters, either more or less. That will show you that the other common stories about me are as false as this one.

But, the fact is, that not one of these stories is true; and if you have heard that I undertake to educate men, and exact money from them for so doing, that it not true either; though I think that it would be a fine thing to be able to educate men, as Gorgias of Leontini, and Prodicus of Ceos, and Hippias of Elis do. For each of them, my friends, can go into any city, and persuade the young men to leave the society of their fellow-citizens, with any of whom they might associate for nothing, and to be only too glad to be allowed to pay money for the privilege of associating with themselves. And I believe that there is another wise man from Paros residing in Athens at this moment. I happened to meet Callias, the son of Hipponicus, a man who has spent more money on the Sophists than every one else put together. So I said to him—he has two sons—Callias, if your two sons had been foals or calves, we could have hired a trainer for them who would have made them perfect in the excellence which belongs to their nature. He would have been either a groom or a farmer. But whom do you intend to take to train them, seeing that they are men? Who understands the excellence which belongs to men and to citizens? I suppose that you must have thought of this, because of your sons. Is there such a person, said I, or not? Certainly there is, he replied. Who is he, said I, and where does he come from, and what is his fee? His name is Evenus, Socrates, he replied: he comes from Paros, and his fee is five minæ. Then I thought that Evenus was a fortunate person if he really understood this art and could teach so cleverly. If I had possessed knowledge of that kind, I should have given myself airs and prided myself on it. But, Athenians, the truth is that I do not possess it.

Perhaps some of you may reply: But, Socrates, what is this pursuit of yours? Whence come these calumnies against you? You must have been engaged in some pursuit out of the common. All these stories and reports of you would never have gone about, if you had not been in some way different from other men. So tell us what your pursuits are, that we may not give our verdict in the dark. I think that that is a fair question, and I will try to explain to you what it is that has raised these calumnies against me, and given me this name. Listen, then: some of you perhaps will think that I am jesting; but I assure you that I will tell you the whole truth. I have gained this name, Athenians, simply by reason of a certain wisdom. But by what kind of wisdom? It is by just that wisdom which is, I believe, possible to men. In that, it may be, I am really wise. But the men of whom I was speaking just now must be wise in a wisdom which is greater than human wisdom, or in some way which I cannot describe, for certainly I know nothing of it myself, and if any man says that I do, he lies and wants to slander me. Do not interrupt me, Athenians, even if you think that I am speaking arrogantly. What I am going to say is not my own: I will tell you who says it, and he is worthy of your credit. I will bring the god of Delphi to be the witness of the fact of my wisdom and of its nature. You remember Chærephon. From youth upwards he was my comrade; and he went into exile with the people, and with the people he returned. And you remember, too, Chærephon's character; how vehement he was in carrying through whatever he took in hand. Once he went to Delphi and ventured to put this question to the oracle,—I entreat you again, my friends, not to cry out,—he asked if there was any man who was wiser than I: and the priestess answered that there was no man. Chærephon himself is dead, but his brother here will confirm what I say.

Now see why I tell you this. I am going to explain to you the origin of my unpopularity. When I heard of the oracle I began to reflect: What can God mean by this dark saying? I know very well that I am not wise, even in the smallest degree. Then what can he mean by saying that I am the wisest of men? It cannot be that he is speaking falsely, for he is a god and cannot lie. And for a long time I was at a loss to understand his meaning: then, very reluctantly, I turned to seek for it in this manner. I went to a man who was reputed to be wise, thinking that there, if anywhere, I should prove the answer wrong, and meaning to point out to the oracle its mistake, and to say, 'You said that I was the wisest of men, but this man is wiser than I am.' So I examined the man—I need not tell you his name, he was a politician—but this was the result, Athenians. When I conversed with him I came to see that, though a great many persons, and most of all he himself, thought that he was wise, yet he was not wise. And then I tried to prove to him that he was not wise, though he fancied that he was: and by so doing I made him, and many of the bystanders, my enemies. So when I went away, I thought to myself, "I am wiser than this man: neither of us probably knows anything that is really good, but he thinks that he has knowledge, when he has not, while I, having no knowledge, do not think that I have. I seem, at any rate, to be a little wiser than he is on this point: I do not think that I know what I do not know." Next I went to another man who was reputed to be still wiser than the last, with exactly the same result. And there again I made him, and many other men, my enemies.

Then I went on to one man after another, seeing that I was making enemies every day, which caused me much unhappiness and anxiety: still I thought that I must set God's command above everything. So I had to go to every man who seemed to possess any knowledge, and search for the meaning of the oracle: and, Athenians, I must tell you the truth; verily, by the dog of Egypt, this was the result of the search which I made at God's bidding. I found that the men, whose reputation for wisdom stood highest, were nearly the most lacking in it; while others, who were looked down on as common people, were much better fitted to learn. Now, I must describe to you the wanderings which I undertook, like a series of Heraclean labours, to make full proof of the oracle. After the politicians, I went to the poets, tragic, dithyrambic, and others, thinking that there I should find myself manifestly more ignorant than they. So I took up the poems on which I thought that they had spent most pains, and asked them what they meant, hoping at the same time to learn something from them. I am ashamed to tell you the truth, my friends, but I must say it. Almost any one of the bystanders could have talked about the works of these poets better than the poets themselves. So I soon found that it is not by wisdom that the poets create their works, but by a certain natural power and by inspiration, like soothsayers and prophets, who say many fine things, but who understand nothing of what they say. The poets seemed to me to be in a similar case. And at the same time I perceived that, because of their poetry, they thought that they were the wisest of men in other matters too, which they were not. So I went away again, thinking that I had the same advantage over the poets that I had over the politicians.

Finally, I went to the artizans, for I knew very well that I possessed no knowledge at all, worth speaking of, and I was sure that I should find that they knew many fine things. And in that I was not mistaken. They knew what I did not know, and so far they were wiser than I. But, Athenians, it seemed to me that the skilled artizans made the same mistake as the poets. Each of them believed himself to be extremely wise in matters of the greatest importance, because he was skilful in his own art: and this mistake of theirs threw their real wisdom into the shade. So I asked myself, on behalf of the oracle, whether I would choose to remain as I was, without either their wisdom or their ignorance, or to possess both, as they did. And I made answer to myself and to the oracle that it was better for me to remain as I was.

By reason of this examination, Athenians, I have made many enemies of a very fierce and bitter kind, who have spread abroad a great number of calumnies about me, and people say that I am 'a wise man.' For the bystanders always think that I am wise myself in any matter wherein I convict another man of ignorance. But, my friends, I believe that only God is really wise: and that by this oracle he meant that men's wisdom is worth little or nothing. I do not think that he meant that Socrates was wise. He only made use of my name, and took me as an example, as though he would say to men, 'He among you is the wisest, who, like Socrates, knows that in very truth his wisdom is worth nothing at all.' And therefore I still go about testing and examining every man whom I think wise, whether he be a citizen or a stranger, as God has commanded me; and whenever I find that he is not wise, I point out to him on the part of God that he is not wise. And I am so busy in this pursuit that I have never had leisure to take any part worth mentioning in public matters, or to look after my private affairs. I am in very great poverty by reason of my service to God.

And besides this, the young men who follow me about, who are the sons of wealthy persons and have a great deal of spare time, take a natural pleasure in hearing men cross-examined: and they often imitate me among themselves: then they try their hands at cross-examining other people. And, I imagine, they find a great abundance of men who think that they know a great deal, when in fact they know little or nothing. And then the persons who are cross-examined, get angry with me instead of with themselves, and say that Socrates is an abominable fellow who corrupts young men. And when they are asked, 'Why, what does he do? what does he teach?' they do not know what to say; but, not to seem at a loss, they repeat the stock charges against all philosophers, and allege that he investigates things in the air and under the earth, and that he teaches people to disbelieve in the gods, and 'to make the worse appear the better reason.' For, I fancy, they would not like to confess the truth, which is that they are shown up as ignorant pretenders to knowledge that they do not possess. And so they have been filling your ears with their bitter calumnies for a long time, for they are zealous and numerous and bitter against me; and they are well disciplined and plausible in speech. On these grounds Meletus and Anytus and Lycon have attacked me. Meletus is indignant with me on the part of the poets, and Anytus on the part of the artizans and politicians, and Lycon on the part of the orators. And so, as I said at the beginning, I shall be surprised if I am able, in the short time allowed me for my defence, to remove from your minds this prejudice which has grown so strong. What I have told you, Athenians, is the truth: I neither conceal, nor do I suppress anything, small or great. And yet I know that it is just this plainness of speech which makes me enemies. But that is only a proof that my words are true, and that the prejudice against me, and the causes of it, are what I have said. And whether you look for them now or hereafter, you will find that they are so.

What I have said must suffice as my defence against the charges of my first accusers. I will try next to defend myself against that 'good patriot' Meletus, as he calls himself, and my later accusers. Let us assume that they are a new set of accusers, and read their indictment, as we did in the case of the others. It runs thus. He says that Socrates is an evil-doer who corrupts the youth, and who does not believe in the gods whom the city believes in, but in other new divinities. Such is the charge. Let us examine each point in it separately. Meletus says that I do wrong by corrupting the youth: but I say, Athenians, that he is doing wrong; for he is playing off a solemn jest by bringing men lightly to trial, and pretending to have a great zeal and interest in matters to which he has never given a moment's thought. And now I will try to prove to you that it is so.

Come here, Meletus. Is it not a fact that you think it very important that the younger men should be as excellent as possible?

MELETUS It is.

SOCRATES Come then: tell the judges, who is it who improves them? You take so much interest in the matter that of course you know that. You are accusing me, and bring me to trial, because, as you say, you have discovered that I am the corrupter of the youth. Come now, reveal to the judges who improves them. You see, Meletus, you have nothing to say; you are silent. But don't you think that this is a scandalous thing? Is not your silence a conclusive proof of what I say, that you have never given a moment's thought to the matter? Come, tell us, my good sir, who makes the young men better citizens?

MELETUS The laws.

SOCRATES My excellent sir, that is not my question. What man improves the young, who starts with a knowledge of the laws?

MELETUS The judges here, Socrates.

SOCRATES What do you mean, Meletus? Can they educate the young and improve them?

MELETUS Certainly.

SOCRATES All of them? or only some of them?

MELETUS All of them.

SOCRATES By Hêrê that is good news! There is a great abundance of benefactors. And do the listeners here improve them, or not?

MELETUS They do.

SOCRATES And do the senators?

MELETUS Yes.

SOCRATES Well then, Meletus; do the members of the Assembly corrupt the younger men? or do they again all improve them?

MELETUS They too improve them.

SOCRATES Then all the Athenians, apparently, make the young into fine fellows except me, and I alone corrupt them. Is that your meaning?

MELETUS Most certainly; that is my meaning.

SOCRATES You have discovered me to be a most unfortunate man. Now tell me: do you think that the same holds good in the case of horses? Does one man do them harm and every one else improve them? On the contrary, is it not one man only, or a very few—namely, those who are skilled in horses—who can improve them; while the majority of men harm them, if they use them, and have to do with them? Is it not so, Meletus, both with horses and with every other animal? Of course it is, whether you and Anytus say yes or no. And young men would certainly be very fortunate persons if only one man corrupted them, and every one else did them good. The truth is, Meletus, you prove conclusively that you have never thought about the youth in your life. It is quite clear, on your own showing, that you take no interest at all in the matters about which you are prosecuting me.

Now, be so good as to tell us, Meletus, is it better to live among good citizens or bad ones? Answer, my friend: I am not asking you at all a difficult question. Do not bad citizens do harm to their neighbours and good citizens good?

MELETUS Yes.

SOCRATES Is there any man who would rather be injured than benefited by his companions? Answer, my good sir: you are obliged by the law to answer. Does any one like to be injured?

MELETUS Certainly not.

SOCRATES Well then; are you prosecuting me for corrupting the young, and making them worse men, intentionally or unintentionally?

MELETUS For doing it intentionally.

SOCRATES What, Meletus? Do you mean to say that you, who are so much younger than I, are yet so much wiser than I, that you know that bad citizens always do evil, and that good citizens always do good, to those

with whom they come in contact, while I am so extraordinarily stupid
as not to know that if I make any of my companions a rogue, he will probably injure me in some way, and as to commit this great crime, as you
allege, intentionally? You will not make me believe that, nor any one else
either, I should think. Either I do not corrupt the young at all; or if I do,
I do so unintentionally: so that you are a liar in either case. And if I corrupt them unintentionally, the law does not call upon you to prosecute
me for a fault like that, which is an involuntary one: you should take me
aside and admonish and instruct me: for of course I shall cease from
doing wrong involuntarily, as soon as I know that I have been doing wrong.
But you declined to instruct me: you would have nothing to do with me:
instead of that, you bring me up before the Court, where the law sends
persons, not for instruction, but for punishment.

The truth is, Athenians, as I said, it is quite clear that Meletus has never
paid the slightest attention to these matters. However, now tell us, Meletus,
how do you say that I corrupt the younger men? Clearly, according to your
indictment, by teaching them not to believe in the gods of the city, but in
other new divinities instead. You mean that I corrupt young men by that
teaching, do you not?

MELETUS Yes: most certainly; I mean that.

SOCRATES Then in the name of these gods of whom we are speaking,
explain yourself a little more clearly to me and to the judges here. I cannot understand what you mean. Do you mean that I teach young men to
believe in some gods, but not in the gods of the city? Do you accuse me of
teaching them to believe in strange gods? If that is your meaning, I myself
believe in some gods, and my crime is not that of absolute atheism. Or do
you mean that I do not believe in the gods at all myself, and that I teach
other people not to believe in them either?

MELETUS I mean that you do not believe in the gods in any way whatever.

SOCRATES Wonderful Meletus! Why do you say that? Do you mean that
I believe neither the sun nor the moon to be gods, like other men?

MELETUS I swear he does not, judges: he says that the sun is a stone, and
the moon earth.

SOCRATES My dear Meletus, do you think that you are prosecuting
Anaxagoras? You must have a very poor opinion of the judges, and think
them very unlettered men, if you imagine that they do not know that the
works of Anaxagoras of Clazomenæ are full of these doctrines. And so
young men learn these things from me, when they can often buy places in
the theatre for a drachma at most, and laugh Socrates to scorn, were he to
pretend that these doctrines, which are very peculiar doctrines too, were
his. But please tell me, do you really think that I do not believe in the gods
at all?

MELETUS Most certainly I do. You are a complete atheist.

SOCRATES No one believes that, Meletus, and I think that you know it to be a lie yourself. It seems to me, Athenians, that Meletus is a very insolent and wanton man, and that he is prosecuting me simply in the insolence and wantonness of youth. He is like a man trying an experiment on me, by asking me a riddle that has no answer. 'Will this wise Socrates,' he says to himself, 'see that I am jesting and contradicting myself? or shall I outwit him and every one else who hears me?' Meletus seems to me to contradict himself in his indictment: it is as if he were to say, 'Socrates is a wicked man who does not believe in the gods, but who believes in the gods.' But that is mere trifling.

Now, my friends, let us see why I think that this is his meaning. Do you answer me, Meletus: and do you, Athenians, remember the request which I made to you at starting, and do not interrupt me if I talk in my usual way.

Is there any man, Meletus, who believes in the existence of things pertaining to men and not in the existence of men? Make him answer the question, my friends, without these absurd interruptions. Is there any man who believes in the existence of horsemanship and not in the existence of horses? or in flute-playing and not in flute-players? There is not, my excellent sir. If you will not answer, I will tell both you and the judges that. But you must answer my next question. Is there any man who believes in the existence of divine things and not in the existence of divinities?

MELETUS There is not.

SOCRATES I am very glad that the judges have managed to extract an answer from you. Well then, you say that I believe in divine beings, whether they be old or new ones, and that I teach others to believe in them; at any rate, according to your statement, I believe in divine beings. That you have sworn in your deposition. But if I believe in divine beings, I suppose it follows necessarily that I believe in divinities. Is it not so? It is. I assume that you grant that, as you do not answer. But do we not believe that divinities are either gods themselves or the children of the gods? Do you admit that?

MELETUS I do.

SOCRATES Then you admit that I believe in divinities: now, if these divinities are gods, then, as I say, you are jesting and asking a riddle, and asserting that I do not believe in the gods, and at the same time that I do, since I believe in divinities. But if these divinities are the illegitimate children of the gods, either by the nymphs or by other mothers, as they are said to be, then, I ask, what man could believe in the existence of the children of the gods, and not in the existence of the gods? That would be as strange as believing in the existence of the offspring of horses and asses, and not in the existence of horses and asses. You must have indicted me in this manner, Meletus, either to test my skill, or because you could not find any crime that you could accuse me of with truth. But you will never contrive to persuade any man, even of the smallest understanding, that a belief in divine things and things of the gods does not necessarily involve a belief in divinities, and in the gods, and in heroes.

But in truth, Athenians, I do not think that I need say very much to prove that I have not committed the crime for which Meletus is prosecuting me. What I have said is enough to prove that. But, I repeat, it is certainly true, as I have already told you, that I have incurred much unpopularity and made many enemies. And that is what will cause my condemnation, if I am condemned; not Meletus, nor Anytus either, but the prejudice and suspicion of the multitude. They have been the destruction of many good men before me, and I think that they will be so again. There is no fear that I shall be their last victim.

Perhaps some one will say: 'Are you not ashamed, Socrates, of following pursuits which are very likely now to cause your death?' I should answer him with justice, and say: 'My friend, if you think that a man of any worth at all ought to reckon the chances of life and death when he acts, or that he ought to think of anything but whether he is acting rightly or wrongly, and as a good or a bad man would act, you are grievously mistaken. According to you, the demigods who died at Troy would be men of no great worth, and among them the son of Thetis, who thought nothing of danger when the alternative was disgrace. For when his mother, a goddess, addressed him, as he was burning to slay Hector, I suppose in this fashion, 'My son, if thou avengest the death of thy comrade Patroclus, and slayest Hector, thou wilt die thyself, for "fate awaits thee straightway after Hector's death;" ' he heard what she said, but he scorned danger and death; he feared much more to live a coward, and not to avenge his friend. 'Let me punish the evil-doer and straightway die,' he said, 'that I may not remain here by the beaked ships, a scorn of men, encumbering the earth.' Do you suppose that he thought of danger or of death? For this, Athenians, I believe to be the truth. Wherever a man's post is, whether he has chosen it of his own will, or whether he has been placed at it by his commander, there it is his duty to remain and face the danger, without thinking of death, or of any other thing, except dishonour.

When the generals whom you chose to command me, Athenians, placed me at my post at Potidæa, and at Amphipolis, and at Delium, I remained where they placed me, and ran the risk of death, like other men: and it would be very strange conduct on my part if I were to desert my post now from fear of death or of any other thing, when God has commanded me, as I am persuaded that he has done, to spend my life in searching for wisdom, and in examining myself and others. That would indeed be a very strange thing: and then certainly I might with justice be brought to trial for not believing in the gods: for I should be disobeying the oracle, and fearing death, and thinking myself wise, when I was not wise. For to fear death, my friends, is only to think ourselves wise, without being wise: for it is to think that we know what we do not know. For anything that men can tell, death may be the greatest good that can happen to them: but they fear it as if they knew quite well that it was the greatest of evils. And what is this but that shameful ignorance of thinking that we know what we do not know? In this matter too, my friends, perhaps I am different from the mass of mankind: and if I were to claim to be at all wiser than others, it would be because I do not think that I have any clear knowledge about the other world, when, in fact, I have none. But I do know very well that it is evil and base to do wrong, and to disobey my superior, whether he be man or god. And I will never do what I know to be evil, and shrink in fear from what, for all that I can tell, may be a good. And so, even if you acquit me now, and do not listen to Anytus' argument that, if I am to be acquitted, I ought never to have been brought to trial at all; and that, as it is, you are bound to put me to death, because, as he said, if I escape, all your children will forthwith be utterly corrupted by practising what Socrates teaches; if you were therefore to say to me, 'Socrates, this time we will not listen to Anytus: we will let you go; but on this condition, that you cease from carrying on this search of yours, and from philosophy; if you are found following those pursuits again, you shall die:' I say, if you offered to let me go on these terms, I should reply:— Athenians, I hold you in the highest regard and love; but I will obey God rather than you: and as long as I have breath and strength I will not cease from philosophy, and from exhorting you, and declaring the truth to every one of you whom I meet, saying, as I am wont, "My excellent friend, you are a citizen of Athens, a city which is very great and very famous for wisdom and power of mind; are you not ashamed of caring so much for the making of money, and for reputation, and for honour? Will you not think or care about wisdom, and truth, and the perfection of your soul?" And if he disputes my words, and says that he does care about these things, I shall not forthwith release him and go away: I shall question him and cross-examine him and test him: and if I think that he has not virtue, though he says that he has, I shall reproach him for setting the lower value on the most important things, and a higher value on those that are of less account. This I shall do to every one whom I meet, young or old, citizen or stranger: but more especially to the citizens, for they are more nearly akin to me. For, know well, God has commanded me to do so. And I think that no better piece of fortune has ever befallen you in Athens than my service to God. For I spend my whole life in going about and persuading you all to give your first and chiefest care to the perfection of your souls, and not till you have done that to think of your bodies, or your wealth; and telling you that virtue does not come from wealth, but that wealth, and every other good thing which men have, whether in public, or in private, comes from virtue. If then I corrupt the youth by this teaching, the mischief is great: but if any man says that I teach anything else, he speaks falsely. And therefore, Athenians, I say, either listen to Anytus, or do not listen to him: either acquit me, or do not acquit me: but be sure that I shall not alter my way of life; no, not if I have to die for it many times.

Do not interrupt me, Athenians. Remember the request which I made to you, and listen to my words. I think that it will profit you to hear them. I am going to say something more to you, at which you may be inclined to cry out: but do not do that. Be sure that if you put me to death, who am what I have told you that I am, you will do yourselves more harm than me. Meletus and Anytus can do me no harm: that is impossible: for I am sure that God will not allow a good man to be injured by a bad one. They may indeed kill me, or drive me into exile, or deprive me of my civil rights; and perhaps Meletus and others think those things great evils. But I do not think so: I think that it is a much greater evil to do what he is doing now, and to try to put a man to death unjustly. And now, Athenians, I am not arguing in my own defence at all, as you might expect me to do: I am trying to persuade you not to sin against God, by condemning me, and rejecting his gift to you. For if you put me to death, you will not easily find another man to fill my place. God has sent me to attack the city, as if it were a great and noble horse, to use a quaint simile, which was rather sluggish from its size, and which needed to be aroused by a gadfly: and I think that I am the gadfly that God has sent to the city to attack it; for I never cease from settling upon you, as it were, at every point, and rousing, and exhorting, and reproaching each man of you all day long. You will not easily find any one else, my friends, to fill my place: and if you take my advice, you will spare my life. You are vexed, as drowsy persons are, when they are awakened, and of course, if you listened to Anytus, you could easily kill me with a single blow, and then sleep on undisturbed for the rest of your lives, unless God were to care for you enough to send another man to arouse you. And you may easily see that it is God who has given me to your city: a mere human impulse would never have led me to neglect all my own interests, or to endure seeing my private affairs neglected now for so many years, while it made me busy myself unceasingly in your interests, and go to each man of you by himself, like a father, or an elder brother, trying to persuade him to care for virtue. There would have been a reason for it, if I had gained any advantage by this conduct, or if I had been paid for my exhortations; but you see yourselves that my accusers, though they accuse me of everything else without blushing, have not had the effrontery to say that I ever either exacted or demanded payment. They could bring no evidence of that. And I think that I have sufficient evidence of the truth of what I say in my poverty.

Perhaps it may seem strange to you that though I am so busy in going about in private with my counsel, yet I do not venture to come forward in the assembly, and take part in the public councils. You have often heard me speak of my reason for this, and in many places: it is that I have a certain divine sign from God, which is the divinity that Meletus has caricatured in his indictment. I have had it from childhood: it is a kind of voice, which whenever I hear it, always turns me back from something which I was going to do, but never urges me to act. It is this which forbids me to take part in politics. And I think that it does well to forbid me. For, Athenians, it is quite certain that if I had attempted to take part in politics, I should have perished at once and long ago, without doing any good either to you or to myself. And do not be vexed with me for telling the truth. There is no man who will preserve his life for long, either in Athens or elsewhere, if he firmly opposes the wishes of the people, and tries to prevent the commission of much injustice and illegality in the State. He who would really fight for justice, must do so as a private man, not in public, if he means to preserve his life, even for a short time.

I will prove to you that this is so by very strong evidence, not by mere words, but by what you value highly, actions. Listen then to what has happened to me, that you may know that there is no man who could make me consent to do wrong from the fear of death; but that I would perish at once rather than give way. What I am going to tell you may be a commonplace in the Courts of Law; nevertheless it is true. The only office that I ever held in the State, Athenians, was that of Senator. When you wished to try the ten generals, who did not rescue their men after the battle of Arginusæ, in a body, which was illegal, as you all came to think afterwards, the tribe Antiochis, to which I belong, held the presidency. On that occasion I alone of all the presidents opposed your illegal action, and gave my vote against you. The speakers were ready to suspend me and arrest me; and you were clamouring against me, and crying out to me to submit. But I thought that I ought to face the danger out in the cause of law and justice, rather than join with you in your unjust proposal, from fear of imprisonment or death. That was before the destruction of the democracy. When the oligarchy came, the Thirty sent for me, with four others, to the Council-Chamber,[1] and ordered us to bring over Leon the Salaminian from Salamis, that they might put him to death. They were in the habit of frequently giving similar orders to many others, wishing to implicate as many men as possible in their crimes. But then I again proved, not by mere words, but by my actions, that, if I may use a vulgar expression, I do not care a straw for death; but that I do care very much indeed about not doing anything against the laws of God or man. That government with all its power did not terrify me into doing anything wrong; but when we left the Council-Chamber, the other four went over to Salamis, and brought Leon across to Athens; and I went away home: and if the rule of the Thirty had not been destroyed soon afterwards, I should very likely have been put to death for what I did then. Many of you will be my witnesses in this matter.

Now do you think that I should have remained alive all these years, if I had taken part in public affairs, and had always maintained the cause of justice like an honest man, and had held it a paramount duty, as it is, to do so? Certainly not, Athenians, nor any other man either. But throughout my whole life, both in private, and in public, whenever I have had

---

[1] A building where the Prytanes had their meals and sacrificed.

to take part in public affairs, you will find that I have never yielded a single point in a question of right and wrong to any man; no, not to those whom my enemies falsely assert to have been my pupils. But I was never any man's teacher. I have never withheld myself from any one, young or old, who was anxious to hear me converse while I was about my mission; neither do I converse for payment, and refuse to converse without payment: I am ready to ask questions of rich and poor alike, and if any man wishes to answer me, and then listen to what I have to say, he may. And I cannot justly be charged with causing these men to turn out good or bad citizens: for I never either taught, or professed to teach any of them any knowledge whatever. And if any man asserts that he ever learnt or heard anything from me in private, which every one else did not hear as well as he, be sure that he does not speak the truth.

Why is it, then, that people delight in spending so much time in my company? You have heard why, Athenians. I told you the whole truth when I said that they delight in hearing me examine persons who think that they are wise when they are not wise. It is certainly very amusing to listen to that. And, I say, God has commanded me to examine men in oracles, and in dreams, and in every way in which the divine will was ever declared to man. This is the truth, Athenians, and if it were not the truth, it would be easily refuted. For if it were really the case that I have already corrupted some of the young men, and am now corrupting others, surely some of them, finding as they grew older that I had given them evil counsel in their youth, would have come forward to-day to accuse me and take their revenge. Or if they were unwilling to do so themselves, surely their kinsmen, their fathers, or brothers, or other relatives, would, if I had done them any harm, have remembered it, and taken their revenge. Certainly I see many of them in Court. Here is Crito, of my own deme and of my own age, the father of Critobulus; here is Lysanias of Sphettus, the father of Æschinus: here is also Antiphon of Cephisus, the father of Epigenes. Then here are others, whose brothers have spent their time in my company; Nicostratus, the son of Theozotides, and brother of Theodotus—and Theodotus is dead, so he at least cannot entreat his brother to be silent: here is Paralus, the son of Demodocus, and the brother of Theages: here is Adeimantus, the son of Ariston, whose brother is Plato here: and Æantodorus, whose brother is Aristodorus. And I can name many others to you, some of whom Meletus ought to have called as witnesses in the course of his own speech: but if he forgot to call them then, let him call them now—I will stand aside while he does so—and tell us if he has any such evidence. No, on the contrary, my friends, you will find all these men ready to support me, the corrupter, the injurer of their kindred, as Meletus and Anytus call me. Those of them who have been already corrupted might perhaps have some reason for supporting me: but what reason can their relatives, who are grown up, and who are uncorrupted, have, except the reason of truth and justice, that they know very well that Meletus is a liar, and that I am speaking the truth?

Well, my friends, this, together it may be with other things of the same nature, is pretty much what I have to say in my defence. There may be some one among you who will be vexed when he remembers how, even in a less important trial than this, he prayed and entreated the judges to acquit him with many tears, and brought forward his children and many of his friends and relatives in Court, in order to appeal to your feelings; and then finds that I shall do none of these things, though I am in what he would think the supreme danger. Perhaps he will harden himself against me when he notices this: it may make him angry, and he may give his vote in anger. If it is so with any of you—I do not suppose that it is, but in case it should be so—I think that I should answer him reasonably if I said: 'My friend, I have kinsmen too, for, in the words of Homer, "I am not born of stocks and stones," but of woman;' and so, Athenians, I have kinsmen, and I have three sons, one of them a lad, and the other two still children. Yet I will not bring any of them forward before you, and implore you to acquit me. And why will I do none of these things? It is not from arrogance, Athenians, nor because I hold you cheap: whether or no I can face death bravely is another question: but for my own credit, and for your credit, and for the credit of our city, I do not think it well, at my age, and with my name, to do anything of that kind. Rightly or wrongly, men have made up their minds that in some way Socrates is different from the mass of mankind. And it will be a shameful thing if those of you who are thought to excel in wisdom, or in bravery, or in any other virtue, are going to act in this fashion. I have often seen men with a reputation behaving in a strange way at their trial, as if they thought it a terrible fate to be killed, and as though they expected to live for ever, if you did not put them to death. Such men seem to me to bring discredit on the city: for any stranger would suppose that the best and most eminent Athenians, who are selected by their fellow-citizens to hold office, and for other honours, are no better than women. Those of you, Athenians, who have any reputation at all, ought not to do these things: and you ought not to allow us to do them: you should show that you will be much more merciless to men who make the city ridiculous by these pitiful pieces of acting, than to men who remain quiet.

But apart from the question of credit, my friends, I do not think that it is right to entreat the judge to acquit us, or to escape condemnation in that way. It is our duty to convince his mind by reason. He does not sit to give away justice to his friends, but to pronounce judgment: and he has sworn not to favour any man whom he would like to favour, but to decide questions according to law. And therefore we ought not to teach you to forswear yourselves; and you ought not to allow yourselves to be taught, for then neither you nor we would be acting righteously. Therefore, Athenians, do not require me to do these things, for I believe them to be neither good nor just nor holy; and, more especially do not ask me to do them to-day, when Meletus is prosecuting me for impiety. For were I to be successful, and to prevail on you by my prayers to break your oaths, I should be clearly teaching you to believe that there are no gods; and I should be simply accusing myself by my defence of not believing in them. But, Athenians, that is very far from the truth. I do believe in the gods as no one of my accusers believes in them: and to you and to God I commit my cause to be decided as is best for you and for me.

(He is found guilty by 281 votes to 220.)

I am not vexed at the verdict which you have given, Athenians, for many reasons. I expected that you would find me guilty; and I am not so much surprised at that, as at the numbers of the votes. I, certainly, never thought that the majority against me would have been so narrow. But now it seems that if only thirty votes had changed sides, I should have escaped. So I think that I have escaped Meletus, as it is: and not only have I escaped him; for it is perfectly clear that if Anytus and Lycon had not come forward to accuse me too, he would not have obtained the fifth part of the votes, and would have had to pay a fine of a thousand drachmæ.

So he proposes death as the penalty. Be it so. And what counter-penalty shall I propose to you, Athenians? What I deserve, of course, must I not? What then do I deserve to pay or to suffer for having determined not to spend my life in ease? I neglected the things which most men value, such as wealth, and family interests, and military commands, and popular oratory, and all the political appointments, and clubs, and factions, that there are in Athens; for I thought that I was really too conscientious a man to preserve my life if I engaged in these matters. So I did not go where I should have done no good either to you or to myself. I went instead to each one of you by himself, to do him, as I say, the greatest of services, and strove to persuade him not to think of his affairs, until he had thought of himself, and tried to make himself as perfect and wise as possible; nor to think of the affairs of Athens, until he had thought of Athens herself; and in all cases to bestow his thoughts on things in the same manner. Then what do I deserve for such a life? Something good, Athenians, if I am really to propose what I deserve; and something good which it would be suitable to me to receive. Then what is a suitable reward to be given to a poor benefactor, who requires leisure to exhort you? There is no reward, Athenians, so suitable for him as a public maintenance in the Prytaneum. It is a much more suitable reward for him than for any of you who has won a victory at the Olympic games with his horse or his chariots. Such a man only makes you seem happy, but I make you really happy: and he is not in want, and I am. So if I am to propose the penalty which I really deserve, I propose this, a public maintenance in the Prytaneum.

Perhaps you think me stubborn and arrogant in what I am saying now, as in what I said about the entreaties and tears. It is not so, Athenians; it is rather that I am convinced that I never wronged any man intentionally, though I cannot persuade you of that, for we have conversed together only a little time. If there were a law at Athens, as there is elsewhere, not to finish a trial of life and death in a single day, I think that I could have convinced you of it: but now it is not easy in so short a time to clear myself of the gross calumnies of my enemies. But when I am convinced that I have never wronged any man, I shall certainly not wrong myself, or admit that I deserve to suffer any evil, or propose any evil for myself as a penalty. Why should I? Lest I should suffer the penalty which Meletus proposes, when I say that I do not know whether it is a good or an evil? Shall I choose instead of it something which I know to be an evil, and propose that as a penalty? Shall I propose imprisonment? And why should I pass the rest of my days in prison, the slave of successive officials? Or shall I propose a fine, with imprisonment until it is paid? I have told you why I will not do that. I should have to remain in prison for I have no money to pay a fine with. Shall I then propose exile? Perhaps you would agree to that. Life would indeed be very dear to me, if I were unreasonable enough to expect that strangers would cheerfully tolerate my discussions and reasonings, when you who are my fellow-citizens cannot endure them, and have found them so burdensome and odious to you, that you are seeking now to be released from them. No, indeed, Athenians, that is not likely. A fine life I should lead for an old man, if I were to withdraw from Athens, and pass the rest of my days in wandering from city to city, and continually being expelled. For I know very well that the young men will listen to me, wherever I go, as they do here; and if I drive them away, they will persuade their elders to expel me: and if I do not drive them away, their fathers and kinsmen will expel me for their sakes.

Perhaps some one will say, 'Why cannot you withdraw from Athens, Socrates, and hold your peace?' It is the most difficult thing in the world to make you understand why I cannot do that. If I say that I cannot hold my peace, because that would be to disobey God, you will think that I am not in earnest and will not believe me. And if I tell you that no better thing can happen to a man than to converse every day about virtue and the other matters about which you have heard me conversing and examining myself and others, and that an unexamined life is not worth living, then you will believe me still less. But that is the truth, my friends, though it is not easy to convince you of it. And, what is more, I am not accustomed to think that I deserve any punishment. If I had been rich, I would have proposed as large a fine as I could pay: that would have done me no harm. But I am not rich enough to pay a fine, unless you are willing to fix it at a sum within my means. Perhaps I could pay you a mina: so I propose that. Plato here, Athenians, and Crito, and Critobulus, and Apollodorus bid me propose thirty minæ, and they will be sureties for me. So I propose thirty minæ. They will be sufficient sureties to you for the money.

(He is condemned to death.)

You have not gained very much time, Athenians, and, as the price of it, you will have an evil name from all who wish to revile the city, and they will cast in your teeth that you put Socrates, a wise man, to death. For they will certainly call me wise, whether I am wise or not, when they want to reproach you. If you would have waited for a little while, your wishes would have been fulfilled in the course of nature; for you see that I am an old man, far advanced in years, and near to death. I am speaking not to all of you, only to those who have voted for my death. And now I am speaking to them still. Perhaps, my friends, you think that I have been defeated because I was wanting in the arguments by which I could have persuaded you to acquit me, if, that is, I had thought it right to do or to say anything to escape punishment. It is not so. I have been defeated because I was wanting, not in arguments, but in overboldness and effrontery: because I would not plead before you as you would have liked to hear me plead, or appeal to you with weeping and wailing, or say and do many other things, which I maintain are unworthy of me, but which you have been accustomed to from other men. But when I was defending myself, I thought that I ought not to do anything unmanly because of the danger which I ran, and I have not changed my mind now. I would very much rather defend myself as I did, and die, than as you would have had me do, and live. Both in a law suit, and in war, there are some things which neither I nor any other man may do in order to escape from death. In battle a man often sees that he may at least escape from death by throwing down his arms and falling on his knees before the pursuer to beg for his life. And there are many other ways of avoiding death in every danger, if a man will not scruple to say and to do anything. But, my friends, I think that it is a much harder thing to escape from wickedness than from death; for wickedness is swifter than death. And now I, who am old and slow, have been overtaken by the slower pursuer: and my accusers, who are clever and swift, have been overtaken by the swifter pursuer, which is wickedness. And now I shall go hence, sentenced by you to death; and they will go hence, sentenced by truth to receive the penalty of wickedness and evil. And I abide by this award as well as they. Perhaps it was right for these things to be so: and I think that they are fairly measured.

And now I wish to prophesy to you, Athenians who have condemned me. For I am going to die, and that is the time when men have most prophetic power. And I prophesy to you who have sentenced me to death, that a far severer punishment than you have inflicted on me, will surely overtake you as soon as I am dead. You have done this thing, thinking that you will be relieved from having to give an account of your lives. But I say that the result will be very different from that. There will be more men who will call you to account, whom I have held back, and whom you did not see. And they will be harder masters to you than I have been, for they will be younger, and you will be more angry with them. For if you think that you will restrain men from reproaching you for your evil lives by putting them to death, you are very much mistaken. That way of escape is hardly possible, and it is not a good one. It is much better, and much easier, not to silence reproaches, but to make yourselves as perfect as you can. This is my parting prophecy to you who have condemned me.

With you who have acquitted me I should like to converse touching this thing that has come to pass, while the authorities are busy, and before I go to the place where I have to die. So, I pray you, remain with me until I go hence: there is no reason why we should not converse with each other while it is possible. I wish to explain to you, as my friends, the meaning of what has befallen me. A wonderful thing has happened to me, judges— for you I am right in calling judges. The prophetic sign, which I am wont to receive from the divine voice, has been constantly with me all through my life till now, opposing me in quite small matters if I were not going to act rightly. And now you yourselves see what has happened to me; a thing which might be thought, and which is sometimes actually reckoned, the supreme evil. But the sign of God did not withstand me when I was leaving my house in the morning, nor when I was coming up hither to the Court, nor at any point in my speech, when I was going to say anything: though at other times it has often stopped me in the very act of speaking. But now, in this matter, it has never once withstood me, either in my words or my actions. I will tell you what I believe to be the reason of that. This thing that has come upon me must be a good: and those of us who think that death is an evil must needs be mistaken. I have a clear proof that that is so; for my accustomed sign would certainly have opposed me, if I had not been going to fare well.

And if we reflect in another way we shall see that we may well hope that death is a good. For the state of death is one of two things: either the dead man wholly ceases to be, and loses all sensation; or, according to the common belief, it is a change and a migration of the soul unto another place. And if death is the absence of all sensation, and like the sleep of one whose slumbers are unbroken by any dreams, it will be a wonderful gain. For if a man had to select that night in which he slept so soundly that he did not even see any dreams, and had to compare with it all the other nights and days of his life, and then had to say how many days and nights in his life he had spent better and more pleasantly than this night, I think that a private person, nay, even the great King himself, would find them easy to count, compared with the others. If that is the nature of death, I for one count it a gain. For then it appears that eternity is nothing more than a single night. But if death is a journey to another place, and the common belief be true, that there are all who have died, what good could be greater than this, my judges? Would a journey not be worth taking, at the end of which, in the other world, we should be released from the self-styled judges who are here, and should find the true judges, who are said to sit in judgment below, such as Minos, and Rhadamanthus, and Æacus, and Triptolemus, and the other demi-gods who were just in their lives? Or what would you not give to converse with Orpheus and Musæus and Hesiod and Homer? I am willing to die many times, if this be true. And for my own part I should have a wonderful interest in meeting there Palamedes, and Ajax the son of Telamon, and the other men of old who have died through an unjust judgment, and in comparing my experiences with theirs. That I think would be no small pleasure. And, above all, I could spend my time in examining those who are there, as I examine men here, and in finding out which of them is wise, and which of them thinks himself wise, when he is not wise. What would we not give, my judges, to be able to examine the leader of the great expedition against Troy, or Odysseus, or Sisyphus, or countless other men and women whom we could name? It would be an infinite happiness to converse with them, and to live with them, and to examine them. Assuredly there they do not put men to death for doing that. For besides the other ways in which they are happier than we are, they are immortal, at least if the common belief be true.

And you too, judges, must face death with a good courage, and believe this as a truth, that no evil can happen to a good man, either in life, or after death. His fortunes are not neglected by the gods; and what has come to me to-day has not come by chance. I am persuaded that it was better for me to die now, and to be released from trouble: and that was the reason why the sign never turned me back. And so I am hardly angry with my accusers, or with those who have condemned me to die. Yet it was not with this mind that they accused me and condemned me, but meaning to do me an injury. So far I may find fault with them.

Yet I have one request to make of them. When my sons grow up, visit them with punishment, my friends, and vex them in the same way that I have vexed you, if they seem to you to care for riches, or for any other thing, before virtue: and if they think that they are something, when they are nothing at all, reproach them, as I have reproached you, for not caring for what they should, and for thinking that they are great men when in fact they are worthless. And if you will do this, I myself and my sons will have received our deserts at your hands.

But now the time has come, and we must go hence; I to die, and you to live. Whether life or death is better is known to God, and to God only.

Sharpe Scholemasters

ROGER ASCHAM

ROGER ASCHAM (1515-1568) was educated at St. John's College, Cambridge, where he applied himself to the study of Greek with such diligence and success that while still a boy, he gave instruction in the language to other boys. He took his bachelor's degree in February, 1534, and a month later was chosen fellow of the college, a position which relieved him from the necessity of support by his adoptive father, Antony Wingfield. After receiving his master's degree in 1537, Ascham became Greek reader and achieved a wide reputation as a scholar and lecturer. To strengthen a weak body and to relieve himself from the fatigue of study, he spent many hours at his favorite sport of archery. To defend this sport against those who thought it an unworthy occupation for a scholar and teacher, Ascham published, in 1544, his Toxophilus, *a book vindicating archery as a salutary and useful diversion. The book was dedicated to Henry VIII, who liked it so well that he awarded Ascham a pension. In 1548 Ascham became tutor to Princess Elizabeth. The years 1550-1553 he spent in travel on the continent, returning in 1553 to become Latin secretary to Queen Mary. When Elizabeth ascended the throne in 1558, Ascham became her private tutor. In 1563 he was invited by Sir Edward Sackville to write* The Scholemaster. *This work was completed before his death in 1568 and later published by his widow.*

In The Scholemaster *Ascham deals chiefly with the education of boys of position. The First Booke, from which the following excerpt is taken, is a general treatise on education.*

I DO gladlie agree with all good Scholemasters in these pointes: to have children brought to good perfitnes in learning: to all honestie in maners: to have all fau(l)tes rightlie amended: to have everie vice severelie corrected: but for the order and waie that leadeth rightlie to these pointes, we somewhat differ. For commonlie, many scholemasters, some, as I have seen moe, as I have heard tell, be of so crooked a nature, as, when they meete with a hard witted scholer, they rather breake him, than bowe him, rather marre him, then mend him. For whan the scholemaster is angrie with some other matter, then will he sonest faul to beate his scholer: and though he him selfe should be punished for his folie, yet must he beate some scholer for his pleasure: though there be no cause for

389

him to do so, nor yet fault in the scholer to deserve so. These ye will say, be fond scholemasters, and fewe they be, that be found to be soch. They be fond in deede, but surelie overmany soch be found everie where. But this will I say, that even the wisest of your great beaters, do as oft punishe nature, as they do correcte faultes. Yea, many times, the better nature, is sorer punished: For, if one, by quicknes of witte, take his lesson readelie, an other, by hardnes of witte, taketh it not so speedelie: the first is alwaies commended, the other is commonlie punished: whan a wise scholemaster, should rather discretelie consider the right disposition of both their natures, and not so moch wey what either of them is able to do now, as what either of them is likelie to do hereafter. For this I know, not onelie by reading of bookes in my studie, but also by experience of life, abrode in the world, that those, which be commonlie the wisest, the best learned, and best men also, when they be olde, were never commonlie the quickest of witte, when they were yonge. The causes why, amongest other, which be many, that move me thus to thinke, be these fewe, which I will recken. Quicke wittes commonlie, be apte to take, unapte to keepe: soone hote and desirous of this and that: as colde and sone wery of the same againe: more quicke to enter speedelie, than hable to pearse farre: even like over sharpe tooles, whose edges be verie soone turned. Soch wittes delite them selves in easie and pleasant studies, and never passe farre forward in hie and hard sciences. And therefore the quickest wittes commonlie may prove the best Poetes, but not the wisest Orators: readie of tonge to speak boldlie, not deepe of judgement, either for good counsell or wise writing. Also, for maners and life, quicke wittes commonlie, be, in desire, newfangle(d), in purpose, unconstant, light to promise any thing, readie to forget every thing: both benefite and injurie: and therby neither fast to frend, nor fearefull to foe: inquisitive of every trifle, not secret in greatest affaires: bolde, with any person: busie, in every matter: so(o)thing, soch as be present: nipping any that is absent: of nature also, alwaies, flattering their betters, envying their equals, despising their inferiors: and, by quicknes of witte, verie quicke and readie, to like none so well as them selves.

On the Conduct of Life; or, Advice to a School-Boy

WILLIAM HAZLITT

WILLIAM HAZLITT (1778-1830), was the youngest son of a Unitarian minister who, when the boy was six, moved to the United States and preached in New York, Philadelphia, and Boston. The Hazlitts returned to England in 1787 and took up residence in an obscure Shropshire village. At fifteen Hazlitt was sent to Hackney Theological College to prepare for the Unitarian ministry, but by 1795 he had abandoned the idea of entering the ministry. He returned to his Shropshire home and spent the following eight years in private reading and study. In 1798 Coleridge came to preach at Shrewsbury and spent the day with the Hazlitts. This led to a meeting with Wordsworth. In spite of an estrangement which developed later, Hazlitt always regarded the meeting with these two men as the most significant experience in his literary and intellectual life.

As a step toward earning a living, Hazlitt studied painting and actually did become an itinerant portrait painter, but dissatisfied with this profession, he turned to writing and became successively a critic, a reporter, and a free-lance journalist. He began to lecture on literature and to publish his lectures and criticism. With Leigh Hunt he began to publish in a journal a series of comments upon life and books called The Round Table. *In 1821 he published a volume of essays called* Table Talk: or, Original Essays. *In these essays Hazlitt poured out his wealth of erudition and observation. In the essay form Hazlitt achieved a place as one of the greatest essayists in the tradition of Addison, Steele, and Goldsmith.*

The essay given here is taken from Table Talk.

MY DEAR LITTLE FELLOW,—You are now going to settle at school, and may consider this as your first entrance into the world. As my health is so indifferent, and I may not be with you long, I wish to leave you some advice (the best I can) for your conduct in life, both that it may be of use to you, and as something to remember me by. I may at least be able to caution you against my own errors, if nothing else.

As we went along to your new place of destination, you often repeated that "You durst say they were a set of stupid, disagreeable people," meaning the people at the school. You were to blame in this. It is a good old rule to hope for the best. Always, my dear, believe things to be right till you find them the contrary; and even then, instead of irritating yourself against them, endeavour to put up with them as well as you can, if you cannot alter them. You said, "You were sure you should not like the school where you were going." This was wrong. What you meant was that you did not like to leave home. But you could not tell whether you should like the school or not, till you had given it a trial. Otherwise, your saying that you should not like it was determining that you would not like it. Never anticipate evils; or, because you cannot have things exactly as you wish, make them out worse than they are, through mere spite and wilfulness. You seemed at first to take no notice of your school-fellows, or rather to set yourself against them, because they were strangers to you. They knew as little of you as you did of them; so that this would have been a reason for their keeping aloof from you as well, which you would have felt as a hardship. Learn never to conceive a prejudice against others, because you know nothing of them. It is bad reasoning, and makes enemies of half the world. Do not think ill of them, till they behave ill to you; and then strive to avoid the faults which you see in them. This will disarm their hostility sooner than pique, or resentment, or complaint.

I thought you were disposed to criticise the dress of some of the boys as not so good as your own. Never despise any one for anything that he cannot help—least of all, for his poverty. I would wish you to keep up appearances yourself as a defence against the idle sneers of the world, but I would not have you value yourself upon them. I hope you will neither be the dupe nor victim of vulgar prejudices. Instead of saying above—"Never despise any one for anything that he cannot help"—I might have said—"Never despise any one at all;" for contempt implies a truimph over and pleasure in the ill of another. It means that you are glad and congratulate yourself on their failings or misfortunes. The sense of inferiority in others, without this indirect appeal to our self-love, is a painful feeling and not an exulting one.

You complain since, that the boys laugh at you and do not care about you, and that you are not treated as you were at home. My dear, that is one chief reason for your being sent to school, to inure you betimes to the unavoidable rubs and uncertain reception you may meet with in life. You cannot always be with me, and perhaps it is as well that you cannot. But you must not expect others to show the same concern about you as I should. You have hitherto been a spoiled child, and have been used to have your own way a good deal, both in the house and among your play-fellows, with whom you were too fond of being a leader: but you have good nature and good sense, and will get the better of this in time. You have now got among other boys who are your equals, or bigger and stronger than yourself, and who have something else to attend to besides humouring your whims and fancies, and you feel this as a repulse or piece of injustice. But the first lesson to learn is that there are other people in the world besides yourself. There are a number of boys in the school where you are, whose amusements and pursuits (whatever they may be) are and ought to be of as much consequence to them as yours can be to you, and to which therefore you must give way in your turn. The more airs of childish self-importance you give yourself, you will only expose yourself to be the more thwarted and laughed at. True equality is the only true morality or true wisdom. Remember always that you are but one among others, and you can hardly mistake your place in society. In your father's house you might do as you pleased: in the world, you will find competitors at every turn. You are not born a king's son, to destroy or dictate to millions: you can only expect to share their fate, or settle your differences amicably with them. You already find it so at school; and I wish you to be reconciled to your situation as soon and with as little pain as you can.

It was my misfortune, perhaps, to be bred up among Dissenters, who look with too jaundiced an eye at others, and set too high a value on their own peculiar pretensions. From being proscribed themselves, they learn to proscribe others; and come in the end to reduce all integrity of principle and soundness of opinion within the pale of their own little communion. Those who were out of it, and did not belong to the class of Rational Dissenters, I was led erroneously to look upon as hardly deserving the name of rational beings. Being thus satisfied as to the select few who are "the salt of the earth," it is easy to persuade ourselves that we are at the head of them, and to fancy ourselves of more importance in the scale of true desert than all the rest of the world put together, who do not interpret a certain text of Scripture in the manner that we have been taught to do. You will (from the difference of education) be free from this bigotry, and will, I hope, avoid everything akin to the same exclusive and narrow-minded spirit. Think that the minds of men are various as their faces—that the modes and employments of life are numberless as they are necessary—that there is more than one class of merit—that though others may be wrong in some things, they are not so in all—and that countless races of men have been born, have lived and died, without ever hearing of any one of those points in which you take a just pride and pleasure—and you will not err on the side of that spiritual pride or intellectual coxcombry which has been so often the bane of the studious and learned!

I observe you have got a way of speaking of your school-fellows as "that Hoare, that Harris," and so on, as if you meant to mark them out for particular reprobation, or did not think them good enough for you. It is a bad habit to speak disrespectfully of others: for it will lead you to think and feel uncharitably towards them. Ill names beget ill blood. Even where there may be some repeated trifling provocation, it is better to be courteous, mild, and forbearing, than captious, impatient, and fretful. The faults of others too often arise out of our own ill temper; or though they should be real, we shall not mend them by exasperating ourselves against them. Treat your playmates as Hamlet advises Polonious to treat the players, "according to your own dignity rather than their deserts." If you fly out at everything in them that you disapprove or think done on purpose to annoy you, you lie constantly at the mercy of their caprice, rudeness, or ill-nature. You should be more your own master.

Do not begin to quarrel with the world too soon: for, bad as it may be, it is the best we have to live in—here. If railing would have made it better, it would have been reformed long ago: but as this is not to be hoped for at present, the best way is to slide through it as contentedly and innocently as we may. The worst fault it has is want of charity: and calling knave and fool at every turn will not cure this failing. Consider (as a matter of vanity) that if there were not so many knaves and fools as we find, the wise and honest would not be those rare and shining characters that they are allowed to be; and (as a matter of philosophy) that if the world be really incorrigible in this respect, it is a reflection to make one sad, not angry. We may laugh or weep at the madness of mankind: we have no right to vilify them, for our own sakes or theirs. Misanthropy is not the disgust of the mind at human nature, but with itself; or it is laying its own exaggerated vices and foul blots at the doors of others! Do not, however, mistake what I have here said. I would not have you, when you grow up, adopt the low and sordid fashion of palliating existing abuses or of putting the best face upon the worst things. I only mean that indiscriminate unqualified satire can do little good, and that those who indulge in the most revolting speculations on human nature do not themselves always set the fairest examples, or strive to prevent its lower degradation. They seem rather willing to reduce it to their theoretical standard. For the rest, the very outcry that is made (if sincere) shows that things cannot be quite so bad as they are represented. The abstract hatred and scorn of vice implies the capacity for virtue: the impatience expressed at the most striking instances of deformity proves the innate idea and love of beauty in the human mind. The best antidote I can recommend to you hereafter against the disheartening effect of such writings as those of Rochefoucault, Mandeville, and others, will be to look at the pictures of Raphael and Correggio. You need not be altogether ashamed, my dear little boy, of belonging to a species which could produce such faces as those; nor despair of doing something worthy of laudable ambition, when you see what such hands have wrought! You will, perhaps, one day have reason to thank me for this advice.

As to your studies and school-exercises, I wish you to learn Latin, French, and dancing. I would insist upon the last more particularly, both because it is more likely to be neglected, and because it is of the greatest consequence to your success in life. Everything almost depends upon first impressions; and these depend (besides person, which is not in our power) upon two things, dress and address, which every one may command with proper attention. These are the small coin in the intercourse of life which are continually in request; and perhaps you will find the year's end, or towards the close of life, that the daily insults, coldness, or contempt, to which you have been exposed by a neglect of such superficial recommendations, are hardly atoned for by the few proofs of esteem or admiration which your integrity or talents have been able to extort in the course of it. When we habitually disregard those things which we know will ensure the favourable opinion of others, it shows we set that opinion at defiance, or consider ourselves above it, which no one ever did with impunity. An inattention to our own persons implies a disrespect to others, and may often be traced no less to a want of good-nature than of good sense. The old maxim—Desire to please, and you will infallibly please— explains the whole matter. If there is a tendency to vanity and affectation on this side of the question, there is an equal alloy of pride and obstinacy on the opposite one. Slovenliness may at any time be cured by an effort of resolution, but a graceful carriage requires an early habit and in most cases the aid of the dancing-master. I would not have you, from not knowing how to enter a room properly, stumble at the very threshold in the good graces of those on whom it is possible the fate of your future life may depend. Nothing creates a greater prejudice against anyone than awkwardness. A person who is confused in manner and gesture seems to have done something wrong, or as if he was conscious of no one qualification to build a confidence in himself upon. On the other hand, openness, freedom, self-possession, set others at ease with you by showing that you are on good terms with yourself. Grace in women gains the affections sooner, and secures them longer, than anything else—it is an outward and visible sign of an inward harmony of soul—as the want of it in men, as if the mind and body equally hitched in difficulties and were distracted with doubts, is the greatest impediment in the career of gallantry and road to the female heart. Another thing I would caution you against is not to pore over your books till you are bent almost double—a habit you will never be able to get the better of, and which you will find of serious ill-consequence. A stoop in the shoulders sinks a man in public and in private estimation. You are at present straight enough, and you walk with boldness and spirit. Do nothing to take away the use of your limbs, or the spring and elasticity of your muscles. As to all wordly advantages, it is to the full of as much importance that your deportment should be erect and manly as your actions.

You will naturally find out all this, and fall into it, if your attention is drawn out sufficiently to what is passing around you; and this will be the case, unless you are absorbed too much in books and those sedentary studies,

> "Which waste the marrow, and consume the brain."

You are, I think, too fond of reading as it is. As one means of avoiding excess in this way, I would wish you to make it a rule, never to read at meal-times, nor in company when there is any (even the most trivial) conversation going on, nor even to let your eagerness to learn encroach upon your play-hours. Books are but one inlet of knowledge; and the pores of the mind, like those of the body, should be left open to all impressions. I applied too close to my studies, soon after I was of your age, and hurt myself irreparably by it. Whatever may be the value of learning, health and good spirits are of more.

I would have you, as I said, make yourself master of French, because you may find it of use in the commerce of life; and I would have you learn Latin, partly because I learnt it myself, and I would not have you without any of the advantages or source of knowledge that I possessed—it would be a bar of separation between us—and secondly, because there is an atmosphere round this sort of classical ground, to which that of actual life is gross and vulgar. Shut out from this garden of early sweetness, we may well exclaim—

> "How shall we part and wander down
> Into a lower world, to this obscure
> And wild? How shall we breathe in other air
> Less pure, accustom'd to immortal fruits?"

I do not think the classics so indispensable to the cultivation of your intellect as on another account, which I have seen explained elsewhere, and you will have no objection to turn with me to the passages. "The study of the classics is less to be regarded as an exercise of the intellect, than as a discipline of humanity. The peculiar advantage of this mode of education consists not so much in strengthening the understanding, as in softening and refining the taste. It gives men liberal views; it accustoms the mind to take an interest in things foreign to itself; to love virtue for its own sake; to prefer fame to life, and glory to riches; and to fix our thoughts on the remote and permanent, instead of narrow and fleeting objects. It teaches us to believe that there is something really great and excellent in the world, surviving all the shocks of accident and fluctuations of opinion, and raises us above that low and servile fear, which bows only to present power and upstart authority. Rome and Athens filled a place in the history of mankind, which can never be occupied again. They were two cities set on a hill, which could not be hid; all eyes have seen them, and their light shines like a mighty sea-mark into the abyss of time.

> 'Still green with bays each ancient altar stands,
> Above the reach of sacrilegious hands;
> Secure from flames, from envy's fiercer rage,
> Destructive war, and all-involving age.
> Hail, bards triumphant, born in happier days,
> Immortal heirs of universal praise!
> Whose honours with increase of ages grow,
> As streams roll down, enlarging as they flow!'

It is this feeling more than anything else which produces a marked difference between the study of the ancient and modern languages, and which, by the weight and importance of the consequences attached to the former, stamps every word with a monumental firmness. By conversing with the mighty dead, we imbibe sentiment with knowledge. We become strongly attached to those who can no longer either hurt or serve us, except through the influence which they exert over the mind. We feel the presence of that power which gives immortality to human thoughts and actions, and catch the flame of enthusiasm from all the nations and ages."

Because, however, you have learnt Latin and Greek, and can speak a different language, do not fancy yourself of a different order of beings from those you ordinarily converse with. They perhaps know and can do more things than you, though you have learnt a greater variety of names to express the same things by. The great object, indeed, of these studies is, to be "a cure for a narrow and selfish spirit," and to carry the mind out of its petty and local prejudices to the idea of a more general humanity. Do not fancy, because you are intimate with Homer and Virgil, that your neighbours who can never attain the same posthumous fame are to be despised, like those impudent valets who live in noble families and look down upon every one else. Though you are master of Cicero's Orations, think it possible for a cobbler at a stall to be more eloquent than you. "But you are a scholar, and he is not." Well, then, you have that advantage over him, but it does not follow that you are to have every other. Look at the heads of the celebrated poets and philosophers of antiquity in the collection at Wilton, and you will say they answer to their works; but you will find others in the same collection whose names have hardly come down to us that are equally fine, and cast in the same classic mould. Do you imagine that all the thoughts, genius, and capacity of those old and mighty nations are contained in a few odd volumes, to be thumbed by school-boys? This reflection is not meant to lessen your admiration of the great names to which you will be accustomed to look up, but to direct it to that solid mass of intellect and power of which they were the most shining ornaments. I would wish you to excel in this sort of learning and to take a pleasure in it, because it is the path that has been chosen for you; but do not suppose that others do not excel equally in their line of study or exercise of skill, or that there is but one mode of excellence in the art or nature. You have got on vastly beyond the point at which you set out; but others have been getting on as well as you in the same or other ways, and have kept pace with you. What then, you may ask, is the use of all the pains you have taken, if it gives you no superiority over mankind in general? It is this—You have reaped all the benefit of improvement and knowledge yourself; and farther, if you had not moved forwards, you would by this time have been left behind. Envy no one, disparage no one, think yourself above no one. Their demerits will not piece out your deficiencies; nor is it a waste of time and labour for you to cultivate your own talents, because you cannot bespeak a monopoly of all advantages. You are more learned than many of your acquaintance who may be more active, healthy, witty, successful in business, or expert in some elegant or useful art than you; but you have no reason to complain, if you have attained the object of your ambition. Or if you should not be able to compass this from a want of genius or parts, yet learn, my child, to be contented with a mediocrity of acquirements. You may still be respectable in your conduct, and enjoy a tranquil obscurity, with more friends and fewer enemies than you might otherwise have had.

There is one almost certain drawback on a course of scholastic study, that it unfits men for active life. The ideal is always at variance with the practical. The habit of fixing the attention on the imaginary and abstracted deprives the mind equally of energy and fortitude. By indulging our imaginations on fictions and chimeras, where we have it all our own way and are led on only by the pleasure of the prospect, we grow fastidious, effeminate, lapped in idle luxury, impatient of contradiction, and unable to sustain the shock of real adversity when it comes; as by being taken up with abstract reasoning or remote events in which we are merely passive spectators, we have no resources to provide against it, no readiness, or expedients for the occasion, or spirit to use them, even if they occur. We must think again before we determine, and thus the opportunity for action is lost. While we are considering the very best possible mode of gaining an object, we find that it has slipped through our fingers, or that others have laid rude fearless hands upon it. The youthful tyro reluctantly discovers that the ways of the world are not his ways, nor their thoughts his thoughts. Perhaps the old monastic institutions were not in this respect unwise, which carried on to the end of life the secluded habits and romantic associations with which it began, and which created a privileged world for the inhabitants, distinct from the common world of men and women. You will bring with you from your books and solitary reveries a wrong measure of men and things, unless you correct it by careful experience and mixed observation. You will raise your standard of character as much too high at first as from disappointed expectation it will sink too low afterwards. The best qualifier of this theoretical mania and of the dreams of poets and moralists (who both treat of things as they ought to be and not as they are) is in one sense to be found in some of our own popular writers, such as our Novelists and periodical Essayists. But you had, after all, better wait and see what things are, than try to anticipate the results. You know more of a road by having travelled it than by all the conjectures and descriptions in the world. You will find the business of life conducted on a much more varied and individual scale than you would expect. People will be concerned about a thousand things that you have no idea of, and will be utterly indifferent to what you feel the greatest interest in. You will find good and evil, folly and discretion, more mingled, and the shades of character running more into each other than they do in the ethical charts. No one is equally wise or guarded at all points and it is seldom that anyone is quite a fool. Do not be surprised, when you go out into the world, to find men talk exceedingly well on different subjects, who do not derive their information immediately from books. In the first place, the light of books is diffused very much abroad in the world in conversation and at second-hand; and besides, common sense is not a monopoly and experience and observation are sources of information open to the man of the world as well as to the retired student. If you know more of the outline and principles, he knows more of the details and "practique part of life." A man may discuss very agreeably the adventures of a campaign in which he was engaged without having read the "Retreat of the Ten Thousand," or give a singular account of the method of drying teas in China without being a profound chemist. It is the vice of scholars to suppose that there is no knowledge in the world but that of books. Do you avoid it, I conjure you; and thereby save yourself the pain and mortification that must otherwise ensue from finding out your mistake continually!

Gravity is one great ingredient in the conduct of life, and perhaps a certain share of it is hardly to be dispensed with. Few people can afford to be quite unaffected. At any rate, do not put your worst qualities foremost. Do not seek to distinguish yourself by being ridiculous; nor entertain that miserable ambition to be the sport and butt of the company. By aiming at a certain standard of behaviour or intellect, you will at least show your taste and value for what is excellent. There are those who blurt out their good things with so little heed of what they are about that no one thinks anything of them; as others by keeping their folly to themselves gain the reputation of wisdom. Do not, however, affect to speak only in oracles, or to deal in bon-mots: condescend to the level of the company, and be free and accessible to all persons. Express whatever occurs to you, that cannot offend others or hurt yourself. Keep some opinions to yourself. Say what you please of others, but never repeat what you hear said of them to themselves. If you have nothing yourself to offer, laugh with the witty—assent to the wise: they will not think the worse of you for it. Listen to information on subjects you are acquainted with, instead of always striving to lead the conversation to some favourite one of your own. By the last method you will shine, but will not improve. I am ashamed myself ever to open my lips on any question I have ever written upon. It is much more difficult to be able to converse on an equality with a number of persons in turn, than to soar above their heads, and excite the stupid gaze of all companies by bestriding some senseless topic of your own and confounding the understandings of those who are ignorant of it. Be not too fond of argument. Indeed, by going much into company (which I do not, however, wish you to do) you will be weaned from this practice, if you set out with it. Rather suggest what remarks may have occurred to you on a subject than aim at dictating your opinions to others or at defending yourself at all points. You will learn more by agreeing in the main with others and entering into their trains of thinking, than by contradicting and urging them to extremities. Avoid singularity of opinion as well as of everything else. Sound conclusions come with practical knowledge, rather than with speculative refinements: in what we really understand, we reason but little. Long-winded disputes fill up the place of common-sense and candid inquiry. Do not imagine that you will make people friends by showing your superiority over them: it is what they will neither admit nor forgive, unless you have a high and acknowledged reputation beforehand, which renders this sort of petty vanity more inexcusable. Seek to gain the good-will of others rather than to extort their applause; and to this end, be neither too tenacious of your own claims, not inclined to press too hard on their weaknesses.

Do not affect the society of your superiors in rank, nor court that of the great. There can be no real sympathy in either case. The first will consider you as a restraint upon them, and the last as an intruder, or upon sufferance. It is not a desirable distinction to be admitted into company as a man of talents. You are a mark for invidious observation. If you say nothing, or merely behave with common propriety and simplicity, you seem to have no business there. If you make a studied display of yourself, it is arrogating a consequence you have no right to. If you are contented to pass as an indifferent person, they despise you; if you distinguish yourself, and show more knowledge, wit or taste than they do, they hate you for it. You have no alternative. I would rather be asked out to sing than to talk. Everyone does not pretend to a fine voice, but every one fancies he has as much understanding as another. Indeed, the secret of this sort of intercourse has been pretty well found out. Literary men are seldom invited to the tables of the great; they send for players and musicians, as they keep monkeys and parrots!

I would not, however, have you run away with a notion that the rich are knaves, or that lords are fools. They are for what I know as honest and as wise as other people. But it is a trick of our self-love, supposing that another has the decided advantage of us in one way, to strike a balance by taking it for granted (as a moral antithesis) that he must be as much beneath us in those qualities on which we plume ourselves, and which we would appropriate almost entirely to our own use. It is hard indeed if others are raised above us not only by the gifts of fortune, but of understanding too. It is not to be credited. People have an unwillingness to admit that the House of Lords can be equal in talent to the House of Commons. So in the other sex, if a woman is handsome, she is an idiot or no better than she should be: in ours, if a man is worth a million of money, he is a miser, a fellow that cannot spell his own name, or a poor creature in some way, to bring him to our level. This is malice, and not truth. Believe all the good you can of every one. Do not measure others by yourself. If they have advantages which you have not, let your liberality keep pace with their good fortune. Envy no one, and you need envy no one.

If you have but the magnanimity to allow merit wherever you see it—understanding in a lord or wit in a cobbler—this temper of mind will stand you instead of many accomplishments. Think no man too happy. Raphael died young. Milton had the misfortune to be blind. If any one is vain or proud, it is from folly or ignorance. Those who pique themselves excessively on some one thing have but that one thing to pique themselves upon, as languages, mechanics, etc. I do not say that this is not an enviable delusion, where it is not liable to be disturbed; but at present knowledge is too much diffused and pretensions come too much into collision for this to be long the case; and it is better not to form such a prejudice at first than to have it to undo all the rest of one's life. If you learn any two things, though they may put you out of conceit one with the other, they will effectually cure you of any conceit you might have of yourself by showing the variety and scope there is in the human mind beyond the limits you had set to it.

You were convinced the first day that you could not learn Latin, which now you find easy. Be taught from this, not to think other obstacles insurmountable that you may meet with in the course of your life, though they seem so at first sight.

Attend above all things to your health; or rather, do nothing wilfully to impair it. Use exercise, abstinence, and regular hours. Drink water when you are alone, and wine or very little spirits in company. It is the last that are ruinous by leading to an unlimited excess. There is not the same headlong impetus in wine. But one glass of brandy and water makes you want another, that other makes you want a third, and so on in an increased proportion. Therefore no one can stop midway who does not possess the resolution to abstain altogether; for the inclination is sharpened with its indulgence. Never gamble. Or if you play for anything, never do so for what will give you uneasiness the next day. Be not precise in these matters; but do not pass certain limits, which it is difficult to recover. Do nothing in the irritation of the moment, but take time to reflect. Because you have done one foolish thing do not do another; nor throw away your health, or reputation, or comfort, to thwart impertinent advice. Avoid a spirit of contradiction, both in words and actions. Do not aim at what is beyond your reach, but at what is within it. Indulge in calm and pleasing pursuits, rather than violent excitements; and learn to conquer your own will, instead of striving to obtain the mastery of that of others.

With respect to your friends, I would wish you to choose them neither from caprice nor accident, and to adhere to them as long as you can. Do not make a surfeit of friendship, through over sanguine enthusiasm, nor expect it to last for ever; Always speak well of those with whom you have once been intimate, or take some part of the censure you bestow on them to yourself. Never quarrel with tried friends, or those whom you wish to continue such. Wounds of this kind are sure to open again. When once the prejudice is removed that sheathes defects, familiarity only causes jealousy and distrust. Do not keep on with a mockery of friendship after the substance is gone—but part, while you can part friends. Bury the carcase of friendship: it is not worth embalming.

As to the books you will have to read by choice or for amusement, the best are the commonest. The names of many of them are already familiar to you. Read them as you grow up with all the satisfaction in your power, and make much of them. It is perhaps the greatest pleasure you will have in life, the one you will think of longest, and repent of least. If my life had been more full of calamity than it has been (much more than I hope yours will be) I would live it over again, my poor little boy, to have read the books I did in my youth.

In politics I wish you to be an honest man, but no brawler. Hate injustice and falsehood for your own sake. Be neither a martyr nor a sycophant. Wish well to the world without expecting to see it much better than it is; and do not gratify the enemies of liberty by putting yourself at their mercy, if it can be avoided with honour.

If you ever marry, I would wish you to marry the woman you like. Do not be guided by the recommendation of friends. Nothing will atone for or overcome an original distaste. It will only increase from intimacy; and if you are to live separate it is better not to come together. There is no use in dragging a chain through life unless it binds one to the object we love. No woman ever married into a family above herself that did not try to make all the mischief she could in it. Be not in haste to marry, nor to engage your affections, where there is no probability of a return. Do not fancy every woman you see the heroine of a romance, a Sophia Western, a Clarissa, or a Julia; and yourself the potential hero of it, Tom Jones, Lovelace, or St. Preux. Avoid this error as you would shrink back from a precipice. All your fine sentiments and romantic notions will (of themselves) make no more impression on one of these delicate creatures than on a piece of marble. Their soft bosoms are steel to your amorous refinements, if you have no other pretensions. It is not what you think of them that determines their choice, but what they think of you. Endeavour, if you would escape lingering torments, and the gnawing of the worm that dies not, to find out this, and to abide by the issue. We trifle with, make sport of, and despise those who are attached to us, and follow those that fly from us. "We hunt the wind—we worship a statue—cry aloud to the desert." Do you, my dear boy, stop short in this career if you find yourself setting out in it, and make up your mind to this—that, if a woman does not like you of her own accord, that is, from involuntary impressions, nothing you can say, or do, or suffer for her sake will make her, but will set her the more against you. So the song goes—

> "Quit, quit for shame; this will not move:
> If of herself she will not love,
> Nothing will make her, the devil take her!"

Your pain is her triumph; the more she feels you in her power, the worse she will treat you: the more you make it appear you deserve her regard, the more she will resent it as an imputation on her first judgment. Study first impressions above all things, for everything depends on them—in love especially. Women are armed by nature and education with a power of resisting the importunity of men, and they use this power according to their discretion. They enforce it to the utmost rigour of the law against those whom they do not like, and relax their extreme severity proportionably in favour of those that they do like, and who in general care as little about them. Hence we see so many desponding lovers and forlorn damsels. Love in women, at least, is either vanity, or interest, or fancy. It is a merely selfish feeling. It has nothing to do, I am sorry to say, with friendship, or esteem, or even pity. I once asked a girl, the pattern of her sex in shape and mind and attractions, whether she did not think Mr. Coleridge had done wrong in making the heroine of his beautiful ballad story of Genevieve take compassion on her hapless lover—

> "When on the yellow forest-leaves
> A dying man he lay;"

and whether she believed that any woman ever fell in love through a sense of compassion, and she made answer—"Not if it was against her inclination!" I would take this lady's word for a thousand pounds on this point. Pain holds antipathy to pleasure, pity is not akin to love; a dying man has more need of a nurse than of a mistress. There is no forcing liking. It is as little to be fostered by reason and good-nature as it can be controlled by prudence or propriety. It is a mere blind, headstrong impulse. Least of all, flatter yourself that talents or virtue will recommend you to the favour of the sex in lieu of exterior advantages. Oh! no. Women care nothing about poets, or philosophers, or politicians. They go by a man's looks and manner. Richardson calls them "an eye-judging sex," and I am sure he knew more about them than I can pretend to do. If you run away with a pedantic notion that they care a pin's point about your head or your heart, you will repent it too late. Some blue-stocking may have her vanity flattered by your reputation, or be edified by the solution of a metaphysical problem or a critical remark, or a dissertation on the state of the nation, and fancy that she has a taste for intellect and is an epicure in sentiment. No true woman ever regarded anything but her lover's person and address. Gravity will here answer all the same purpose without understanding, gaiety without wit, folly without good-nature, and impudence without any other pretension. The natural and instinctive passion of love is excited by qualities not peculiar to artists, authors, and men of letters. It is not the jest but the laugh that follows, not the sentiment but the glance that accompanies it, that tells—in a word, the sense of actual enjoyment that imparts itself to others, and excites mutual understanding and inclination. Authors, on the other hand, feel nothing spontaneously. The common incidents and circumstances of life with which others are taken up, make no alteration in them, nor provoke any of the common expressions of surprise, joy, admiration, anger or merriment. Nothing stirs their blood or accelerates their juices or tickles their veins. Instead of yielding to the first natural and lively impulses of things, in which they would find sympathy, they screw themselves up to some far-fetched view of the subject in order to be unintelligible. Realities are not good enough for them, till they undergo the process of imagination and reflection. If you offer them your hand to shake, they will hardly take it; for this does not amount to a proposition. If you enter their room suddenly, they testify neither surprise nor satisfaction: no new idea is elicited by it. Yet if you suppose this to be a repulse you are mistaken. They will enter into your affairs or combat your ideas with all the warmth and vehemence imaginable as soon as they have a subject started. But their faculty for thinking must be set in motion, before you can put any soul into them. They are intellectual dram-drinkers; and without their necessary stimulus, are torpid, dead insensible to everything. They have great life of mind, but none of body. They do not drift with the stream of company or of passing occurrences, but are straining at some hyberbole, or striking out a bye-path of their own. Follow them who list. Their minds are a sort of Herculaneum, full of old, petrified images;—are set in stereotype, and little fitted to the ordinary occasions of life.

What chance, then, can they have with women, who deal only in the pantomine of discourse, in gesticulation and the flippant bye-play of the senses, "nods and winks and wreathed smiles;" and to whom to offer a remark is an impertinence, or a reason an affront? The only way in which I ever knew mental qualities or distinction tell was in the clerical character; and women do certainly incline to this with some sort of favourable regard. Whether it is that the sanctity of pretension piques curiosity, or that the habitual submission of their understandings to their spiritual guides subdues the will, a popular preacher generally has the choice among the elite of his female flock. According to Mrs. Inchbald (see her Simple Story) there is another reason why religious courtship is not without its charms! But as I do not intend you for the church, do not, in thinking to study yourself into the good graces of the fair, study yourself out of them, millions of miles. Do not place thought as a barrier between you and love: do not abstract yourself into the regions of truth, far from the smile of earthly beauty. Let not the cloud sit upon your brow: let not the canker sink into your heart, Look up, laugh loud, talk big, keep the colour in your cheek and the fire in your eye, adorn your person, maintain your health, your beauty, and your animal spirits, and you will pass for a fine man. But should you let your blood stagnate in some deep metaphysical question, or refine too much in your ideas of the sex, forgetting yourself in a dream of exalted perfection, you will want an eye to cheer you, a hand to guide you, a bosom to lean on, and will stagger into your grave, old before your time, unloved and unlovely. If you feel that you have not the necessary advantages of person, confidence, and manner, and that it is up-hill work with you to gain the ear of beauty, quit the pursuit at once, and seek for other satisfactions and consolations.

A spider, my dear, the meanest creature that crawls or lives, has its mate or fellow: but a scholar has no mate or fellow. For myself, I had courted thought, I had felt pain; and Love turned away his face from me. I have gazed along the silent air for that smile which had lured me to my doom. I no more heard those accents which would have burst upon me like a voice from heaven. I loathed the light that shone on my disgrace. Hours, days, years passed away, and only turned false hope to fixed despair. And as my frail bark sails down the stream of time, the God of Love stands on the shore, and as I stretch out my hands to him in vain, claps his wings, and mocks me as I pass!

There is but one other point on which I meant to speak to you, and that is the choice of a profession. This, probably, had better be left to time or accident or your own inclination. You have a very fine ear, but I have somehow a prejudice against men-singers, and indeed against the stage altogether. It is an uncertain and ungrateful soil. All professions are bad that depend on reputation, which is "as often got without merit as lost without deserving." Yet I cannot easily reconcile myself to your being a slave to business, and I shall be hardly able to leave you an independence. A situation in a public office is secure, but laborious and mechanical, and without the two great springs of life, Hope and Fear. Perhaps, however, it might ensure you a competence, and leave you leisure for some other favourite amusement or pursuit. I have said all reputation is hazardous, hard to win, harder to keep. Many never attain a glimpse of what they have all their lives been looking for, and others survive a passing shadow of it. Yet if I were to name one pursuit rather than another, I should wish you to be a good painter, if such a thing could be hoped. I have failed in this myself, and should wish you to be able to do what I have not—to paint like Claude or Rembrandt or Guido or Vandyke, if it were possible. Artists, I think, who have succeeded in their chief object, live to be old, and are agreeable old men. Their minds keep alive to the last. Cosway's spirits never flagged till after ninety, and Nollekins, though nearly blind, passed all his mornings in giving directions about some group or bust in his workshop. You have seen Mr. Northcote, that delightful specimen of the last age. With what avidity he takes up his pencil, or lays it down again to talk of numberless things! His eye has not lost its lustre, nor "paled its ineffectual fire." His body is a shadow: he himself is a pure spirit. There is a kind of immortality about this sort of ideal and visionary existence that dallies with Fate and baffles the grim monster, Death. If I thought you could make as clever an artist and arrive at such an agreeable old age as Mr. Northcote, I should declare at once for your devoting yourself to this enchanting profession; and in that reliance, should feel less regret at some of my own disappointments, and little anxiety on your account!

The Danger of a Little Learning

ALEXANDER POPE

ALEXANDER POPE (1688-1744), most representative poet of the eighteenth century, was the son of a Roman Catholic linen-draper of London. Handicapped by bad health and physical deformity, he was largely self-educated. His first poems, written when he was seventeen and published four years later, showed his metrical skill and brought him to the attention of the literary figures of the day. In 1711 he published An Essay on Criticism, *a didactic poem in heroic couplets. The next year he published his mock-heroic poem,* The Rape of the Lock. *He brought out an edition of Shakespeare, and translated the* Iliad *and the* Odyssey. *His literary work brought him a small fortune so that he was enabled to buy Twickenham, a small estate near London, where he spent the remainder of his life.*

A LITTLE *learning* is a dangerous thing;
Drink deep, or taste not the Pierian spring:
There shallow draughts intoxicate the brain,
And drinking largely sobers us again.
Fired at first sight with what the Muse imparts,
In fearless youth we tempt the heights of arts,
While from the bounded level of our mind,
Short views we take, nor see the lengths behind;
But more advanced, behold with strange surprise
New distant scenes of endless science rise!
So pleased at first the towering Alps we try,
Mount o'er the vales and seem to tread the sky,
The eternal snows appear already pass'd,
And the first clouds and mountains seem the last:
But, those attain'd, we tremble to survey
The growing labours of the lengthen'd way,
The increasing prospect tires our wandering eyes,
Hills peep o'er hills, and Alps on Alps arise!

I Consider Mr. Chips

JOHN P. MARQUAND

JOHN P. MARQUAND, novelist and short-story writer, was born in Wilmington, Delaware, in 1893. After his graduation from Newburyport High School, he entered Harvard College and was graduated in three years with the class of 1915. Two weeks later he was working as a reporter on the Boston Transcript. *After service in World War I he worked on the New York* Tribune *and later in the copy department of a national advertising agency. His career as a novelist began during a summer in Massachusetts in which he wrote a novel which was bought by the* Ladies' Home Journal. *His next story was sold to the* Saturday Evening Post, *in which much of his subsequent work has been published.*

In 1937 his novel The Late George Apley *won the Pulitzer Prize as the best novel of the year.*

H. M. Pulham, Esquire, *from which the following selection is taken, first ran as a serial in* McCall's Magazine *under the title* Gone Tomorrow. *Like* The Late George Apley *this novel recounts the life of a Boston Brahmin.*

A GOOD deal of life as I know it really began when I went to boarding school. When I left Westwood one September afternoon, home grew smaller and faded into the clouds, like the land when you leave for Europe. After that I was always going away and always coming back, but whenever I came back part of me did not belong there.

"Father's going to take you in the Winton," Mary said.

My trunk was on the floor of my room with all the things I needed, such as a blue suit and stiff white collars and two laundry bags and a shoe bag and blankets and a comforter and sheets and pillow slips and a Bible and stockings and corduroy knickerbockers.

"Father told Patrick this afternoon," Mary said, "and Patrick has been working on the engine all day."

Then Hugh came in. He opened the door without knocking.

"Now, now, now," Hugh said. "What would Madam say if she knew you were in here, Miss Mary?"

"Oh, go bunch," Mary said.

"Such a way for a little lady to talk," said Hugh, and he smiled at me. "They will beat the living daylights out of you, Master Harry. I know what they did to Master Alfred Frothingham, who was a much nicer-spoken young gentleman than you. Master Alfred walked lame when he came back for the Christmas holidays."

Hugh liked to talk of the Frothinghams, a much better place than his present one.

"Oh, go chase yourself," I said.

"Now, now," said Hugh, "such a way to talk, such language. The young gentleman tied Master Alfred up by his thumbs. Master Alfred told me so himself. And they put weights on his feet, and they stuck red-hot needles in Master Alfred, so that his flesh all burned and smoked and sizzled like a steak over coals, and then they beat Master Alfred with cricket bats."

"Oh, go soak your head," I said. "They don't have cricket bats in America."

"That's right, Harry," Mary said. "Hugh is nothing but a great big nasty liar. They don't have cricket bats in America."

"Excuse me, miss," Hugh said. "Baseball bats, I should have said. Master Alfred still had lumps on him when I left the place, horrible big welts all over him, and holes where they inserted the needles. Master Alfred was covered with running sores."

"*Ach,*" I heard Fräulein say to her, "Mrs. Pulham, you are so brave!"

"Fräulein, dear," my mother answered, "I'm only doing what anyone ought to do."

I know only too well that there is nothing like a mother, and a man, I think, understands this better than a woman. That is why the best tributes to motherhood come from men. I recall particularly Whistler's portrait of his mother, which always gives me a burning feeling in my throat when I see it, and that poem of Kipling's about "Mother o' Mine." I have been told that it is sentimental, but I think that it is very true.

Those nervous headaches of hers, which grew worse as she grew older, were particularly severe that September. I remember being struck by my father's expression when he thought she did not see him. He looked puzzled and not entirely sympathetic, and once when I was walking down the hall, their door was open and I heard Father say:

"Now, Mary, he's only going to school."

The morning before I left I was sent to say good-by to everyone on the place, to Patrick and then to Charley and Joe in the garden, and to the two Italians who came in by the day to help, and then to Mr. and Mrs. Roland, who lived in the cottage by the gate. I had been aware for some time that my status with all of them was altering, and I was embarrassed when the men wiped their hands before they shook hands with me. I even felt constrained with Bob Roland. Bob was the superintendent's son and just about my age.

"Well," I said, "so long."

I saw Bob looking at my new clothes. We stood there, eyeing each other like strangers, although we were very good friends.

"So long," Bob said.

"I'll see you at Christmas," I told him.

It was a fine September day. The sunlight was soft, and a breeze was blowing through the elm trees.

"We'll all miss Master Harry, madam," Hugh was saying.

Patrick was cranking the Winton. It would cough and then it would stop, and he would run over to the steering wheel and move the spark and the gas, and then he would crank it again and run back to the steering wheel. Finally the engine responded, and he crawled into the tonneau in back. Father pulled his cap over his eyes and pulled on his leather gauntlets.

"All right," he called. We had to speak very loudly, and Mother waved. I had a queer feeling in the pit of my stomach—but there is no use describing what everyone has felt.

"Don't fall out," Mother called. "Hold on tight, darling."

I can remember the sun and the colors of the trees and all the country roads. There were no roadside stands or gasoline pumps and no advertising signs. I remember the yellow trees in Weston and how a horse in front of the general store reared and broke his bridle. I remember the piles of pumpkins and squashes outside the barns near Sudbury and the carts full of apple barrels. I was tired when we got to Worcester, where we stopped for the night.

"Well," said Father in the hotel dining room, "you'll be there tomorrow."

I had never been with him for such a long time in my life, but we did not say much.

"I wish I were going with you," he said. "You see, I never went to boarding school. They were newfangled things in my day. Now everybody goes."

We did not reach school until about four the next afternoon. We were delayed by two blowouts and a puncture on the Springfield Road. All that road is paved and unfamiliar now, but when I was there last the school had not changed much. There were some new buildings, but that was all. There was the same smell of oil on the floor and the same impersonal and cleanly, but human, smell coming from the cubicles of the small boys' dormitory.

Parents were helping put things in bureau drawers and everyone was very cheerful. Father had taken me downstairs to shake hands with Mr. Ewing, and one of the Third Form boys had shown us where I was to live.

"Well," Father said, "I guess that's about all. You'll write me if you want anything, won't you?"

"Yes, sir."

"Well, all right," Father said. "Is there anything we've forgotten?"

"The coat hangers," I said.

"I'll send them by express," Father said, and he blew his nose. "That's all, isn't it?"

"Yes, sir."

"Don't bother to go down with me," Father said. "You'd better go to the lavatory and wash your face and hands—in good cold water. Use a lot of good cold water. There isn't anything else, is there?"

"No, I guess that's all," I answered.

"Well, behave yourself." My father looked around the dormitory and blew his nose again. "And have a good time. You're going to have a fine time."

"Yes, sir."

"And if you don't," Father said, "don't let anyone know it. Well, good-by, Harry."

If you have not prepared for college at one of the older and larger schools, with traditions and a recognized headmaster, you have missed a great experience. You have missed something fine in intimate companionship. You have missed that indefinable thing known as school spirit, which is more important than books or teaching, because it lasts when physics and algebra and Latin are forgotten. The other day I tried to read a page of Cicero and I could not get through a single line, although I got a B on my Latin entrance examination, but I can still remember the school hymn word for word. I am quite sure even today that I can tell, after a five minutes' talk with anyone, whether he attended a public or private school thirty years before. I believe that I can go even further than that. I can tell whether he went to a really good boarding school or to a second-rate one. The answer is always written in his voice and manner. That is why school is so enormously important.

I owe a debt of gratitude to my school, and I believe it was the best school then and it is the best school now. No matter what else has happened to me in the way of failure and disappointment I am glad that I went to St. Swithin's. More than once the particular thing I learned there, which you can call manners or attitude, for want of better words, has helped me in my darkest moments, and I have Mr. Ewing to thank for it, my old headmaster.

"In order to be a leader," Mr. Ewing used to say in chapel, "and to take the place which is made for you, you must learn first to obey and serve."

This sort of thing is hard to express to anyone who has never been there. I have tried to explain it to Bill King more than once. I told him on one occasion that I was sorry that he had not gone to St. Swithin's, that he would have been quite a different person if he had gone there.

"You're damned well right I would have," Bill said, "but I like to think I couldn't have stood it."

"You could have, Bill," I told him, "if you had started in the First Form. The way to get the most out of school is to start at the beginning. Very few boys are taken in after that, because they don't get the most out of it."

"You mean, they have minds of their own," Bill said.

"That isn't what I mean at all," I told him. "The Skipper can't do a proper job on a boy unless he has him all the way through."

"Skipper!" Bill said. "Can't you stop calling him the Skipper?"

"That's all right," I told him. "The graduates of any good school have a nickname for the headmaster. I wish you really knew the Skipper, Bill. If you really knew him you wouldn't indulge in so many half-truths."

"I do know him," Bill said. "I crossed the ocean with him once."

"That isn't really knowing him," I said. "You can only know the Skipper when he's up at school doing his job. He's different anywhere else."

"Wherever that old jellyfish is," Bill said, "he's a conceited, pandering poop."

"My God, Bill," I said, and I had to laugh. "You just don't know the Skipper. He hadn't been more than a few years out of Harvard when he came there. You should have seen him on the football field! The Skipper's sixty now and he still plays games."

"Mr. Chips," Bill said. "*Good-bye, Mr. Chips.*"

"And what's wrong with Mr. Chips?" I asked.

"What's wrong with Mr. Chips?" Bill said. "Frankly, everything was wrong with Mr. Chips."

"You aren't talking sense," I said. "I can think of nothing finer than Mr. Chips's last remark. 'Children? . . . I've had hundreds of them, and all of them are boys.'"

"Don't," Bill said. "You'll have to go away if you make me want to cry. Could anything be more unnatural than herding a lot of adolescent males together who ought to be with their parents and their sisters and their friends' sisters, learning the usual amenities of life?"

"The school wasn't unnatural," I said. "We were all able to see family life there, Bill, a good deal happier and more successful than what lots of us saw at home."

"How much did you see of it?" Bill asked.

"We used to see a lot of it," I said. "We were all brought up with the Skipper's children. Why, Mrs. Ewing always saw that every boy came in once a week to tea, and the Sixth Form always came in on Sundays for a pick-up supper."

"It sounds like a biological laboratory," Bill said. "It's like the neurologists at all those nervous-breakdown places. They have to have a happy married life or else they'll be fired. Well, go ahead. What did the Skipper teach you?"

"You can sneer at it all you like, Bill," I told him. "It doesn't affect me, because you don't understand. The Skipper had the guts to stand for what he stood for. That's more than either you or I have."

"We don't get a house and a salary for it," Bill said. "We don't get paid for having guts. Don't get mad, Harry. You couldn't help it. Most of us were sent away from home somewhere and made to adjust ourselves to some arbitrary, artificial world that was built up by some positive and not intelligent individual. The only thing you can do is to try to snap out of it. Say good-by to it fast. Good-by, Mr. Chips."

"There are a lot of things you never say good-by to," I said, "if you go to a first-rate school."

"Yes," Bill said, "that's true. Not when they catch you young."

"You have to have standards to live," I said.

"Did you ever meet a poor boy there?" Bill asked. "Did you ever learn that people are abused and hungry, or what a minimum wage is? Did you ever get outside and go downtown? Did anybody ever teach you what the other ninety-nine per cent of people think about?"

"You learn that later," I said. "I spent the happiest time of my life there, the most worth-while time. I wish I were back there now."

"The old subconscious desire," Bill said, "to crawl back into your mother's womb."

Now, I can be amused by people when they talk that way. I am even broad-minded enough to see their point of view, but there is nothing easier than to make fun of something that you do not understand.

I wish I might go back there again, because I did well at school. I was never one of the leaders. I never stood high in my form. I was too light for football, but of course I played it, because everyone had to play. I never did like baseball, but I wrote things for *The Crier*, the school paper. None of this meant very much, but I was an integral part of something—a part of a group.

I wish I could go back. Whenever autumn comes, even now, if I am in the country, I seem to be close to school. I still have all the indefinable sensations which mark the beginnings of a new year. I think of the fresh pages of new books and of the Upper Field and of the Lower Field, with their goalposts, and of the tennis courts and of the red and yellow of the maples. And I can see the Skipper, younger then.

"That was well played, Pulham," I can hear him saying. "Show fight, always show fight."

Every autumn I can see the faces of my form. Their names run through my mind, and their nicknames, and their physical peculiarities. It was a good form. Out of it came a banker and a state senator, two doctors and a scientist, a drunkard, and a good many brokers and lawyers. One was killed along the Meuse in the Argonne drive, and one was killed in a motor accident, and one has died of heart failure—five of them have been divorced, two of them are dead-broke—on the whole not a bad record. I wish that I were back. I have often said that to myself before I have gone to sleep. I wish that I were back where there was someone like the Skipper to tell me what to do, someone who knew absolutely what was right and what was wrong, someone who had an answer to everything. There was always an answer at school, and a good answer. No matter what the world was like you could still play the game. I wish to God that I were back.

A Pedant Conducts a Latin Recitation

JOHN MARSTON

JOHN MARSTON (1575?-1634), dramatist, was educated at Brasenose College, Oxford. Finding the study of the law distasteful, he began to write satire for the stage, but about 1607 he abandoned playwriting and took holy orders. He resigned from his living in 1631 and in 1633 published a collection of his plays. He died in the following year.

The comedy, What You Will, *was first published in 1607.*

(A schoolroom. The PEDANT draws the curtains, revealing BATTUS, NOUS, SLIP, NATHANIEL and HOLOFERNES PIPPO, his pupils, with books in their hands.)

ALL   *Salve, magister!* [1]

PEDANT   *Salvete pueri, estote salvi, vos salvere exopto vobis salutem. Batte, mi fili, mi Batte!* [2]

BATTUS   *Quid vis?* [3]

PEDANT   Stand forth: repeat your lesson without book.

BATTUS   A noun is the name of a thing that may be seen, felt, heard, or understood.

PEDANT   Good boy: on, on.

BATTUS   Of nouns, some be substantives and some be substantives.

PEDANT   Adjectives.

BATTUS   Adjectives. A noun substantive either is proper to the thing that it betokeneth——

PEDANT   Well, to numbers.

BATTUS   In nouns be two numbers, the singular and the plural: the singular number speaketh of one, as *lapis*, a stone; the plural speaketh of more than one, as *lapides*, stones.

PEDANT   Good child. Now thou art past *lapides*, stones, proceed to the cases. Nous, say you next, Nous. Where's your lesson, Nous?

NOUS   I am in a verb, forsooth.

PEDANT   Say on, forsooth: say, say.

NOUS   A verb is a part of speech declined with mood and tense, and betokeneth doing, as *amo*, I love.

[1] "Hail, master."
[2] "Good morning, my boys, I hope you are well, Battus, my boy, my Battus."
[3] "What is your wish?"

414

PEDANT   How many kinds of verbs are there?

NOUS   Two: personal and impersonal.

PEDANT   Of verbs personal, how many kinds?

NOUS   Five: active, passive, neuter, deponent, and common. A verb active endeth in *o*, and betokeneth to do, as *amo*, I love; and by putting to *r*, it may be a passive, as *amor*, I am loved.

PEDANT   Very good child. Now learn to know the deponent and common. Say you, Slip.

SLIP   *Cedant arma togæ, concedat laurea linguæ.*[4]

PEDANT   What part of speech is *lingua? Inflecte, inflecte.*

SLIP   *Singulariter, nominativo hæc lingua.*

PEDANT   Why is *lingua* the feminine gender?

SLIP   Forsooth because it is the feminine gender.

PEDANT   Ha, thou ass! thou dolt! *idem per idem,* mark it: *lingua* is declined with *hæc*, the feminine, because it is a household stuff, particularly belonging and most resident under the roof of women's mouths. Come on, you Nathaniel, say you, say you next; not too fast; say tretably [5]; say.

NATHANIEL   *Mascula dicuntur monosyllaba nomina quædam.*[6]

PEDANT   Faster! faster!

NATHANIEL   *Ut sal, sol, ren et splen: car, ser, vir, vas, vadis, as, mas.*
Bes, cres, pres et pes, glis, gliris habens genetivo,
Mos, flos, ros et tros, muns, dens, mons, pons—

PEDANT   *Rup, tup, snup, slug, bor, hor, cor, mor.* Holla! holla! holla! you Holofernes Pippo, put him down. Wipe your nose: fie, on your sleeve! where's your muckender [7] your grandmother gave you? Well, say on; say on.

HOLOFERNES   Pree, master, what word's this?

PEDANT   Ass! ass!

HOLOFERNES   —*As in presenti perfectum format in, n, in—*

PEDANT   In what, sir?

HOLOFERNES (confused)   *Perfectum format . . .* In what, sir?

PEDANT   In what, sir?—*in avi.*

HOLOFERNES   In what, sir?—*in avi. Ut no, nas, navi: vocito, vocitas, voci . . . voci . . . voci—*[8]

PEDANT   What's next?

HOLOFERNES   *Voci*—what's next?

PEDANT   Why, thou ungracious child! thou simple animal! thou barnacle! Nous, snare him; take him up: [9] and you were my father, you should up.

---

[4] "Let arms yield to the gown, the laurel give place to the tongue"—i.e. the arts and honours of peace take the place of war.

[5] With clear utterance.

[6] Certain monosyllabic nouns are called masculine.

[7] Handkerchief.

[8] "-*as* in the present forms its perfect in -avi, as *no, nas, navi; vocito, vocitas, vocitavi.*"

[9] Take up: mount, hoist on the back ready for a thrashing.

HOLOFERNES   Indeed I am not your father. O Lord! now, for God sake let me go out. My mother told a thing: I shall bewray all else. Hark, you master: my grandmother entreats you to come to dinner to-morrow morning.

PEDANT (his anger increasing)   I say, untruss; take him up. Nous, dispatch! what, not perfect in an—*as in presenti?*

HOLOFERNES   In truth I'll be as perfect an *as in presenti* as any of this company, with the grace of God, law: this once—this once—and I do so any more—

PEDANT   I say, hold him up!

HOLOFERNES   Ha, let me say my prayers first. You know not what you ha' done now; all the syrup of my brain is run into my buttocks, and ye spill the juice of my wit well. Ha, sweet! ha, sweet! honey, Barbary sugar, sweet master.

PEDANT   Sans tricks, trifles, delays, demurrers,[10] procrastinations, or retardations, mount him, mount him.

[10] Legal objection.

A Searching of Schoolmasters

H. G. WELLS

H. G. WELLS, English novelist and scientific writer, was born in 1866, the son of a small shopkeeper. Between periods of work as a draper's and a druggist's apprentice Wells attended the Midhurst Grammar School, where he was an outstanding pupil. He subsequently attended the Royal College of Science and in 1888 was graduated with honors from London University. He then became a teacher until ill health forced him to give up all work. When he had recovered his health, he went to London and began his career as a journalist and novelist.

Wells was a prolific and versatile writer, his work including fantastic and imaginative romances, realistic novels, and novels which serve as vehicles for his social and political theories. He died in 1946.

Joan and Peter, from which the following selection is taken, makes education the chief motive in the lives of two young people.

Bᴜᴛ here Justice demands an interlude.

Before we go on to tell of how Joan and Peter grew up to adolescence in these schools that Oswald—assisted by Aunt Phyllis in the case of Joan—found for them, Mr. Mackinder must have his say, and make the Apology of the Schoolmaster. He made it to Oswald when first Oswald visited him and chose his school out of all the other preparatory schools, to be Peter's. He appeared as a little brown man with a hedgehog's nose and much of the hedgehog's indignant note in his voice. He came, shy and hostile, into the drawing-room in which Oswald awaited him. It was, by the by, the most drawing-room-like drawing-room that Oswald had ever been in; it was as if some one had said to a furniture dealer, "People expect me to have a drawing-room. Please let me have exactly the sort of drawing-room that people expect." It displayed a grand piano towards the French window, a large standard lamp with an enormous shade, a pale silk sofa, an Ottoman, a big fern in an ornate pot, and water-colours of Venetian lagoons. In the midst of it all stood Mr. Mackinder, in a highly contracted state, mutely radiating an interrogative "Well?"

"I'm looking for a school for my nephew," said Oswald.

"You want him here?"

"Well—Do you mind if first of all I see something of the school?"

"We're always open to investigation," said Mr. Mackinder, bitterly.

"I want to do the very best I can for this boy. I feel very strongly that it's my duty to him and the country to turn him out—as well as a boy can be turned out."

Mr. Mackinder nodded his head and continued to listen.

This was something new in private schoolmasters. For the most part they had opened themselves out to Oswald, like sunflowers, like the receptive throats of nestlings. They had embraced and silenced him by the wealth of their assurances.

"I have two little wards," he said. "A boy and a girl. I want to make all I can of them. They ought to belong to the Elite. The strength of a country —of an empire—depends ultimately almost entirely on its Elite. This empire isn't overwhelmed with intelligence, and most of the talk we hear about the tradition of statesmanship——"

Mr. Mackinder made a short snorting noise through his nose that seemed to indicate his opinion of contemporary statesmanship.

"You see I take this schooling business very solemnly. These upper-class schools, I say, these schools for the sons of prosperous people and scholarship winners, are really Elite-making machines. They really make—or fail to make—the Empire. That makes me go about asking schoolmasters a string of questions. Some of them don't like my questions. Perhaps they are too elementary. I ask: what is this education of yours up to? What is the design of the whole? What is this preparation of yours for? This is called a Preparatory School. You lay the foundations. What is the design of the building for which these foundations are laid?"

He paused, determined to make Mr. Mackinder say something before he discoursed further.

"It isn't so simple as that," was wrung from Mr. Mackinder. "Suppose we just walk round the school. Suppose we just see the sort of place it is and what we are doing here. Then perhaps you'll be able to see better what we contribute—in the way of making a citizen."

The inspection was an unusually satisfactory one. White Court was one of the few private schools Oswald had seen that had been built expressly for its purpose. Its class rooms were well lit and well arranged, its little science museum seemed good and well arranged and well provided with diagrams; its gymnasium was businesslike; its wall blackboards unusually abundant and generously used, and everything was tidy. Nevertheless the Catechism for Schoolmasters was not spared. "Now," said Oswald, "now for the curriculum?"

"We live in the same world with most other English schools," Mr. Mackinder sulked. "This is a preparatory school."

"What are called English subjects?"

"Yes."

"How do you teach geography?"

"With books and maps."

Oswald spoke of lantern slides and museum visits. The cinema had yet to become an educational possibility.

"I do what I can," said Mr. Mackinder; "I'm not a millionaire."

"Do you *do* classics?"

"We do Latin. Clever boys do a little Greek. In preparation for the public schools."

"Grammar of course? . . .

"What else? . . .

"French, German, Latin, Greek, bits of mathematics, botany, geography, bits of history, book-keeping, music lessons, some water-colour painting; it's very mixed," said Oswald.

"It's miscellaneous."

Mr. Mackinder roused himself to a word of defence: "The boys don't specialize."

"But this is a diet of scraps," said Oswald, reviving one of the most controversial topics of the catechism. "Nothing can be done thoroughly."

"We are necessarily elementary."

"It's rather like the White Knight in *Alice in Wonderland* packing his luggage for nowhere."

"We have to teach what is required of us," said Mr. Mackinder.

"But what is education up to?" asked Oswald.

As Mr. Mackinder offered no answer to that riddle, Oswald went on. "What *is* Education in England up to, anyhow? In Uganda we knew what we were doing. There was an idea in it. The old native tradition was breaking up. We taught them to count and reckon English fashion, to read and write, we gave them books and the Christian elements, so that they could join on to our civilization and play a part in the great world that was breaking up their little world. We didn't teach them anything that didn't serve mind or soul or body. We saw the end of what we were doing. But half this school teaching of yours is like teaching in a dream. You don't teach the boy what he wants to know and needs to know. You spend half his time on calculations he has no use for, mere formal calculations, and on this dead language stuff—! It's like trying to graft mummy steak on living flesh. It's like boiling fossils for soup."

Mr. Mackinder said nothing.

"And damn it!" said Oswald petulantly; "your school is about as good a school as I've seen or am likely to see. . . .

"I had an idea," he went on, "of just getting the very best out of those two youngsters—the boy especially—of making every hour of his school work a gift of so much power or skill or subtlety, of opening the world to him like a magic book. . . . The boy's tugging at the magic covers. . . ."

He stopped short.

"There are no such schools," said Mr. Mackinder compactly. "This is as good a school as you will find."

And there he left the matter for the time. But in the evening he dined with Oswald at his hotel, and it may be that iced champagne had something to do with a certain relaxation from his afternoon restraint. Oswald had already arranged about Peter, but he wanted the little man to talk more. So he set him an example. He talked of his own life. He represented it as a life of disappointment and futility. "I envy you your life of steadfast usefulness." He spoke of his truncated naval career and his disfigurement. Of the years of uncertainty that had followed. He talked of the ambitions and achievements of other men, of the large hopes and ambitions of youth.

"I too," said Mr. Mackinder, warming for a moment, and then left his sentence unfinished. Oswald continued to generalize. . . .

"All life, I suppose, is disappointment—is anyhow largely disappointment," said Mr. Mackinder presently.

"We get something done."

"Five per cent., ten per cent., of what we meant to do."

The schoolmaster reflected. Oswald refilled his glass for him.

"To begin with I thought, none of these other fellows really know how to run a school. I will, I said, make a nest of Young Paragons. I will take a bunch of boys and get the best out of them, the best possible; watch them, study them, foster them, make a sort of boy so that the White Court brand shall be looked for and recognized. . . ."

He sipped his faintly seething wine and put down the glass.

"Five per cent.," he said; "ten per cent., perhaps." He touched his lips with his dinner-napkin. "I have turned out some creditable boys."

"Did you make any experiments in the subjects you taught?"

"At first. But one of the things we discover in life as we grow past the first flush of beginning, is just how severely we are conditioned. We are conditioned. We seem to be free. And we are in a net. You have criticized my curriculum today pretty severely, Mr. Sydenham. Much that you say is absolutely right. It is wasteful, discursive, ineffective. Yes. . . . But in my place I doubt if you could have made it much other than it is. . . .

"One or two things I do. Latin grammar here is taught on lines strictly parallel with the English and French and German—that is to say, we teach languages comparatively. It was troublesome to arrange, but it makes a difference mentally. And I take a class in Formal Logic; English teaching is imperfect, expression is slovenly, without that. The boys write English verse. The mathematical teaching too, is as modern as the examining boards will let it be. Small things, perhaps. But you do not know the obstacles.

"Mr. Sydenham, your talk today has reminded me of all the magnificent things I set out to do at White Court, when I sank my capital in building White Court, six and twenty years ago. When I found that I couldn't control the choice of subjects, when I found that in that matter I was ruled by the sort of schools and colleges the boys had to go on to and by the preposterous examinations they would have to pass, then I told myself, 'at least I can cultivate their characters and develop something like a soul in them, instead of crushing out individuality and imagination as most schools do. . . .'

"Well, I think I have a house of clean-minded and cheerful and willing boys, and I think they all tell the truth. . . ."

"I don't know what I'm to do with the religious teaching of these two youngsters of mine," said Oswald abruptly. "Practically, they're Godless."

Mr. Mackinder did not speak for a little while. Then he said, "It is almost unavoidable, under existing conditions, that the religious teaching in a school should be—formal and orthodox.

"For my own part—I'm liberal," said Mr. Mackinder, and added, "very liberal. Let me tell you, Mr. Sydenham, exactly how I see things."

He paused for a moment as if he collected his views.

"If a little boy has grown up in a home, in the sort of home which one might describe as God-fearing, if he has not only heard of God but seen God as a living influence upon the people about him, then—then, I admit, you have something real. He will believe in God. He will know God. God—simply because of the faith about him—will be a knowable reality. God is a faith. In men. Such a boy's world will fall into shape about the idea of God. He will take God as a matter of course. Such a boy can be religious from childhood—yes . . . But there are very few such homes."

"Less, probably, than there used to be?"

Mr. Mackinder disavowed an answer by a gesture of hands and shoulders. He went on, frowning slightly as he talked. He wanted to say exactly what he thought. "For all other boys, Mr. Sydenham, God, for all practical purposes, does not exist. Their worlds have been made without him; they do not think in terms of him; and if he is to come into their lives at all he must come in from the outside—a discovery, like a mighty rushing wind. By what is called Conversion. At adolescence. Until that happens you must build the soul on pride, on honour, on the decent instincts. It is all you have. And the less they hear about God the better. They will not understand. It will be a cant to them—a kind of indelicacy. The two greatest things in the world have been the most vulgarized. God and sex . . . If I had my own way I would have no religious services for my boys at all."

"Instead of which?"

Mr. Mackinder paused impressively before replying.

"The local curate is preparing two of my elder boys for Confirmation at the present time."

He gazed gloomily at the tablecloth. "If one could do as one liked!" he said. "If only one could do as one liked!"

But now Oswald was realizing for the first time the eternal tragedy of the teacher, that sower of unseen harvests, that reaper of thistles and the wind, that serf of custom, that subjugated rebel, that feeble, persistent antagonist of the triumphant things that rule him. And behind that immediate tragedy Oswald was now apprehending for the first time something more universally tragic, an incessantly recurring story of high hopes and a grey ending; the story of boys and girls, clean and sweet-minded, growing up into life, and of the victory of world inertia, of custom drift and the tarnishing years.

Mr. Mackinder spoke of his own youth. Quite early in life had come physical humiliations, the realization that his slender and delicate physique debarred him from most active occupations, and his resolve to be of use in some field where his weak and undersized body would be at no great disadvantage. "I made up my mind that teaching should be my religion," he said.

He told of the difficulties he had encountered in his attempts to get any pedagogic science or training. "This is the most difficult profession in the world," he said, "and the most important. Yet it is not studied; it has no established practice; it is not endowed. Buildings are endowed and institutions, but not teachers." And in Great Britain, in the schools of the classes that will own and rule the country, ninety-nine per cent. of the work was done by unskilled workmen, by low-grade, genteel women and young men. In America the teachers were nearly all women. "How can we expect to raise a nation nearly as good as we might do under such a handicap?" He had read and learnt what he could about teaching; he had served for small salaries in schools that seemed living and efficient; finally he had built his own school with his own money. He had had the direst difficulties in getting a staff together. "What can one expect?" he said. "We pay them hardly better than shop assistants—less than bank clerks. You see the relative importance of things in the British mind." What hope or pride was there to inspire an assistant schoolmaster to do good work?

"I thought I could make a school different from all other schools, and I found I had to make a school like most other fairly good schools. I had to work for what the parents required of me, and the ideas of the parents had been shaped by their schools. I had never dreamt of the immensity of the resistance these would offer to constructive change. In this world there are incessant changes, but most of them are landslides or epidemics. . . . I tried to get away from stereotyping examinations. I couldn't. I tried to get away from formal soul-destroying religion. I couldn't. I tried to get a staff of real assistants. I couldn't. I had to take what came. I had to be what was required of me. . . .

"One works against time always. Over against the Parents. It is not only the boys one must educate, but the parents—let alone one's self. The parents demand impossible things. I have been asked for Greek and for bookkeeping by double-entry by the same parent. I had—I had to leave the matter—as if I thought such things were possible. After all, the Parent is master. One can't run a school without boys."

"You'd get *some* boys," said Oswald.

"Not enough. I'm up against time. The school has to pay."

"Can't you hold out for a time? Run the school on a handful of oatmeal?"

"It's running it on an overdraft I don't fancy. You're not a married man, Mr. Sydenham, with sons to consider."

"No," said Oswald shortly. "But I have these wards. And, after all, there's not only today but tomorrow. If the world is going wrong for want of education—— If you don't give it your sons will suffer."

"Tomorrow, perhaps. But today comes first. I'm up against time. Oh, I'm up against time."

He sat with his hands held out supine on the table before him.

"I started my school twenty-seven years ago next Hilary. And it seems like yesterday. When I started it I meant it to be something memorable in schools. . . . I jumped into it. I thought I should swim about. . . . It was like jumping into the rapids of Niagara. I was seized, I was rushed along. . . . Ai! Ai! . . ."

"Time's against us all," said Oswald. "I suppose the next glacial age will overtake us long before we're ready to fight out our destiny."

"If you want to feel the generations rushing to waste," said Mr. Mackinder, "like rapids—like rapids—you must put your heart and life into a private school."

My Memories and Miseries As a Schoolmaster

STEPHEN LEACOCK

STEPHEN LEACOCK (1869-1944), Canadian humorist and for many years a teacher of political economy at McGill University, Montreal, was born in England. His parents emigrated to Canada in 1876 and settled on a farm in Ontario. Leacock was sent to Upper Canada College, Toronto, and to the University of Toronto, from which he was graduated in 1891. For the next eight years he taught at his old school, an experience which left him "with a profound sympathy for the many gifted and brilliant men who are compelled to spend their lives in the most dreary, most thankless, and the worst-paid profession in the world."

In 1899 Leacock gave up school teaching, and after taking a Ph.D. degree, joined the faculty of McGill University, where he taught until his retirement.

Fᴏʀ ten years I was a schoolmaster. About thirty years ago I was appointed to the staff of a great Canadian school. It took me ten years to get off it. Being appointed to the position of a teacher is like being hooked up through the braces and hung up against a wall. It is hard to get down again.

From those ten years I carried away nothing in money and little in experience; indeed, no other asset whatever, unless it be, here and there, a pleasant memory or two and the gratitude of my former pupils. There was nothing really in my case for them to be grateful about. They got nothing from me in the way of intellectual food but a lean and perfunctory banquet; and anything that I gave them in the way of sound moral benefit I gave gladly and never missed.

But schoolboys have a way of being grateful. It is the decent thing about them. A schoolboy, while he is at school, regards his masters as a mixed assortment of tyrants and freaks. He plans vaguely that at some future time in life he will "get even" with them. I remember well, for instance, at the school where I used to teach, a little Chilean boy, who kept a stiletto in his trunk with which he intended to kill the second mathematical master.

But somehow a schoolboy is no sooner done with his school and out in the business of life than a soft haze of retrospect suffuses a new colour over all that he has left behind. There is a mellow sound in the tones of the school bell that he never heard in his six years of attendance. There is a warmth in the colour of the old red bricks that he never saw before; and such a charm and such a sadness in the brook or in the elm trees beside the school playground that he will stand beside them with a bowed and reverent head as in the silence of a cathedral. I have seen an "Old Boy" gaze into the open door of an empty classroom and ask, "And those are the same old benches?" with a depth of meaning in his voice. He has been out of school perhaps five years and the benches already seem to him infinitely old. This, by the way, is the moment and this the mood in which the "Old Boy" may be touched for a subscription to the funds of the school. This *is* the way, in fact, in which the sagacious head master does it. The foolish head master, who has not yet learned his business, takes the "Old Boy" round and shows him all the *new* things, the fine new swimming pool built since his day and the new gymnasium with up-to-date patent apparatus. But this is all wrong. There is nothing in it for the "Old Boy" but boredom. The wise head master takes him by the sleeve and says, "Come"; he leads him out to a deserted corner of the playground and shows him an old tree behind an ash house and the "Old Boy" no sooner sees it than he says:

"Why, Great Cæsar! that's the same old tree that Jack Counsell and I used to climb up to hook out of bounds on Saturday night! Old Jimmy caught us at it one night and licked us both. And look here, here's my name cut on the boarding at the back of the ash house. See? They used to fine us five cents a letter if they found it. Well! Well!"

The "Old Boy" is deep in his reminiscences, examining the board fence, the tree and the ash house.

The wise head master does not interrupt him. He does not say that he knew all along that the "Old Boy's" name was cut there and that that's why he brought him to the spot. Least of all does he tell him that the boys still "hook out of bounds" by this means and that he licked two of them for it last Saturday night. No, no, retrospect is too sacred for that. Let the "Old Boy" have his fill of it, and when he is quite down and out with the burden of it, then as they walk back to the school building, the head master may pick a donation from him that falls like a ripe thimbleberry.

And most of all, by the queer contrariety of things, does this kindly retrospect envelop the person of the teachers. They are transformed by the alchemy of time into a group of profound scholars, noble benefactors through whose teaching, had it been listened to, one might have been lifted into higher things. Boys who never listened to a Latin lesson in their lives look back to the memory of their Latin teacher as the one great man that they have known. In the days when he taught them they had no other idea than to put mud in his ink or to place a bent pin upon his chair. Yet they say now that he was the greatest scholar in the world and that if they'd only listened to him they would have got more out of his lessons than from any man that ever taught. He wasn't and they wouldn't—but it is some small consolation to those who have been schoolmasters to know that after it is too late this reward at least is coming to them.

Hence it comes about that even so indifferent a vessel as I should reap my share of schoolboy gratitude. Again and again it happens to me that some unknown man, well on in middle life, accosts me with a beaming face and says: "You don't remember me. You licked me at Upper Canada College," and we shake hands with a warmth and heartiness as if I had been his earliest benefactor. Very often if I am at an evening reception or anything of the sort, my hostess says, "Oh, there is a man here so anxious to meet you," and I know at once why. Forward he comes, eagerly pushing his way among the people to seize my hand. "Do you remember me?" he says. "You licked me at Upper Canada College." Sometimes I anticipate the greeting. As soon as the stranger grasps my hand and says, "Do you remember me?" I break in and say, "Why, let me see, surely I licked you at Upper Canada College." In such a case the man's delight is beyond all bounds. Can I lunch with him at his Club? Can I dine at his home? He wants his wife to see me. He has so often told her about having been licked by me that she too will be delighted.

I do not like to think that I was in any way brutal or harsh, beyond the practice of my time, in beating the boys I taught. Looking back on it, the whole practice of licking and being licked, seems to me mediæval and out of date. Yet I do know that there are, apparently, boys that I have licked in all quarters of the globe. I get messages from them. A man says to me, "By the way, when I was out in Sumatra there was a man there that said he knew you. He said you licked him at Upper Canada College. He said he often thought of you." I have licked, I believe, two Generals of the Canadian Army, three Cabinet Ministers, and more Colonels and Majors than I care to count. Indeed all the boys that I have licked seem to be doing well.

I am stating here what is only simple fact, not exaggerated a bit. Any schoolmaster and every "Old Boy" will recognise it at once; and indeed I can vouch for the truth of this feeling on the part of the "Old Boys" all the better in that I have felt it myself. I always read Ralph Connor's books with great interest for their own sake, but still more because, thirty-two years ago, the author "licked me at Upper Canada College." I have never seen him since, but I often say to people from Winnipeg, "If you ever meet Ralph Connor—he's Major Charles Gordon, you know—tell him that I was asking about him and would like to meet him. He licked me at Upper Canada College."

But enough of "licking." It is, I repeat, to me nowadays a painful and a disagreeable subject. I can hardly understand how we could have done it. I am glad to believe that at the present time it has passed or is passing out of use. I understand that it is being largely replaced by "moral suasion." This, I am sure, is a great deal better. But when I was a teacher moral suasion was just beginning at Upper Canada College. In fact I saw it tried only once. The man who tried it was a tall, gloomy-looking person, a university graduate in psychology. He is now a well-known Toronto lawyer so I must not name him. He came to the school only as a temporary substitute for an absent teacher. He was offered a cane by the college janitor whose business it was to hand them round. But he refused it. He said that a moral appeal was better: he said that psychologically it set up an inhibition stronger than the physical. The first day that he taught—it was away up in a little room at the top of the old college building on King Street—the boys merely threw paper wads at him and put bent pins on his seat. The next day they put hot beeswax on his clothes and the day after that they brought screw drivers and unscrewed the little round seats of the classroom and rolled them down the stairs. After that day the philosopher did not come back, but he has since written, I believe, a book called "Psychic Factors in Education"; which is very highly thought of.

But the opinion of the "Old Boy" about his teachers is only a part of his illusionment. The same peculiar haze of retrospect hangs about the size and shape and kind of boys who went to school when he was young as compared with the boys of to-day.

"How small they are!" is always the exclamation of the "Old Boy" when he looks over the rows and rows of boys sitting in the assembly hall. "Why, when I went to school the boys were ever so much bigger."

After which he goes on to relate that when he first entered the school as a youngster (the period apparently of maximum size and growth), the boys in the sixth form had whiskers! These whiskers of the sixth form are a persistent and perennial school tradition that never dies. I have traced them, on personal record from eyewitnesses, all the way from 1829 when the college was founded until to-day. I remember well, during my time as a schoolmaster, receiving one day a parent, an "Old Boy," who came accompanied by a bright little son of twelve whom he was to enter at the school. The boy was sent to play about with some new acquaintances while I talked with his father.

"The old school," he said in the course of our talk, "is greatly changed, very much altered. For one thing the boys are very much younger than they were in my time. Why, when I entered the school—though you will hardly believe it—the boys in the sixth form had whiskers!"

I had hardly finished expressing my astonishment and appreciation when the little son came back and went up to his father's side and started whispering to him. "Say, dad," he said, "there are some awfully big boys in this school. I saw out there in the hall some boys in the sixth form with whiskers."

From which I deduced that what is whiskers to the eye of youth fades into fluff before the disillusioned eye of age. Nor is there need to widen the application or to draw the moral.

The parents of the boys at school naturally fill a broad page in the schoolmaster's life and are responsible for many of his sorrows. There are all kinds and classes of them. Most acceptable to the schoolmaster is the old-fashioned type of British father who enters his boy at the school and says:

"Now I want this boy well thrashed if he doesn't behave himself. If you have any trouble with him let me know and I'll come and thrash him myself. He's to have a shilling a week pocket money and if he spends more than that let me know and I'll stop his money altogether." Brutal though this speech sounds, the real effect of it is to create a strong prejudice in the little boy's favor and when his father curtly says, "Good-bye, Jack," and he answers, "Good-bye, father," in a trembling voice, the schoolmaster would be a hound indeed who could be unkind to him.

But very different is the case of the up-to-date parent. "Now I've just given Jimmy fifty dollars," he says to the schoolmaster with the same tone as he would to an inferior clerk in his office, "and I've explained to him that when he wants more he's to tell you to go to the bank and draw for him what he needs." After which he goes on to explain that Jimmy is a boy of very peculiar disposition, requiring the greatest nicety of treatment; that they find if he gets in tempers the best way is to humour him and presently he'll come round. Jimmy, it appears can be led, if led gently, but never driven. During all of which time the schoolmaster, insulted by being treated as an underling (for the iron bites deep into the soul of every one of them), has already fixed his eye on the undisciplined young pup called Jimmy with a view to trying out the problem of seeing whether he can't be driven after all.

But the greatest nuisance of all to the schoolmaster is the parent who does his boy's home exercises and works his boy's sums. I suppose they mean well by it. But it is a disastrous thing to do for any child. Whenever I found myself correcting exercises that had obviously been done for the boys in their homes I used to say to them:

"Paul, tell your father that he *must* use the ablative after *pro*."

"Yes, sir," says the boy.

"And, Edward, you tell your grandmother that her use of the dative case simply won't do. She's getting along nicely and I'm well satisfied with the way she's doing, but I cannot have her using the dative right and left on every occasion. Tell her it won't do."

"Yes, sir," says little Edward.

I remember one case in particular of a parent who did not do the boy's exercise but, after letting the boy do it himself, wrote across the face of it a withering comment addressed to me and reading: "From this exercise you can see that my boy, after six months of your teaching, is completely ignorant. How do you account for it?"

I sent the exercise back to him with the added note: "I think it must be heredity."

In the whole round of the school year, there was, as I remember it, but one bright spot—the arrival of the summer holidays. Somehow as the day draws near for the school to break up for holidays, a certain touch of something human pervades the place. The masters lounge round in cricket flannels smoking cigarettes almost in the corridors of the school itself. The boys shout at their play in the long June evenings. At the hour when, on the murky winter nights, the bell rang for night study, the sun is still shining upon the playground and the cricket match between House and House is being played out between daylight and dark. The masters— good fellows that they are—have cancelled evening study to watch the game. The head master is there himself. He is smoking a briar-root pipe and wearing his mortar board sideways. There is wonderful greenness in the new grass of the playground and a wonderful fragrance in the evening air. It is the last day of school. Life is sweet indeed in the anticipation of this summer evening.

If every day in the life of a school could be the last, there would be little fault to find with it.

Of Studies

FRANCIS BACON

FRANCIS BACON (1561-1626) entered Trinity College, Cambridge, at the age of twelve. Little is known of his life there beyond a reminiscence of his own which shows that at this early age he had begun to observe natural phenomena. "I remember," he says, "in Trinity College in Cambridge there was an upper chamber, which being thought weak in the roof of it, was supported by a pillar of iron . . . which if you had struck, it would make a little flat noise in the room where it was struck, but it would make a great bomb in the chamber beneath." After three years at Cambridge Bacon lived for a time in France to prepare for a career in diplomacy, but after his father's death, he returned to England and studied law. He entered Parliament in 1584, hoping meanwhile for an office which should place him above want and give him leisure to pursue his intellectual interests. In the course of time Bacon became Attorney General, Lord Keeper, and Lord Chancellor. In 1621 he was charged with bribery. He confessed that he was guilty of corruption but denied that he had ever perverted justice. He was deprived of his office, fined, and imprisoned, but the sentence was only partially carried out. He retired to private life and spent his remaining years in literary and philosophical work.

Of his literary works the most important are the Essays first published in 1597.

STUDIES serve for delight, for ornament, and for ability. Their chief use for delight is in privateness and retiring; for ornament, is in discourse; and for ability, is in the judgment and disposition of business. For expert men can execute, and perhaps judge of particulars, one by one; but the general counsels, and the plots and marshaling of affairs, come best from those that are learned. To spend too much time in studies is sloth; to use them too much for ornament is affectation; to make judgment wholly by their rules is the humor of a scholar. They perfect nature, and are perfected by experience; for natural abilities are like natural plants, that need proyning by study; and studies themselves do give forth directions too much at large, except they be bounded in by experience. Crafty men contemn studies, simple men admire them; and wise men use them: for they teach not their own use; but that is a wisdom without them and above them, won by observation. Read not to contradict and confute; nor to believe and take for granted; nor to find talk and discourse; but to weigh and consider. Some books are to be tasted, others to be swallowed, and some few to be chewed and digested: that is, some books are to be read only in parts; others to be read, but not curiously; and some few to be read wholly, and with diligence and attention. Some books also may be read by deputy, and extracts made of them by others; but that would be only in the less important arguments, and the meaner sort of books; else distilled books are like common distilled waters, flashy things. Reading maketh a full man; conference a ready man; and writing an exact man. And therefore, if a man write little he had need have a great memory; if he confer little, he had need have a present wit; and if he read little, he had need have much cunning, to seem to know that he doth not. Histories make men wise; poets witty; the mathematics subtle; natural philosophy deep; moral grave; logic and rhetoric able to contend. *Abeunt studia in mores.* Nay, there is no stond or impediment in the wit, but may be wrought out by fit studies: like as diseases of the body may have appropriate exercises. Bowling is good for the stone and reins; shooting for the lungs and breast; gentle walking for the stomach; riding for the head; and the like. So if a man's wit be wandering, let him study the mathematics; for in demonstrations, if his wit be called away never so little, he must begin again: if his wit be not apt to distinguish or find differences, let him study the schoolmen; for they are *cymini sectores:* if he be not apt to beat over matters, and to call one thing to prove and illustrate another, let him study the lawyers' cases: so every defect of the mind may have a special receipt.

The New Principal

THOMAS WOLFE

THOMAS WOLFE (1900-1938) was born in Asheville, North Carolina. At the age of fifteen he entered the University of North Carolina, where he edited the college paper and magazine, studied playwriting, and wrote plays. In 1920 he enrolled in Professor G. P. Baker's English 47 at Harvard and continued to write plays. He received his M.A. from Harvard in 1922 and after a period of travel became in 1924 an instructor in English at Washington Square College of New York University. Six years later he went abroad on a Guggenheim fellowship. Meantime his first novel Look Homeward, Angel, *had been published in 1929. In the remaining eight years of his life Wolfe wrote furiously. Before his death in 1938 he had published two long novels and completed work on two others which have been published posthumously.*

The first two selections here given are taken from Look Homeward, Angel. *The manuscript of this novel was bought in 1939 at a sale for the benefit of German refugees and presented to the Harvard College Library.*

THE spring grew ripe. There was at mid-day a soft drowsiness in the sun. Warm sporting gusts of wind howled faintly at the eaves; the young grass bent; the daisies twinkled.

He pressed his high knees uncomfortably against the bottom of his desk, grew nostalgic on his dreams. Bessie Barnes scrawled vigorously two rows away, displaying her long full silken leg. Open for me the gates of delight. Behind her sat a girl named Ruth, dark, with milk-white skin, eyes as gentle as her name, and thick black hair, parted in the middle. He thought of a wild life with Bessie and of a later resurrection, a pure holy life, with Ruth.

One day, after the noon recess, they were marshalled by the teachers— all of the children in the three upper grades—and marched upstairs to the big assembly hall. They were excited, and gossiped in low voices as they went. They had never been called upstairs at this hour. Quite often the bells rang in the halls: they sprang quickly into line and were marched out in double files. That was fire drill. They liked that. Once they emptied the building in four minutes.

This was something new. They marched into the big room and sat down in blocks of seats assigned to each class: they sat with a seat between each of them. In a moment the door of the principal's office on the left—where little boys were beaten—was opened, and the principal came out. He walked around the corner of the big room and stepped softly up on the platform. He began to talk.

He was a new principal. Young Armstrong, who had smelled the flower so delicately, and who had visited Daisy, and who once had almost beaten Eugene because of the smutty rhymes, was gone. The new principal was older. He was about thirty-eight years old. He was a strong rather heavy man a little under six feet tall; he was one of a large family who had grown up on a Tennessee farm. His father was poor but he had helped his children to get an education. All this Eugene knew already, because the principal made long talks to them in the morning and said he had never had their advantages. He pointed to himself with some pride. And he urged the little boys, playfully but earnestly, to "be not like dumb driven cattle, be a hero in the strife." That was poetry, Longfellow.

The principal had thick powerful shoulders; clumsy white arms, knotted with big awkward country muscles. Eugene had seen him once hoeing in the schoolyard; each of them had been given a plant to set out. He got those muscles on the farm. The boys said he beat very hard. He walked with a clumsy stealthy tread—awkward and comical enough, it is true, but he could be up at a boy's back before you knew it. Otto Krause called him Creeping Jesus. The name stuck, among the tough crowd. Eugene was a little shocked by it.

The principal had a white face of waxen transparency, with deep flat cheeks like the Pentlands, a pallid nose, a trifle deeper in its color than his face, and a thin slightly-bowed mouth. His hair was coarse, black, and thick, but he never let it grow too long. He had short dry hands, strong, and always coated deeply with chalk. When he passed near by, Eugene got the odor of chalk and of the schoolhouse: his heart grew cold with excitement and fear. The sanctity of chalk and school hovered about the man's flesh. He was the one who could touch without being touched, beat without being beaten. Eugene had terrible fantasies of resistance, shuddering with horror as he thought of the awful consequences of fighting back: something like God's fist in lightning. Then he looked around cautiously to see if any one had noticed.

The principal's name was Leonard. He made long speeches to the children every morning, after a ten-minute prayer. He had a high sonorous countrified voice which often trailed off in a comical drawl; he got lost very easily in revery, would pause in the middle of a sentence, gaze absently off with his mouth half-open and an expression of stupefaction on his face, and return presently to the business before him, his mind still loose, with witless distracted laugh.

He talked to the children aimlessly, pompously, dully for twenty minutes every morning: the teachers yawned carefully behind their hands, the students made furtive drawings, or passed notes. He spoke to them of "the higher life" and of "the things of the mind." He assured them that they were the leaders of to-morrow and the hope of the world. Then he quoted Longfellow.

He was a good man, a dull man, a man of honor. He had a broad streak of coarse earthy brutality in him. He loved a farm better than anything in the world except a school. He had rented a big dilapidated house in a grove of lordly oaks on the outskirts of town: he lived there with his wife and his two children. He had a cow—he was never without a cow: he would go out at night and morning to milk her, laughing his vacant silly laugh, and giving her a good smacking kick in the belly to make her come round into position.

He was a heavy-handed master. He put down rebellion with good corn-field violence. If a boy was impudent to him he would rip him powerfully from his seat, drag his wriggling figure into his office, breathing stertorously as he walked along at his clumsy rapid gait, and saying roundly, in tones of scathing contempt: "Why, you young upstart, we'll just see who's master here. I'll just show you, my sonny, if I'm to be dictated to by every two-by-four whippersnapper who comes along." And once within the office, with the glazed door shut, he published the stern warning of his justice by the loud exertion of his breathing, the cutting swish of his rat-tan, and the yowls of pain and terror that he exacted from his captive.

He had called the school together that day to command it to write him a composition. The children sat, staring dumbly up at him as he made a rambling explanation of what he wanted. Finally he announced a prize. He would give five dollars from his own pocket to the student who wrote the best paper. That aroused them. There was a rustle of interest.

They were to write a paper on the meaning of a French picture called The Song of the Lark. It represented a French peasant girl, barefooted, with a sickle in one hand, and with face upturned in the morning-light of the fields as she listened to the bird-song. They were asked to describe what they saw in the expression of the girl's face. They were asked to tell what the picture meant to them. It had been reproduced in one of their readers. A larger print was now hung up on the platform for their inspection. Sheets of yellow paper were given them. They stared, thoughtfully masticating their pencils. Finally, the room was silent save for a minute scratching on paper.

The warm wind spouted about the eaves; the grasses bent, whistling gently.

Eugene wrote: "The girl is hearing the song of the first lark. She knows that it means Spring has come. She is about seventeen or eighteen years old. Her people are very poor, she has never been anywhere. In the winter she wears wooden shoes. She is making out as if she was going to whistle. But she doesn't let on to the bird that she has heard him. The rest of her people are behind her, coming down the field, but we do not see them. She has a father, a mother, and two brothers. They have worked hard all their life. The girl is the youngest child. She thinks she would like to go away somewhere and see the world. Sometimes she hears the whistle of a train that is going to Paris. She has never ridden on a train in her life. She would like to go to Paris. She would like to have some fine clothes, she would like to travel. Perhaps she would like to start life new in America, the Land of Opportunity. The girl has had a hard time. Her people do not understand her. If they saw her listening to the lark they would poke fun at her. She has never had the advantages of a good education, her people are so poor, but she would profit by her opportunity if she did, more than some people who have. You can tell by looking at her that she's intelligent."

It was early in May; examinations came in another two weeks. He thought of them with excitement and pleasure—he liked the period of hard cramming, the long reviews, the delight of emptying out abundantly on paper his stored knowledge. The big assembly room had about it the odor of completion, of sharp nervous ecstasy. All through the summer it would be drowsy-warm; if only here, alone, with the big plaster cast of Minerva, himself and Bessie Barnes, or Miss—Miss——

"We want this boy," said Margaret Leonard. She handed Eugene's paper over to her husband. They were starting a private school for boys. That was what the paper had been for.

Leonard took the paper, pretended to read half a page, looked off absently into eternity, and began to rub his chin reflectively, leaving a slight coating of chalk-dust on his face. Then, catching her eye, he laughed idiotically, and said: "Why, that little rascal! Huh? Do you suppose——?"

Feeling delightfully scattered, he bent over with a long suction of whining laughter, slapping his knee and leaving a chalk print, making a slobbering noise in his mouth.

"The Lord have mercy!" he gasped.

"Here! Never you mind about that," she said, laughing with tender sharp amusement. "Pull yourself together and see this boy's people." She loved the man dearly, and he loved her.

A few days later Leonard assembled the children a second time. He made a rambling speech, the purport of which was to inform them that one of them had won the prize, but to conceal the winner's name. Then, after several divagations, which he thoroughly enjoyed, he read Eugene's paper, announced his name, and called him forward.

Chalkface took chalkhand. The boy's heart thundered against his ribs. The proud horns blared, he tasted glory.

Awakening

WITH thick chalked fingers John Dorsey thoughtfully massaged his torso from loin to chin.

"Now, let me see," he whined with studious deliberation, "what he gives on this." He fumbled for the notes.

Tom Davis turned his reddening cheeks toward the window, a low sputter of laughter escaping from his screwed lips.

Guy Doak gazed solemnly at Eugene, with a forked hand stroking his grave pallid face.

"*Entgegen*," said Eugene, in a small choked voice, "follows its object."

John Dorsey laughed uncertainly, and shook his head, still searching the notes.

"I'm not so sure of that," he said.

Their wild laughter leaped like freed hounds. Tom Davis hurled himself violently downward over his desk. John Dorsey looked up, adding uncertainly his absent falsetto mirth.

From time to time, in spite of himself, they taught him a little German, a language of which he had been quite happily ignorant. The lesson had become for them a daily hunger: they worked it over with mad intensity, speeding and polishing their translation in order to enjoy his bewilderment. Sometimes, deliberately, they salted their pages with glib false readings, sometimes they interpolated passages of wild absurdity, waiting exultantly for his cautious amendment of a word that did not exist.

"Slowly the moonlight crept up the chair in which the old man was sitting, reaching his knees, his breast, and finally,"—Guy Doak looked up slyly at his tutor, "giving him a good punch in the eye."

"No-o," said John Dorsey, rubbing his chin, "not exactly. 'Catching him squarely in the eye' gets the idiom better, I think."

Tom Davis thrust a mouthful of strange gurgling noises into his desk, and waited for the classic evasion. It came at once.

"Let me see," said John Dorsey, turning the pages, "what he gives on this."

Guy Doak scrawled a brief message across a crumpled wad and thrust it on Eugene's desk. Eugene read:

> "Gebe mir ein Stück Papier,
> Before I bust you on the ear."

He detached two slick sheets from his tablet, and wrote in answer:

> "Du bist wie eine bum-me."

They read sweet gluey little stories, fat German tear-gulps: *Immensee, Höher als die Kirche, Der Serbrochene Krug*. Then, *Wilhelm Tell*. The fine lyrical measure of the opening song, the unearthly siren song to the fisher-boy, haunted them with its faery music. The heavy melodrama of some of the scenes was unhackneyed to them: they bent eagerly to the apple-shooting scene, and the escape by boat. As for the rest, it was, they wearily recognized, Great Literature. Mr. Schiller, they saw, was religiously impressed, like Patrick Henry, George Washington, and Paul Revere, with the beauties of Liberty. His embattled Swiss bounded ponderously from crag to crag, invoking it in windy speeches.

"The mountains," observed John Dorsey, touched, in a happy moment, by the genius of the place, "have been the traditional seat of Liberty."

Eugene turned his face toward the western ranges. He heard, far off, a whistle, a remote thunder on the rails.

A Letter of Gratitude and Indebtedness

When Thomas Wolfe was a student at Harvard in his twenty-first year, he wrote the following letter of recommendation of his boyhood teacher, Mrs. J. M. Roberts, to the Superintendent of Schools in Asheville, Mr. Frank Wells.

My friend and former teacher, Mrs. J. M. Roberts, has lately written me, explaining that some testimonial is desired as to her quality as a teacher, and asking me if I would care to record any opinion I have on that subject. I esteem it an honor and a privilege to do this, although I find myself in constant difficulties when I try to keep my pen from leaping away with a red-hot panegyric.

But—with all the moderation and temperance and earnestness at my command I can do no less than consider Mrs. Roberts as one of the three great teachers who have ever taught me,—this with all honor to Harvard, who has not yet succeeded in adding a fourth name to my own Hall of Fame.

More than anyone else I have ever known, Mrs. Roberts succeeded in getting under my skull with an appreciation of what is fine and altogether worth while in literature. That, in my opinion, is the vital quality. That is the essential thing—the mark of a real teacher.

I didn't know, until Mrs. Roberts wrote me, that she had no University degree, but that is a matter of not the slightest consequence to me. So far does she surpass certain college graduates I know, who are teaching, in respect to actual knowledge, appreciation, and the ability to stimulate and inspire, that any difficulty as to a degree would be negligible, I think.

I have spoken of Mrs. Roberts merely as a teacher. This is perhaps the only testimonial you want. But I cannot stop before I speak of another matter that has been of the highest importance to me. During the years Mrs. Roberts taught me she exercised an influence that is inestimable on almost every particular of my life and thought.

With the other boys of my age I know she did the same. We turned instinctively to this lady for her advice and direction and we trusted to it unfalteringly.

I think that kind of relation is one of the profoundest experiences of anyone's life,—I put the relation of a fine teacher to a student just below the relation of a mother to her son and I don't think I could say more than this.

You can readily understand that the intimacy of such a relation is much more important in those formative years at grammar school or high school than afterwards at college. At college you don't get it but you don't need it so much. The point is that I did get it at a time when it was supremely important that I get it. It is, therefore, impossible that I ever forget the influence of Mrs. Roberts. She is one of my great people, and happy are those who can claim her as their teacher!

Mr. Thompson Meets the Headmaster

ANNA GORDON KEOWN

ANNA GORDON KEOWN, English novelist, was born in 1897 and educated at the Cheltenham Ladies College and in Dresden.

The following chapters are taken from Mr. Thompson In The Attic, *a delightful story of the vagaries of an eccentric schoolteacher who rejoices in the possession of an attic room in a boys' school.*

THE strange formality of that first interview between Thompson and his headmaster, strange, that is, in the light of future events, should perhaps be recorded. Though the time was to come, and that at no very distant date, when Thompson (drinking sherry for the first time and with a naive enjoyment) was to discourse upon the principles of navigation, the property of poetry, the difference between love and lust, and the constituency of melancholy; to hold forth, indeed, upon a hundred and one delightful subjects for the edification of a headmaster captivated by his eloquence, at the moment neither of them guessed it.

Since his purchase of this school at the War's end, John Silver must have interviewed some twenty assistant-masters, engaging them without enthusiasm, dismissing them without regret, tolerating them in the meantime with a perfect admixture of politeness and condescension. How, then, should he know that he was destined to let down a drawbridge almost rusted from disuse to the new mathematical master?

As for Thompson himself, had he been told that the companionship of his headmaster was to become pleasant and even dear to him in the future, the news would have interested him but little. Here was a being whom early caution had instructed to put his eggs in the most unlikely baskets; baskets, moreover, involving nothing so unaccountable as the human relationships. Whatever the future might hold, whatever pleasant intimacies might in time be arrived at, this preliminary interview lacked nothing in circumspection.

• • •

The ominous clanging of the door-bell had sent the headmaster burrowing protectively behind the pages of *The Times.* Now, gazing at the new-comer across the chaotic piles of papers upon his desk he was to know a moment of real anxiety. For the first time in his life John Silver had engaged an assistant-master without the precaution of a preliminary interview; small wonder, then, that he should examine the result of his hardihood with the liveliest possible apprehension, and (since that result was Thompson) with a certain sense of shock.

This apprehension was not lost upon its cause; he sensed it without either surprise or resentment. A man does not live forty-nine years and remain unaware, however vaguely, of the effect he is likely to produce upon his fellows; it was Thompson's considerate habit to allow the general public time to recover itself. For this reason he gazed calmly out of the window.

Not that the man's personality was disagreeable; far from it. He had dignity, a quality dear to the headmaster's heart, dignity and an unaffected friendliness by which one was instantly charmed. The word disagreeable, used in connection with so attractive a being, must have been absurdly wide of the mark. Rather, he belonged to that order of persons, who, on account of their very divergence from the general pattern, take a good deal of getting used to. In a single minute the headmaster found himself confronted by the loftiest brow and the most fantastically-fitting suit of his experience. In all his life, he thought, he had never seen so unlikely-looking a schoolmaster.

Thompson, on the other hand, thought he had rarely seen a finer marine view. Sitting there completely at his ease, he admired the bending of branches against the afternoon sky, the noble sweep of the cliffs, the white foaming of the sea amid its bays and rocks and secret caves. What could be more pleasant than to allow one's thoughts to wander at leisure along so promising a coast while warming one's body before this spirited log fire which leapt and curveted up the wide chimney?

Now, withdrawing his gentle gaze from the view (prompted as it seemed rather by courtesy than by any special interest), he transferred it to that extraordinarily handsome façade, the headmaster; to his crutch, leaning idly against the desk, to his lame leg, stretched stiffly before him upon a convenient stool, and inwards, to the man's personality.

"Full of trouble," he told himself.

Aloud he said, speaking almost for the first time and in a voice of rare sweetness,

"I trust, sir, that I see you in good health. I have had a most delightful journey. I fear I may be a little late, and that is because, falling a prey to temptation, I climbed the hill behind the house and sat for some time on a stile."

"Stile?" said the headmaster, genuinely startled. "I'd no idea there was a stile behind my house."

Thompson smiled. "Then I bring you good news. There is an excellent stile. The view obtained from that point is particularly instructive, and I was very pleased to discover that your church roof, although shingled in the older manner, would seem to be in the most beautiful state of preservation. The church itself, on the other hand, appears to be far from happy. Am I right?"

Very much against his better judgment, John Silver smiled. Secretly, the eccentricity of this question pleased him. For years now he had conducted interviews with men who, while nervously pulling at their ties, assured him of their devotion to his school, to his person, and to his particularly uninspiring system of timetable; in Thompson's happy nonchalance be read a promise of possible diversion. Ready money always excepted, there was no commodity of which our headmaster stood in greater need. Ignoring the possible infidelity of the church, he said abruptly:

"Have a sherry."

Rather to his disappointment, Thompson refused it. From a decanter hidden, but for its shining stopper, among masses of paper, he poured himself a liberal glass.

"You don't drink? That's a pity. Yes, you are a bit late, still I dare say if I don't keep you too long you'll find some tea going. Perhaps we'd better get straight to business. As you probably realize yourself, Thompson, in engaging you I have taken a considerable risk. I am aware, of course, of your very distinguished qualifications; on the other hand, knowledge is no guarantee of the ability to teach. Quite frankly, it yet remains to be seen whether you will be able to adapt yourself to the requirements of a humdrum preparatory school. I understand from my agents that, apart from university lecturing, you have never done any actual teaching?"

Thompson had stretched his long legs towards the hearth. His shoes, cheered by so much sudden good fortune, began to get up a magnificent steam. This he observed with unbounded satisfaction.

"Extremely well put," he said politely.

The headmaster shot him a glance. Was the man mocking him? Apparently not. There was an ingenuousness about him which disarmed suspicion. Curious spectacles he wore!—they appeared inches thick. The headmaster continued:

"As you have probably heard often enough from the phrase-mongers, teaching is a special gift. At the same time, I think myself that side of the thing can be overstated. Patience and experience will do much; I've known the most hopeless cases improve out of all knowledge. Actually, of course, it comes down to a question of discipline. Just at first it's bound to be difficult: you must be prepared for that. My boys are no worse and no better than other boys; they are neither angels nor devils; they simply require a firm hand. But there's one thing I do want you to remember. I am always anxious to help you. At any time of the day, however busy I may be, don't hesitate to interrupt me. That's what I'm here for."

Thompson looked thoughtful.

"I am entirely grateful," he said. "And it is extremely kind. At the same time," he added unexpectedly, "I will be frank. I anticipate no difficulty whatsoever."

This is scarcely the reply the headmaster expects from his new assistant. Silver's surprise found its way into his voice.

"Indeed?"

"I should hope not," said Thompson. "I should most devoutly hope not. I have always understood," he continued, taking off his glasses and polishing them vigorously, a habit with him when he was warming to his subject—"I have always understood, and I take it to be true, that any lack of attention upon the part of the boys is nothing but the direct result of lack of confidence upon the part of the master. Now I, sir, have every confidence in myself; the very idea of doubting my own capacity is foreign, I am thankful to say, from my whole make-up. I both know and believe myself to be entirely capable of inspiring any boy (provided he be not some particularly hopeless kind of idiot) to a love and desire for understanding. That last, I take it, is of the first importance in one who aspires to instruct."

"Certainly it is," agreed the headmaster. "Certainly it is. At the same time——"

"Granted that," continued Thompson, "I think there need be no anxiety upon the score of my future as a schoolmaster. Indeed, there need never be any anxiety upon the score of *any* future were we but wise enough to realize that important truth. What, after all, is anxiety but an unwieldy obstacle which we deliberately throw down in our path in order to put ourselves to the pain of unnecessary jumping exercises? Anxiety springs solely from lack of faith, and lack of faith (I feel sure you will agree with me) is the last and most deadly blasphemy."

If the headmaster had formulated in his mind the words, "Exactly so," he did not immediately give them voice. Instead he sat and stared at Thompson, and it was with some difficulty that he preserved his gravity. The humour of being lectured by a complete novice was not lost upon him. A mathematical genius, no doubt, and a genius boasting after his name precisely those letters so well calculated to light up the rather dim pages of a school prospectus. But a novice nevertheless. The situation struck him as preposterous, and not the least preposterous feature was his own inability to resent it more keenly. Recovering himself with an effort he said:

"Exactly so. At the same time," and here he fell back upon the headmaster's traditional throat-clearing to ensure himself against further interruption—"At the same time, Thompson, glad though I am that you should commence your work in so hopeful a spirit, yet I must beg to point out (and I think you will admit that my ten years of teaching experience qualify me to do so) there must necessarily arise questions of discipline concerning which it would perhaps be ill-advised to set aside the judgment of more experienced colleagues."

The headmaster, in listening to his own words of wisdom, could not help feeling that they sounded rather well; his colleague, too, appeared impressed.

"It would not only be ill-advised," said Thompson, "it would be extremely discourteous." But his attention was in reality wandering.

How the wind shrieked and whooped out there! It beat the bushes in the garden until, flattened against the sky behind them, they appeared as a succession of immense black hoops. Growing momentarily short of breath, it released them, so that they sprang stiffly to attention; then they might have been a row of soldiers. Anon it caught and flattened them with renewed zest; then they were hoops again. This little game was very amusing to watch.

Although he could not actually *see* them from the chair in which he sat, Thompson knew that the yew trees growing round the church were twisting and shouting like maniacs. And the storm was increasing, that was the best of it; it swept the side of the house with a dull, subdued roaring. To this sound Thompson listened with growing exultation.

"They're in for a terrible drubbing, sir," said he, rubbing his hands in unmistakable delight.

The headmaster looked puzzled. To whom was the man alluding? Surely not to his pupils . . . he allowed corporal punishment only in the most extreme cases. . . .

Thompson hastened to explain the misunderstanding. "Bushes," he said, smiling, "not boys. Has it ever occurred to you, sir, that whereas we humans are chastised in infancy because we have lied, stolen, or given way to the hideous lure of gluttony, the young tree is chastised for no better reason than that there is a certain amount of meteorological indigestion in some far-off continent? If the soul of the young trees be not perpetually embittered by the injustice of the thing, then we are forced to conclude that the vegetable kingdom is gifted with a breadth of vision and a largeness of charity altogether lacking in ourselves."

"As to that," said Silver, speaking somewhat dryly, "I am not interested in trees, and I do think, if you don't mind my saying so, it would be better to keep to the subject in hand. By the way, isn't there a peculiar smell in the room?"

Thompson looked pleased. "It's my shoes," he said. "They were originally very damp. Now they are beginning to roast. I will withdraw them from the fire immediately." He did so, twining and untwining his arms and legs in a fashion which demonstrated that chairs, as such, were never designed for the accommodation of that long-limbed, angular body.

"By all means do," said the headmaster. "God, what an odour! I noticed it quite suddenly."

Thompson's spectacles glittered intelligently.

"As regards leather," he said, "that is the way with it. One moment it is practically non-existent, a mere covering for the feet. The next, it almost knocks one over. I once had a pair of shoes . . . ."

But the headmaster had no intention of allowing himself to be cajoled into a discussion upon the habits of leather. Ignoring the digression he said: .

"Now as to the school staff, it consists of yourself, Mr. Baxter, Mr. Rathbone, and Miss Sevenoaks, who teaches the younger boys. My wife, of course, is very active in the school, and with such a small number of boys (we've only fifty-two, I'm sorry to say, though we can take seventy) you will easily understand that a certain elasticity of arrangement in time-tables, which would not be possible in a larger school, is easily possible here." And he went on to explain what Thompson had already suspected, that all his fifty-two boys were backward. Not mentally incapable, that was to say, but merely backward. From a variety of causes—measles, eye trouble, mumps, and pampering at home, etc. . . .

"To be sure," said Thompson. He was not listening. He would be familiar with the details of the school soon enough. He devoted his attention (the headmaster's voice rambling on and on) to the view of the distant cliffs. The words, "but I'll not keep you now. You'll be wanting to unpack," brought him back to himself.

"We can talk things over to-morrow," said the headmaster.

"God forbid," thought Thompson.

The headmaster now rang the bell, and to the comely country girl standing in the doorway he said:

"Kindly show Mr. Thompson to his room."

After Thompson had gone he helped himself to yet another glass of sherry.

Mr. Thompson Inhabits the Attic and Observes the School

Thompson was not greatly concerned with the headmaster, his habit of mind, his staff, or the general disposition of his school. Throughout the interview in that unbelievably untidy study downstairs the consideration which had exercised him was as follows: What kind of views will the windows of my room afford me? Will they give upon sea or upon country? Will my bedroom possess a table or desk upon which a man may write at his leisure? And lastly, given a table, will there be leisure in which to write?

True, to these important considerations was now added a natural appreciation of the housemaid's country freshness (for Thompson, after all, was no clod, but a man like the rest of us, and the girl was charming); nevertheless, his main concern lay with the discovery ahead.

"What do they call you?" he asked.

"Betsy," replied the girl blushing.

Thompson nodded approvingly.

"It is an excellent name," said he.

Together they climbed the shallow staircase, Betsy leading, Thompson following in her wake. He did not need to be informed of the proximity of the classrooms upon the first floor. A distant roaring not unlike that which one hears upon approaching near to the Zoological Gardens now fell upon his ears. Thompson was a proud man; hearing that fatal sound, he did not permit himself any cowardly sinking of heart. All the same, he could scarcely have believed human beings to be capable of emitting so sinister a sound.

Now, the thick pile carpet giving way to strips of matting, the matting giving way, in its turn, to a frank patterning of linoleum (the stairs ever winding steeply and ruthlessly aloft) Betsy's manner became increasingly apologetic.

"It's dreadfully long way up, sir," she complained. "Mind the stair-rods. . . . They work loose. There's the boys' dormitories down there. And there's the other masters' rooms." And now, less for her companion's benefit than her own, for she was a thoughtful girl and given to thinking aloud, she added, "This be no fit staircase for a gentleman."

"Then it'll do very well for me," Thompson assured her cheerfully. At the moment he cared little or nothing for gentlemen. What he did care for was a propitious ending to his journey of exploration. Would his room boast one window or two? If (horrible possibility) the prospect proved unpleasing, failing to include those wonderful elms on the village green, would he be justified in handing in his resignation to-morrow? And the window-sills. Would the window-sills prove sufficiently wide to accommodate his beloved fish-tanks?

The fact that they had attained the upper regions of the ancient house, regions reserved, as he shrewdly suspected, for servants and mice; the fact that at moments his heels, sinking through the cracks in the decayed stair-treads, hung as it were over immeasurable space, moved him not at all.

"It's an admirable staircase," he said, taking pity on Betsy's shame. It was scarcely this girl's fault that they had seen fit to put him up here among the rats. He paused now. They both paused. Leaning far out over the well-shaped staircase, Thompson whistled—a shrill, bird-like note.

"Exactly as I thought," he said. They resumed their climbing.

Betsy was clearly at sea.

"What was that, then?" she asked, looking back at him over her pretty shoulder.

"Acoustics deplorable," said Thompson. "They always are in these old houses."

Betsy shook her head. She did not attempt to understand the gentleman's language. It was her duty to show him to his room, and to this business she sensibly confined herself, standing now indeed with her hand
upon the door-handle. Here was a fateful moment.

With that Thompson entered—to find himself in possession of one of the
most satisfactory rooms he had seen in the whole course of his life.

"Perfect," he breathed, "quite perfect."

He would have liked to hide from Betsy his immense, overwhelming
satisfaction; but she, reading his radiant face, watching him stand in the
centre of the room as though in a moment of dedication, needed no telling.

"You look pleased, sir. You'll find hot water and towels. Is there any
luggage to be brought up?"

But Thompson seemed scarcely to hear her. Already he had thrown up
the windows, one after another; already a salt wind was sweeping the room
clean and cold as a knife blade. Betsy shivered.

"Tea's down in the refectory. They ring a gong."

"Do they indeed?" said Thompson; and he added recklessly, "let them
ring."

Betsy shut the door, leaving him in Paradise.

.   .   .

And now as to this bedroom which Thompson, in his joyful credulity,
confounds with the heavenly regions.

It is an attic. It possesses six windows. Running beneath the extreme
right gable of the old farmhouse, it occupies the entire width from front to
back; its front windows giving upon the sea, its side windows upon the
village green, and its back windows upon the downs. The ceilings, very
sudden and surprisingly, show faintly pink; the walls (except in the early
morning) show whatever colour the shadows choose to impose upon them.
The carpet, improperly wedded to the ancient floorboards, yawns prodigi-
ously in the draught.

Articles of furniture there are but three. One, an iron bedstead standing
head-on to the sole windowless wall (a bedstead counterpaned in blue
and violet checks, very fresh and pleasant). Two, a rush-bottomed chair.
Three, a table of the well-scrubbed deal variety. This table is so exactly
suited to its owner's requirements, that, had he been privileged to create
it by the simple expedient of, let us say, simply clapping his hands, he
would have been at pains to improve on it.

Considered as a whole, then, could any combination of circumstances
point to greater happiness at the outset of a schoolmaster's career? It
appears doubtful.

The size, the exquisite proportions of his attic, will provide a continual
delight to the eye. The table of well-scrubbed deal will provide a home for
his books, his drawings, his papers relating to the *Balance of Beauty
among Beasts*. The window-sills will accommodate his fish-cases. While

as for the prospect afforded by windows of such varied aspects, it promises to be little short of magnificent.

In this attic, set so high above the levels of earth, so low beneath the branching of the giant rafters, the floors sing and groan with every visiting buffet of the wind.

"A veritable cradle," says Thompson; and he adds fiercely, "but not of the Muses." Upon this he glares across his shoulder as though at some invisible enemy. For he is determined, sorely tempted though he may be, that he will write no single line of poetry in this enchanted place.

Here are Peace, Harmony, and the beauty of extreme simplicity; if these between them constitute Paradise, then it may very well be that Thompson, in his original conjecture, was not so far out as may have been at first imagined.

For a long time he stands dreaming over by the windows.

. . .

He possessed a watch, a great unwieldy timepiece, with a face shining and ingenuous as that of the full moon; a contrivance little removed, in point of elegance, from the timepieces of our forefathers. This he would upon occasion produce, admire, tap, and even wind; to consult it with relation to the passing hour rarely occurred to him.

Wandering down the crazy stairs upon his first evening of arrival, the consideration that he was already late troubled him little, and it was entirely without self-consciousness that he stood in the arch of the refectory door (directed thither by the cheerful aroma of muffins), an interested observer of a household busy with its tea.

Looking down upon the assembled school from the elevation of the three steps leading from the passage-way, its conformation was to impress itself upon his mind in a pattern as inevitable and decorous as that of the village viewed from the hill at the back of the house; the one radiating outwards from the central hub of the church, the other from those central piles set at regular intervals along the tables, the mellow, magnificent piles of the buttered muffins. With relation to these it seemed, boys, masters, and steaming urns played their symmetrical (if strictly minor) parts; and Thompson could not fail to observe with pleasure how that same Betsy, who not half an hour ago had bestowed upon him, golden-handed, his exquisite attic, now came and went, the one fluctuating quantity in a design ravenously static.

In an assembly occupied with its muffins the new master was not immediately remarked; and it was Rathbone who first, peering up into an archway no whit more shadowy than his own regretful mind, caught sight of the tall figure dreaming there. Prevented from immediate speech by a mouth inconveniently full of muffin, he contented himself by attracting the attention of his colleague Baxter, busy at the table-end with the replenishing of the cups.

Baxter looked up.

"Oh, Thompson! Come along and join us. Betsy! bring a chair."

Thompson now took his place between the two masters; Rathbone, pale, cadaverous, and hostile; Baxter, stout, fresh-complexioned, and important. All around him, and for a long distance up the table, lay a flood-tide of earthenware cups. With these and with an urn notably out of hand Baxter wrestled, carrying on an animated conversation meanwhile in his thin, high-pitched voice.

"Awful thing this urn. Boys, pass those across. Always behaves like this at the beginning of the term. Rathbone, send along something for Thompson to eat, can't you? Or, better still, Thompson, you make a long arm for the food. Never get anything here if you don't fight for it. By the way, where *did* you get to this afternoon? Saw you in the bus and then you simply weren't there. Never spotted you going, neither did the boys, for that matter. How did you manage it?"

"I merely stepped down," said Thompson, cheerfully.

On his right hand Rathbone growled.

"If you intended to walk after all, why the hell didn't you walk up with me? I asked you, you know, and you went off without a word. Didn't like the look of me, perhaps?"

Thompson, pausing in the demolition of a muffin, eyed his neighbour thoughtfully.

"To be quite candid," he said, "I didn't."

There followed a short pause.

Rathbone was also engaged in eating a muffin. This he now put down. Wiping the butter from his fingers with a spotted handkerchief, he stared at Thompson.

"Well I . . . did you get that, Baxter? Well of all . . ."

"It's his little joke," shouted Baxter pacifically, above the noise of boys and boiling water. Anxiety was apparent in his face and voice; the tea ran out over the forty-ninth cup, streaming on to the tablecloth; the urn, resourceful in its manifestations of power as Vesuvius, began to rumble oddly.

"Only a joke, I'm certain, Rathbone," he screamed.

It was Thompson's turn to look hurt.

"On the contrary," he protested, "I was never more serious in my life."

Turning to reconsider Rathbone with that mild disarming gaze of his, he said kindly:

"I should, however, be the first to admit that upon closer acquaintance I like you very much better."

Rathbone glared.

"Oh, you do, do you?"

"Most certainly I do," said Thompson; and he added gently, "I trust I have not offended you.'

Rathbone lowered his head over the teacups. Retaliation, as a general rule, held for him no mysteries; on this occasion he felt himself to be entirely nonplussed. Never in his wildest dreams had he met any one in the least like Thompson. Oaths and witticisms in turn suggested themselves to his mind only to be rejected; here was an adversary whom, for all his fragile appearance and strange manners, he was bound to respect. Incidentally, the man was his senior by some twenty-five years. Kicking his chair against the table, he slouched angrily from the room.

The cups were by this time dealt with, and Baxter, a man every bit as prone to hunger as the rest of humanity, was at leisure. Building around his plate a solid fortification of butter, jam, and what remained of the muffins (greasy-looking and disillusioning, these last), he fell upon his tea with tremendous nervous energy.

Between the bites he shouted, "You're taking a great risk, Thompson. Rathbone's an ugly customer when he's roused. . . . What's that? More tea? Tell the greedy little pigs they'll get no more. . . . Take it from me, Thompson. Besides, well, I mean, the poor devil can't help his face."

Thompson agreed.

"Naturally not, naturally not. And I sincerely hope," he said, "that I have not hurt his feelings. Nothing was farther from my intention."

"Well, you can't expect him to be exactly pleased, can you?"

"I don't see that," said Thompson. But his mind was busy with more pleasant issues. For the first time since his arrival he was considering his future pupils with something like interest.

This interest on Thompson's part was returned sevenfold, and there was a good deal of nudging, scuffling, and whispering along the lower reaches of the board. The new master held those lower reaches with his eye, and the whispering fell away, rather remarkably, into an uneasy silence. Baxter looked up.

"Boys, you can go. Don't wait for me, Thompson. I'm going to eat for a long time yet. You know your way to the common-room, I suppose? We meet in Mrs. Silver's drawing-room before dinner. Seven o'clock. . . . I'm taking prep. to-night."

Baxter returned to his tea.

.   .   .

The new master made his way along the brick-floored passage. Boys were running everywhere. Considering that there were but fifty-two in all, the manner in which they duplicated themselves was quite extraordinary! They appeared to be engaged in rushing out of one room only to rush into another for the pleasure of rushing back again. A seemingly unprofitable pastime! Had Thompson but known it, these youthful creatures were very busy indeed, and their present occupation, that of "scouting the new boob," demanded both caution and judgment. At any moment the headmaster might appear in the door of his study.

The Bax, thank God, was still stuffing himself with muffins, old Bones they knew to be safely unpacking in his bedroom on the third floor.

Blissfully unconscious of the scrutiny of impious eyes, Thompson warmed himself beside the log fire burning in the hall. The boys' pert "Good evening, sir," seemed to him to be without importance, and he returned the greeting, when he returned it at all, with indifference which impressed them in spite of themselves. Accustomed to the general run of new masters, men with nervous smiles, ingratiating manners, and (for the first fortnight at least) a ladylike determination to be polite, this indifference to their good opinion struck them as rather magnificent.

In passages, in schoolrooms, and in the dormitories above where the head-master's wife, in the absence of the matron, was helping the boys to unpack, they raised inquiring eyebrows and left it at that. Too soon, of course, to deliver any considered judgment. Besides, they would naturally wait until Spottiswood pronounced his verdict.

Spottiswood's opinion, needless to say, carried weight. It was rumoured that this new man had been an explorer. He didn't look in the least like an explorer; that was probably all eye-wash. Robinson was certain of it, but Robinson was usually wrong. Was it likely that a real explorer would choose to be a schoolmaster? Anyhow, the term was yet young . . . time would tell.

"Yes, Mrs. Silver, I know. Mother sent a message she was sorry to pack my things unmended. But she was in a great rush, and had no time the last few days."

"And my socks aren't darned, Mrs. Silver. Shall I throw them into the laundry bag? I haven't got a single pair to put on."

"Mrs. Silver! I've left my mac in the train. It's a new one. Dad will be furious."

"Oh, Mrs. Silver! My hair-wash bottle has broken all over everything in my bag. It's all over the place. Everything's sopped. And the smell, Mrs. Silver! Verbena! Take a sniff, you chaps." And so on. . . . and so on. . . .

Meanwhile, Thompson, ascending thoughtfully to Paradise, was observed nosing around the corridors and galleries. One might almost have imagined he had bought the place. The age of the house, its dignity, the workmanship of its banisters and panelling pleased him enormously; the lines of its staircase and the proportions of its windows all seemed to him exceptionally fine. Oblivious to rapidly growing audience, he carried out certain surveying operations; tapping with thoughtful finger upon beam and plaster, striking matches, polishing his glasses, and even in one instance (and to the general satisfaction) lying full length in the corridor in order to examine the cracks of the decaying woodwork.

The sight of a new master lying flat upon his stomach and squinting down cracks was almost more than the school could bear in silence. Sundry squeaks and sniggers of suppressed joy escaped now and then from heads appearing round doors and banisters. If Thompson heard them, he made no sign. Presently, tiring of his investigations, he completed the ascent to his attic.

It was now that the great Spottiswood, head of the school and captain of the cricket, came out into the open. Made his pronouncement:

"I'll say this, you chaps. That fellow's got a nerve. Damned if he hasn't."

That settled it. Thompson, before he had been in the house three hours, had proved himself a man of mettle.

The Boys

Phrase most inadequate wherewith to designate a group of human beings entirely different one from another. Did not the Mother Country long ago recognize this deplorable diversity? Did it not invent, as a result of that painful recognition, the great Public School System, a machine whereby, generation after generation, this persistently recurring individuality might be transformed into something at least resembling a decent uniformity? It did.

Did it not cram its small boys into caps, top hats, blazers, green, red, or yellow, in order that despite a certain lamentable variety of feature, voice, and personality these boys might present to a gratified world a uniform front—indistinguishable peas in a scholastic pod? Again, the answer is, Yes.

"Boys are all alike," Baxter once said. "All exactly alike. Except," he added, "that some are nastier than others."

Thompson, when he came to teach, knew better. No two salamanders are alike. No two dustmen. No two schoolboys. It was indeed the very lack of sameness manifested by his small charges which in some measure he learned to dread. Variety spells charm, charm spells enslavement; it was (as we already know) Thompson's ambition to hold himself free from enslavement, and more especially from enslavement to human beings. The very names of the boys acted upon his sensitive ear with something of the fatality of a spell. Piedmond, D'Orsy, Tate, Wimperis . . . Wimperis, Tate, D'Orsy, Piedmond. And the very fact that these charges of his were little more than unsophisticated children did but add to their attraction.

"It's the same with colts," Thompson had protested, arguing the matter in the common-room. "Once the colt is broken in, it takes its place in the placid world of horses. An unbroken colt is a flame, a whirlwind, a creature straight from God. Life will break the spirits of these boys soon enough without any great assistance from ourselves."

Baxter, busy with his charts and coloured inks, asked rather peevishly:

"But why colts? Why colts? How do you know that an unbroken colt is a creature straight from God? I never thought of it myself."

"Possibly you didn't," said Thompson. "But that in itself does not constitute a calamity. It was my good fortune, once, to live upon a ranch in

Texas; there it was my job to break in horses. Have you ever tried it, Baxter?"

"I haven't," said Baxter; and he nodded to himself over his inks as much as to say, "That explains it."

Aloud he said, "You haven't always been a schoolmaster then, Thompson?"

Thompson smiled.

"No, Baxter, no. In fact, not by any means."

Always a schoolmaster! The idea tickled him immensely. If the truth were to be told, school-mastering must rank among the few activities which Thompson, in his varied existence, had never before attempted.

"Wait until you've taught a little longer, then," said Baxter. "You'll soon agree with me that schoolboys are a worthless lot. Would you oblige me with that ruler. I'm busy," he added impatiently, "preparing the bath lists."

Thompson obliged with the ruler.

"Ah," he said, "the bath lists."

"Yes. The bath lists. Thanks very much. We had quite a little rumpus last night," said Baxter brightening. "What *do* you think? Robinson sneaked Tate's bath, so of course Tate sneaked Anderson's. The result was that Anderson had to go without his bath, and all because Robinson was simply too lazy to apply to Miss Sevenoaks for his proper bath-time. So now Tate has to be squeezed in somehow on Wednesdays. It's all terribly difficult. I really believe I can only allow him a quarter of an hour. Is that sufficient, Thompson, should you say?"

"Is what sufficient?"

"Is a quarter of an hour sufficient for Tate's bath? Naturally, we shouldn't rush him like this if we could avoid it; but what are we to do?"

"Why do anything?" asked Thompson sadly. From what he had seen of Tate it didn't seem to him that a quarter of an hour would be nearly sufficient. "Why do anything?" he repeated. It was always the same. The moment he deserted the privacy of his attic for the publicity of the common-room he would find himself involved in conversations so trivial and irritating that he was forced to beat a hasty retreat.

He now wandered disconsolately away. Baxter, busy with the bath lists, was not a stimulating sight.

Thompson's mind was still occupied with this question concerning the individuality of the boys. First of all D'Orsy, at whose fresh features it was impossible to look, even in asking him to define a square root, without calling to mind that blue-eyed too-elegant mother of his, a woman liable to turn up without the slightest warning, and from the ends of the earth, and for no better reason than to plague the head-master's wife with fads and instructions. After a half-hour's session with this particularly exhausting woman April Silver (as he had observed) would appear fagged out; that gently humorous disposition could be no match for the cracking vitality of her visitor. Mrs. D'Orsy had transmitted to her son the priceless heritage: ability to wear down all comers by sheer force of animal spirits.

Or take Tubbs. Tubbs, who although a duffer in the fullest sense of the word, turned out, under Thompson's tutelage, and with the aid of a pin and a piece of string, to be a magical fisherman. Tubbs had scarcely time to lower his line into the village pond before registering a catch. It was really remarkable.

Thirdly, Piedmond, who confessed to a liking for Latin verbs, and wore, so the other boys reported, wool next to his skin.

Then there was Spottiswood the elegant, thirteen years of age, captain of the cricket, head of the school, with a brother at Rugby and a tongue like a whispering gallery. A shameless old maid of a gossip for all his pretences. . . . And the Kelly twins, those two delightful little Irishmen, with their great red paws for hands and their eyes like dewy violets. Who in his senses could claim that all schoolboys are alike.

. . .

Sitting behind his desk at the end of the sunny classrooms Thompson would survey the rows of heads with the affectionate unconcern which, in his attitude to the boys, saved him so much pain. He would never (as did April Silver) give his heart into their irresponsible keeping, he would never allow himself to be tied to them by ties of affection. He refused to subscribe to Baxter's theory that they were worthless devils, yet he was not, like the headmaster, disillusioned or scandalized by their dishonesties, their immodesties, or their seemingly heartless cruelty. He accepted them as they were, and they perhaps for that very reason, liked Thompson rather better than any of the masters.

For one thing, although they walked in wholesome fear, they yet found old Tomp definitely amusing. Never by any chance did they feel the slightest inclination to go to sleep during his classes; just at that moment when things had begun to look a little dull, what with the heat and the business of wrestling with compound subtraction, matters would suddenly take a turn for the better.

Thompson would go off on some story of fish or bird, and it needed very little encouragement, as they soon discovered, to extend the range of his observations to the most exciting subjects; aviation, the construction of sky-scrapers, banditry, the futility of academic distinctions as opposed to the possession of sound horse-sense, the dangers of intellectual overwork (pretty hearing this latter for schoolboys wrestling with their sums)— many and many a stimulating topic whose pros and cons Thompson would set before them with fascinating clarity.

And this he did, not from any desire to instruct his pupils (a caddish advantage which they would have been quick to resent), but rather for the reason that, given an audience, Thompson was not the man to refrain from addressing it.

In the capacity of listeners the boys perceived themselves to occupy a rôle comparatively unimportant; it did indeed occur to them at times that Thompson, although he stood before them, was often, and for long periods, quite unaware of their presence in the classroom. This suspicion mystified while it impressed them. But that which puzzled them most upon Thompson's first appearances, was his power.

Nine schoolboys out of ten would have summed him up at a glance, and summed him up wrongly, as an ideal man to rag. There were, to put the matter briefly, no flies on Thompson. Yet he should, by all the rules of the game, have been as innocent a fly-catcher as ever lived.

With that straggling walk, that bumpy forehead, and those glittering spectacles, he might, in their opinion, have gone straight on to the stage as a mug, a half-boiled egg, a scream. The strangeness of the things provided them with matter for many an after-lights-out conversation, when, lying row upon row on their squeaking mattresses, they discussed at length (and in loud whispers which must have been audible to any one in the corridor outside) the affairs of the world at large and the school in particular.

Thompson's classes, they remembered with regret, passed miraculously quickly. To him they came for relief and excitement.

They were rarely disappointed.

Mr. Thompson Becomes a Cricketer

The Boys v. Masters match, the last match of the term, was an occasion so impressive that it might safely be described by the editor of the school magazine, and in advance, as a brilliant affair. Those very words, typed dizzily in a violet ink, lay snugly on the editor's desk before ever a ball had been hit or a batsman bowled out down in the fragrant greenness of the school meadow.

For three days now the roller had been grinding its rusty song to and fro across the length of the pitch, for three days the school pony had dragged the inadequate mowing-machine behind his flying tail in ever-increasing circles of respect around that strip of sacred green. Nothing short of rain, an epidemic, or an earthquake could now rob the dignified preparations of their just fruition, and of these the first, as being the more likely, was the most generally feared.

Needless fear. On the day of the cricket match the world rose to a flawless morning, a morning so brilliant that the merciful sun had wrapped himself about, as though for the protection of waking eyes, in a white heat-haze. This haze, drifting lazily inland in ragged wisps, played strange tricks with cottage chimney and church spire, now obscuring, now revealing; Thompson, who had scarcely slept a wink, observed with considerable interest, and from his look out among the pillows, that nothing but the boots of the milkman on his early morning rounds appeared to be traversing the village green. The intrepid advance of those boots, apparently uninhabited, together with the glint of a milk-pail swinging, as it seemed, upon nothing more substantial than the salty air itself, set him meditating upon the irrelevance of men in the general scheme of things; and now, a bicycle, manifesting nothing save two wheels and two flying pedals, appearing in the wake of the milkman, the irrelevance of women no less. The bicycle he knew to be the property of a Mrs. Buffle come to light fires and pump water.

"God bless my soul," sighed the man among the pillows, "Here's a pretty state of affairs! For since boots have taken to walking, pails to swinging, and bicycle wheels to revolving of their own accord, we may look for flying-fish, I shouldn't wonder, before the day is out."

He now placed a thoughtful finger in his right ear and poked it furiously: then he listened. Which of us can have failed to note a like gesture among swimmers newly come to the shore, swimmers who, once having relieved their heads of the roaring of salt-water, hold those same heads at attention; listening, weighing the evidence of their singing senses, seeming to ask themselves (since no miracle can well prove more miraculous than this, the containing of all the oceans within the orbit of one inconsiderable cranium), "What next?" Which of us, I say, can have failed to note the gesture?

To tell the truth, Thompson was apt to find himself a little deaf in the mornings; hence the poking, the listening, the expression of careful anxiety. Even before putting his right hand out of bed for his spectacles, he would attend to this very necessary task.

Now, spectacles on nose, he again gave his attention to the sea-mist. Very curiously it travelled, like old lengths of chiffon floating out from some invisible flag-pole. Very skilfully it revealed the roots of things; feet of milkmen, lower stones of churchyard walls, trunks of trees, rendering them doubly vivid upon account of their hidden parts. Cheerfully it folded from sight all superfluities; men, women, tree-tops, and hills. That there was a method in its madness one was obliged to suspect. Thickly through the obscurity came the crowing of cocks, the clanging of seven from the church tower, the shiver of the sea folded away under the cliff.

"It's the day of the thingummy," reflected Thompson, and his heart sank a little, for the day promised brilliant sunshine. By "thingummy" he meant cricket match, and the word expressed most eloquently his attitude to the whole affair. Reproving himself for his own selfishness, he tried to be glad for the sake of the boys, those same boys who, in another half-hour, would be up and shouting, throwing things around the dormitories, thrusting their heads anxiously out of the windows, snatching one another's bathing-towels. In another half-hour, Thompson himself, springing out of bed and hastily dressing, would partake of the general excitement; bursting through his attic door and down the narrow staircase with the suddenness of a thunder-bolt, throwing open the doors of the dormitories, rushing from top to bottom of the tall old house, from woodwork to linoleum, from linoleum to cork matting, from cork matting to the thick pile upon the lower flight, with increasing determination and speed. Nevertheless, the thought of the "thingummy" depressed him.

.   .   .

Lessons to-day were bound to be a haphazard affair. The pitch had to be examined and discussed, the ability of the various batsmen disputed; by twelve o'clock absurdly overexcited parents in half as many cars had arrived for a one o'clock lunch. Betsy, attended by three maidens hired from the village, was to be seen hurrying frantically to and fro past the doors of the classrooms. April had been up since six. Even Miss Sevenoaks appeared occupied.

These abnormal activities, making themselves felt even within the peaceful area of Thompson's classroom, disturbed him more than he would have cared to admit. For once he could get no sense out of the boys; abandoning all attempt at mathematics he told them to please themselves for fifteen minutes. He himself purposed to have a nap. But he was allowed little peace.

"Sir, how many runs do you think Mr. Rathbone made last year?"

"How many."

"A duck, sir."

"Indeed."

"Sir."

"D'Orsy?"

"What is your record match innings, sir?"

Mindful of his claims as a diver, the boys listened for his answer with no little interest.

Thompson put his elbows on his desk, placing his hands meticulously together, palm to palm, finger to finger.

"That is a simple question to answer," he said. "I have never played in a cricket match in the whole course of my life."

The class stared at him, speechless. He might have been some strange monster they saw before them.

"Baseball," said Thompson, with dignity. "Hockey. Hickle-spin. Ping-pong. Old-maid. But never cricket."

"But, sir, you are going to play this afternoon."

"Certainly I am going to play this afternoon," agreed Thompson, "and I cannot say that I particularly enjoy the prospect; but that, D'Orsy, is not from any anxiety as to my style as a batsman. If I am not looking forward to play, it is because I very much prefer to be idle, and because, from what I know of the game, it appears to me to be an entirely unreasonable form of sport. It is perhaps a little late in the day," he added regretfully, "to reorganize the ethics of cricket; nevertheless, one cannot help feeling it might have been accorded more careful consideration at the outset."

The boy's excited, "Dash it all, sir! Look here, sir," was cut short by a realization that Thompson's eyes were shut.

. . .

Lunch was at one o'clock.

The headmaster's table, decorated with roses, was a veritable arbour; across the tops of the flowers parents and masters nodded politely around them; Betsy and her attendant nymphs (loudly-breathing), glorious in new aprons and caps, carried the vegetable dishes with shaking hands and with terror in their hearts. The carrying of these dishes was sufficient indication of ceremony; usually the vegetables for the whole school were served by April herself from two enormous bowls.

Even the boys' table boasted its decorations, its severely starched serviettes, its unfamiliar silver and glass. Dazzled by so much unaccustomed splendour, subdued by the presence of strangers, the boys sat quietly, their sunburnt faces as eloquent an advertisement for the school as their good behaviour. April, when she could spare a moment, beamed in their direction.

"Poor darlings," she thought, "another twenty years or so and I'm afraid they'll look very much like their parents. What a pity it is children have to grow up."

Her husband was in his element. In his old sporting check (actually pre-War in date), he looked far more the country squire than the schoolmaster; without effort he carved and conversed—an easy, charming host. Looking down the length of the table April gave him a lingering glance; quite obviously she admired him enormously. Thompson caught that glance; suffered a pain against which he was powerless to fight. Never in his life before had he experienced precisely that agony. He knew it for what it was.

"Jealousy," he said aloud, and the little woman seated on his left, a little woman with homely features and anxious eyes, gave a nervous start. Twice already she had attempted conversation, but had received no encouragement. She now begged his pardon.

"I was not aware of having spoken," said Thompson stiffly. "Perhaps you would have the extreme goodness to pass the mustard."

A creditable buzz of conversation was by this time running the gamut of the tables. In this conversation Thompson bore no part. Barely silent, he sat between the homely woman and a youthful baldheaded father as one in a dream.

He wasn't, thought the headmaster, glancing in his direction, looking particularly well. That chill, doubtless—he'd never really got over it.

"Worrying about having to put up some kind of a show this afternoon, I daresay. Don't blame him. Cricket's bound to be an ordeal to a man like Thompson. . . ."

The sonorous voice of Baxter could be heard during the pauses.

"Not so much noise there, boys; a little quieter, please." While from Betsy and her assistants came the clatter of plates piled inexpertly on a side table.

The large windows lay open upon the perfect summer's day without; to the parents, very land-lubbers for the most part, the salty air blowing straight in off the sea set up an intoxication as potent almost as that following upon Major Silver's excellent claret. What sunlight! By laying your hand in one of those golden pools upon the tablecloth you might almost hope to have it bronzed before the meal's end. And the lawns outside! How deliciously green.

Mrs. D'Orsy, on April's left, became positively lyrical on the subject of the garden. With her blue eyes and her musical-comedy air (had she not, indeed, before her marriage to Julian D'Orsy, graced the boards with no uncertain success?) she looked charming in that metallic manner which fashionable women affect. It was as though her charm, through very overwork, had hardened overnight; so that no longer spontaneous, since spontaneity involves sincerity, it clung to her with the tenacity of a cloak which she was powerless either to throw off or to draw around her more closely.

In her own way, and after her own cynical fashion, she enjoyed these school occasions.

"Marvellous day," said Mrs. D'Orsy. "Really too marvellous. A marvellous drive down. Marvellous coming over the downs. Quite marvellous."

April, looking the picture of charming unsophistication by contrast with her left-hand neighbour, regarded Mrs. D'Orsy with a thoughtful eye.

"Why is it," she wondered, "that the stage, that home of eloquence, beggars the vocabulary of its adherents to such an extent that the poor things find themselves out in a cold world equipped with a range of words which would put the veriest child to the blush? For set the Mrs. Buffles of this life beside the Pamela D'Orsys, and we shall soon see whose conversation proves the richest. Mrs. Buffles' Elizabethan bawdy as opposed to the others' 'Marvellous' would be like a thick home-brewed beer beside so much watered wine. Why, then," April asked herself, "unless baldness of speech be the universal aim, do we trouble ourselves about education, schools, school fees, or schoolmasters? Why, indeed?"

And she looked along the table to where her husband, finished with his carving, was listening to his neighbour with every appearance of enjoyment. Every appearance, we repeat, for in reality he was not listening to one word. He was asking himself how in the world so attractive a creature as Mrs. D'Orsy could have married that weakling, Julian, whom he had both known and kicked in the old Rugby days. And he regretted the lay-out of the lunch table. Mrs. D'Orsy should have been sitting beside *him*. It was surely so obvious. Then, Mrs. Culpepper could have sat beside April. April was always so excellent with bores.

"And I think you will agree with me," Mrs. Culpepper was saying, "that the young boy in these days is faced with so many new inventions and theories that life is going to be very difficult for him. Very, very difficult. All this flying and gadding about. Now, when you get to my age . . ." she added coyly.

Silver rewarded this remark with an incredulous, an almost tender smile. Mrs. Culpepper flushed with gratified vanity.

"I entirely agree with you," he said, "though in your case I should have thought there need be no anxiety on the score of age. Now, take an old crock like myself. . . ."

He heard Mrs. D'Orsy say:

"I'm so keen on fishin'. Such a good sport. We used to fish quite a lot when we lived at Portland. It was too marvellous. Julian's at sea again, you know."

From half-way up the table the mother of Robinson spoke for the first time and to nobody in particular.

"I have a theory," said she, all in calmly folding a seviette which, her sharp eye assured her, stood in need of a stitch—"I have a theory that if one is born by the sea one is likely to have a special love for it. I cannot believe that people born inland ever know the real *thrill* of coming back to the sea. What do you say, Mrs. Silver?"

April thought without hurry. Then she said:

"Sometimes I love the sea. There are times when I detest it. I was born in Switzerland."

Mrs. D'Orsy took matters into her capable hands. Gazing adoringly in the headmaster's direction (and what a pity it did seem there should be such a litter of flowers, plates, knives, forks, and odd human beings between herself and that perfectly delightful-looking man), she asked:

"And you, Major Silver?"

Silver, happily relieved for the moment of his responsibilities to the right, transferred his smile from Mrs. Culpepper to the charmer.

"I'm a simple country man," he said bluffly; "I was born in Cornwall and I like the sea well enough. I don't pretend to be mad about it. . . . What do you say, Thompson?"

This sudden challenge was deliberately launched. Quite time, thought the headmaster, that the fellow should come out of his day-dream. Every eye was now trained upon the fellow. What a strange individual, with his enormous brow and his serviette tucked, French fashion, into his jacket! The parents didn't seem to remember having seen him before. Thompson, or some such name, they believed. . . .

Blinking a little, Thompson cleared his throat. When he spoke it was in that penetrating voice of his which could be heard in every corner of the room.

"As for my birthplace," he said, "I have always been given to understand that I was born at the end of a jetty. And it is quite undeniable," he added pleasantly, "that I am addicted to shellfish."

These words, innocent enough in themselves, appeared to settle like some peculiarly deadly blight upon the body of the conversation. Heads were craned forward, the boys at the tables behind giggled and snuffled, Betsy all but dropped the trifle upon what must have been one of the most expensive and irreplaceable hats in Sussex. Not that the words, "jetty" or "shellfish" conveyed any special meaning to her mind: simply, she was affected by that sense of shock which ran the length of the table like some incalculable streak of lightning.

"How amusin'," said Mrs. D'Orsy.

"Very," said Mrs. Culpepper severely.

"I think," suggested April, "it would be a good idea if we drank our coffee out in the garden. There's shade under the trees, and it does seem such a pity to be in the house. The match won't begin for another hour. Would you like to do that?"

The ladies said they would like it very much. They followed April out of doors. Garden chairs of the camp variety had been set under the copper beech. Here the ladies drank their coffee. Here the gnats bit the ladies. Here, in due course, ladies and gnats were joined by the opposing teams resplendent in cricketing flannels.

.   .   .

The "thingummy."

It began punctually at two-thirty. The boys examined the parental team with a mixture of condescension and amusement. Terribly funny, they thought it. Eleven of the senior boys, captained by Spottiswood, represented the school. Opposed to these were the masters, Rathbone, Baxter, two curates from Harminster, and six male parents. It only needed the arrival of Thompson to complete the picture. And now, the field beginning to grow impatient, a small boy was dispatched to hurry him along.

To do Thompson justice he had cherished every intention of being on time, but the unaccustomed procedure of changing into cricket things had proved more difficult than he could have foreseen. For one thing, the headmaster's shoes, which he had borrowed for the occasion, having spoilt his own, bathing, were nowhere to be found, and had not Mrs. Buffle herself assisted in the search, stood over him while he put them on, and practically pushed him out of the deserted house, it seems likely that the public might have been deprived of the sight of him for the rest of the day.

At length he was observed strolling, unhurried and serene, in the direction of the cricketing pavilion; and if there was a very general relief among the players on the score of his safe arrival, yet it cannot be said that his appearance inspired any particular confidence in the bosoms of the male parents. They had heard his remark about shellfish at lunch: that was enough. Very rightly they disapproved of his cricket shirt, a cast-off of Rathbone's and too big for him, and of his trousers, lent for the occasion by Baxter, and too short for him. His whole appearance, in their view, looked surprisingly un-English; and as for that ridiculous hat, it was not, they felt, and again rightly, the hat of a cricketer. Nevertheless, in these little preparatory school matches one must, of course, be prepared to play with the oddest assortment of persons; that, after all, was half the fun of the thing. The male parents cheered up when their captain won the toss, thus establishing prior batting rights.

All through the tossing ceremony Thompson had stood, detached from the main body, gazing mildly out to sea. The question which agitated him was as follows: Was that, or was it not, a bird which bobbed and dipped out there on the extreme horizon? Impossible that it should be so, yet, viewed from this distance, it bore an astonishing resemblance to a gigantic duck. And the sea itself! Might one not, by a stretch of imagination, have been looking out across a tremendous pond, immensely blue, immensely calm, upon which that duck came riding buoyantly into sight over the edge of the world?

Not until he heard shouting behind him did he realize that his own side, with the exception of the two first batsmen in, had withdrawn to the edge of the field. He himself retired in good order, sitting beside a man whom he suspected of being one of the curates, and upon the steps of the cricket pavilion. A conversation somewhat unsuited to the occasion of a cricket match now ensued.

The curate began it.

"Excuse me. May I presume to ask what you are looking at?"

Thompson pointed. "Naturally, you may. I am looking exactly to the left of that white crag of cliff and on the extreme horizon. You see it?"

The curate scanned the horizon from end to end.

"Certainly not. I can see nothing."

"I am sorry to hear it," said his companion, a tall odd-looking man whom the curate took to be one of the masters. "It is certainly *there* all right. I should explain, perhaps, that even without my glasses, I have the good fortune to be exceptionally long-sighted."

"And so, curiously enough, am I," said the curate disagreeably. The heat of the day combined with a five-mile bicycle ride had done little to foster good humour. "As a matter of fact," he added with careless pride, "I am accustomed to go birding in Norfolk, and if there is one thing that teaches a man quickness of eye, it is birding."

"Birding?" repeated Thompson.

"Birding," said the curate. Thompson looked at him. "Eggs, you know."

"To be sure," said Thompson. "Then in that case I do hope you will be able to distinguish the strange object at which I am gazing when it draws a little closer. I have reason to suspect that here we have an unknown bird of gargantuan proportions. A smoking bird," he added, for a tiny wisp of smoke now began to appear in the wake of the mysterious craft.

"Do but observe it! It is travelling fast. I feel sure you will see it now."

The curate withdrew his gaze from Thompson, at whom he had been staring curiously, and looked once more out to sea. He admitted, grudgingly, that he saw something.

"It turns out to be a liner," said Thompson, smiling. "So I fear we can scarcely hope for any eggs."

Thwack! The batsmen were in full going order, the bowlers were excelling themselves. The sun, sheathed no longer in its protective haze, was almost literally splitting the trees. Was there, in all England upon this particular afternoon, a more cheerful scene? It seemed doubtful. In the extreme background shone the sun-baked downs, their copses and woods shining darkly, like a three-days' bristle upon the chin of a giant; lower down, the roofs of cottages and the church spire peeped from among the chestnuts, while in the foreground the figures of the cricketers, white and flat as though cut from paper, showed against the shadow of the trees in clearest relief. Nearer at hand, upon wooden seats, sat the ladies, picturesque in flowered voiles and shady hats, while about the cricket pavilion clustered that impressive array of masculinity waiting to bat. At the distance of one meadow away, his head across his accustomed gate, dreamed the school pony—a homely touch—and from the farm across the green came the quacking of ducks and lowing of oxen.

"It's simply delightful," said Thompson. And so it was. Not sixteen yards away from him, in the extreme middle of one of the wooden seats, sat April, loveliness itself in her simple cream dress and flopping sun hat. By screwing up his eyes against the glare, Thompson could distinguish her features, could see her lips moving, though he could not hear what she said. From that distance, merely because he loved her, he felt a power to interpret her thoughts. He knew that for her this was bound to be a day fraught with anxiety, that no defensive magic could protect her from Mrs. Culpepper's accounts of her rheumatism, or cure for her that inconvenient shyness with which she had been affected while entertaining D'Orsy's mother at lunch.

(Unobservant as Thompson may have appeared, relationships between April and her left-hand neighbour had been as apparent to him as though he had turned opera-glasses upon the pair of them.)

His gaze now travelled beyond April and her guests. "There's that husband of hers," he said to himself. There the headmaster certainly was. Lying back in one of the only two available camp chairs, he was engaged in happily chatting to Mrs. D'Orsy. Looking genuinely gay. Obviously no thoughts of a melancholy nature oppressed him at the moment; the proximity of a pretty woman not his wife was more than sufficient to distract him from sordid worries.

"At a meagre reckoning," thought Thompson, whose weakness for economics often led him into surprisingly practical calculations, "the man must be a good thousand pounds in debt. Given another five years, going as he is going, he'll be up to the neck in it. And that in spite of his wife's pathetic attempts at economy, her amber-handled darning basket, her wasting of delicious mornings and golden afternoons. Five years! His study will be littered to the ceiling. The bath water will be colder than ever. And I? Where shall I be?"

"Thompson, you're in next. Put on these pads."

The voice of Rathbone, and for him a voice strangely gentle and sympathetic.

"Here! I'll help you."

Down on one of his immaculately trousered knees on the grass Rathbone fastened the buckle.

"I know you won't resent a little advice," he breathed, in a voice considerately lowered, "but do just bear this in mind. Face the bowler. *Always* face the bowler. Keep your eye on the ball. And don't be too anxious."

Looking down at Rathbone kneeling on the grass before him, Thompson noted the extreme redness of his face. Ignorant of the fact that this kneeling hero had the best excuse in the world for a red face, that is to say, twenty-five runs to his credit, Thompson wondered whether the heat had not proved a little too much for him. Anxious? The very thought struck him as ridiculous. It wasn't difficult to see which of the two, himself or Rathbone, was betraying anxiety.

"On the contrary, Rathbone," he said brightly, "I feel every confidence in myself. I'm looking forward to my innings tremendously."

Rathbone fastened the last buckle with an approving "That's the spirit." But he did not appear entirely reassured.

"You'll remember to face the bowler, Thompson," he reiterated tactlessly, as Thompson, seizing the bat from a breathless ex-batsman, prepared to take the field. This perpetual repetition about facing the bowler irritated Thompson, and he strode out fiercely as one in whose ear buzzes some inconvenient insect.

True, there had been an occasion earlier in the term when he had failed in just some such particular as that of facing the bowler: that, however, was over and done with.

"Let dead dogs lie," said Thompson to himself as he took up his stance. "But what an ugly phrase to be sure." Dead dogs. Ugh! He'd seen enough of those on his explorations. He never wanted to see a dead dog again.

But now for this great cricketing affair. At the end of the first over his fellow-batsman, a rotund analytical chemist, had made seven runs; now, the over ended, it was Thompson's turn to bat. For this great moment he prepared with alacrity. Forgetting the second of Rathbone's urgent directions, he picked out his west-bound vessel, steaming along well within the limits of the horizon, as a suitable target. In that direction, and in no other, he would hit the ball. Upon that, and not upon the ball, he would keep his eye. If, by some magical manipulation of space, he might succeed in crushing in the foremost of the belching funnels, bringing the ship's company hysterically on deck, so much the better. April was watching him. April would account it a feat worthy of accomplishment. Cheered on by that fact, he felt he could guarantee to hit practically anything; stood awaiting his first ball.

The warm air around his eyes rocked and swam, he could hear his heart beating, or was it his turnip-watch, the field appeared vast, the bowler minute, spectators, fieldsmen, and umpires waited upon his slightest whim. Up came the ball.

Slash! He had hit the empty air.

"My own fault," he thought; "I took my eye off that funnel." And at the coming of the second ball he trained his eye severely; lashed out. There was a slight hush on the part of nature, even the birds seemed to have ceased singing. No need to run; Thompson had hit a boundary.

The analytical chemist gazed respectfully down the length of the pitch. Who would have expected a man wearing a hat like that to hit so hard? Nobody. There were cheers from the pavilion, cheers from the wooden seats, a separate cheer it may be, but of this Thompson could not be sure, from his friend the school pony. Now once more he trained his eye upon the ship's funnel, once more he hit the ball.

"Run," and "run again," shouted his fellow-batsman, and he ran and ran again. He was back at his original wicket. (April was watching him.)

On came the ball, a curious and deceptive ball, well calculated to disturb the equanimity of a less indifferent batsman. Fortunately Thompson did not see it. With the centre of his bat he caught it a resounding crack: it went flying into the air. To be dropped by Robinson III. Resounding cheers.

"More luck than good management," said Thompson aloud. "I won't do *that* again. Now, where's this funnel? Dear me, it's getting up steam with a vengeance. Smoking like a chimney."

"What's that?" said the wicket-keeper.

"Don't annoy me," said Thompson. Once more he addressed the ball, once more he hit it in the direction of the ship. But he reckoned without his hat. This he had worn, batting as he was in the very eye of the sun, tipped well over his nose. Always two sizes too small for him, it had maintained, up to the present, a precarious and difficult seat.

"Run," shouted the chemist, and he ran; but halfway between the wickets his hat slipped from his head. Alas! No sooner had he darted back to pick it up than certain funny business was carried on at the other end of the pitch, and he was given to understand, but he did *not* understand it, that he was out. Stumped.

Thompson would have liked to argue the point, but he thought better of it, and his natural chagrin at this turn of events was softened by the ovation accorded to him by the spectators, when, bat in hand, he cheerfully hopped in the direction of the pavilion. Quite obviously he was considered a great success. His spirits soared. A cricketer! He who'd always counted himself out of the running upon any such occasion as the present. Hitting a boundary! . . . well, it was not, after all, surprising. He'd felt, as he'd frankly remarked to Rathbone, and in spite of the fact that his trousers were too tight for him, every confidence in himself. If it hadn't been for that hat he might have made a century. If he had only been wearing his own shoes!

The school crowded round.

"Jolly good, sir! Jolly well done, sir! Have a drink, sir! You hit it a ripping swipe."

With his spectacles just clear of the lemonade glass he peered blandly in April's direction. Very satisfactory. Not only was she looking admiringly towards him, he made no doubt she was speaking of him in glowing terms. Once again Love lent him ears, and he could almost hear her saying:

"That's Thompson, our mathematical master. He's only played three times in his life, and yet, look, he hits a boundary without effort. If it hadn't been for his hat he'd have made a century. Excuse me, I really must go over and congratulate him."

If these were indeed the words issuing from April's gently moving lips, she made no movement. She continued to sit on the wooden seat between Mrs. Mullinger (Mullinger junior) and Mrs. Culpepper. Neither, to tell the truth, did her words concern Thompson, or even more remotely, cricket. At that very moment she was in the middle of a sentence which had begun in this fashion:

"I'm afraid I can't promise to do that, Mrs. Mullinger. You see, my husband is very much against favouritism of any sort among the boys, and although I know you didn't intend this as favouritism, it might be misunderstood. But I'll do what I can. I'll have a talk with the school carpenter and see if we can't get rid of the draught. To put another boy in *his* bed wouldn't be quite fair I am afraid. I'd no idea there *was* a draught. I do wish the boys would bring their complaints to me."

Mrs. Mullinger said, in the voice of one who doggedly reiterates a grievance, "James had one of those noisy, snuffling colds when he was home in the holidays, and the moment I arrived to-day I heard him sneezing. Of course it may be the merest coincidence; please don't think I'm complaining. But I thought I'd just mention that dormitory window."

"I'm so glad you did," said April brightly. She was not glad. She didn't care a button at the moment if every window in the schoolhouse was blown sky-high. She would dearly have loved to steal off, if only for a few moments; leaving a dummy headmaster's wife beneath the brim of her wide hat while she herself in spirit soared gloriously out to sea, up into the wide air, anywhere. She wanted to cry. It wasn't only having got up so early, the heat, the difficulties of persuading Betsy to wear a decent cap and apron, or the continual strain of appearing interested when one simply wasn't. No, nor the fact that she hadn't exchanged three words with John since breakfast, whereas he . . . She glanced shyly in his direction. It was a sensation, unfamiliar to her, of complete lassitude, which to-day assailed her.

"I feel," said she to herself, while still discussing the affair of the dormitory window with Mullinger's mother, "I feel like a fish, soft and without any bones. A fish or a ghost. I'm terribly afraid I don't appear to know much about the cricket match. A quarter past three; soon be tea-time. Let's hope they'll remember to clean out the tea urn really thoroughly. There was sand in it last time. . . . What on earth makes Mr. Thompson stare so fixedly in this direction? Poor dear! Surely *somebody* could have produced trousers for him that didn't end round his knees. Why do I feel so limp? I can't, I simply cannot, go on. I'm not the least bit tired. I'm just dead."

She turned now to her right, and even Mrs. Culpepper, immersed in her own interests, noticed that the headmaster's wife, whom she considered "unusually good-looking," was very white. Squinting around April's hat brim with eyes beady as those of some elderly female buzzard, she absorbed, not without satisfaction, the drama of the two camp chairs.

"So that's how it is," she thought. "Well, we all have our troubles. If it's not rheumatism, it's husbands. Naturally, if one marries such a dangerously attractive man! How glad I am dear James is too young to notice such things." Aloud, she agreed with Robinson's mother that it was nice to see so much green grass about.

In due course the parents and masters were out, and for sixty-two runs. Now the mothers, erstwhile drowsy and frankly bored by the sight of their husbands batting, an activity unfairly stigmatized in their minds as "showing off," sat to attention. Now that it was a question of SONS, the whole affair took on a very different complexion. No afternoon heat, no hardness of seating arrangements, could distract their devoted contemplation from the issue at stake.

With each successive batsman, and it must be admitted that upon this occasion the batsmen succeeded one another with disheartening rapidity, the outbreak of hand-clapping spread like a rash among spectators feverishly alert.

There were cries of "Oh, hard luck! Dear me, too bad!" and "Stick to it, do," together with an undercurrent of: "What a handsome boy, the one hitting the ball at this moment. But why has Rickett's father suddenly sat down? Did he do it purposely, or has he slipped? There is my James over there just behind the wicket-keeper, by the pavilion. His asthma is a great trouble to me. There's Starling—Alice Maddison's boy, you know, the one who married the rich coal man against her parents' wishes and came to live quite near us at Chaldeburys. They say . . . but I don't know, of course . . . probably mere rumour . . . disgraceful. . . ."

Throughout the peerless afternoon the villagers had joined their applause to that of the school, and the meadows, the green, the school field itself was invaded by unknown persons, probably tourists down for the day, come to stare and to clap. By four-thirty the school was out for fifty runs, a fine score considering everything; stumps were drawn, mutual cheering called for by the captains of the opposing side, and the whole party, with the exception of the pony, repaired to the schoolhouse for tea.

. . .

The jade curtains were drawn half-way across the window, shutting out the glare. There was a hissing of the urn, a lively chatter. Thompson, standing with a teacup in one hand, a bun in the other, felt that he wanted to shout. In all his life he had never been so elated.

First of all, from this day onward, he was a proven cricketer. Secondly, April had applauded him. With his own eyes he had seen her clapping, with his heart he had guessed at those kind and complimentary words with which she had spoken of him. Now, standing near her where she poured out tea for her guests, he neither ate, drank, nor offered to hand round the cakes; he was unaware of the crowd, the sunshine, of everything save his own happiness. Greater happiness was still to come.

Looking up suddenly from her hissing urn, smiling straight into his eyes, so that he had ample time wherein to observe the dark lines round her own, April said:

"Well played, Mr. Thompson."

Well played, she had said, and stooped once more to the urn. He could scarcely believe his own good fortune. Abandoning his cup and his bun, he escaped from the company.

Once in his own attic he shut the door carefully behind him. He wanted to remember that smile and to keep it with him for ever and ever. Gazing in the direction of the windows he looked out over his fish-cases into the world beyond. The moment was too ecstatic, too painful. He must think about something else. Scarcely knowing what he did, he now opened his *Fisherman's Manual,* and read aloud the first paragraph which came to hand, a paragraph embodying Scroop's advice to fishermen upon the art of wading. Like a charm he repeated the words over and over again:

"Never go deeper into the water than the fourth button of the waistcoat. Should you be wading when it may chance to freeze very hard, pull down your stockings and examine your legs. Should they be black, or even purple, it might, perhaps, be as well to get on dry land; but if they are only rubicund you may continue to enjoy the water, if it so pleases you."

When he had first discovered these words in his manual, they had afforded Thompson exquisite amusement. Now he was not amused. He had no more idea of their portent than the man in the moon.

Jane Enters Lowood

CHARLOTTE BRONTË

CHARLOTTE BRONTË (1816-1855) was the oldest of the three famous Brontë sisters. Their father, son of an Irish peasant, was educated at Cambridge, and, from 1820 until his death in 1861, was curate of Haworth, an isolated village in Yorkshire. In 1824, he sent four of his daughters to a cheap boarding school for clergymen's daughters. Living conditions at the school were wretched; the two oldest daughters died as a result of inadequate food and poor sanitation; Charlotte and Emily were, fortunately, withdrawn. Charlotte then entered Miss Wooler's school at Roe Head, to which in 1835 she returned as a teacher. She disliked teaching, but it was the only occupation open to her at the time, and she was under the necessity of augmenting the meagre family income. Despite her dislike of teaching, Charlotte thought of opening a school of her own, and, to secure the necessary training for such an undertaking, she and Emily enrolled in a school in Brussels. The experience was unhappy; the sisters returned to Haworth the following year. In 1845 Charlotte discovered by accident the manuscript of Emily's poems. In 1846 they were published along with poems by Charlotte and Anne under the title Poems by Currer, Ellis, and Acton Bell. *The book had no sale, but, undaunted, the three sisters set to work, each upon a novel. Anne's novel* Agnes Gray *and Emily's* Wuthering Heights *were accepted by a publisher, but Charlotte's novel,* The Professor, *remained unpublished until after her death. Charlotte then went to work on* Jane Eyre, *which was published in 1847 and achieved immediate success.*

The following chapter from Jane Eyre *is based upon Charlotte's own experiences at boarding school.*

FIVE o'clock had hardly struck on the morning of the 19th of January, when Bessie brought a candle into my closet, and found me already up and nearly dressed. I had risen half an hour before her entrance, and had washed my face, and put on my clothes by the light of a half-moon just setting, whose rays streamed through the narrow window near my crib. I was to leave Gateshead that day by a coach which passed the lodge gates at six a. m. Bessie was the only person yet risen; she had lit a fire in the nursery, where she now proceeded to make my breakfast. Few children can eat when excited with the thoughts of a journey; nor could I. Bessie, having pressed me in vain to take a few spoonfuls of the boiled milk and bread she had prepared for me, wrapped up some biscuits in a paper and put them into my bag; then she helped me on with my pelisse and bonnet, and, wrapping herself in a shawl, she and I left the nursery. As we passed Mrs. Reed's bedroom, she said, "Will you go in and bid Missis good-bye?"

"No Bessie: she came to my crib last night when you were gone down to supper, and said I need not disturb her in the morning, or my cousins either; and she told me to remember that she had always been my best friend, and to speak of her and be grateful to her accordingly."

"What did you say, Miss?"

"Nothing: I covered my face with the bed-clothes, and turned from her to the wall."

"That was wrong, Miss Jane."

"It was quite right, Bessie: your Missis has not been my friend: she has been my foe."

"Oh, Miss Jane! don't say so!"

"Good-bye to Gateshead!" cried I, as we passed through the hall and went out at the front door.

The moon was set, and it was very dark; Bessie carried a lantern, whose light glanced on wet steps and gravel road sodden by a recent thaw. Raw and chill was the winter morning: my teeth chattered as I hastened down the drive. There was a light in the porter's lodge: when we reached it, we found the porter's wife just kindling her fire: my trunk, which had been carried down the evening before, stood corded at the door. It wanted but a few minutes of six, and shortly after that hour had struck the distant roll of wheels announced the coming coach; I went to the door, and watched its lamps approach rapidly through the gloom.

"Is she going by herself?" asked the porter's wife.

"Yes."

"And how far is it?"

"Fifty miles."

"What a long way! I wonder Mrs. Reed is not afraid to trust her so far alone."

The coach drew up; there it was at the gates with its four horses and its top laden with passengers: the guard and coachman loudly urged haste; my trunk was hoisted up; I was taken from Bessie's neck, to which I clung with kisses.

"Be sure and take good care of her," cried she to the guard, as he lifted me into the inside.

"Ay, ay!" was the answer: the door was slapped to, a voice exclaimed, "All right," and on we drove. Thus was I severed from Bessie and Gateshead: thus whirled away to unknown, and, as I then deemed, remote and mysterious regions.

I remember but little of the journey: I only know that the day seemed to me of a preternatural length, and that we appeared to travel over hundreds of miles of road. We passed through several towns, and in one, a very large one, the coach stopped; the horses were taken out, and the passengers alighted to dine. I was carried into an inn, where the guard wanted me to have some dinner; but as I had no appetite, he left me in an immense room with a fire-place at each end, a chandelier pendent from the ceiling and a little red gallery high up against the wall filled with musical instruments. Here I walked about for a long time, feeling very strange, and mortally apprehensive of some one coming in and kidnapping me; for I believed in kidnappers, their exploits having frequently figured in Bessie's fireside chronicles. At last the guard returned: once more I was stowed away in the coach, my protector mounted his own seat, sounded his hollow horn, and away we rattled over the "stony street" of L————.

The afternoon came on wet and somewhat misty: as it waned into dusk, I began to feel that we were getting very far indeed from Gateshead: we ceased to pass through towns; the country changed; great gray hills heaved up round the horizon: a twilight deepened, we descended a valley, dark with wood, and long after night had overclouded the prospect I heard a wild wind rushing among trees.

Lulled by the sound, I at last dropped asleep: I had not long slumbered when the sudden cessation of motion awoke me; the coach door was open, and a person like a servant was standing at it: I saw her face and dress by the light of the lamps.

"Is there a little girl called Jane Eyre here?" she asked. I answered "Yes," and was then lifted out; my trunk was handed down, and the coach instantly drove away.

I was stiff with long sitting, and bewildered with the noise and motion of the coach: gathering my faculties, I looked about me. Rain, wind, and darkness filled the air; nevertheless, I dimly discerned a wall before me and a door open in it; through this door I passed with my new guide: she shut and locked it behind her. There was now visible a house or houses— for the building spread far—with many windows, and lights burning in some; we went up a broad pebbly path, splashing wet, and were admitted at a door; then the servant led me through a passage into a room with a fire, where she left me alone.

I stood and warmed my numbed fingers over the blaze, then I looked round; there was no candle, but the uncertain light from the hearth showed, by intervals, papered walls, carpet, curtains, shiny mahogany furniture: it was a parlor, not so spacious or splendid as the drawing-room at Gateshead, but comfortable enough. I was puzzling to make out the subject of a picture on the wall, when the door opened, and an individual carrying a light entered; another followed close behind.

The first was a tall lady with dark hair, dark eyes, and a pale and large forehead; her figure was partly enveloped in a shawl, her countenance was grave, her bearing erect.

"The child is very young to be sent alone," said she, putting her candle down on the table. She considered me attentively for a minute or two, then further added:

"She had better be put to bed soon; she looks tired: are you tired?" she asked, placing her hand on my shoulder.

"A little, ma'am."

"And hungry too, no doubt: let her have some supper before she goes to bed, Miss Miller. Is this the first time you have left your parents to come to school, my little girl?"

I explained to her that I had no parents. She inquired how long they had been dead; then how old I was, what was my name, whether I could read, write, and sew a little: then she touched my cheek gently with her fore-finger, and saying, "She hoped I should be a good child," dismissed me along with Miss Miller.

The lady I had left might be about twenty-nine; the one who went with me appeared some years younger: the first impressed me by her voice, look, and air. Miss Miller was more ordinary: ruddy in complexion, though of a care-worn countenance; hurried in gait and action, like one who had always a multiplicity of tasks on hand: she looked, indeed, what I afterward found she really was, an under-teacher. Led by her, I passed from compartment to compartment, from passage to passage, of a large and irregular building; till, emerging from the total and somewhat dreary silence pervading that portion of the house we had traversed, we came upon the hum of many voices, and presently entered a wide, long room with great deal tables, two at each end, on each of which burned a pair of candles, and seated all round on benches, a congregation of girls of every age, from nine or ten to twenty. Seen by the dim light of the dips, their number to me appeared countless, though not in reality exceeding eighty; they were uniformly dressed in brown stuff frocks of quaint fashion, and long holland pinafores. It was the hour of study; they were engaged in conning over their to-morrow's task, and the hum I heard was the combined result of their whispered repetitions.

Miss Miller signed to me to sit on a bench near the door, then walking up to the top of the long room, she cried out,

"Monitors, collect the lesson-books and put them away!"

Four tall girls arose from different tables, and going round, gathered the books and removed them. Miss Miller again gave the word of command:

"Monitors, fetch the supper-trays!"

The tall girls went out and returned presently, each bearing a tray, with portions of something, I knew not what, arranged thereon, and a pitcher of water and mug in the middle of each tray. The portions were handed round; those who liked took a draught of the water, the mug being common to all. When it came to my turn, I drank, for I was thirsty, but did not touch the food, excitement and fatigue rendering me incapable of eating: I now saw, however, that it was a thin oaten cake, shared into fragments.

The meal over, prayers were read by Miss Miller, and the classes filed off, two and two, up stairs. Overpowered by this time with weariness, I scarcely noticed what sort of a place the bedroom was; except that, like the school-room, I saw it was very long. To-night I was to be Miss Miller's bed-fellow; she helped me to undress: when laid down I glanced at the long rows of beds, each of which was quickly filled with two occupants; in ten minutes the single light was extinguished; amidst silence and complete darkness, I fell asleep.

The night passed rapidly: I was too tired even to dream; I only once awoke to hear the wind rave in furious gusts, and the rain fall in torrents, and to be sensible that Miss Miller had taken her place by my side. When I again unclosed my eyes, a loud bell was ringing: the girls were up and dressing; day had not yet begun to dawn, and a rush-light or two burned in the room. I too rose reluctantly; it was bitter cold, and I dressed as well as I could for shivering, and washed when there was a basin at liberty, which did not occur soon, as there was but one basin to six girls on the stands down the middle of the room. Again the bell rang: all formed in file, two and two, and in that order descended the stairs and entered the cold and dimly-lit school-room: here prayers were read by Miss Miller: afterward she called out, "Form classes!"

A great tumult succeeded for some minutes, during which Miss Miller repeatedly exclaimed, "Silence!" and "Order!" When it subsided, I saw them all draw up in four semicircles, before four chairs, placed at the four tables; all held books in their hands, and a great book, like a Bible, lay on each table, before the vacant seat. A pause of some seconds succeeded, filled up by the low, vague hum of numbers; Miss Miller walked from class to class, hushing this indefinite sound.

A distant bell tinkled: immediately three ladies entered the room, each walked to a table and took her seat; Miss Miller assumed the fourth vacant chair, which was that nearest the door, and around which the smallest of the children were assembled: to this inferior class I was called, and placed at the bottom of it.

Business now began: the day's Collect was repeated, then certain texts of Scripture were said, and to these succeeded a protracted reading of chapters in the Bible, which lasted an hour. By the time that exercise was terminated, day had fully dawned. The indefatigable bell now sounded for the fourth time: the classes were marshaled and marched into another room to breakfast: how glad I was to behold a prospect of getting something to eat! I was now nearly sick from inanition, having taken so little the day before.

The refectory was a great, low-ceiled, gloomy room; on two long tables smoked basins of something hot, which, however, to my dismay, sent forth an odor far from inviting. I saw a universal manifestation of discontent when the fumes of the repast met the nostrils of those destined to swallow it: from the van of the procession, the tall girls of the first class, rose the whispered words, "Disgusting! The porridge is burned again!"

"Silence!" ejaculated a voice; not that of Miss Miller, but one of the upper teachers, a little and dark personage, smartly dressed, but of somewhat morose aspect, who installed herself at the top of one table, while a more buxom lady presided at the other. I looked in vain for her I had first seen the night before; she was not visible. Miss Miller occupied the foot of the table where I sat, and a strange, foreign looking, elderly lady, the French teacher, as I afterward found, took the corresponding seat at the other board. A long grace was said, and a hymn sung; then a servant brought in some tea for the teachers, and the meal began.

Ravenous, and now very faint, I devoured a spoonful or two of my portion without thinking of its taste; but the first edge of hunger blunted, I perceived I had got in hand a nauseous mess: burned porridge is almost as bad as rotten potatoes; famine itself soon sickens over it. The spoons were moved slowly: I saw each girl taste her food and try to swallow it; but in most cases the effort was soon relinquished. Breakfast was over, and none had breakfasted. Thanks being returned for what we had not got, and a second hymn chanted, the refectory was evacuated for the school-room. I was one of the last to go out, and in passing the tables, I saw one teacher take a basin of the porridge and taste it; she looked at the others; all their countenances expressed displeasure, and one of them, the stout one, whispered, "Abominable stuff! How shameful!"

A quarter of an hour passed before lessons again began, during which the school-room was in a glorious tumult; for that space of time, it seemed to be permitted to talk loud, and more freely, and they used their privilege. The whole conversation ran on the breakfast, which one and all abused roundly. Poor things! it was the sole consolation they had. Miss Miller was now the only teacher in the room: a group of great girls standing about her, spoke with serious and sullen gestures. I heard the name of Mr. Brocklehurst pronounced by some lips; at which Miss Miller shook her head disapprovingly; but she made no great effort to check the general wrath: doubtless she shared in it.

A clock in the school-room struck nine; Miss Miller left her circle, and standing in the middle of the room, cried, "Silence! To your seats!"

Discipline prevailed; in five minutes the confused throng was resolved into order, and comparative silence quelled the Babel clamor of tongues. The upper teachers now punctually resumed their posts: but still, all seemed to wait. Ranged on benches down the sides of the room, the eighty girls sat motionless and erect: a quaint assemblage they appeared, all with plain locks combed from their faces, not a curl visible; in brown dresses, made high and surrounded by a narrow tucker about the throat, with little pockets of holland (shaped something like a Highlander's purse) tied in front of their frocks, and destined to serve the purpose of a work-bag: all, too, wearing woolen stockings and country-made shoes, fastened with brass buckles. Above twenty of those clad in this costume were full-grown girls, or rather young women; it suited them ill, and gave an air or oddity even to the prettiest.

I was still looking at them, and also at intervals examining the teachers—none of whom precisely pleased me; for the stout one was a little coarse, the dark one not a little fierce, the foreigner harsh and grotesque, and Miss Miller, poor thing! looked purple, weather-beaten, and overworked—when, as my eye wandered from face to face, the whole school rose simultaneously, as if moved by a common spring.

What was the matter? I had heard no order given: I was puzzled. Ere I had gathered my wits, the classes were again seated: but as all eyes were now turned to one point, mine followed the general direction, and encountered the personage who had received me last night. She stood at the bottom of the long room, on the hearth; for there was a fire at each end: she surveyed the two rows of girls silently and gravely. Miss Miller approaching, seemed to ask her a question, and having received her answer, went back to her place, and said, aloud, "Monitor of the first class, fetch the globes!"

While the direction was being executed, the lady consulted moved slowly up the room. I suppose I have a considerable organ of Veneration, for I retain yet the sense of admiring awe with which my eyes traced her steps. Seen now, in broad daylight, she looked tall, fair, and shapely; brown eyes, with a benignant light in their irids, and a fine penciling of long lashes round, relieved the whiteness of her large front; on each of her temples her hair, of a very dark brown, was clustered in round curls, according to the fashion of those times, when neither smooth bands nor long ringlets were in vogue; her dress, also in the mode of the day, was of purple cloth, relieved by a sort of Spanish trimming of black velvet; a gold watch (watches were not so common then as now) shone at her girdle. Let the reader add, to complete the picture, refined features; a complexion, if pale, clear; and a stately air and carriage, and he will have, at least, as clearly as words can give it, a correct idea of the exterior of Miss Temple—Maria Temple, as I afterward saw the name written in a prayer-book intrusted to me to carry to church.

The superintendent of Lowood (for such was this lady) having taken her seat before a pair of globes placed on one of the tables, summoned the first class round her, and commenced giving a lesson in geography; the lower classes were called by the teachers: repetitions in history, grammar, etc., went on for an hour; writing and arithmetic succeeded, and music lessons were given by Miss Temple to some of the elder girls. The duration of each lesson was measured by the clock, which at last struck twelve. The superintendent rose: "I have a word to address to the pupils," said she.

The tumult of cessation from lessons was already breaking forth, but it sank at her voice. She went on: "You had this morning a breakfast which you could not eat; you must be hungry: I have ordered that a lunch of bread and cheese shall be served to all."

The teachers looked at her with a sort of surprise.

"It is to be done on my responsibility," she added, in an explanatory tone to them, and immediately afterward left the room.

The bread and cheese was presently brought in and distributed, to the high delight and refreshment of the whole school. The order was now given "To the garden!" Each put on a coarse straw bonnet, with strings of colored calico, and a cloak of gray frieze. I was similarly equipped, and, following the stream, I made my way into the open air.

The garden was a wide inclosure, surrounded with walls so high as to exclude every glimpse of prospect; a covered verandah ran down one side, and broad walks bordered a middle space divided into scores of little beds: these beds were assigned as gardens for the pupils to cultivate, and each had an owner. When full of flowers they would doubtless look pretty; but now, at the latter end of January, all was wintry blight and brown decay. I shuddered as I stood and looked round me: it was an inclement day for outdoor exercise; not positively rainy, but darkened by a drizzling yellow fog; all underfoot was still soaking wet with the floods of yesterday. The stronger among the girls ran about and engaged in active games, but sundry pale and thin ones herded together for shelter and warmth in the verandah; and among these, as the dense mist penetrated to their shivering frames, I heard frequently the sound of a hollow cough.

As yet I had spoken to no one, nor did any body seem to take notice of me; I stood lonely enough: but to the feeling of isolation I was accustomed; it did not oppress me much. I leaned against a pillar of the verandah, drew my gray mantle close about me, and, trying to forget the cold which nipped me without, and the unsatisfied hunger which gnawed me within, delivered myself up to the employment of watching and thinking. My reflections were too undefined and fragmentary to merit record: I hardly yet knew where I was; Gateshead and my past life seemed floated away to an immeasurable distance; the present was vague and strange, and of the future I could form no conjecture. I looked round the convent-like garden, and then up at the house; a large building, half of which seemed gray and old, the other half quite new. The new part, containing the school-room and dormitory, was lit by mullioned and latticed windows, which gave it a church-like aspect; a stone tablet over the door bore this inscription:

LOWOOD INSTITUTION

THIS PORTION WAS REBUILT A. D. ——, BY NAOMI BROCKLEHURST,
OF BROCKLEHURST HALL, IN THIS COUNTY.

*Let your light so shine before men that they may see your good works,
and glorify your Father which is in heaven.*—St. Matt. v: 16.

I read these words over and over again: I felt that an explanation belonged to them, and was unable fully to penetrate their import. I was still pondering the signification of "Institution," and endeavoring to make out a connection between the first words and the verse of Scripture, when the sound of a cough close behind me made me turn my head. I saw a girl sitting on a stone bench near; she was bent over a book, on the perusal of which she seemed intent: from where I stood I could see the title—it was "Rasselas;" a name that struck me as strange, and consequently attractive. In turning, she happened to look up, and I said to her directly, "Is your book interesting?" I had already formed the intention of asking her to lend it to me some day.

"I like it," she answered, after a pause of a second or two, during which she examined me.

"What is it about?" I continued. I hardly know where I found the hardihood thus to open a conversation with a stranger; the step was contrary to my nature and habits: but I think her occupation touched a chord of sympathy somewhere; for I too liked reading, though of a frivolous and childish kind; I could not digest or comprehend the serious or substantial.

"You may look at it," replied the girl, offering me the book.

I did so; a brief examination convinced me that the contents were less taking than the title: "Rasselas" looked dull to my trifling taste; I saw nothing about fairies, nothing about genii; no bright variety seemed spread over the closely-printed pages. I returned it to her; she received it quietly, and without saying any thing she was about to relapse into her former studious mood: again I ventured to disturb her: "Can you tell me what the writing on that stone over the door means? What is Lowood Institution?"

"This house where you are come to live."

"And why do they call it Institution? Is it in any way different from other schools?"

"It is partly a charity-school: you and I, and all the rest of us, are charity-children. I suppose you are an orphan: are not either your father or your mother dead?"

"Both died before I can remember."

"Well, all the girls here have lost either one or both parents, and this is called an institution for educating orphans."

"Do we pay no money? Do they keep us for nothing?"

"We pay, or our friends pay, fifteen pounds a year for each."

"Then why do they call us charity-children?"

"Because fifteen pounds is not enough for board and teaching, and the deficiency is supplied by subscription."

"Who subscribes?"

"Different benevolent-minded ladies and gentlemen in this neighborhood and in London."

"Who was Naomi Brocklehurst?"

"The lady who built the new part of this house as that tablet records, and whose son overlooks and directs every thing here."

"Why?"

"Because he is treasurer and manager of the establishment."

"Then this house does not belong to that tall lady who wears a watch, and who said we were to have some bread and cheese."

"To Miss Temple? Oh no! I wish it did: she has to answer to Mr. Brocklehurst for all she does. Mr. Brocklehurst buys all our food and all our clothes."

"Does he live here?"

"No—two miles off, at a large hall."

"Is he a good man?"

"He is a clergyman, and is said to do a great deal of good."

"Did you say that tall lady was called Miss Temple?"

"Yes."

"And what are the other teachers called?"

"The one with red cheeks is called Miss Smith; she attends to the work, and cuts out—for we make our own clothes, our frocks, and pelisses, and every thing; the little one with black hair is Miss Scatcherd; she teaches history and grammar, and hears the second-class repetitions; and the one who wears a shawl, and has a pocket-handkerchief tied to her side with a yellow ribbon, is Madame Pierrot; she comes from Lisle, in France, and teaches French."

"Do you like the teachers?"

"Well enough."

"Do you like the little black one, and the Madame——? I can not pronounce her name as you do."

"Miss Scatcherd is hasty—you must take care not to offend her; Madame Pierrot is not a bad sort of person."

"But Miss Temple is the best—isn't she?"

"Miss Temple is very good, and very clever; she is above the rest, because she knows far more than they do."

"Have you been long here?"

"Two years."

"Are you an orphan?"

"My mother is dead."

"Are you happy here?"

"You ask rather too many questions. I have given you answers enough for the present: now I want to read."

But at the moment the summons sounded for dinner: all re-entered the house. The odor which now filled the refectory was scarcely more appetizing than that which had regaled our nostrils at breakfast: the dinner was served in two huge tin-plated vessels, whence rose a strong steam redolent of rancid fat. I found the mess to consist of indifferent potatoes and strange shreds of rusty meat, mixed and cooked together. Of this preparation a tolerably abundant plateful was apportioned to each pupil. I ate what I could, and wondered within myself whether every day's fare would be like this.

After dinner, we immediately adjourned to the school-room: lessons recommenced, and were continued till five o'clock.

The only marked event of the afternoon was, that I saw the girl with whom I had conversed in the verandah dismissed in disgrace by Miss Scatcherd from a history class, and sent to stand in the middle of the large school-room. The punishment seemed to me in a high degree ignominious, especially for so great a girl—she looked thirteen or upward. I expected she would show signs of great distress and shame; but to my surprise she neither wept nor blushed: composed, though grave, she stood the central mark of all eyes. "How can she bear it so quietly—so firmly?" I asked of myself. "Were I in her place, it seems to me I should wish the earth to open and swallow me up. She looks as if she were thinking of something beyond her punishment—beyond her situation: of something not round her nor before her. I have heard of day-dreams—is she in a day-dream now? Her eyes are fixed on the floor, but I am sure they do not see it— her sight seems turned in, gone down into her heart: she is looking at what she can remember, I believe; not at what is really present. I wonder what sort of a girl she is—whether good or naughty?"

Soon after five p.m. we had another meal, consisting of a small mug of coffee, and half a slice of brown bread. I devoured my bread and drank my coffee with relish; but I should have been glad of as much more—I was still hungry. Half an hour's recreation succeeded, then study: then the glass of water and the piece of oat-cake, prayers, and bed. Such was my first day at Lowood.

A Down-Right Scholar

JOHN EARLE

JOHN EARLE was born at York about 1601. In 1619 he probably entered Christ's Church College, Oxford, though he seems to have studied also at Merton College. In 1628 he published Microcosmographie, *a collection of character essays on the model of Theophrastus. In this work Earle analyzes inconspicuous types of men, such as the plain country fellow, a modest man, a poor man. This work was popular and ran through three editions in the year of its publication. The best of Earle's characters deal with types familiar in the universities of his time. Four of these are given here.*

Is one that has much learning in the ore, unwrought and untried, which time and experience fashions and refines. He is good metal in the inside, though rough and unscoured without, and therefore hated of the courtier, that is quite contrary. The time has got a vein of making him ridiculous, and men laugh at him by tradition, and no unlucky absurdity, but is put upon his profession, and done like a scholar. But his fault is only this, that his mind is (somewhat) too much taken up with his mind, and his thoughts not loaden with any carriage besides. He has not put on the quaint garb of the age, which is now a man's. (*Imprimis and all the Item.*[1]) He has not humbled his meditations to the industry of complement, nor afflicted his brain in an elaborate leg. His body is not set upon nice pins, to be turning and flexible for every motion, but his scrape is homely and his nod worse. He cannot kiss his hand and cry, madam, nor talk idle enough to bear her company. His smacking of a gentlewoman is somewhat too savory, and he mistakes her nose for her lips. A very woodcock would puzzle him in carving, and he wants the logick of a capon. He has not the glib faculty of sliding over a tale, but his words come squeamishly out of his mouth, and the laughter commonly before the jest. He names this word college too often, and his discourse beats too much on the university. The perplexity of mannerliness will not let him feed, and he is sharp set at an argument when he should cut his meat. He is discarded for a gamester at all games but one and thirty, and at tables he reaches not beyond doublets. His fingers are not long and drawn out to handle a fiddle, but his fist clunched with the habit of disputing. He ascends a horse somewhat sinisterly, though not on the left side, and they both go jogging in grief

[1] *Now become a man's total,* first edit.

479

together. He is exceedingly censured by the inns-of-court men, for that
heinous vice being out of fashion. He cannot speak to a dog in his own
dialect, and understands Greek better than the language of a falconer.
He has been used to a dark room, and dark clothes, and his eyes dazzle at
a sattin suit. The hermitage of his study, has made him somewhat un-
couth in the world, and men make him worse by staring on him. Thus is
he (silly and) ridiculous, and it continues with him for some quarter of
a year out of the university. But practise him a little in men, and brush
him over with good company, and he shall out-ballance those glisterers, as
far as a solid substance does a feather, or gold, gold-lace.

A Young Gentleman of the University

Is one that comes there to wear a gown, and to say hereafter, he has been
at the university. His father sent him thither because he heard there were
the best fencing and dancing-schools; from these he has his education,
from his tutor the over-sight. The first element of his knowledge is to be
shewn the colleges, and initiated in a tavern by the way, which hereafter
he will learn of himself. The two marks of his seniority, is the bare velvet
of his gown, and his proficiency at tennis, where when he can once play
a set, he is a fresh man no more. His study has commonly handsome
shelves, his books neat silk strings, which he shews to his father's man,
and is loth to unty or take down for fear of misplacing. Upon foul days
for recreation he retires thither, and looks over the pretty book his tutor
reads to him, which is commonly some short history, or a piece of Euphor-
mio; for which his tutor gives him money to spend next day. His main
loytering is at the library, where he studies arms and books of honour,
and turns a gentleman critick in pedigrees. Of all things he endures not to
be mistaken for a scholar, and hates a black suit though it be made of
sattin. His companion is ordinarily some stale fellow, that has been notorious for an ingle to gold hatbands, whom he admires at first, afterward
scorns. If he have spirit or wit he may light of better company, and may
learn some flashes of wit, which may do him knight's service in the country
hereafter. But he is now gone to the inns-of-court, where he studies to
forget what he learned before, his acquaintance and the fashion.

A Plodding Student

Is a kind of alchymist or persecutor of nature, that would change the dull
lead of his brain into finer metal, with success many times as unprosperous,

or at least not quitting the cost, to wit, of his own oil and candles. He has a strange forced appetite to learning, and to atchieve it brings nothing but patience and a body. His study is not great but continual, and consists much in the sitting up till after midnight in a rug-gown and a night-cap, to the vanquishing perhaps of some six lines; yet what he has, he has perfect, for he reads it so long to understand it, till he gets it without book. He may with much industry make a breach into logick, and arrive at some ability in an argument; but for politer studies he dare not skirmish with them, and for poetry accounts it impregnable. His invention is no more than the finding out of his papers, and his few gleanings there; and his disposition of them is as just as the bookbinders, a setting or glewing of them together. He is a great discomforter of young students, by telling them what travel it has cost him, and how often his brain turned at philosophy, and makes others fear studying as a cause of duncery. He is a man much given to apothegms, which serve him for wit, and seldom breaks any jest but which belongs to some Lacedemonian or Roman in Lycosthenes. He is like a dull carrier's horse, that will go a whole week together, but never out of a foot pace; and he that sets forth on the Saturday shall overtake him.

A Pretender to Learning

Is one that would make all others more fools than himself, for though he know nothing, he would not have the world know so much. He conceits nothing in learning but the opinion, which he seeks to purchase without it, though he might with less labour cure his ignorance than hide it. He is indeed a kind of scholar-mountebank, and his art our delusion. He is tricked out in all the accoutrements of learning, and at the first encounter none passes better. He is oftener in his study than at his book, and you cannot pleasure him better than to deprehend him; yet he hears you not till the third knock, and then comes out very angry as interrupted. You find him in his slippers and a pen in his ear, in which formality he was asleep. His table is spread wide with some classick folio, which is as constant to it as the carpet, and hath laid open in the same page this half year. His candle is always a longer sitter up than himself, and the boast of his window at midnight. He walks much alone in the posture of meditation, and has a book still before his face in the fields. His pocket is seldom without a Greek testament or Hebrew bible, which he opens only in the church, and then when some stander-by looks over. He has sentences for company, some scatterings of Seneca and Tacitus, which are good upon all occasions. If he reads any thing in the morning, it comes up all at dinner; and as long as that lasts, the discourse is his. He is a great plagiary of tavern wit, and comes to sermons only that he may talk of Austin. His parcels are the meer scrapings from company, yet he complains at parting what time he has lost. He is wondrously capricious to seem a judgment, and listens with a sower attention to what he understands not. He talks much of Scaliger, and Casaubon, and the Jesuits, and prefers some unheard-of Dutch name before them all. He has verses to bring in upon these and these hints, and it shall go hard but he will wind in his opportunity. He is critical in a language he cannot conster, and speaks seldom under Arminius in divinity. His business and retirement and caller away is his study, and he protests no delight to it comparable. He is a great nomenclator of authors, which he has read in general in the catalogue, and in particular in the title, and goes seldom so far as the dedication. He never talks of any thing but learning, and learns all from talking. Three encounters with the same men pump him, and then he only puts in or gravely says nothing. He has taken pains to be an ass, though not to be a scholar, and is at length discovered and laughed at.

The Latin School

GEORGE SANTAYANA

GEORGE SANTAYANA was born in Madrid in 1863 and lived in Spain until 1872, when his parents took up residence in Boston. The son of a Spanish father, Santayana has kept his Spanish citizenship though the better part of his life has been spent in the United States. He received his education at the Boston Latin School and at Harvard College, to which he returned to teach philosophy in 1889. He left Harvard in 1912 and went abroad to live.

The following chapter from his autobiography Persons and Places *recalls his Latin School days.*

WHEN I search my memory for events and feelings belonging to my earlier boyhood in America, from the age of eight to sixteen, I find for the most part a blank. There are only stray images, like those of early childhood, with no sense of any consecutive interest, any affections or sorrows. And yet I know that my feelings in those years were intense, that I was solitary and unhappy, out of humor with everything that surrounded me, and attached only to a persistent dream-life, fed on books of fiction, on architecture and on religion. I was not precocious; I may have had more ability than the average boy, but it was lavished on boyish thoughts; and a certain backwardness, or unwilling acceptance of reality, characterizes my whole life and philosophy, not indeed as a maxim but as a sentiment.

Why have I forgotten all those years? The causes are no doubt physical, but the effects may be expressed in literary terms. The past cannot be re-enacted except in the language and with the contrasts imposed by the present. The feelings of children, in particular, although intense, are not ordinarily long-lived or deeply rooted. We cry desperately or we silently hate, for not being allowed to do this or to have that; but these objects are trifles. If we remember those occasions they would seem to us indifferent; we should be ashamed to confess those feelings, or we should laugh at them with superior airs: as if the things that now preoccupy us, if we outgrew them, could seem to us more momentous. Thus vast portions of the past—almost all our dreams, almost all our particular thoughts and conversations—become unrecoverable. Our accepted, organized, practically compulsory habits shut them out. But these habits themselves will change more or less with time and with circumstances. Even what we still think we remember will be remembered differently; so that a man's memory may almost become the art of continually varying and misrepresenting his past, according to his interests in the present. This, when it is not intentional or dishonest, involves no deception. Things truly wear those aspects to one another. A point of view and a special lighting are not distortions. They are conditions of vision, and spirit can see nothing not focused in some living eye.

Something like this was in Goethe's mind when he entitled his essay on his life *Fiction and Truth* or *Truth and Poetry;* not that any facts were to be reported inaccurately or invented, but that his mature imagination, in which those facts were pictured, could not but veil them in an atmosphere of serenity, dignity, and justice, utterly foreign to his original romantic experience. I am no Goethe; the atmosphere of my aging mind is not Olympian, and in retrospect it cannot help lending to my insignificant contacts with the world some flavors that Goethe's wisdom had washed out, though they were not absent from his younger days: I mean salt, pepper, and pity for mankind.

Of Miss Welchman's Kindergarten in Chestnut Street, my first school in Boston, I remembered only that we had cards with holes pricked in them, and colored worsted that we were invited to pass through the holes, making designs to suit our own fancy. I suppose this was calculated to develop artistic originality, not to convince us how trivial that originality is, and how helpless without traditional models. I remember also that I used to walk home with another boy, not so old as I, but also much older than the other children; that there were banks of snow on both sides of the path; and that one day—this must have been in spring for there was a bush with red flowers in his grass plot—he said something very strange as he left me, and ran up the steps into his house. I reported what he had said to Susana, who pronounced it *pantheism:* perhaps it was that those red flowers were opening because God was awakening in them. This shows how far my English had got in that Kindergarten and how we lisped metaphysics there.

The Brimmer School, where I went during the next winter, 1873-1874, was the public grammar school of our city district, although more than a mile from our house, in the depths of the South End. I had to walk the whole level length of Beacon Street, cross the Common, and go some distance downhill in Tremont Street to Common Street, where the school was situated, looking like a police station. It was a poor boys' free school, the roughest I was ever in, where the rattan played an important part, although usually behind the scenes, and where there was an atmosphere of rowdiness and ill-will, requiring all sorts of minor punishments, such as standing in the corner or being detained after school. I don't know what lessons we had, except that there were oral spelling-matches, in which naturally I didn't shine. A word spelt aloud (as some Americans like to do facetiously, instead of pronouncing it) still puzzles me and leaves me dumb. Nevertheless, partly because I was older and bigger than most of the boys, I soon became "monitor," and had my little desk beside the teacher's, a woman, facing the whole class. This distinction was invidious, and there were attempts at chasing me or hooting at me when we got out of school. Only once did it come to blows; and inexpert as I was at fisticuffs, or rather wrestling, I was taller, and managed to hold my own, and make my nasty little enemy sneak away sullenly. And I was not friendless. There was another boy from the West End, Bob Upham by name, with whom I usually crossed the Common; this was the danger-zone, since in the streets there were policemen who understood these things and would stop hostilities. On that occasion Bob Upham behaved according to the strictest rules of honor, standing by me sympathetically, but without interfering, and he afterwards said that the other boy had "Very nearly got me." But I hadn't been at all hurt, and never have had another opportunity to try my hand at the manly art, in which no doubt I should have been a miserable failure.

By a happy chance it was possible to transfer me the next year to a much better school, the historic Latin School, where from the earliest times until my day at least, all well-educated Bostonians had been prepared for College. The School Committee in the City government had that year decided to try an experiment, and establish a preparatory course of two years, to precede the six traditional classes. The experiment was not long continued, but I profited by it, and passed eight full years in the Latin School, thus being more of a Latin School boy than almost anybody else. We were not lodged during those preliminary years in the regular School-house, but at first in Harrison Avenue, and later in Mason Street. Both these places, as well as the Schoolhouse in Bedford Street, were in a central quarter of the town. I still had to cross the Common, but now to West Street, whence it was but a step to those schoolhouses.

More than once in my life I have crossed a desert in all that regards myself, my thoughts, or my happiness; so that when I look back over those years, I see objects, I see public events, I see *persons and places,* but I don't see myself. My inner life, as I recall it, seems to be concentrated in a few oases, in a few halter-places, *Green Inns,* or Sanctuaries, where the busy traveller stopped to rest, to think, and to be himself. I say the *busy* traveller, because those long stretches of spiritual emptiness were filled with daily actions and feelings, later in my case often with giving lectures and writing books: yet all was done under some mechanical stimulus, the college bell, the desk, the pen, or the chapter planned: old thoughts and old words flowing out duly from the reservoir, until the college bell rang again, and the water was turned off. Of myself in those years I have no recollection; it is as if I hadn't existed, or only as a mechanical sensorium and active apparatus, doing its work under my name. Somnambulistic periods, let me call them; and such a period now seems to begin and to last for two-thirds of my Latin School days.

Certain detached images, with the crude spectral coloring of a child's picture-book, remain from this first somnambulist season. At the school in Harrison Avenue I can see the yellow wainscoting of the schoolroom, and the yellow desks; and especially I can see the converging leaden sides of the sink, where on one winter morning the teacher—now a man—sent me to thaw out my ears, frozen stiff on the way to school. I was to bathe them in cold water; there was sharp pain and subsequently enormous blisters; but the accident never recurred, although I resolutely refused all scarves, pads, or ridiculous cloth rosettes, such as the women recommended to protect those asinine organs. I found that a little pressure, applied at the right moment, at once brought the warm blood coursing back, and prevented trouble. Cold, rain, and wind, unless there were dust, never spoilt my pleasure in the open air when I was young; on the contrary, I liked them.

I remember also my first Headmaster at the Latin School, Mr. Gardner by name: a tall, gaunt figure in some sort of flowing long coat—of course not a gown—with a diminutive head like the knob of a mannikin. The insignificant occiput was enlarged, however, as if by a halo, by a great crop of dusty brown hair. Was it a wig? That suspicion seemed to my mocking young mind curiously comic and exciting. What if it were a wig and should fall off? What if we hung a hook on an invisible wire over the door, to catch it as he sailed out? One day on his rounds of inspection the Headmaster found us having our French lesson. A headmaster has to pretend to know everything, and the pretense soon becomes a conviction. Mr. Gardner at once took over the duty of teaching us his super-French. "The French word *bonne*," he said, "is pronounced in Paris—I have been in Paris myself—exactly as the English word *bun*." Now, I had heard a good deal of French out of school. There had been the French *bonne* Justine, the Alsatian tutor who loved *avec rage*, and the Catholic families in Boston who chatted in French together. And hadn't I inherited from my sisters *La Jeune Abeille du Parnasse Français* and couldn't I say by heart:

> *Et ma plus belle couronne*
> *De lilas*
> *Sera à toi, ma bonne,*
> *Si tu me dis où Dieu n'est pas?*

If *bonne* sounds exactly like bun, would Mr. Gardner maintain that *couronne*, save for that first letter, sounds exactly like *you run?* I was sure that it was as ridiculous to call a *bonne* a bun as to call a bun a *bonne*. But apparently headmasters were like that; and I kept my phonetic science to myself with the immense satisfaction of feeling that I knew better than my teacher.

I may add that at that time our French master was not a Frenchman, but a Yankee farmer named Mr. Capen, whom we called Old Cudjo, and who had a physiological method of acquiring a Parisian accent without needing to accompany the Headmaster to Paris. He would open his mouth wide, like the hippopotamus at the Zoo, and would insert a pencil, to point out exactly what parts of the tongue, lips, palate or larynx we should contract or relax in order to emit the pure French sounds of *u, an, en, in, un,* and *on.* Nobody laughed. I think the boys were rather impressed for the moment by the depth of Mr. Capen's science, and the hopelessness of profiting by it. He was not a man to be trifled with. He had a most thunderous way of playing what he called Voluntaries on the piano; and rumor had it that he had stolen a march, under a heavy handicap of years, on his own son, by marrying the girl his son was engaged to.

Scraps of rude, quaint, grotesque humanity: bits of that Dickensian bohemia still surviving in my day in certain old-fashioned places, of which I shall have occasion to speak again. But the image that for me sets the key to them all appeared when we moved to the Bedford Street schoolhouse. It seemed a vast, rattling old shell of a building, bare, shabby, and forlorn to the point of squalor; not exactly dirty, but worn, shaky, and stained deeply in every part by time, weather, and merciless usage. The dingy red brick—and everything in that world was dingy red brick—had none of that plastic irregularity, those soft pink lights and mossy patina that make some old brick walls so beautiful: here all the surfaces remained stark and unyielding, thin and sharp, like impoverished old maids. This house was too modern to be as solid as the Hollis and Stoughton Halls that I afterwards lived in at Harvard; it had been built in a hurry, and not to last long. The windows were much larger, but blank and somber; their cold, glassy expanse with its slender divisions looked comfortless and insecure. When up three or four worn granite steps you entered the door, the interior seemed musty and ill-lighted, but spacious, even mysterious. Each room had four great windows, but the street and the courts at the side and rear were narrow, and over-shadowed by warehouses or office-buildings. No blackboard was black; all were indelibly clouded with ingrained layers of old chalk; the more you rubbed it out, the more you rubbed it in. Every desk was stained with generations of ink-spots, cut deeply with initials and scratched drawings. What idle thoughts had been wandering for years through all those empty heads in all those tedious school hours! In the best schools, almost all schooltime is wasted. Now and then something is learned that sticks fast; for the rest the boys are merely given time to grow and are kept from too much mischief.

A ramshackle wooden staircase wound up through the heart of the building to the fourth story, where the Hall was; and down those steep and dangerous curves the avalanche of nail-hoofed boys would come thundering, forty or eighty or two hundred together. However short their legs might be, it was simpler and safer, if not altogether inevitable, to rush down spontaneously with the herd rather than to hold back and be pushed or fall out, or be tramped upon or deserted.

And the teachers, though it is not possible for me now to distinguish them all in memory, were surely not out of keeping with their surroundings: disappointed, shabby-genteel, picturesque old Yankees, with a little bitter humor breaking through their constitutional fatigue. I daresay that for them as for me, and for all the boys who were at all sensitive, the school was a familiar symbol of fatality. They hadn't chosen it, they hadn't wanted it, they didn't particularly like it; they knew no reason why it should be the sort of school it was: but there it stood, there they somehow found themselves entangled; and there was nothing else practicable but to go on there, doing what was expected and imposed upon them. You may say that for the teachers at least, in that age of individual initiative and open careers, a thousand alternatives were, or had been, possible; and you may say that they could not have been altogether insensible of their high vocation and the high vocation of their country to create gradually and securely a better world, a world free from superstition, from needless hatreds, from unjust inequalities, and from devastating misery. Yes: but all that was negative; it consisted of things to be got rid of and avoided, and in America the more obvious of them had actually been escaped. Officially, especially now that slavery had been abolished, everything was all right. Everybody was free. Everybody was at work. Almost everybody could be well educated. Almost everbody was married. Therefore almost everybody was, or ought to be, perfectly happy. But were the teachers at the Latin School, perhaps the best of American schools, happy? Or were the boys? Ah, perhaps we should not ask whether they were happy, for they were not rich, but whether they were not enthusiastically conscious of a great work, an endless glorious struggle and perpetual victory, set before them in the world. And I reply, not for myself, since I don't count, being an alien, but in their name, that they decidedly were conscious of no such thing. They had heard of it; but in their daily lives they were conscious only of hard facts, meagerness, routine, petty commitments, and ideals too distant and vague to be worth mentioning.

Those teachers were stray individuals; they had not yet been standardized by educational departments and pedagogy. Some were like village schoolmasters or drudges; elderly men, like Mr. Capen, with crotchets, but good teachers, knowing their particular book and knowing how to keep order, and neither lax nor cruel. Others, especially Mr. Fiske, afterwards headmaster, and Mr. Groce, were younger, with a more modern education. They might have been college professors; they loved their subjects, Greek and English, and allowed them to color their minds out of school hours. In a word, they were *cultivated* men. I was an unprofitable though not unappreciative pupil to Mr. Fiske, because I didn't learn my Greek properly. That was not his fault. If I could have had him for a private tutor I should have become a good Grecian: it would have added immensely to my life and to my philosophy. But I was only one of forty; I was expected to study dryly, mechanically, without the side-lights and the stimulus of non-verbal interest attached to the words. In Latin, I could supply these side-lights and non-verbal interests out of my own store. Latin was the language of the Church, it was old Spanish. The roots were all my roots. But Greek roots were more often foreign and at first unmeaning; they had to be learned by hammering, to which my indolence was not inclined. And there was another difficulty. My apprehension of words is auricular; I must *hear* what I read. I knew, with small variations, what was the sound of Latin. I had heard it all my life; slovenly and corrupt as the Spanish pronunciation of it may be, at least it is something traditional. But what of Greek pronunciation? How should Homer sound? How should Sophocles? How should Xenophon or Plato? The artificial German Greek that we were taught—without even a proper *o*—was impossible. I tried many years later, when I was in Greece, to learn a little of the modern language, in hopes that it might react on my sense for the ancient texts and make me feel at home in them: but the time was too short, my opportunities limited, and I was too old to be quick in such a matter.

Even as it was, however, I learned a little Greek at School after my fashion, and one day surprised Mr. Fiske by reciting a long speech out of *Œdipus Tyrannus* for my ordinary declamation. He couldn't believe his ears, and afterwards privately congratulated me on my pronunciation of the *o*'s. But that didn't make me master of the Greek vocabulary or the Greek inflections. I didn't *study* enough. I learned and remembered well what I could learn from Mr. Fiske without studying. He was an exceedingly nervous, shy man; evidently suffered at having to address any one, or having to find words in which to express his feelings. His whole body would become tense, he would stand almost on tiptoe, with two or three fingers in the side pocket of his trousers, and the other two or three moving outside, as if reaching for the next word. These extreme mannerisms occasioned no ridicule: the boys all saw that there was a clear mind and a good-will behind them; and Mr. Fiske was universally liked and admired. This, although his language was as contorted as his gestures. He always seemed to be translating literally and laboriously from the Greek or the German. When he wished to fix in our minds the meaning of a Greek word he would say, for instance: "χἄράδρα, a ravine, from which our word character, the deeply graven result of long-continued habit." Or "χαταρρέω, to flow down, whence our word *catarrh*, copious down-flowings from the upper regions of the head." We didn't laugh, and we remembered.

Very different was dapper Mr. Groce, our teacher of English composition and literature, a little plump man, with a keen, dry, cheerful, yet irritable disposition, a sparkling bird-like eye, and a little black mustache and diminutive chin-beard. I suspect that he was too intelligent to put up patiently with all the conventions. Had he not been a public-school teacher, dependent on the democratic hypocrisies of a government committee, he might have said unconventional things. This inner rebellion kept him from being sentimental, moralistic, or religious in respect to poetry; yet he *understood* perfectly the penumbra of emotion that good and bad poetry alike may drag after them in an untrained mind. He knew how to rescue the structural and rational beauties of a poem from that bog of private feeling. To me this was a timely lesson, for it was precisely sadness and religiosity and grandiloquence that first attracted me in poetry; and perhaps I owe to Mr. Groce the beginnings of a capacity to distinguish the musical and expressive charm of poetry from its moral appeal. At any rate, at sixteen, I composed my first longish poem, in Spenser's measure, after *Childe Harold* and *Adonais,* full of pessimistic, languid, Byronic sentiments, describing the various kinds of superiority that Night has over Day. It got the prize.

That year I won several other prizes, and began to be a personage in my own estimation, because other people, in my little world, began to take notice of me. At home I had never been petted or praised, and my conceit, which was rather disdain for other things than claims for myself, had had only itself to feed upon. Being noticed had a good effect on me in awakening my sympathy in return without, however, either establishing or much modifying my good opinion of myself. Neither praise nor blame has ever done so. On the contrary, if people praise me I almost always feel that they praise me for the wrong things, for things which they impute to me out of their preconceptions, and which are not in me; and the blame often, though not always, has the same source. Yet blame is apt to be more keen-scented than praise; praise is often silly; but blame, though it may be baseless objectively, probably indicates a true perception of divergence from the critic's standards: so that relatively to the critic, it is seldom mistaken.

I have mentioned declamation: that was another stimulus to vanity. Inwardly it was one more dramatic indulgence, one more occasion for fantastically playing a part, and dreaming awake; as I did in making plans of vast palaces and imaginary islands, where I should one day be monarch, like Sancho Panza; and this slides into the sphere of my youthful religiosity, of which more presently. But, socially considered, declamation was an effort *de se faire valoir,* to make oneself count, to gain a momentary and fictitious ascendency over others. Momentary and fictitious, because our declamation was pure oratory. It had nothing of that political timeliness which characterizes young people's debates in England. With us, the subject matter was legendary, the language learned by rote, stilted and inflated, the thought platitudinous. Apart from the training in mere *elocution* (as indeed it was called) it was practice in feigning, in working up a verbal enthusiasm for any cause, and seeming to prophesy any event. Very useful, no doubt, for future lawyers, politicians, or clergymen—training for that reversible sophistry and propaganda that intoxicates the demagogue and misleads the people.

That prize-day in June, 1880, in the old Boston Music Hall, marked my emergence into public notice. It abolished, or seemed to abolish, my shyness and love of solitude, I could now face any public and speak before it; and this assurance never forsook me afterwards, except when sometimes, in my unwritten lectures or speeches, I found myself out of my element, had nothing to say, or was weary of saying it. In reality I was always out of my element in teaching and in society, and was saying something forced. The dramatic practice of accepting a brief, or developing an argument, helped me for a time. I could be sincere and spontaneous in the logic of my theme, even if the ultimate issue were unreal or problematical; and in reviewing the history of philosophy this critical honesty is enough, and supplies the information and the dialectical training that are officially required. Nevertheless, this was not preaching a gospel. It did not come from the heart. It left the pupil unguided and morally empty, and in the end the teacher felt himself a drudge. My shyness came back in what Hegelians would call a higher form: I was no longer timid or without resource, but rebellious against being roped in and made to play some vulgar trick in a circus. My love of solitude reasserted itself, not that I feared the world, but that I claimed my liberty and my *Lebensraum* beyond it. In solitude it is possible to love mankind; in the world, for one who knows the world, there can be nothing but secret or open war. For those who love war the world is an excellent field, but I am a born cleric or poet. I must see both sides and take neither, in order, ideally, to embrace both, to sing both, and love the different forms that the good and the beautiful wear to different creatures. This comprehensiveness in sympathy by no means implies that good and evil are indistinguishable or dubious. Nature sets definite standards for every living being: the good and the beautiful could not exist otherwise; and the failure or lapse of natural perfection in each is an irreparable evil. But it is, in every case, a ground of sorrow to the spirit, not of rage; for such failure or lapse is fated and involuntary. This sorrow in my case, however, has always been mitigated by the gift of laughter. Laughter helped me both to perceive those defects and to put up with them.

Between the laughing and the weeping philosopher there is no opposition: *the same facts* that make one laugh make one weep. No wholehearted man, no sane art, can be limited to either mood. In me this combination seems to be readier and more pervasive than in most people. I laugh a great deal, laugh too much, my friends tell me; and those who don't understand me think that this merriment contradicts my disillusioned philosophy. *They* apparently, would never laugh if they admitted that life is a dream, that men are animated automata, and that the forms of good and beautiful are as various and evanescent as the natural harmonies that produce them. They think they would collapse or turn to stone, or despair and commit suicide. But probably they would do no such thing: they would adapt themselves to the reality, and laugh. They might even feel a new zest in living, join in some bold adventure, become heroes, and think it glorious to die with a smile for the love of something beautiful. They do not perceive that this is exactly what national leaders and religious martyrs have always done, except that their warm imagination has probably deceived them about the material effects of what they were doing.

My lachrymose prize poem about the beauties of darkness was not my only effusion. The habit of scribbling mocking epigrams has accompanied me through life and invaded the margins of my most serious authors. Mockery is the first puerile form of wit, playing with surfaces without sympathy: I abounded in it. During the winter of 1880-1881 our class, then the second class, formed a society to meet once a week in the evening and have a debate. We hired a bare room in Tremont Street, opposite the Common, with a few benches or chairs in it; some one would propose a resolution or advance an opinion, and the discussion would follow. When my turn came, I read a little satire on all our teachers, in verse, saying very much what I have said about them above; only that my account was more complete, included them all, and treated them less kindly. It had a great success, and the boys wanted to have it printed. Printed it was, but not as it originally stood. "Holy Moses," for instance, which was the nickname current for our headmaster, Moses Merrill, was changed to the less irreverent and more exact phrase: "lordly Moses," and many other things were modified. Then the whole was enveloped in a tirade, of a sentimental sort, about the Bedford Street Schoolhouse, which was about to be abandoned for a new building in the South End. A lot of copies were printed, perhaps two or three hundred; and on the day of our Farewell Public Declamation in the Hall, the Headmaster somehow got wind of its existence, and said, "We hear that one of the boys has written a poem about leaving this old Schoolhouse: will he get up and read it." I had a copy in my pocket: I got up, and read the longish sentimental part and then sat down again, leaving out the personalities. For the moment all was well; but other boys and some outsiders got copies; and the disrespectful gibes at the teachers became public under their noses.

It was a day or two before Christmas, and the School was not to meet again for ten days or more: however, after consulting with the family at home, I went to see the Headmaster at his own house, and explained how everything had happened. He wasn't severe; I had been really very complimentary to him, and had come spontaneously to apologize. But he said I had better write to the various teachers, explaining that I had only intended the thing as a private joke, without any thought that it would become public; and that I must particularly apologize to Mr. Chadwick, whom I had spoken of unkindly, and who felt the blow. When School met again, Mr. Merrill made us a long speech; but nothing more happened, and official sentiment towards me was not unfavorably affected. This appeared at the opening of the next term. My class had to elect the Lieutenant Colonel of the Boston School Regiment, the Colonel that year coming from the English High School; and by a majority of one vote they elected Dick Smith, and then me unanimously for Major of our Battalion. But the Headmaster reversed the order, and appointed me Lieutenant Colonel and Dick Smith Major, without giving reasons, at which legal but arbitrary exhibition of favoritism on the Headmaster's part Dick Smith's father took him out of the School; and I became both Lieutenant Colonel and Major, both offices being almost sinecures.

These incidents established me during my last year as, in a sense, the leading boy in my school, far as I was from being the head of my class: yet in my irregular way I was not bad at my studies, and got six honorable mentions in my Harvard entrance examinations. This capacity of mine to pass examinations and to win prizes was doubtless what had caused Mr. Merrill to prefer me to Dick Smith for the head of the School Battalion; because Dick Smith was a clean manly boy and a gentleman, but not an intellectual luminary. This sporadic brilliancy of mine seemed to render me a better representative of the School as a whole—a surprising and only momentary phenomenon. In reality I remained there, as I remained later at Harvard for twenty-five years, a stranger at heart; and all the false appearances to the contrary would not have misled anybody (as they did not mislead President Eliot and the intelligent public at Harvard) if *athletics* had been important at that time in the School. Now, although there was, I believe, a baseball team, it was an obscure unofficial affair; else my complete uselessness, either as a performer or as manager in such sports, would have at once set me down for a stray individual of no importance to the life of the place. Not that I had then, or ever, any *ideal* hostility to sport or to polite society or even to politics or trade. As customs, as institutions, as historical dramas, these things interest and please me immensely and excite my imagination to sympathy with this form of them or antipathy to that other form. But I can truly live only in the reaction of the mind upon them in religion, poetry, history, and friendship. If I take a practical part, it is only by putting on a domino for the carnival. I am capable of that impulse, I can feel the fun and the intoxication of it; but the louder the rout the greater the frivolity, and the more complete the relief of stripping off the motley, washing away the paint, and returning to solitude, to silence, and to sincerity.

Brookfield and Chips

JAMES HILTON

JAMES HILTON was born in 1900, the son of a London schoolmaster. In 1921 he was graduated from Christ's College, Cambridge. At this time he had already done some writing for the Manchester Guardian *and had published a novel. In 1933 he was asked by the* British Weekly *to write a story for its special Christmas supplement. As the deadline approached with the story still unwritten, Hilton took a trip on his bicycle to clear his mind and, returning, wrote* Good-bye, Mr. Chips *in four days. The* Atlantic Monthly *published the story in its April, 1934, issue. In June of the same year it appeared in book form and became a best-seller. The following chapters are taken from this charming tale of an English schoolmaster.*

ACROSS the road behind a rampart of ancient elms lay Brookfield, russet under its autumn mantle of creeper. A group of eighteenth-century buildings centred upon a quadrangle, and there were acres of playing field beyond; then came the small dependent village and the open fen country. Brookfield, as Wetherby had said, was an old foundation; established in the reign of Elizabeth, as a grammar school, it might, with better luck, have become as famous as Harrow. Its luck, however, had been not so good; the School went up and down, dwindling almost to nonexistence at one time, becoming almost illustrious at another. It was during one of these latter periods, in the reign of the first George, that the main structure had been rebuilt and large additions made. Later, after the Napoleonic Wars and until mid-Victorian days, the School declined again, both in numbers and in repute. Wetherby, who came in 1840, restored its fortunes somewhat; but its subsequent history never raised it to front-rank status. It was, nevertheless, a good school of the second rank. Several notable families supported it; it supplied fair samples of the history-making men of the age—judges, members of parliament, colonial administrators, a few peers and bishops. Mostly, however, it turned out merchants, manufacturers, and professional men, with a good sprinkling of country squires and parsons. It was the sort of school which, when mentioned, would sometimes make snobbish people confess that they rather thought they had heard of it.

These four selections from *Good-bye, Mr. Chips*, by James Hilton, are reprinted by permission of Little, Brown & Company and The Atlantic Monthly Press.

But if it had not been this sort of school it would probably not have taken Chips. For Chips, in any social or academic sense, was just as respectable, but no more brilliant, than Brookfield itself.

It had taken him some time to realize this, at the beginning. Not that he was boastful or conceited, but he had been, in his early twenties, as ambitious as most other young men at such an age. His dream had been to get a headship eventually, or at any rate a senior mastership in a really first-class school; it was only gradually, after repeated trials and failures, that he realized the inadequacy of his qualifications. His degree, for instance, was not particularly good, and his discipline, though good enough and improving, was not absolutely reliable under all conditions. He had no private means and no family connections of any importance. About 1880, after he had been at Brookfield a decade, he began to recognize that the odds were heavily against his being able to better himself by moving elsewhere; but about that time, also, the possibility of staying where he was began to fill a comfortable niche in his mind. At forty, he was rooted, settled, and quite happy. At fifty, he was the doyen of the staff. At sixty, under a new and youthful Head, he *was* Brookfield—the guest of honor at Old Brookfieldian dinners, the court of appeal in all matters affecting Brookfield history and traditions. And in 1913, when he turned sixty-five, he retired, was presented with a check and a writing desk and a clock, and went across the road to live at Mrs. Wickett's. A decent career, decently closed; three cheers for old Chips, they all shouted, at that uproarious end-of-term dinner.

Three cheers, indeed; but there was more to come, an unguessed epilogue, an encore played to a tragic audience.

Chips Returns to Brookfield

1916. . . . The Somme Battle. Twenty-three names read out one Sunday evening.

Toward the close of that catastrophic July, Chatteris talked to Chips one afternoon at Mrs. Wickett's. He was overworked and overworried and looked very ill. "To tell you the truth, Chipping, I'm not having too easy a time here. I'm thirty-nine, you know, and unmarried, and lots of people seem to think they know what I ought to do. Also, I happen to be diabetic, and couldn't pass the blindest M.O., but I don't see why I should pin a medical certificate on my front door."

Chips hadn't known anything about this; it was a shock to him, for he liked Chatteris.

The latter continued: "You see how it is. Ralston filled the place up with young men—all very good, of course—but now most of them have joined up and the substitutes are pretty dreadful, on the whole. They poured ink down a man's neck in prep one night last week—silly fool— got hysterical. I have to take classes myself, take prep for fools like that, work till midnight every night, and get cold-shouldered as a slacker on top of everything. I can't stand it much longer. If things don't improve next term I shall have a breakdown."

"I do sympathize with you," Chips said.

"I hoped you would. And that brings me to what I came here to ask you. Briefly, my suggestion is that—if you felt equal to it and would care to—how about coming back here for a while? You look pretty fit, and, of course, you know all the ropes. I don't mean a lot of hard work for you— you needn't take anything strenuously—just a few odd jobs here and there, as you choose. What I'd like you for more than anything else is not for the actual work you'd do—though that, naturally, would be very valuable —but for your help in other ways—in just *belonging* here. There's nobody ever been more popular than you were, and are still—you'd help to hold things together if there were any danger of them flying to bits. And perhaps there *is* that danger. . . ."

Chips answered, breathlessly and with a holy joy in his heart: "I'll come. . . ."

Chips Becomes Acting Headmaster of Brookfield

He still kept on his rooms with Mrs. Wickett; indeed, he still lived there; but every morning, about half-past ten, he put on his coat and muffler and crossed the road to the School. He felt very fit, and the actual work was not taxing. Just a few forms in Latin and Roman History—the old lessons—even the old pronunciation. The same joke about the Lex Canuleia —there was a new generation that had not heard it, and he was absurdly gratified by the success it achieved. He felt a little like a music-hall favorite returning to the boards after a positively last appearance.

They all said how marvelous it was that he knew every boy's name and face so quickly. They did not guess how closely he had kept in touch from across the road.

He was a grand success altogether. In some strange way he did, and they all knew and felt it, help things. For the first time in his life he felt *necessary*—and necessary to something that was nearest his heart. There is no sublimer feeling in the world, and it was his at last.

He made new jokes, too—about the O.T.C. and the food-rationing sys- tem and the anti-air-raid blinds that had to be fitted on all the windows. There was a mysterious kind of rissole that began to appear on the School

menu on Mondays, and Chips called it *abhorrendum*—"meat to be abhorred." The story went round—heard Chip's latest?

Chatteris fell ill during the winter of '17, and again, for the second time
in his life, Chips became Acting Head of Brookfield. Then in April Chatteris died, and the Governors asked Chips if he would carry on "for the
duration." He said he would, if they would refrain from appointing him
officially. From that last honor, within his reach at last, he shrank instinctively, feeling himself in so many ways unequal to it. He said to Rivers:
"You see, I'm not a young man and I don't want people to—um—expect
a lot from me. I'm like all these new colonels and majors you see everywhere—just a war-time fluke. A ranker—that's all I am really."

1917. 1918. Chips lived through it all. He sat in the headmaster's study
every morning, handling problems, dealing with plaints and requests. Out
of vast experience had emerged a kindly, gentle confidence in himself. To
keep a sense of proportion, that was the main thing. So much of the world
was losing it; as well keep it where it had, or ought to have, a congenial
home.

On Sundays in Chapel it was he who now read out the tragic list, and
sometimes it was seen and heard that he was in tears over it. Well, why
not, the School said; he was an old man; they might have despised anyone
else for the weakness.

One day he got a letter from Switzerland, from friends there; it was
heavily censored, but conveyed some news. On the following Sunday,
after the names and biographies of old boys, he paused a moment and
then added:—

"Those few of you who were here before the War will remember Max
Staefel, the German master. He was in Germany, visiting his home, when
war broke out. He was popular while he was here, and made many friends.
Those who knew him will be sorry to hear that he was killed last week, on
the Western Front."

He was a little pale when he sat down afterward, aware that he had
done something unusual. He had consulted nobody about it, anyhow; no
one else could be blamed. Later, outside the Chapel, he heard an argument:—

"On the Western Front, Chips said. Does that mean he was fighting for
the Germans?"

"I suppose it does."

"Seems funny, then, to read his name out with all the others. After all,
he was an *enemy*."

"Oh, just one of Chip's ideas, I expect. The old boy still has 'em."

Chips, in his room again, was not displeased by the comment. Yes, he
still had 'em—those ideas of dignity and generosity that were becoming
increasingly rare in a frantic world. And he thought: Brookfield will take
them, too, from me; but it wouldn't from anyone else.

Once, asked for his opinion of bayonet practice being carried on near the cricket pavilion, he answered, with that lazy, slightly asthmatic intonation that had been so often and so extravagantly imitated: "It seems —to me—umph—a very vulgar way of killing people."

The yarn was passed on and joyously appreciated—how Chips had told some big brass hat from the War Office that bayonet fighting was vulgar. Just like Chips. And they found an adjective for him—an adjective just beginning to be used: he was pre-War.

Chips Carries On

And once, on a night of full moonlight, the air-raid warning was given while Chips was taking his lower fourth in Latin. The guns began almost instantly, and, as there was plenty of shrapnel falling about outside, it seemed to Chips that they might just as well stay where they were, on the ground floor of School House. It was pretty solidly built and made as good a dugout as Brookfield could offer; and as for a direct hit, well, they could not expect to survive that, wherever they were.

So he went on with his Latin, speaking a little louder amid the reverberating crashes of the guns and the shrill whine of anti-aircraft shells. Some of the boys were nervous; few were able to be attentive. He said, gently: "It may possibly seem to you, Robertson—at this particular moment in the world's history—umph—that the affairs of Caesar in Gaul some two thousand years ago—are—umph—of somewhat secondary importance —and that—umph—the irregular conjugation of the verb *tollo* is—umph— even less important still. But believe me—umph—my dear Robertson— that is not really the case." Just then there came a particularly loud explosion—quite near. "You cannot—umph—judge the importance of things— umph—by the noise they make. Oh dear me, no." A little chuckle. "And these things—umph—that have mattered—for thousands of years—are not going to be—snuffed out—because some stink merchant—in his laboratory —invents a new kind of mischief." Titters of nervous laughter; for Buffles, the pale, lean, and medically unfit science master, was nicknamed the Stink Merchant. Another explosion—nearer still. "Let us—um—resume our work. If it is fate that we are soon to be—umph—interrupted, let us be found employing ourselves in something—umph—really appropriate. Is there anyone who will volunteer to construe?"

Maynard, chubby, dauntless, clever, and impudent, said: "I will, sir."

"Very good. Turn to page forty and begin at the bottom line."

The explosions still continued deafeningly; the whole building shook as if it were being lifted off its foundations. Maynard found the page, which was some way ahead, and began, shrilly:—

"*Genus hoc erat pugnae*—this was the kind of fight—*quo se Germani exercuerant*—in which the Germans busied themselves. Oh, sir, that's good —that's really very funny indeed, sir—one of your very best—"

Laughing began, and Chips added: "Well—umph—you can see—now— that these dead languages—umph—can come to life again—sometimes— eh? Eh?"

Afterward they learned that five bombs had fallen in and around Brookfield, the nearest of them just outside the School grounds. Nine persons had been killed.

The story was told, retold, embellished. "The dear old boy never turned a hair. Even found some old tag to illustrate what was going on. Something in Caesar about the way the Germans fought. You wouldn't think there were things like that in Caesar, would you? And the way Chips laughed . . . you know the way he *does* laugh . . . the tears all running down his face . . . never seen him laugh so much. . . ."

He was a legend.

With his old and tattered gown, his walk that was just beginning to break into a stumble, his mild eyes peering over the steel-rimmed spectacles, and his quaintly humorous sayings, Brookfield would not have had an atom of him different.

November 11, 1918.

News came through in the morning; a whole holiday was decreed for the School, and the kitchen staff were implored to provide as cheerful a spread as war-time rationing permitted. There was much cheering and singing, and a bread fight across the Dining Hall. When Chips entered in the midst of the uproar there was an instant hush, and then wave upon wave of cheering; everyone gazed on him with eager, shining eyes, as on a symbol of victory. He walked to the dais, seeming as if he wished to speak; they made silence for him, but he shook his head after a moment, smiled, and walked away again.

It had been a damp, foggy day, and the walk across the quadrangle to the Dining Hall had given him a chill. The next day he was in bed with bronchitis, and stayed there till after Christmas. But already, on that night of November 11, after his visit to the Dining Hall, he had sent in his resignation to the Board of Governors.

When School reassembled after the holidays he was back at Mrs. Wickett's. At his own request there were no more farewells or presentations, nothing but a handshake with his successor and the word "acting" crossed out on official stationery. The "duration" was over.

Education

ALDOUS HUXLEY

ALDOUS HUXLEY is the grandson of Thomas Henry Huxley, the English biologist. His mother is the granddaughter of the famous Dr. Arnold, headmaster of Rugby. He was sent to Eton, where he had begun to specialize in biology when he became almost completely blind. Within two years he had recovered sufficiently to be able to read, but a scientific career was impossible, and he went to Oxford to study English literature and philology. Four years after receiving his degree from Oxford he began to work on the staff of the Athenaeum, *chiefly writing dramatic, art, and musical criticism. Years of travel followed which finally led him to the United States, where he is now living.*

Though Huxley has written many novels, he has also done brilliant work as an essayist. The following essay on education is from Ends and Means.

Discipline is not the only instrument of character training. One of the major psychological discoveries of modern times was the discovery that the play, not only of small children, but (even more significantly) of adolescents and adults could be turned to educational purposes. Partly by accident, partly by subtle and profound design, English educators of the second half of the nineteenth century evolved the idea of organizing sport for the purpose of training the character of their pupils. At Rugby, during Tom Brown's schooldays, there were no organized games. Dr. Arnold was too whole-heartedly a low-church social reformer, too serious-minded a student of Old Testament history, to pay much attention to a matter seemingly so trivial as his boys' amusements. A generation later, cricket and football was compulsory in every English Public School, and organized sport was being used more and more consciously as a means of shaping the character of the English gentleman.

Like every other instrument that man has invented, sport can be used either for good or for evil purposes. Used well, it can teach endurance and courage, a sense of fair play and a respect for rules, co-ordinated effort and the subordination of personal interests to those of the group. Used badly, it can encourage personal vanity and group vanity, greedy desire for victory and hatred for rivals, an intolerant *esprit de corps* and contempt for people who are beyond a certain arbitrarily selected pale. In either case sport inculcates responsible co-operation; but when it is used badly the co-operation is for undesirable ends and the result upon the individual character is an increase of attachment; when it is used well, the character is modified in the direction of non-attachment. Sport can be either a preparation for war or, in some measure, a substitute for war; a trainer either of potential war-mongers or of potential peace-lovers; an educative influence forming either militarists or men who will be ready and able to apply the principles of pacifism in every activity of life. It is for us to choose which part the organized amusements of children and adults shall play. In the dictatorial countries the choice has been made, consciously and without compromise. Sport there is definitely a preparation for war—doubly a preparation. It is used, first of all, to prepare children for the term of military slavery which they will have to serve when they come of age—to train them in habits of endurance, courage and co-ordinated effort, and to cultivate that *esprit de corps*, that group-vanity and group-pride which are the very foundations of the character of a good soldier. In the second place, it is used as an instrument of nationalistic propaganda. Football matches with teams belonging to foreign countries are treated as matters of national prestige, victory is hailed as a triumph over an enemy, a sign of racial or national superiority; a defeat is put down to foul play and treated almost as a *casus belli*. Optimistic theorists count sport as a bond between nations. In the present state of nationalistic feeling it is only another cause of international misunderstanding. The battles waged on the football field and the race-track are merely preliminaries to, and even contributory causes of, more serious contests. In a world that has no common religion or philosophy of life, but where every national group practises its own private idolatry, international football matches and athletic contests can do almost nothing but harm.

On Reasoning with Children

JEAN JACQUES ROUSSEAU

JEAN JACQUES ROUSSEAU (1712-1778) was born at Geneva, the son of a watchmaker. His early schooling was irregular and haphazard. In 1728 he ran away from home and began the series of wanderings recounted in his Confessions. *In 1745 he was living in Paris and on familiar terms with Diderot. In 1749 he published an essay,* Discours Sur Les Arts et Sciences, *in which he developed the paradox of the superiority of the savage state over the cultivated state. The essay appealed to the taste of the day, and Rousseau became famous. In 1760 he published* La Nouvelle Héloïse, *and in 1762 appeared the* Contrat Social *and* Emile. *The ideas in these novels were not popular with those in authority, and so Rousseau soon found the atmosphere of Paris unfriendly. He took up residence in Neuchâtel, but his unpopularity increasing, he sought asylum in England, where he was befriended by David Hume. A year later, following a quarrel with Hume, he returned to France, where he died in 1778.*

The following selection is taken from Emile.

"Reason with children" was Locke's chief maxim; it is in the height of fashion at present, and I hardly think it is justified by its results; those children who have been constantly reasoned with strike me as exceedingly silly. Of all man's faculties, reason, which is, so to speak, compounded of all the rest, is the last and choicest growth, and it is this you would use for the child's early training. To make a man reasonable is the coping stone of a good education, and yet you profess to train a child through his reason! You begin at the wrong end, you make the end the means. If children understood reason they would not need education, but by talking to them from their earliest age in a language they do not understand you accustom them to be satisfied with words, to question all that is said to them, to think themselves as wise as their teachers; you train them to be argumentative and rebellious; and whatever you think you gain from motives of reason, you really gain from greediness, fear, or vanity with which you are obliged to reinforce your reasoning.

Most of the moral lessons which are and can be given to children may be reduced to this formula:

MASTER You must not do that.

CHILD Why not?

MASTER Because it is wrong.

CHILD Wrong! What is wrong?

MASTER What is forbidden you.

CHILD Why is it wrong to do what is forbidden?

MASTER You will be punished for disobedience.

CHILD I will do it when no one is looking.

MASTER We shall watch you.

CHILD I will hide.

MASTER We shall ask you what you were doing.

CHILD I shall tell a lie.

MASTER You must not tell lies.

CHILD Why must not I tell lies?

MASTER Because it is wrong, etc.

That is the inevitable circle. Go beyond it, and the child will not understand you. What sort of use is there in such teaching? I should greatly like to know what you would substitute for this dialogue. It would have puzzled Locke himself. It is no part of a child's business to know right and wrong, to perceive the reason for a man's duties.

Nature would have them children before they are men. If we try to invert this order we shall produce a forced fruit immature and flavourless, fruit which will be rotten before it is ripe; we shall have young doctors and old children. Childhood has its own ways of seeing, thinking, and feeling; nothing is more foolish than to try and substitute our ways; and I should no more expect judgment in a ten-year-old child than I should expect him to be five feet high. Indeed, what use would reason be to him at that age? It is the curb of strength, and the child does not need the curb.

When you try to persuade your scholars of the duty of obedience, you add to this so-called persuasion compulsion and threats, or still worse, flattery and bribes. Attracted by selfishness or constrained by force, they pretend to be convinced by reason. They see as soon as you do that obedience is to their advantage and disobedience to their disadvantage. But as you only demand disagreeable things of them, and as it is always disagreeable to do another's will, they hide themselves so that they may do as they please, persuaded that they are doing no wrong so long as they are not found out, but ready, if found out, to own themselves in the wrong for fear of worse evils. The reason for duty is beyond their age, and there is not a man in the world who could make them really aware of it; but the fear of punishment, the hope of forgiveness, importunity, the difficulty of answering, wrings from them as many confessions as you want; and you think you have convinced them when you have only wearied or frightened them.

What does it all come to? In the first place, by imposing on them a duty which they fail to recognise, you make them disinclined to submit to your tyranny, and you turn away their love; you teach them deceit, falsehood,

and lying as a way to gain rewards or escape punishment; then by accus-
toming them to conceal a secret motive under the cloak of an apparent
one, you yourself put into their hands the means of deceiving you, of
depriving you of a knowledge of their real character, of answering you
and others with empty words whenever they have the chance. Laws, you
say, though binding on conscience, exercise the same constraint over
grown-up men. That is so, but what are these men but children spoilt by
education? This is just what you should avoid. Use force with children and
reasoning with men; this is the natural order; the wise man needs no laws.

The Last Class

ALPHONSE DAUDET

ALPHONSE DAUDET (1840-1897) was born at Nîmes, in Southern France. His father was the prosperous owner of a silk factory until the Revolution of 1848 ruined the business and plunged the family into poverty. Young Daudet attended the Lycée at Lyons, and at sixteen accepted a position as proctor in a school at Alais. Life in this school proving intolerable, Daudet went to Paris in 1857 to make his way in literature. His first publication was a volume of poems which attracted the attention of the Empress Eugénie and gained for Daudet the position of private secretary to the Duke of Morny. He turned to the writing of fiction and plays and with the publication of Le Petit Chose *in 1868 achieved a position as a man of letters. He died in Paris in 1897.*

ON that morning I was late getting started to school, and I was very much afraid of being scolded, all the more so as Mr. Hamel had told us that he would question us about the participles, and I did not know the first word about them. For a moment I thought of absenting myself from the class and of making my way off across the fields. The weather was so bright and warm.

You could hear the blackbirds calling at the edge of the woods, and in Rippert's field, behind the sawmill were the Prussian soldiers drilling. All that attracted me much more than the rules about the participles. But I had the will-power to resist, and I ran along very fast to school.

Passing the town hall I noticed that there were a number of people gathered before the little bulletin board. For two years it had been from there that came all the bad news of battles lost, of requisitions, of orders from the Commandant, and I thought to myself, without stopping:

"And now what is the matter?"

Then, as I was running across the Square, the old blacksmith Wachter, who was there with his apprentice reading the notice, called out to me:

"Don't hurry so fast, my lad; you'll get to your school in plenty of time!"

I thought he was laughing at me, and I, all out of breath, entered Mr. Hamel's little court.

Usually, at the beginning of the class, there was a big uproar which one could hear clear out in the street, desks opened and closed, lessons which everybody together was reciting aloud, stopping up his ears in order the better to learn, and the master's big ruler thumping on the table.

"A little silence, please!"

I was counting upon all that turmoil to gain my seat without being seen; but actually, on that day, everything was as silent as on a Sunday morning. Through the open window, I could see my comrades already in their places, and Mr. Hamel, moving back and forth with his terrible iron ruler under his arm. I had to open the door and enter in the midst of that great calm! You can imagine how red was my face, and how scared I was!

But no, Mr. Hamel just looked at me with no anger at all, and said very gently to me:

"Take your seat quickly, my little Frantz; we were about to begin without you."

I climbed over the bench and sat down immediately at my desk. Then only, somewhat recovered from my fear, did I notice that our master was wearing his fine, green frock-coat, his ruffled frill and his embroidered, black silk skullcap which he would wear only on days when the Committee came to visit school, and to distribute prizes. However, there was something unusual, and very solemn about the whole School. But what surprised me most was to see, at the back of the schoolroom, sitting on the benches which were ordinarily empty, some of the townspeople, all as silent as we were. There was old Hauser with his tricorne, the former mayor, the old postman, and several more people. All of them seemed sad; and Hauser had brought with him an old, tattered spelling book which he was holding wide open on his knees, with his big glasses lying across its pages.

While I was recovering from my astonishment at all that, Mr. Hamel had mounted the platform, and with the same grave and gentle voice with which he had received me, he said to us:

"My children, this is the last time that I shall hold the class. The order has come from Berlin to teach no longer anything except German in the schools of Alsace and Lorraine. The new master will arrive tomorrow. Today we have our last lesson in French. So please be very attentive."

These few words overwhelmed me. Ah! The wretches! That is what they had posted at the townhall!

My last French lesson!

And I who hardly knew how to write! And now I should never learn! And I should have to stop there! Now how I begrudged the time I had lost, the classes I had skipped in order to go hunting for birds' nests, or to go sliding in the sand on the banks of the Saar! My books which just now I was still finding so boring, so heavy to carry, my grammar, my spelling book, my Bible studies, all seemed now to be old friends the parting with whom gave me great pain. And it was just the same with Mr. Hamel. The thought that he was going to leave us, that I should never see him again, make me forget the punishments and the blows of his ruler.

Poor man! It was in honour of this last class that he had donned his Sunday garb, and now I understood why all those old people from the village had come in and sat down at the back of the schoolroom. It seemed to say that they were sorry for not having come more often to school. It was also a way of thanking our old master for his forty years of faithful service, and of paying their respects to our fatherland which was going away . . .

I was at that point in my thoughts when I heard my name called. It was my turn to recite. What would I not have given to be able to quote the whole length of that famous rule of the participles! To say it loudly, and clearly without one mistake! But I was confused at the first words, and I stood there at my bench, shuffling my foot in confusion, with a heavy heart, not daring to raise my head. I heard Mr. Hamel speaking to me:

"I shall not scold you, my little Frantz, for you are punished enough already. That is the way it is. Everyday one says to himself: "Bah! I have time enough. I will learn it tomorrow." And you see what happens. . . . Ah, that has been the great misfortune of our Alsace, always putting off its instruction until tomorrow. Now these people have the right to say to us: "What! you claim to be French, and you don't know how either to speak or write your own language!" In all that, my poor Frantz, it is not you who are the most guilty. We all have our own good share of reproaches to make ourselves. Your parents have not been eager enough to see you learn. They preferred to send you to work in the fields, or to the spinning shops in order to have a few more sous. And I, have I nothing to reproach myself about? Haven't I often made you water my garden instead of learning your lessons? And when I wished to go trout fishing did I hesitate at all to give you a holiday?"

Then from one thing to another Mr. Hamel went on, and finally began to talk to us about the French language, saying that it was the most beautiful language in the world, the clearest, the most substantial; that we must keep it alive amongst ourselves, and never forget it, because when a race of people falls into slavery, it is as if it held a key to its prison so long as it holds fast to its language. Then he took a grammar and read us our lesson. I was astonished to see how well I understood it. Everything that he was saying seemed clear to me, and easy. And I think also that I had never before listened so attentively, and that he had never before made his explanations with such patience. One would have said that, before going away the poor man wished to give us all his knowledge, to drive it all into our heads with one stroke.

The grammar lesson finished, we went on to the writing lesson. For that day, Mr. Hamel had prepared for us entirely new examples, upon which he had written in his beautiful roundhand: France, Alsace, France, Alsace. It was like having little flags floating around the classroom, hung at the corners of our desks. You should have seen how hard everyone was working, and what a silence there was! You could hear nothing but the scratching of our pens. Once some Junebugs came in, but nobody paid any attention to them, not even the smallest children who were busy tracing their strokes as if it were already French which they were writing, so heartily and so conscientiously. On the roof of the schoolhouse some pigeons were cooing softly, and I said to myself hearing them: "Are they going to make them, too, sing in German?"

From time to time, raising my eyes above my page, I would see Mr. Hamel motionless on the platform staring at the objects around him as if he wished to carry away with him in his vision his whole little schoolhouse. Just think! He had been there in the same place with his court before him, and his class always just the same. Only the benches had been polished and rubbed by use; the walnut trees in the yard had grown big, and the hop vine which he himself had planted, now twined around all the windows, clear to the roof. How heart-breaking all that must be to that poor man who was going away, and to hear his sister moving about in the room above, busy closing their trunks! For they were to leave the very next morning, and to go away from their country forever!

All the same he had the courage to keep our class right to the end. After the writing lesson we had our history; then the little children sang all together the ba, be, bi, bo, bu. Yonder, at the back of the room old Hauser had put on his spectacles, and holding his spelling book in both hands, he spelled out the words with them. You could see that he too was applying himself to the lesson; his voice trembled with emotion, and it was so funny to hear him that we all felt like laughing and crying. Ah! I shall remember that last class . . .

All at once the clock from the church struck noon, and then the Angelus. At that very moment the trumpets of the Prussians who were returning from Drill, broke out under our windows. Mr. Hamel rose very pale from his chair. Never had he seemed to me so tall.

"My friends," said he, "my friends, I . . . I . . ."

But something seemed to choke him. He was unable to finish the sentence. Then he turned towards the blackboard, took a piece of chalk, and bearing down with all his strength, he wrote in letters as large as he could:

"Vive la France!"

He remained there, with his head leaned against the wall, and, without speaking, with his hand he motioned to us:

"It is all over, go now!"

Oxford Education

EDWARD GIBBON

EDWARD GIBBON (1737-1794) was educated at Westminster and at Magdalen College, Oxford. He remained at Oxford only fourteen months, "the most idle and unprofitable of my whole life." At the age of sixteen he became a Roman Catholic, but, after studying under a Calvinist minister at Lausanne, he was reconverted to Protestantism. In 1758 he returned to London and for a year devoted his time to reading. From 1759 to 1763 he served in the Hampshire militia. In the following year, while touring in Italy, he formed the plan of his History of the Decline and Fall of the Roman Empire. The work was completed in 1788.

The following excerpt dealing with Gibbon's unhappy experience at Oxford is taken from his Memoirs, published two years after his death.

A TRAVELLER, who visits Oxford or Cambridge, is surprised and edified by the apparent order and tranquillity that prevail in the seats of the English muses. In the most celebrated universities of Holland, Germany, and Italy, the students, who swarm from different countries, are loosely dispersed in private lodgings at the houses of the burghers: they dress according to their fancy and fortune; and in the intemperate quarrels of youth and wine, their *swords,* though less frequently than of old, are sometimes stained with each other's blood. The use of arms is banished from our English universities; the uniform habit of the academics, the square cap, and black gown, is adapted to the civil and even clerical profession; and from the Doctor in Divinity to the undergraduate, the degrees of learning and age are externally distinguished. Instead of being scattered in a town, the students of Oxford and Cambridge are united in colleges; their maintenance is provided at their own expense or that of the founders; and the stated hours of the hall and chapel represent the discipline of a regular, and as it were, a religious community. The eyes of the traveller are attracted by the size or beauty of the public edifices; and the principal colleges appear to be so many palaces, which a liberal nation has erected and endowed for the habitation of science. My own introduction to the university of Oxford forms a new era in my life; and at the distance of forty years I still remember my first emotions of surprise and satisfaction. In my fifteenth year I felt myself suddenly raised from a boy to a man; the persons whom I respected as my superiors in age and academical rank entertained me with every mark of attention and civility; and my vanity was flattered by the velvet cap and silk gown, which distinguish a gentleman commoner from a plebeian student. A decent allowance, more money than a schoolboy had ever seen, was at my own disposal; and I might command, among the tradesmen of Oxford, an indefinite and dangerous latitude of credit. A key was delivered into my hands, which gave me the free use of a numerous and learned library, my apartment consisted of three elegant and well-furnished rooms in the new building, a stately pile, of Magdalen College, and the adjacent walks, had they been frequented by Plato's disciples, might have been compared to the Attic shade on the banks of the Ilissus. Such was the fair prospect of my entrance (April 3, 1752) into the University of Oxford. . . .

I spent fourteen months at Magdalen College; they proved the fourteen months the most idle and unprofitable of my whole life: the reader will pronounce between the school and the scholar; but I cannot affect to believe that Nature had disqualified me for all literary pursuits. The specious and ready excuse of my tender age, imperfect preparation, and hasty departure may doubtless be alleged, nor do I wish to defraud such excuses of their proper weight. Yet in my sixteenth year I was not devoid of capacity or application; even my childish reading had displayed an early though blind propensity for books; and the shallow flood might have been taught to flow in a deep channel and a clear stream. . . .

Perhaps, in a separate annotation, I may coolly examine the fabulous and real antiquities of our sister universities, a question which has kindled such fierce and foolish disputes among their fanatic sons. In the meanwhile it will be acknowledged that these venerable bodies are sufficiently old to partake of the prejudices and infirmities of age. The schools of Oxford and Cambridge were founded in a dark age of false and barbarous science; and they are still tainted with the vices of their origin. Their primitive discipline was adapted to the education of priests and monks; and the government still remains in the hands of the clergy, an order of men whose manners are remote from the present world, and whose eyes are dazzled by the light of philosophy. The legal incorporation of these societies by the charters of popes and kings had given them a monopoly of the public instruction; and the spirit of monopolists is narrow, lazy, and oppressive; their work is more costly and less productive than that of independent artists; and the new improvements so eagerly grasped by the competition of freedom, are admitted with slow and sullen reluctance in those proud corporations, above the fear of a rival, and below the confession of an error. We can scarcely hope that any reformation will be a voluntary act; and so deeply are they rooted in law and prejudice, that even the omnipotence of parliament would shrink from an inquiry into the state and abuses of the two universities. . . .

In all the universities of Europe, excepting our own, the languages and sciences are distributed among a numerous list of effective professors: the students, according to their taste, their calling, and their diligence, apply themselves to the proper masters; and in the annual repetition of public and private lectures, these masters are assiduously employed. Our curiosity may enquire what number of professors has been instituted at Oxford? (for I shall now confine myself to my own university;) by whom are they appointed and what may be the probable chances of merit or incapacity? how many are stationed to the three faculties, and how many are left for the liberal arts? what is the form and what the substance, of their lessons? But all these questions are silenced by one short and singular answer, "That in the university of Oxford, the greater part of the public professors have for these many years given up altogether even the pretence of teaching." Incredible as the fact may appear, I must rest my belief on the positive and impartial evidence of a master of moral and political wisdom, who had himself resided at Oxford. Dr. Adam Smith assigns as the cause of their indolence, that instead of being paid by voluntary contributions, which would urge them to increase the number, and to deserve the gratitude of their pupils, the Oxford professors are secure in the enjoyment of a fixed stipend, without the necessity of labour, or the apprehension of control. . . .

The college of St. Mary Magdalen was founded in the fifteenth century by Wainfleet, Bishop of Winchester; and now consists of a President, forty fellows, and a number of inferior students. It is esteemed one of the largest and most wealthy of our academical corporations, which may be compared to the Benedictine abbeys of Catholic countries; and I have loosely heard that the estates belonging to Magdalen College, which are leased by those indulgent landlords at small quit-rents and occasional fines, might be raised, in the hands of private avarice, to an annual revenue of nearly thirty thousand pounds. Our colleges are supposed to be schools of science as well as of education; nor is it unreasonable to expect that a body of literary men, devoted to a life of celibacy, exempt from the care of their own subsistence, and amply provided with books, should devote their leisure to the prosecution of study, and that some of their studies should be manifested to the world. The shelves of their library groan under the weight of the Benedictine folios, of the editions of the fathers, and the collections of the middle ages, which have issued from the single abbey of St. Germain des Préz at Paris. A composition of genius must be the offspring of one mind; but such works of industry as may be divided among many hands, and must be continued during many years, are the peculiar province of a laborious community. If I inquire into the manufactures of the monks of Magdalen, if I extend the inquiry to the other colleges of Oxford and Cambridge, a silent blush, or a scornful frown, will be the only reply. The fellows or monks of my time were decent easy men, who supinely enjoyed the gifts of the founder; their days were filled by a series of uniform employments; the chapel and the hall, the coffee-house and the common room, till they retired, weary and well satisfied, to a

long slumber. From the toil of reading, or thinking, or writing, they had
absolved their conscience; and the first shoots of learning and ingenuity
withered on the ground, without yielding any fruits to the owners or the
public. As a gentleman commoner, I was admitted to the society of the
fellows, and fondly expected that some questions of literature would be
the amusing and instructive topics of their discourse. Their conversation
stagnated in a round of college business, Tory politics, personal anecdotes, and private scandal: their dull and deep potations excused the brisk
intemperance of youth; and their constitutional toasts were not expressive
of the most lively loyalty for the House of Hanover. A general election was
now approaching: the great Oxfordshire contest already blazed with all
the malevolence of party zeal. Magdalen College was devoutly attached
to the old interest! and the names of Wenman and Dashwood were more
frequently pronounced than those of Cicero and Chrysostom. The example of the senior fellows could not inspire the undergraduates with a
liberal spirit of studious emulation; and I cannot describe, as I never
knew, the discipline of college. Some duties may possibly have been imposed on the poor scholars, whose ambition aspired to the peaceful honours of a fellowship (*ascribi quietis ordinibus . . . Deorum*); but no independent members were admitted below the rank of a gentleman commoner, and our velvet cap was the cap of liberty. A tradition prevailed
that some of our predecessors had spoken Latin declamations in the hall,
but of the ancient custom no vestige remained: the obvious methods of
public exercises and examinations were totally unknown; and I have never
heard that either the president or the society interfered in the private
economy of the tutors and their pupils.

Going Back to School

MAX BEERBOHM

*MAX BEERBOHM, English novelist and essayist, was born in London in
1872. He was educated at Charterhouse and at Merton College, Oxford,
where he was well known for his wit and his satiric cartoons. He went to
London to engage in journalism and in 1898 succeeded Bernard Shaw as
dramatic critic of the* Saturday Review. *He became famous for his parodies
and for his caricatures, both of which were aimed at literary mannerisms
and social pretense.*

*As an essayist he is a master of deft irony. E. F. Benson once said of him
that he "purifies the mind not by pity and terror, but by laughter."*

THE other evening, at about seven o'clock, I was in a swift hansom.
My hat was tilted at a gay angle, and, for all I was muffled closely, my
gloves betokened a ceremonious attire. I was smoking *la cigarette d'ap-
pétit*, and was quite happy. Outside Victoria my cab was stopped by a file
of other cabs, that were following one another in at the main entrance of
the station. I noticed, on one of them, a small hat-box, a newish trunk and
a corded play-box, and I caught one glimpse of a very small, pale boy in
a billicock-hat. He was looking at me through the side-window. If Envy
was ever inscribed on any face, it was inscribed on the face of that very
small, pale boy. "There," I murmured, "but for the grace of God, goes
Max Beerbohm!"

My first thought, then, was for myself. I could not but plume me on the
contrast of my own state with his. But, gradually, I became fulfilled with a
very great compassion for him. I understood the boy's Envy so well. It was
always the most bitter thing, in my own drive to the station, to see other
people, quite happy, as it seemed, with no upheaval of their lives; people
in cabs, who were going out to dinner and would sleep in London;
grown-up people! Than the impotent despair of those drives—I had exactly fifteen of them—I hope that I shall never experience a more awful
emotion. Those drives have something, surely, akin with drowning. In
their course the whole of a boy's home-life passes before his eyes, every
phase of it standing out against the black curtain of his future. The author
of *Vice-Versa* has well analyzed the feeling, and he is right, I think, in

saying that all boys, of whatsoever temperament, are preys to it. Well do I remember how, on the last day of the holidays, I used always to rise early, and think that I had got twelve more whole hours of happiness, and how those hours used to pass me with mercifully slow feet. . . . Three more hours! . . . Sixty more minutes! . . . Five! . . . I used to draw upon my tips for a first-class ticket, that I might not be plunged suddenly among my companions, with their hectic and hollow mirth, their dreary disinterment of last term's jokes. I used to revel in the thought that there were many stations before G—— . . . The dreary walk, with my small bag, up the hill! I was not one of those who made a rush for the few cabs! . . . The awful geniality of the House Master! The jugs in the dormitory! . . . Next morning, the bell that woke me! The awakening!

Not that I had any special reason for hating school! Strange as it may seem to my readers, I was not unpopular there. I was a modest, good-humoured boy. It is Oxford that has made me insufferable. At school, my character remained in a state of undevelopment. I had a few misgivings, perhaps. In some respect, I was always too young, in others, too old, for a perfect relish of the convention. As I hovered, in grey knickerbockers, on a cold and muddy field, round the outskirts of a crowd that was tearing itself limb from limb for the sake of a leathern bladder, I would often wish for a nice, warm room and a good game of hunt-the-slipper. And, when we sallied forth, after dark, in the frost, to the swimming-bath, my heart would steal back to the fireside in Writing School and the plot of Miss Braddon's latest novel. Often, since, have I wondered whether a Spartan system be really well for youths who are bound mostly for Capuan Universities. It is true, certainly, that this system makes Oxford or Cambridge doubly delectable. Under-graduates owe their happiness chiefly to the consciousness that they are no longer at school. The nonsense which was knocked out of them at school is all put gently back at Oxford or Cambridge. And the discipline to which they are subject is so slight that it does but serve to accentuate their real freedom. The sudden reaction is rather dangerous, I think, to many of them.

Even now, much of my own complacency comes of having left school. Such an apparition as that boy in the hansom makes me realise my state more absolutely. Why, after all, should I lavish my pity on him and his sorrows? *Dabit deus his quoque finem.* I am at a happier point in Nature's cycle. That is all. I have suffered every one of his ordeals, and I do not hesitate to assure him, if he chance to see this essay of mine, how glad I am that I do not happen to be his contemporary. I have no construe of Xenophon to prepare for to-morrow morning, nor any ode of Horace to learn, painfully, by heart. I assure him that I have no wish nor any need to master, as he has, at this moment, the intricate absurdities of that proposition in the second book of Euclid. I have no locker, with my surname printed on it and a complement of tattered school-books. I burnt all my school-books, when I went up to Oxford. Were I to meet, now, any one of those masters who are monsters to you, my boy, he would treat me even more urbanely, it may be, than I should treat him. When he sets you a hundred lines, you write them without pleasure, and he tears them up. When I, with considerable enjoyment and at my own leisure, write a hundred lines or so, they are printed for all the world to admire, and I am paid for them enough to keep you in pocket-money for many terms. I write at a comfortable table, by a warm fire, and occupy an arm-chair, whilst you are sitting on a narrow form. My boots are not made "for school-wear," nor do they ever, like yours, get lost in a litter of other boots in a cold boot-room. In a word, I enjoy myself immensely. To-night, I am going to a theatre. Afterwards, I shall sup somewhere and drink wine. When I come home and go to bed, I shall read myself to sleep with some amusing book. . . . You will have torn yourself from your bed, at the sound of a harsh bell, have washed, quickly, in very cold water, have scurried off to Chapel, gone to first school and been sent down several places in your form, tried to master your next construe, in the interval of snatching a tepid breakfast, been kicked by a bigger boy, and had a mint of horrible experiences long before I, your elder by a few years, have awakened, very gradually, to the tap of knuckles on the panel of my bed-room-door. I shall make a leisurely toilet. I shall descend to a warm breakfast, open one of the little budgets which my "damned good-natured friend," Romeike, is always sending me, and glance at that morning paper which appeals most surely to my sense of humour. And when I have eaten well of all the dishes on the table, I shall light a cigarette. Through the haze of its fragrant smoke, I shall think of the happy day that is before me.

Old School-Day Romances

JAMES WHITCOMB RILEY

JAMES WHITCOMB RILEY, Hoosier poet, was born in Indiana in 1849. His formal schooling was acquired at a three-room public school where the standard text was McGuffey's Reader. *School held little interest for him; far more interesting were his visits to the courthouse with his lawyer father, his contacts with the manners and speech of Indiana country folk. At sixteen he left school and began his career in journalism as editor of the town newspaper. In 1877 he was at work on the Indianapolis* Journal, *contributing the homely verses in rustic dialect that eventually brought him fame. His first collection of poems was published in 1883. Other volumes followed, and soon Riley was well known for his use of Hoosier dialect, his sentimentality, and his cheerful philosophy. Before his death in 1916 he had become a national figure.*

O F the wealth of facts and fancies
    That our memories may recall,
The old school-day romances
    Are the dearest, after all!—
When some sweet thought revises
    The half-forgotten tune
That opened "Exercises"
    On "Friday Afternoon."

We seem to hear the clicking
    Of the pencil and the pen,
And the solemn ceaseless ticking
    Of the time-piece ticking then;
And we note the watchful master,
    As he waves the warning rod,
With our own heart beating faster
    Than the boy's who threw the wad.

Some little hand uplifted,
    And the creaking of a shoe:—

A problem left unsifted
  For the teacher's hand to do.
The murmured hum of learning,
  And the flutter of a book—
The smell of something burning,
  And the school's inquiring look.

The bashful boy in blushes;
  And the girl, with glancing eyes,
Who hides her smiles, and hushes
  The laugh about to rise,—
Then, with a quick invention,
  Assumes a serious face,
To meet the words, "Attention!
  Every scholar in his place!"

The opening song, page twenty—
  Ah! dear old "Golden Wreath,"
You willed your sweets in plenty;
  And some who look beneath
The leaves of Time will linger,
  And loving tears will start,
As Fancy trails her finger
  O'er the index of the heart.

"Good news from Home"—We hear it
  Welling tremulous, yet clear
And holy as the spirit
  Of the song we used to hear—
"Good news for me"—(A throbbing
  And an aching melody)—
"Has come across the"—(sobbing,
  Yea, and salty) "dark blue sea!"

Or the pæan "Scotland's burning!"
  With its mighty surge and swell
Of chorus, still returning
  To its universal yell—
Till we're almost glad to drop to
  Something sad and full of pain—
And "Skip verse three," and stop, too,
  Ere our hearts are broke again.

Then "the big girls'" compositions,
  With their doubt, and hope, and glow

Of heart and face,—conditions
    Of "the big boys"—even so,
When themes of "Spring" and "Summer,"
    And of "Fall" and "Wintertime"
Droop our heads and hold us dumber
    Than the sleighbell's fancied chime.

Elocutionary Science—
    Still in changeless infancy!—
With its "Cataline's Defiance,"
    And "The Banner of the Free":
Or—lured from Grandma's attic,
    A ramshackle rocker there
Adds a skreek of the dramatic
    To the poet's "Old Arm-Chair."

Or the "Speech of Logan" shifts us
    From the pathos to the fire;
    And Tell (with Gessler) lifts us
    Many noble notches higher—
Till a youngster, far from sunny,
    With sad eyes of watery blue,
Winds up with something "funny,"
    Like "Cock-a-doodle-doo!"

Then a Dialogue—selected
    For its realistic worth:—
The Cruel Boy detected
    With a turtle turned to earth
Back-downward; and, in pleading,
    The Good Boy—strangely gay
At such a sad proceeding—
    Says, "Turn him over, pray!"

So the exercises taper,
    Through gradations of delight,
To the reading of "The Paper"
    Which is entertaining—quite!—
For it goes ahead and mentions
    "If a certain Mr. O.
Has serious intentions
    That he ought to tell her so."

It also "Asks permission
    To intimate to 'John'

The dubious condition
    Of the ground he's standing on;"
And, dropping the suggestion
    To "mind what he's about,"
It stuns him with the question
    "Does his mother know he's out?"

And among the contributions
    To this "academic Press"
Are "Versified Effusions"
    By—"Our Lady Editress"—
Which fact is proudly stated
    By the Chief of the concern,—
Though the verse communicated
    Bears the pen-name "Fanny Fern."

When all has been recited,
    And the teacher's bell is heard,
And visitors, invited,
    Have dropped a kindly word,
A hush of holy feeling
    Falls down upon us there,
As though the day were kneeling,
    With the twilight for the prayer.

Midst the wealth of fact and fancies
    That our memories may recall,
Thus the old school-day romances
    Are the dearest, after all!—
When some sweet thought revises
    The half-forgotten tune
That opened "Exercises"
    On "Friday Afternoon."

Parents

HORACE DUTTON TAFT

HORACE DUTTON TAFT (1861-1943), brother of President William Howard Taft, was the founder and for forty-six years headmaster of Taft School, at Watertown, Connecticut. Before deciding to found a boys' school, Taft had practiced law in his brother's Cincinnati office and later had tutored in Latin at Yale. In 1890 he opened a school at Pelham Manor with seven day pupils and ten boarders; he later installed the school in an old summer hotel at Watertown, Connecticut, and there it grew and prospered. Of education Taft once said: "I am a great believer in the vital importance for character building of that which comes from training in old-fashioned obedience."

A SCHOOLMASTER can hardly indulge in reminiscences without giving a chapter to parents. Whenever masters of schools, still more headmasters, get together for a chat, you may be sure that they will be very unfair to parents. Naturally, being like other people, they like to talk of the unusual. They like to talk of the mother who thinks that all the members of the faculty ought to devote their time to her boy, or the father who begins his letter by saying that no one is more in favor of school discipline than himself, and then goes on to ask a favor that would upset the entire system. Moreover, a very few parents can sometimes make a headmaster's life miserable and give him a distorted view of the whole matter. Thring, the great English Headmaster of Uppingham, begins his diary one day with the remark, "I am sick of parental jaw." Another English headmaster is credited with the statement, "Parents are the last people on earth who ought to have children."

Yet, taking them all together, any headmaster must acknowledge the help, the common sense, and the loyalty of the great majority of parents. Of course every parent has a tremendous prejudice in favor of his or her offspring, and the world would be a dreadfully cold place to live in if this were not true; but most parents realize this fact, use self-restraint, and endeavor to help the school in every way possible. For myself, I cherish the friendships, some of them intimate and precious, which have grown up in an experience of half a century with the parents of my boys, these sometimes including parents whose boys have been subjected to extreme discipline. I have seen heroism of parents displayed in the great influenza epidemic. I have seen big sacrifices made at home for the boys without complaint, these sacrifices sometimes appreciated at their full value by the boys, and sometimes not.

I have seen, as has every headmaster, the comical and the selfish. I remember the extraordinary idea of a school shown by a mother who had taken up no end of my time on a busy morning, asking a million questions about the school. She was thinking of leaving her boy with us, and I was trying to bring the conversation to a close, an effort in which different headmasters have various methods and various degrees of success. At last she asked, "Does this school give the boy all the care he gets at home?"

"Certainly not. Neither does any school."

This shocked her a bit, and then she said, "Well, don't they sometimes get their feet wet?"

"Eight or ten years ago there was a boy here who got his feet wet. He got by me."

It made her so angry that I could not treat soberly so serious a matter that she promptly left. I had achieved my object.

I remember another very wealthy lady who wrote to ask about putting her two boys with us and, when I sent the usual questions and the usual request for references, replied that she could not dream of sending her boys to a school in which there was the slightest question as to their being an addition to the social life of the school. I found out that they had been in another boarding school, the headmaster of which was very much amused at her reply. He said that the boys were a pair of degenerates and he did not wonder that the mother resented an inquiry. There was an English headmaster to whom a snobbish mother wrote that before she sent her boy to his school she must ask whether he was very particular about the social background of his pupils. He answered: "Dear Madam: As long as your son behaves himself and his fees are paid, no questions will be asked about his social background."

It was a college president who was pestered by maternal questions as to the college course and the treatment of the students, and who finally telegraphed: "Satisfaction guaranteed or we return the boy."

A mother appeared in my office one morning with a boy whose head was a little larger than a baseball, told of his troubles with his schooling, and ended with the remark: "The great trouble with Johnny is that he does not know how to concentrate. It is a great pity, too, because he has great ability in some directions. He is just a born clog dancer." I said solemnly, "It is a very unusual accomplishment." My brother Will wrote me of this interview that I was a narrow-minded pedagogue not to have courses fitted for all the talents.

Makepeace's biography of Sherman Thacher describes a rather exceptional situation in which Sherman found himself, owing to the fact that many mothers came to live in the Ojai Valley so that they might be near their dear ones. Makepeace quotes from Sherman: "I have no fundamental objection to mothers. Indeed I love them. I do not agree with the prophet who said that 'a wise son maketh a glad father, but a foolish son is just like his mother.' It is only when Mother, like Mary's lamb, follows him to school that Teacher is annoyed."

Schoolmasters are made aware of differences of opinion in families in regard to the education of the children, and sometimes this is embarrassing. Some twenty-five years ago I had the unpleasant duty of dismissing a boy for very substantial reasons. A few days afterward his father came in to ask whether I could not take the boy back. I told him that it would be quite impossible, that the boys themselves would be shocked to hear of his return. He said, "Well, what am I going to do with him?"

"The only thing to do is to find him a good hard job and put him to work. He will waste his time in school and go to the devil in college. Hard work out in the world will probably sober him up."

"I believe you are dead right. That is what I will do." When he reached the door, however, he turned around and said, "But you remember that *I have made a hell of a fight to get him back into the school!*"

One dear friend of mine, who had been most reasonable about her boy and was emphatically in the list of good parents, kept bothering me morning after morning. Her boy had been kicked on the end of the spine and retired to the infirmary. Dr. Martin assured me that with a little rest and refraining from exercise he would be all right and there was nothing to worry about; but she kept calling me up in the busiest time of the morning, until I said: "Mary, you make me tired. You are wasting valuable time every morning for me. I tell you the boy is all right. I will only add that it is the other end of his spine that I am worried about." She laughed and reported that to her family, and that was the end of it.

Sometimes it is amazing to see the way in which a parent will shift responsibility to the school. A father of a boy who was attending a private day school was very indignant because the boy was expelled for gambling. He wrote to the head of the school that he did not object to the rule against gambling or think the punishment excessive. He only felt that the school was at fault for not instructing him about the evils of gambling, adding, "If a boy is not going to learn at school the evils of dishonesty, immorality, and gambling, *where will he learn them?*"

A man is amazed to find how very little thought a parent has put upon a given problem. A college graduate, a man of ability, was visiting the school to see his boy and walked in on me. He said, "I do not think much of the way you teach English these days."

"Neither do I."

"When I was a boy I used to browse in my father's library."

"So did I."

"I read Cooper and Scott and Dickens and Thackeray with no prodding or compulsion."

"So did I."

Then we two foolish men proceeded to match the books we had read, whereupon he said, "I would rather have done that reading on my own than have the compulsory reading which is involved in your English course."

"So would I."

He then looked at me as though he thought it was my move.

"You realize, of course," I said, "that browsing is a voluntary thing and depends on the boy, himself, on his whole environment, but especially on his home influence. You have had that boy of yours fifteen years all to yourself, with the influence of the entire family brought to bear on the single boy. I have it from his own lips that he never read a single book except what he was compelled to read by school authorities. Fifteen years! And yet you send him to me, one of two hundred and fifty boys, and expect me to teach him to browse! Could anything be more absurd?" I added, "We have a goodly number of boys here who have read more than you and I together, and they go on browsing whenever they have time for it."

I am only pointing out how amazing it is that an intelligent man could miss a point as plain as this.

One of our best old boys, a senior at Yale, was talking with another brilliant student:

"Gans, I did a dreadful thing yesterday."

"What was that?"

"I cut that infernal football game and took a long walk in the woods. It was a beautiful day, and it was good to get away and enjoy it."

"I did worse than that."

"What could you do that was worse?"

"I stayed at home and read a good book. You know, Billy, there is a great deal of *clandestine good reading* going on on this campus."

The expression tickled me.

Of course a whole volume could be written on spoiled boys. Too much money will spoil them. On the whole, however, the general home atmosphere is what determines whether a boy is spoiled or not. He may come from a rich family in which life is simple and in which his responsibilities are emphasized, or he may come from a comparatively poor family in which his opinions and comforts are regarded as of the utmost importance.

We have all seen boys who are spoiled through the weakness of their parents. The head of a big business who is made of iron when dealing with his subordinates announces that his boy is going to lead the simple life and not be ruined by indulgence. He weakens at the first attack, especially if the mother's influence is thrown on the wrong side. But I remember an amazing instance in which the father's attitude was quite different:

He walked into the office of the Dean of an eastern college and announced, "Mr. X, I have been looking around your college and have concluded that this is the place for my boy."

"That is very gratifying. We will do the best we can for him."

"Yes, I went out to Texas twenty-five years ago with hardly a dollar in my pocket, and I have made good. I have made millions. That boy is not going to have any of the trouble I had. He is going to have all the money he wants."

"All the money he wants? An automobile?"

"Two of them, if he wants them."

"And may he go to New York?"

"Well, of course, I want him to keep your rules but, as far as I am concerned, he may go to New York when he pleases and spend what he wishes to."

"I rather think you had better send him somewhere else."

"What in the world do you mean by that?"

"I mean that the boy is going to the devil as fast as he can, and that in all probability he will take a number of other boys with him."

The father was hotly indignant. "You don't know what you are talking about. He is a good boy."

"I will take your word for that, but, unless he is a miracle, you are going to make him into a bad boy. Have you as much money as the Vanderbilts and the Rockefellers?"

"Why, no, I don't suppose that I am in their class."

"Well, we have had a number of their boys here and, as far as I can see, they are just as good and clean as the sons of poor families. Their fathers don't talk the way you do. They know the dangers of money. They give their boys allowances, and they watch those allowances as carefully as any part of their business accounts. We have some boys here whose fathers have taken the view of life that you have. They are going to the devil with drink and women, and that is where your boy is going unless he is very exceptional."

The man walked up and down for a time and finally said, "I don't know what I am going to do, but I want to thank you, sir, for giving me something to think over."

The question naturally comes up, how could a man who had brains enough to make a fortune in any line have as little sense as this? He could not read the Bible, he could not read a novel, he could not read a newspaper, he could not talk with men of the world, without hearing of young men whose lives were ruined by indulgence; and yet he deliberately planned such a life.

As I have said, most parents are sensible and helpful and anxious for the development of their boys in every good way. Occasionally you find a father—or more often a mother—whose ambition for the boy is simply that he may be trained to be a member of Society with a big S. She thinks of life entirely from that angle and, though of different social standing, she would sympathize with the mother of the Kentucky mountaineer who said of her son: "He don't gamble; he don't drink; he don't chaw; he don't smoke—he ain't got no resources within himself."

The school influence that tends to correct a boy spoiled in the home is largely that of the other boys. They are democratic, punish undue selfishness with a directness that no master could use, and from the penalty they inflict there is no appeal. Boys in the main are not snobbish, and money will not bring popularity. When I say they are not snobbish perhaps I ought to add, except in regard to automobiles. I have seen comical cases in which a boy who was absolutely without a trace of snobbery in any other way would feel ashamed if his parents came to visit the school in a Ford machine. They know altogether too much about the different makes of automobiles, and sometimes acquire a silly ambition to own the best. I am told, however, that this is changing and that Fords and station wagons are now considered the "smart" thing.

However, the war has come, and many of these youngsters have got to learn to use their legs or bicycles. The value of automobiles is going up at such a rate as to make probable the story of a man at a club who said to his friend:

"Heavens and earth, Jim! What is the matter with you? You look as though you had lost your last friend."

"You would, too, if you had been through what I have been through."

"What has happened?"

"I got home last night and found that my wife had taken my car and run away with another man."

"My God, man! Not your *new* car."

In the matter of money, parents may make a mistake in either way. It is easy to blame them, but before the schoolmaster judges he ought to consider the actual situation. It is easy to say that a boy ought to have only just so much pocket money, or that he must not attend dances or movies more than so often during vacation; but there is, especially for boys living in cities—and most of them do live in cities—a real problem as to how far it is well to make a boy different from his mates in regard to money and privileges. I have sometimes been tickled to see the change of attitude in teachers who have been very critical, the change coming when they, themselves, joined the ranks of parents. They find the problem is more complicated than they had dreamed. I have known a headmaster, even, to change his opinion as to the value of scholarship when his boys turned out to be wretched scholars but great athletes. I have known masters who were quite contemptuous of parents who were not willing to leave to the school authorities the question whether a boy should be promoted with his class, but who showed as much partiality in the case of their own boys and as much objection to the enforcing of the school rules as any parent they had laughed at.

Nearly all of these questions are solved by a normal healthy companionship between boys and parents, a companionship that does not prevent discipline, but makes discipline almost unnecessary.

Parents, like the rest of us, are in the current of modern thinking and customs, and their position is often a hard one. A Parents' Association in one city resolved that during the vacations their children ought not to go out to parties or the theater more than so many times a week. The other evenings they ought to spend at home. It occured to the thoughtful ones, however, that this was absurd unless the parents also stayed at home those nights. So the conscientious ones declined invitations for certain nights in order to be with their children. The amusing thing was that they did not know what to do with themselves or with the children, because that kind of companionship was new to them. The atmosphere of the old home circle, as we knew it in my childhood, was not there. There was nothing but a sense of duty on one side and of repression on the other.

I am often asked whether the boy of today is better or worse than the boy of my own days. It seems to me that the boys of today are made of the same stuff, good, bad, and indifferent, as the boys of earlier days. The only trouble is that they need to be a great deal better. The movies, the radio, the automobile, make it more difficult for boys in any grade of society to lead the simple life and to avoid undue dissipation of their thoughts and energies.

A father said to a good friend of his who was an important member of a college faculty, "You are not doing much of a job in education these days."

"What is the matter with you now? You have got a splendid boy, and he is doing well."

"Yes, he is a fine boy and I love him. Perhaps I am a little proud of him. But when I was a boy I lived fifty miles from Blank College. At the beginning or end of a term I walked that distance, taking two days to it and sending my baggage the cheapest way. I never dreamed of complaining and I never missed an hour in the college exercises. That boy of mine missed the whole first day of the last term, and do you know why?"

His friend shook his head.

"*Because he couldn't get a lower berth on the sleeping car.* Damn an education that makes a boy as soft as that!"

Perhaps it was not the college that was in fault in such a case.

I hope later to say something on the general character of American education. Here I am concerned only with what parents can do who are convinced of the shortcomings of our schools, who feel responsible for the education of their children beyond the mere choice of a school, and who would gladly make up for the deficiencies of the school education if they knew how. They cannot change the school—they must choose among those offered them, especially in the case of the primary school; and it is in the primary that the first and greatest loss occurs.

The poor quality of the teachers is something that is beyond their power to change. But few parents have any idea what hearty co-operation with the school means. We can never have in this country, even if we should wish it, a system such as obtained in Germany before the World War and in France, where the school authorities had power, not only over the boy, but over the entire family.

Two or three things, however, are of vital importance. The first is that the home, and therefore, the boy, shall take school seriously, shall consider it the business of the boy's life for the present. Lecturing and preaching will do little good. The boy will know quickly enough whether his parents regard his work and conduct at school as a serious matter. Another condition that is absolutely requisite is that the home, and therefore the boy, shall consider the school authorities supreme in their own sphere. I do not mean merely that a boy shall go to recitations, be regular in attendance, and obey the rules, but that his frame of mind shall be sympathetic and respectful and serious toward his work and toward the school authorities.

The free-for-all discussion at home of the discipline of the school or of the value to the boy of what he is studying, a discussion which the American boy hears and often takes part in, is a singular thing known only to America to any extent. I have wrestled with many boys in the study of Latin and have been well aware that they have listened to comments at home on the utter futility of that particular study. This is a splendid preparation for the beginning of the work that is necessary for the mastery of a difficult study. It is as though the parents should send a boy to the doctor and say, "His medicine is of no use, and I would not take any more of it than he compels you to take." The question before the parents in the cases I referred to was not the value of the study of Latin. They knew that he was going to study it. Surely any study is better for the boy's development, both mental and moral, if he devotes himself to it honestly and conscientiously; and any teacher, competent or incompetent, is a better teacher if he has the moral advantage of that attitude toward the school which ought to exist in every home.

Criticism of individual teachers, of school rules, of the course of study is not only allowed, but encouraged in many a family. It would surprise the heads of these families to know that those very criticisms and the condemnations and the ridicule often involved have lowered the standard of the schools, have made the work of the teacher much more difficult, and have been a grave injury to all the boys of the school, including their own. Criticism of school matters, while often amply justified, should be confined to the discussion of the grown-up members of the family. But the school has a right to much more than silence. The whole influence of the home, earnestly and positively, should be exercised to uphold and increase the power of the school authorities.

As for the simple life, preaching goes for little. Parents cannot have their boys lead a simple life while they, themselves, lead one of luxury, frivolity, and ease. I repeat, it is the home atmosphere that counts, and that atmosphere comes not from lectures to the boys, but from the life of the parents.

Much can be done by the use of the long vacations. Our vacations have been arranged in a perfectly haphazard way with very little consideration for the rest that an ordinarily strong, healthy boy needs. William S. Learned in a pamphlet written before the World War on "An American Teacher in a Prussian Gymnasium" says that the German boys attend school on six days a week instead of five, making a difference in the school year of forty days or two American school months. This means that from six to sixteen the German gains more than two full years, even leaving out of account our long vacations. Let us remember that we suffer, not only the loss arising from the fact that the boys do not go ahead, but also the loss of forgetting and growing rusty. What teacher is without the experience of the struggle in September to bring pupils up to the point that they had reached in June?

Granted that parents feel their responsibility; granted that they do not laugh at the ignorance their children show of spelling and arithmetic, and simply regard it as a sign of the degeneracy of the times for which they are not answerable, there is still the question of what definite steps they can take to better the situation. Well, there is the long vacation, three full months, in which two hours a day for more than half the time at least would not be an unreasonable allowance for a boy to devote to his studies, especially when he is attending a primary school, the work of which is of so exceedingly mild a type.

First, let us do what the school has done badly. The average boy in the average American school is, according to any reasonable standard, poor in spelling, superficial and inaccurate in arithmetic, and more so in English grammar, if the modern fads have not banished that study from his curriculum altogether. By English grammar I mean the simple structure of sentences, the parts of speech, punctuation, voices and moods of verbs, the different kinds of clauses and their relations to each other—all simple enough, but offering training in logic that was rightly valued by John Stuart Mill, as adapted to that early age, and still more valued by the unfortunate teacher who tries to teach another language to a boy who has not learned thoroughly the simple grammar common to all languages. I take these branches of study first, because on knowledge and training in these depends the work in more advanced studies. Let us not despise them. The main thing is that the boy shall at home acquire that standard of thoroughness, so far as he may, which he has not acquired at school. Moreover, remember the time saved now is time saved later. Many a father or mother has been distressed that the boy is late in entering college and has failed to realize that the real loss of time occurred before the age of the secondary school. A man ran hard, but missed his train. A friend said, "You didn't run fast enough." He replied, "I did, too. I didn't start soon enough."

It is not a great task for conscientious parents to find out what a boy lacks in these simple branches. There is very little danger of holding him up to too high standards. One word of warning—don't consider his standing in his class or the average given him by the school as any proof of proficiency, unless you have reason to believe in the standard of the school. In any good secondary school the tragedy of the sudden discovery of exceptional deficiency in a boy by his parents is a common occurrence. A reasonably high standard in our American schools is rare. Think of the clamor against the severity of the College Board examinations, examinations which in any European country would seem very lenient. Of the whole number of students entering American colleges and universities in any given September, only a very small percentage could pass these examinations.

It is not difficult to find out what a boy lacks in the school branches, and it is hardly more difficult to supply it. It means some review of textbooks but, before all, a rigid adherence to a schedule of hours. This does require the right spirit of obedience to duty in the family, a very reasonable bit of self-sacrifice on the part of parent as well as boy.

What is there to do in work which the schools do not attempt, or which they hardly attempt? Perhaps the most common complaint of parents is that the boys care nothing for good reading, that their taste in reading, if they have any, is for trash. Sometimes the complaint is simply absurd, coming as it does from parents who never open a book that is not trash and whose minds are mainly on automobiles, bridge, and the comic opera. Men do not as yet gather figs from thistles. But the cry comes from parents who have a real liking for good reading and who grieve to see no development of such liking in their children.

Here, again, we must pay the price. That price consists of accompanying the boy through a considerable part of his early reading. I have spoken of this in my father's case. A perfectly natural family discussion of characters and situations, of humor and pathos puts the matter of reading in an entirely different light, so that the superiority of good reading to trash is easy for the boy to see.

There are many harder tasks for a man or a woman in this world than to review his Scott, Dickens, Thackeray or Stevenson. As far as the boy is concerned, one or two novels of each would suffice. Even Shakespeare might lose his terrors, and I am confident that in many cases that marvel of marvels, a taste for history in a boy, might develop by perfectly natural reading and discussion of such interesting books as Fiske's "American Revolution" or any one of fifty fine biographies.

In the very early years there is the important subject of reading aloud, a subject that impresses itself on me more and more. If a man takes twenty boys at the beginning of their secondary school course and finds that part of them have been trained to read aloud with expression and with evident grasp of the meaning, and part of them are conspicuous for their failure to do this, we shall find that the former have an advantage in the understanding of literature, in expressing their own thoughts, in learning a new language, that one would hardly connect with this exercise. The structure of a sentence, the value of words, the relation of clauses, many things that it is hard to describe are inevitably taught in teaching a boy to read aloud with intelligence and appreciation. With the best intentions in the world teachers can give very little instruction or practice in this. An hour's exercise in a class of twenty would give only three minutes apiece.

Many a conscientious mother has spent as much time as that suggested here, but has devoted it to reading aloud to her son, a process which, wisely used, achieves some good results, but which more often merely entertains the boy and produces in him an intellectual laziness which is hard to overcome.

But try the other plan. Of course let the book be of a kind to interest the boy. Let the reading take at least half an hour a day. Let them share the reading, but let the boy do most of it, the mother being careful to correct the faults of her boy's reading, but also being careful not to expect perfection all at once. Her own reading is necessary because some progress in the story is needed to promote the interest. A single summer would do wonders, but the reading should go on till the boy becomes an easy and intelligent reader of any literature of reasonable difficulty.

We hear more and more today of a reading disability. Such a course as I have described would either cure such a disability or demonstrate early the need of the help of a specialist.

I hardly dare go into the subject of memory training. This is of immense importance, but it is perhaps hardly worth while to begin it unless the parent is prepared to lay out a definite course and carry it through. English boys have a great advantage over our own, because, at the age when rote memory can be wonderfully developed, they have systematic drill in it of a very regular and severe kind. An Oxford man told me that he had begun learning by heart at his mother's knee and had continued the daily practice till he went to the University. I have heard Dr. Peabody of Groton tell of the marvelous (for an American) ease with which English boys could learn either Latin or English by heart. With such training a boy not only has acquired a facility that is of immense advantage to him in languages, in history, and in many of the sciences, but he has, somewhere in the back of his mind, a familiarity with the words, phrases, and spirit of many of the masterpieces of English literature, beginning with the most beautiful parts of our English Bible. I have no space here to discuss the many ways in which such a training helps in the mental progress of a boy. Suffice it to say that we Americans have despised this humble but most useful function of a mind and have paid dearly for our mistake. This is a training which anybody can give the boy and which brings marvelous results at a very early age.

One word more. American parents are apt to think that, while vacation work may be proper and advantageous for backward boys, it can have no rational place in the training of bright ones. Nothing is more remarkable than the difference between the attitude of an ambitious American father of a bright boy and that of an English father of a boy of the same kind. Though the English boy receives a much better education in his school than the American, the father has no notion of leaving to the school the entire responsibility.

The English school, itself, goes to the other extreme from ours and devotes more time and energy to the bright boys than to the dull ones. The attitude of the American teacher was, and is, that the bright boy can take care of himself, and most of the work of our teachers is devoted, therefore, to the other end of the class. Naturally the loss to the boy and to the community is greater when a boy of fine ability fails to develop up to his reasonable limitations than when an ordinary or backward boy fails in this. The ideal system is that by which each boy is trained according to his ability and develops the best that is in him.

A Good Book

JOHN MILTON

•

JOHN MILTON was born in London, in 1608. His father was a cultivated man, a musician and a composer, who trained his son in the Puritan faith, in poetry and languages, music and mathematics. In 1625 he entered Christ's College, Cambridge, where he remained for seven years, devoting his time to the study of literature, history, religion, and philosophy. After leaving Cambridge, Milton lived for five years in the village of Horton with his father, continuing the humanistic studies he had begun in Cambridge and composing L'Allegro, Il Penseroso, Comus, *and* Lycidas. *During the years 1638-1639 he traveled abroad, conversing with distinguished persons and collecting a library for future reading and study. At Florence, where he spent four months, he visited Galileo. By this time Milton was certain that his mission in life was to become a great poet. In 1640 he settled in London, resumed his literary work, and taught a few private pupils. Nine years later he was made Latin Secretary under the government of the Commonwealth. In the following year he became blind in one eye and three years later was totally blind. He published* Paradise Lost *in 1667. He died in 1674.*

The following quotation is from Areopagitica.

I DENY not, but that it is of greatest concernment in the church and commonwealth, to have a vigilant eye how books demean themselves, as well as men; and thereafter to confine, imprison, and do sharpest justice on them as malefactors; for books are not absolutely dead things, but do contain a potency of life in them to be as active as that soul was whose progeny they are; nay, they do preserve as in a vial the purest efficacy and extraction of that living intellect that bred them. I know they are as lively, and as vigorously productive, as those fabulous dragon's teeth: and being sown up and down, may chance to spring up armed men. And yet, on the other hand, unless wariness be used, as good almost kill a man as kill a good book: who kills a man kills a reasonable creature, God's image; but he who destroys a good book, kills reason itself, kills the image of God, as it were, in the eye. Many a man lives a burden to the earth; but a good book is the precious life-blood of a master-spirit, embalmed and treasured up on purpose to a life beyond life. It is true, no age can restore a life, whereof, perhaps, there is no great loss; and revolutions of ages do not oft recover the loss of a rejected truth, for the want of which whole nations fare the worse. We should be wary, therefore, what persecution we raise against the living labours of public men, how we spill that seasoned life of man, preserved and stored up in books; since we see a kind of homicide may be thus committed, sometimes a martyrdom; and if it extend to the whole impression, a kind of massacre, whereof the execution ends not in the slaying of an elemental life, but strikes at the ethereal and fifth essence, the breath of reason itself; slays an immortality rather than a life.

The Concert

HORACE ANNESLEY VACHELL

HORACE ANNESLEY VACHELL, English novelist and playwright, was born in 1861 and received his education at Harrow and at Sandhurst. While waiting for his commission in the Rifle Brigade, he came to the United States and visited California. This state so pleased him that in 1883 he resigned his commission, returned to California, and for some years made his home there. He returned to the land of his birth in 1899 and has lived there ever since.

The following selection is taken from The Hill, *a story of school life, published in 1905.*

> Forty years on, when afar and asunder,
>   Parted are those who are singing to-day,
> When you look back, and forgetfully wonder
>   What you were like in your work and your play;
> Then, it may be, there will often come o'er you
>   Glimpses of notes like the catch of a song,—
> Visions of boyhood shall float them before you,
>   Echoes of dreamland shall bear them along.

BEFORE the end of the summer term, both Desmond and Scaife received their "caps" and a word of advice from Lawrence.

"There are going to be changes here," said he; "and I wish I could see 'em, and help to bring 'em about. Now, I'm not given to buttering fellows up, but I see plainly that the rebuilding of this house depends a lot upon you two. Don't speak! It's not likely that you're able to measure your influence; if you could, there wouldn't be much to measure. But take it from me, not a word, not an action of yours is without weight with the lower boys. Everything helps or hinders. Next term there will be war—to the knife—between Warde and some fellows I needn't name, and Warde will win. Remember I said so. I hope you," he looked hard at Desmond, "will fight on the right side."

The boys returned to their room, jubilant because the house-cap was theirs, but uneasy because of the words given with it. As soon as they were alone, Scaife said sullenly—

Chapter VI of *The Hill*, by Horace Annesley Vachell, is reprinted by permission of Dodd, Mead & Company, Inc.

"Does Lawrence expect us to stand in with Warde against Lovell and his pals? If he does, he's jolly well mistaken, as far as I'm concerned."

Desmond flushed. He had spent nearly five terms at Harrow, but only two at the Manor. Of what had been done or left undone by certain fellows in the Fifth he was still in twilight ignorance. He discerned shadows, nothing more, and, boylike, he ran from shadows into the sunlight. Desmond knew that there were beasts at the Manor. Had you forced from him an expression approaching, let us say, definiteness, he would have admitted that beasts lurked in every house, in every school in the kingdom. You must keep out of their way (and ways)—that was all. And he knew also that too many beasts wreck a house, as they wreck a regiment or a nation.

But once or twice within the past few months he had suspected that his cut-and-dried views on good and evil were not shared by Scaife. Scaife confessed to Desmond that the Old Adam was strong in him. He liked, craved for, the excitement of breaking the law. Hitherto, this breaking of the law had been confined to such offenses as smoking or drinking a glass of beer at a "pub," [1] or using cribs, or, generally speaking, setting at naught authority. That Scaife had escaped severe punishment was due to his keen wits.

Now, when Scaife gave Desmond the unexpurgated history of the row which so nearly resulted in the expulsion of six boys, Desmond had asked a question—

"Do you *like* whisky? I loathe it."

Scaife laughed before he answered. Doubtless one reason why he exacted interest and admiration from Desmond lay in a rare (rare at fifteen) ability to analyse his own and others' actions.

"I loathe it too," he admitted. "Really, you know, we drank precious little, because it *is* such beastly stuff. But I liked, we all liked, to believe that we were doing the correct thing—eh? And it warmed us up. Just a taste made the Caterpillar awfully funny."

"I see."

"Do you see? I doubt it, Cæsar. Perhaps I shall horrify you when I tell you that vice interests me. I used to buy the *Police News* when I was a kid and simply wallow in it. I told a woman that last Easter, and she laughed—she was as clever as they make 'em—and said that I suffered from what the French call the homesickness for the gutter. Rather personal, but dev'lish sharp, wasn't it?"

"I think she was a beast."

"Not she, she's a sort of cousin; she came from the same old place herself, that's why she understood. You don't want to know what goes on in the slums, but I do. Why? Because my grand-dad was born in 'em."

"He pulled himself out by brains and muscles."

[1] All "public houses" are out of bounds.

"But he went back—sometimes. Oh yes, he did. And the governor—I'm up to some of *his* little games. I could tell you——"

"Oh—shut up!" said Cæsar, the colour flooding his cheeks.

Upon the last Saturday of the term the School Concert took place. Few of the boys in the Manor, and none out of it, knew that John Verney had been chosen to sing the treble solo; always an attractive number of the programme. John, indeed, was painfully shy in regard to his singing, so shy that he never told Desmond that he had a voice. And the music-master, enchanted by its quality, impressed upon his pupil the expediency of silence. He wished to surprise the School.

The concerts at Harrow take place in the great Speech-room. Their characteristic note is the singing of Harrow songs. To any boy with an ear for music and a heart susceptible of emotion these songs must appeal profoundly, because both words and music seem to enshrine all that is noble and uplifting in life. And, sung by the whole School (as are most of the choruses), their message becomes curiously emphatic. The spirit of the Hill is acclaimed, gladly, triumphantly, unmistakably, by Harrovians repeating the creed of their fathers, knowing that creed will be so repeated by their sons and sons' sons. Was it happy chance or a happier sagacity which decreed that certain verses should be sung by the School Twelve, who have struggled through form after form and know (and have not yet had time to forget) the difficulties and temptations which beset all boys? They, to whom their fellows unanimously accord respect at least, and often—as in the case of a Captain of the Cricket Eleven—enthusiastic admiration and fealty; these, the gods, in a word, deliver their injunction, transmit, in turn, what has been transmitted to them, and invite their successors to receive it. To many how poignant must be the reflection that the trust they are about to resign might have been better administered! But to many there must come upon the wings of those mighty, rushing choruses the assurance that the Power which has upheld them in the past will continue to uphold them in the future. In many—would one could say in all—is quickened, for the first time, perhaps, a sense of what they owe to the Hill, the overwhelming debt which never can be discharged.

Desmond sat beside Scaife. Scaife boasted that he could not tell "God save the Queen" from "The Dead March in Saul." He confessed that the concert bored him. Desmond, on the other hand, was always touched by music, or, indeed, by anything appealing to an imagination which gilded all things and persons. He was Scaife's friend, not only, (as John discovered) because Scaife had a will strong enough to desire and secure that friendship, but because—a subtler reason—he had never yet seen Scaife as he was, but always as he might have been.

Desmond told Scaife that he could not understand why John had bottled up the fact that he was chosen to sing upon such an occasion. Scaife smiled contemptuously.

"You never bottle up anything, Cæsar," said he.

"Why should I? And why should he?"

"I expect he'll make an awful ass of himself."

"Oh, no, he won't," Desmond replied. "He's a clever fellow is Jonathan."

As he gave John his nickname, Desmond's charming voice softened. A boy of less quick perceptions than Scaife would have divined that the speaker liked John, liked him, perhaps, better than he knew. Scaife frowned.

"There are several Old Harrovians," he said, indicating the seats reserved for them. "It's queer to me that they come down for this caterwauling."

Desmond glanced at him sharply, with a wrinkle between his eyebrows. For the moment he looked as if he were short-sighted, as if he were trying to define an image somewhat blurred, conscious that the image itself was clear enough, that the fault lay in the obscurity of his own vision.

"They come down because they're keen," he replied. "My governor can't leave his office, or he'd be here. I like to see 'em, don't you, Demon?"

"I could worry along without 'em," the Demon replied, half-smiling. "You see," he added, with the blend of irony and pathos which always captivated his friend, "you see, my dear old chap, I'm the first of my family at Harrow, and the sight of all your brothers and uncles and fathers makes me feel like Mark Twain's good man, rather—*lonesome.*"

At once Desmond responded, clutching Scaife's arm.

"You're going to be Captain of the cricket and footer Elevens, and the School racquet-player, and a monitor; and after you leave you'll come down here, and you'll see that Harrow hasn't forgotten you, and then you'll know why these fellows cut engagements. My governor says that an hour at a School Concert is the finest tonic in the world for an Old Harrovian."

"Oh, shut up!" said Scaife; "you make me feel more of an outsider than good old Snowball." He glanced at a youth sitting close to them. Snowball was as black as a coal: the son of the Sultan of the Sahara. "Yes, Cæsar, you can't get away from it, I *am* an 'alien.'"

"You're a silly old ass! I say, who's the guest of honour?"

Next to the Head Master was sitting a thin man upon whose face were fixed hundreds of eyes. The School had not been told that a famous Field Marshal, the hero of a hundred fights, was coming to the concert. And, indeed, he had accepted an invitation given at the last moment—accepted it, moreover, on the understanding that his visit was to be informal. None the less, his face was familiar to all readers of illustrated papers. And, suddenly, conviction seized the boys that a conqueror was among them, an Old Etonian, making, possibly, his first visit to the Hill. Scaife whispered his name to Desmond.

"Why, of course," Desmond replied eagerly. "How splendid!"

He leaned forward, devouring the hero with his eyes, trying to pierce the bronzed skin, to read the record. From his seat upon the stage John,

also, stared at the illustrious guest. John was frightfully nervous, but looking at the veteran he forgot the fear of the recruit. Both Desmond and he
were wondering what "it felt like" to have done so much. And—they compared notes afterwards—each boy deplored the fact that the great man was
not an Old Harrovian. There he sat, cool, calm, slightly impassive. John
thought he must be rather tired, as a man ought to be tired after a life of
strenuous endeavour and achievement. He had done—so John reflected—
an awful lot. Even now, he remained the active, untiring servant of Queen
and country. And he had taken time to come down to Harrow to hear the
boys sing. And, dash it all! he, John, was going to sing to him.

At that moment Desmond was whispering to Scaife—

"I say, Demon: I'm jolly glad that I've not got to sing before *him*. I bet
Jonathan is in a funk."

"A big bit of luck," replied Scaife, reflectively. Then, seeing the surprise on Desmond's face, he added, "If Jonathan can sing—and I suppose
he can, or he wouldn't be chosen—this is a chance——"

"Of what?"

"Cæsar, sometimes I think you've no brains. Why, a chance of attracting
the notice of a tremendous swell—a man, they say, who never forgets—
never! Jonathan may want a commission in the Guards, as I do; and if he
pleases the great man, he may get it."

"Jonathan's not thinking of that," said Desmond. "Shush-h-h!"

The singers stood up. They faced the Field Marshal, and he faced
them. He looked hardest at Lawrence, pointed out to him by the Head
Master. Perhaps he was thinking of India; and the name of Lawrence
indelibly cut upon the memories of all who fought in the Mutiny. And
Lawrence, you may be sure, met his glance steadily, being fortified by it.
The good fellow felt terribly distressed, because he was leaving the Hill;
and, being a humble gentleman, the old songs served to remind him, not
of what he had done, but of what he left undone—the words unspoken,
the actions never now to be performed. The chief caught his eyes, smiled,
and nodded, as if to say, "I claim your father's son as a friend."

When the song came to an end, John was seized with an almost irresistible impulse to bolt. His turn had come. He must stand up to sing before nearly six hundred boys, who would stare down with gravely critical
and courteously amused eyes. And already his legs trembled as if he were
seized of a palsy. John knew that he could sing. His mother, who sang
gloriously, had trained him. From her he had inherited his vocal chords,
and from her he drew the knowledge how to use them.

When he stood up, pale and trembling, the silence fell upon his sensibilities as if it were a dense, yellow fog. This silence, as John knew, was an
unwritten law. The small boy selected to sing to the School, as the representative of the School, must have every chance. Let his voice be heard!
The master playing the accompaniment paused and glanced at his pupil.
John, however, was not looking at him; he was looking within at a John

he despised—a poltroon, a deserter about to run from his first engagement. He knew that the introduction to the song was being played a second time, and he saw the Head Master whispering to his guest. Paralysed with terror, John's intuition told him that the Head Master was murmuring, "That's the nephew of John Verney. Of course you know him?" And the Field Marshal nodded. And then he looked at John, as John had seen him look at Lawrence, with the same flare of recognition in the steel-grey eyes. Out of the confused welter of faces shone that pair of eyes—twin beacons flashing their message of encouragement and salvation to a fellow-creature in peril—at least, so John interpreted that piercing glance. It seemed to say, far plainer than words, "I have stood alone as you stand; I have felt my knees as wax; I have wished to run away. But—*I didn't.* Nor must you. Open your mouth and sing!"

So John opened his mouth and sang. The first verse of the lyric went haltingly.

Scaife growled to Desmond, "He *is* going to make an ass of himself."

And Desmond, meeting Scaife's eyes, half thought that the speaker wished that John would fail—that he grudged him a triumph. None the less, the first verse, sung feebly, with wrong phrasing and imperfect articulation, revealed the quality of the boy's voice; and this quality Desmond recognized, as he would have recognized a fine painting or a bit of perfect porcelain. All his short life his father had trained him to look for and acclaim quality, whether in things animate or inanimate. He caught hold of Scaife's arm.

"Make an ass of himself!" he whispered back. "Not he. But he may make an ass of me."

Even as he spoke he was aware that tears were horribly near his eyes. Some catch in John's voice, some subtle inflection, had smitten his heart, even as the prophet smote the rock.

"Rot!" said Scaife, angrily.

He was angry, furiously angry, because he saw that Cæsar was beyond his reach, whirled innumerable leagues away by the sound of another's voice. John had begun the second verse. He stared, as if hypnotized, straight into the face of the great soldier, who in turn stared as steadily at John; and John was singing like a lark, with a lark's spontaneous delight in singing, with an ease and self-abandonment which charmed eye almost as much as ear. Higher and higher rose the clear, sexless notes, till two of them met and mingled in a triumphant trill. To Desmond, that trill was the answer to the quavering, troubled cadences of the first verse; the vindication of the spirit soaring upwards unfettered by the flesh—the pure spirit, not released from the pitiful human clay without a fierce struggle. At that moment Desmond loved the singer—the singer who called to him out of heaven, who summoned his friend to join him, to see what he saw—"the vision splendid."

John began the third and last verse. The famous soldier covered his face with his hand, releasing John's eyes, which ascended, like his voice, till they met joyfully the eyes of Desmond. At last he was singing to his friend—*and his friend knew it.* John saw Desmond's radiant smile, and across that ocean of faces he smiled back. Then, knowing that he was nearer to his friend than he had ever been before, he gathered together his energies for the last line of the song—a line to be repeated three times, loudly at first, then more softly, diminishing to the merest whisper of sound, the voice celestial melting away in the ear of earth-bound mortals. The master knew well the supreme difficulty of producing properly this last attenuated note; but he knew also that John's lungs were strong, that the vocal chords had never been strained. Still, if the boy's breath failed; if anything—a smile, a frown, a cough—distracted his attention, the end would be weakness, failure. He wondered why John was staring so fixedly in one direction.

Now—now!

The piano crashed out the last line; but far above it, dominating it, floated John's flute-like notes. The master played the same bars for the second time. He was still able to sustain, if it were necessary, a quavering, imperfect phrase. But John delivered the second repetition without a mistake, singing easily from the chest. The master put his foot upon the soft pedal. Nobody was watching him. Had any one done so, he would have seen the perspiration break upon the musician's forehead. The piano purred its accompaniment. Then, in the middle of the phrase, the master lifted his hands and held them poised above the instrument. John had to sing three notes unsupported. He was smiling and staring at Desmond. The first note came like a question from the heart of a child; the second, higher up, might have been interpreted as an echo to the innocent interrogation of the first, the head no wiser than the heart; but the third and last note had nothing in it of interrogation: it was an answer, all-satisfying—sublime! Nor did it seem to come from John at all, but from above, falling like a snowflake out of the sky.

And then, for one immeasureable moment—*silence.*

John slipped back to his seat, crimson with bashfulness, while the School thundered applause. The Field Marshal shouted "Encore!" as loudly as any fag; but the Head Master whispered—

"We don't encourage *encores.* A small boy's head is easily turned."

"Not his," the hero replied.

Two numbers followed, and then the School stood up, and with them all Old Harrovians, to sing the famous National Anthem of Harrow, "Forty Years on." Only the guests and the masters remained seated.

> *Forty years on, growing older and older,*
> *Shorter in wind, as in memory long,*
> *Feeble of foot and rheumatic of shoulder,*
> *What will it help you that once you were strong?*

> *God give us bases to guard or beleaguer,*
> *Games to play out, whether earnest or fun;*
> *Fights for the fearless, and goals for the eager,*
> *Twenty, and thirty, and forty years on!*
> *Follow up! Follow up! Follow up! Follow up!*
> *Till the field ring again and again,*
> *With the tramp of the twenty-two men.*
> *Follow-up!*

As the hundreds of voices, past and present indissolubly linked together, imposed the mandate, *"Follow up!"* the Head Master glanced at his guest, but left unsaid the words about to be uttered. Tears were trickling down the cheeks of the man who, forty years before, had won his Sovereign's Cross—For Valour.

After the concert, but before he left the Speech-room, the Field Marshal asked the Head Master to introduce Lawrence and John, and, of course, the Head of the School. When John came up, there was a twinkle in the veteran's eye.

"Ha—ha!" said he; "you were in a precious funk, John Verney."

"I was, sir," said John.

"Gad! Don't I know the feeling? Well, well," he chuckled, smiling at John, "you climbed up higher than I've ever been in my life. What was it—hey? 'F' in 'alt'?"

" 'G,' sir."

"You sang delightfully. Tell your uncle to bring you to see me next time you are in town. You must consider me a friend," he chuckled again—"an old friend. And look ye here," his pleasant voice sank to a whisper, "I daren't tip these tremendous swells, but I feel that I can take such a liberty with you. Shush-h-h! Good-bye."

John scurried away, bursting with pride, feeling to the core the strong grip of the strong man, hearing the thrill of his voice, the thrill which had vibrated in thousands of soldier-hearts. Outside, Fluff was awaiting him.

"Oh, Jonathan, you can sing, and no mistake!"

"Five—six—seven mistakes," John answered.

The boys laughed. John told Fluff what the hero had said to him, and showed the piece of gold.

"What ho! The Creameries! Come on, Esmé!"

At the Creameries several boys congratulated John, and the Caterpillar said—

"You astonished us, Jonathan; 'pon my soul you did! Have a 'dringer' with me? And Fluff too? By the way, be sure to keep your hair clipped close. These singing fellows with manes may be lions in their own estimation, but the world looks upon 'em as asses."

"That's not bad for you, Caterpillar," said a boy in the Fifth.

"Not my own," said the Caterpillar, solemnly—"my father's. I take from him all the good things I can get hold of."

John polished off his "dringer," listening to the chaff, but his thoughts were with Desmond. He had an intuition that Desmond would have something to say to him. As soon as possible he returned to the Manor.

There he found his room empty. John shut the door and sat down, looking about him half-absently. The Duffer had not contributed much to the mural decoration, saying, loftily, that he preferred bare walls to rubbishy engravings and Japanese fans. But, with curious inconsistency (for he was the least vain of mortals), he had bought at a "leaving auction" a three-sided mirror—once the property of a great buck in the Sixth. The Duffer had got it cheap, but he never used it. The lower boys remarked to each other that Duff didn't dare to look in it, because what he would see must not only break his heart but shatter the glass. Generally, it hung, folded up, close to the window, and the Duffer said that it would come in handy when he took to shaving.

John's eye rested on this mirror, vacantly at first, then with gathering intensity. Presently he got up, crossed the room, opened the two folding panels, and examined himself attentively, pursing up his lips and frowning. He could see John Verney full face, three-quarter face, and half face. And he could see the back of his head, where an obstinate lock of hair stuck out like a drake's tail. John was so occupied in taking stock of his personal disadvantage that a ringing laugh quite startled him.

"Why, Jonathan! Giving yourself a treat—eh?"

John turned a solemn face to Desmond. "I think my head is hideous," he said ruefully.

"What do you mean?"

"It's too long," John explained. "I like a nice round head like yours, Cæsar. I wish I wasn't so ugly."

Desmond laughed. John always amused him. Cæsar was easily amused, saw the funny side of things, and contrasts tickled his fancy agreeably. But he stopped laughing when he realized that John was hurt. Then, quickly, impulsively, he said—

"Your head is all right, old Jonathan. And your voice is simply beautiful." He spoke seriously, staring at John as he had stared in the Speech-room when John began to sing. "I came here to tell you that. I felt odd when you were singing—quite weepsy, you know. You like me, old Jonathan, don't you?"

"Awfully," said John.

"Why did you look at me when you sang that last verse? Did you know that you were looking at me?"

"Yes."

"You looked at me because—well, because—bar chaff—you—liked—me?"

"Yes."

"You like me better than any other fellow in the school?"

"Yes; better than any other fellow in the world."

"Is it possible?"

"I have always felt that way since—yes—since the very first minute I saw you."

"How rum! I've forgotten just where we did meet for the first time."

"I shall never forget," said John, in the same slow, deliberate fashion, never taking his eyes from Desmond's face. Ever since he had sung, he had known that this moment was coming. "I shall never forget it," he repeated—"never. You were standing near the Chapel. I was poking about alone, trying to find the shop where we buy our straws. And I was feeling as all new boys feel, only more so, because I didn't know a soul."

"Yes," said Desmond, gravely; "you told me that. I remember now; I mistook you for young Hardacre."

"You smiled at me, Cæsar. It warmed me through and through. I suppose that when a fellow is starving he never forgets the first meal after it."

"I say. Go on; this is awfully interesting."

"I can remember what you wore. One of your bootlaces had burst——"

"Well; I'm——"

"I had a wild sort of wish to run off and buy you a new lace——"

"Of all the rum starts I——"

"Afterwards," John continued, "I tried to suck-up. I asked you to come and have some 'food.' Do you remember?"

"I'll bet I came, Jonathan."

"No; you didn't. You said 'No.'"

"Dash it all! I certainly said, 'No, thanks.'"

"I dare say. The 'No' hurt awfully because I did feel that it was cheek asking you."

"Jonathan, you funny old buster, I'll never say 'No' again. 'Pon my word, I won't. So I said 'No.' That's odd, because it's not easy for me to say 'No.' The governor pointed that out last hols. Somehow, I can't say 'No,' particularly if there's any excitement in saying 'Yes.' And my beastly 'No' hurt, did it? Well, I'm very, *very* sorry."

He held out his hands, which John took. Then, for a moment, there was a pause before Desmond continued awkwardly—

"You know, Jonathan, that the Demon is my pal. You like him better than you did, don't you?"

John had the tact not to speak; but he shook his head dolefully.

"And I couldn't chuck him, even if I wanted to, which I don't—which I don't," he repeated, with an air of satisfying himself rather than John. And John divined that Scaife's hold upon Desmond's affections was not so strong as he had deemed it to be. Desmond continued, "But I want you, too, old Jonathan, and if—if——"

"All right," said John, nobly. He perceived that Desmond's loyalty to

Scaife made him hesitate and flush. "I understand, Cæsar, and if I can't be first, let me be second; only, remember, with me you're first, rain or shine."

Desmond looked uneasy. "Isn't that a case of 'heads I win, tails you lose'?"

John considered; then he smiled cheerfully, "You know you are a winner, Cæsar. You're cut out for a winner; you can win whatever you want to win."

"Oh, that's all rot," said Desmond. He looked very grave, and in his eyes lay what John had never seen before.

And so ended John's first year at Harrow.

How the Wise Man Taught His Son

ANONYMOUS

THE BABEES' BOOK is a collection of treatises on manners which formed part of the education of children in medieval times. In its medieval form, courtesy was an accompaniment to the practices of chivalry and probably first appeared in France. Certainly most of the English books on the subject came from French sources. Many of the maxims dealing with courtesy were put into verse so that children might memorize them easily, for these books on manners formed part of the schooling of the day.

In medieval times the character of a child's education depended on his social position. The sons of rich men were often received into the homes of gentlemen to be trained in serving. Some children had a tutor at home or in the household of the great man with whom they were placed; others were sent to monastic and conventual institutions and later to grammar schools and the universities. At first the universities were frequented chiefly by poor men's sons and scarcely at all by gentlemen's sons. Chaucer's Clerk of Oxenford, be it remembered, was poor and threadbare and had little gold. During the sixteenth century, however, a university education became so fashionable that rich men's sons crowded in. Still there were those who opposed it. Pace in his De Fructu, in 1517, quotes a "gentleman" as follows: "I swear by God's body I would rather that my son should hang than study letters. For it becomes the sons of gentlemen to blow the horn nicely, and to hunt skilfully, and elegantly carry and train a hawk. But the study of letters should be left to the sons of rustics. . . ."

In general, the system of education implied in the Babees' Book *is chiefly concerned with riding, jousting, harping, singing and dancing.*

Listen, lordlings, and ye shall hear how the wise man taught his son. Take good heed to this matter and learn it if ye can, for this song was made with good intent to make men true and steadfast, and a thing well begun makes often a good ending.

There was a wise man taught his son while he was yet a child of tender years, meek and fair to look upon, very eager for learning and with a great desire to all goodness; and his father taught him well and featly by good example and fair words.

Selections from *The Babees' Book* are here reprinted by permission of Chatto & Windus, London.

He said: "My son, take good heed every morning, ere ye do worldly thing, lift up your heart to God, and pray as devoutly as you can for grace to lead a good life, and to escape sin both night and day, and that heaven's bliss may be your meed.

"And, my son, wherever you go, be not full of tales; beware what you say, for your own tongue may be your foe. If you say aught, take good heed where and to whom, for a word spoken to-day may be repented seven years after.

"And, son, whatever manner of man ye be, give yourself not to idleness, but busy yourself every day according to your estate. Beware of rest and ease, which things nourish sloth. Ever to be busy, more or less, is a full good sign of honesty.[1]

"And, son, I warn you also not to desire to bear office, for then can it be no other than that you must either displease and hurt your neighbours, or else forswear yourself and not do as your office demands; and get yourself, maugré,[2] here and there, an hundredfold more than thanks.

"And, son, as far as you may, go on no evil quests, nor bear false witness in any man's matter. It were better for you to be deaf and dumb than to enter wrongfully into a quest. Think, son, on the dreadful doom that God shall deem [3] us at the last!

"And, son, of another thing I warn you, on my blessing take good heed of tavern-haunting, and of the dice, and flee all lechery, lest you come to an evil end, for it will lead astray all your wits and bring you into great mischief.

"And, son, sit not up too long at even, or have late suppers, though ye be strong and hale, for with such outrage your health shall worsen. And of late walking comes debate,[4] and of sitting and drinking out of time, therefore beware and go to bed betimes and wink.

"And, son, if ye would have a wife, take her not for her money, but inquire wisely of all her life, and give good heed that she be meek, courteous and prudent, even though she be poor; and such an one will do you more good service in time of need, than a richer.

"And if your wife be meek and good, and serve you well and pleasantly, look ye be not so mad as to charge her too grievously, but rule her with a fair hand and easy, and cherish her for her good deeds. For a thing unskilfully overdone makes needless grief to grow, and it is better to have a meal's meat of homely fare with peace and quiet, than an hundred dishes with grudging and much care. And therefore learn this well that if you want a wife to your ease, take her never the more for the riches she may have, though she might endow you with lands.

"And ye shall not displease your wife, nor call her by no villainous

---

[1] Truth, literally.
[2] In spite of yourself.
[3] Judge.
[4] Strife.

names, for it is a shame to you to miscall a woman; and in so doing, ye are not wise, for if ye defame your own wife, no wonder that another should do so! Soft and fair will tame alike hart and hind, buck and doe.

"On the other hand, be not too hasty to fight or chide, if thy wife come to you at any time with complaint of man or child; and be not avenged till you know the truth, for you might make a stir in the dark, and afterwards it should rue you both.

"And, son, if you be well at ease, and sit warm among your neighbours, do not get new-fangled ideas, or be hasty to change, or to flit;[1] for if ye do, ye lack wit and are unstable, and men will speak of it and say: 'This fool can bide nowhere!'

"And, son, the more goods you have, the rather bear you meekly, and be humble, and boast not overmuch; it is wasted, for by their boasting men know fools.

"And look you pay well what you owe, and set no great store by other riches, for death takes both high and low, and then—farewell, all that there is! And therefore do by my counsel, and take example from other men, how little their goods avail them when they be dolven[2] in their dens;[3] and one that was not of his kin hath his wife, and all that there is.

"Son, keep you from deadly sin, and assay to enter Paradise. Make amends for your trespasses and deal out of your goods to poor men, make friends of your foes, and strive to gain salvation for your soul, for the world is false and frail, and every day doth worsen. Son, set nought by this world's weal, for it fares as a ripe cherry. And death is ever, I trow, the most certain thing that is; and nothing is so uncertain as to know the time thereof. Therefore, my son, think on this, on all that I have said, and may Jesus, who for us bare the crown of thorns, bring us to His bliss."

AMEN

How the Good Wife Taught Her Daughter

The good wife taught her daughter,
    Full many a time and oft,
A full good woman to be;
For said she: "Daughter to me dear,
Something good now must thou hear,
    If thou wilt prosper thee.

Daughter, if thou wilt be a wife,
    Look wisely that thou work;

[1] Move house (Scotch still).
[2] Buried.
[3] Graves.

Look lovely and in good life,
　Love God and Holy Kirk.
Go to church whene'er thou may,
　Look thou spare for no rain,
For best thou farest on that day;
　To commune with God be fain.
　　He must needs well thrive,
　　That liveth well all his life,
　　　My lief [1] child.

Gladly give thy tithes and thy offerings both,
To the poor and the bed-rid—look thou be not loth.
Give of thine own goods and be not too hard,
For seldom is the house poor where God is steward.
　　Well is he provéd
　　Who the poor hath lovéd,
　　　My lief child.

When thou sittest in the church, o'er thy beads bend;
Make thou no jangling with gossip or with friend.
Laugh thou to scorn neither old body nor young,
But be of fair bearing and of good tongue.
　　Through thy fair bearing
　　Thy worship hath increasing,
　　　My lief child.

If any man offer thee courtship, and would marry thee,
Look that thou scorn him not, whatsoever he be;
But show it to thy friends and conceal it naught.
Sit not by him nor stand where sin might be wrought,
　　For a slander raised of ill
　　Is evil for to still,
　　　My lief child.

The man that shall thee wed before God with a ring,
Love thou him and honour most of earthly thing.
Meekly thou him answer and not as an atterling,[2]
So may'st thou slake his mood,[3] and be his dear darling.
　　A fair word and a meek
　　Doth anger slake,
　　　My lief child.

Fair of speech shalt thou be, glad and of mild mood,
True in word and in deed, and in conscience good.

[1] Dear.
[2] Shrew.
[3] Quiet his wrath.

Keep thee from sin, from villainy and from blame;
And look thou bear thee so that none say of thee shame,
   For he that in good life hath run,
   Full oft his weal hath won,
     My lief child.

Be of seemly semblance, wise, and other good cheer;
Change not thy countenance for aught that thou may hear.
Fare not as a gig,[4] for nought that may betide.
Laugh thou not too loud nor yawn thou not too wide.
   But laugh thou soft and mild,
   And be not of cheer too wild,
     My lief child.

And when thou goest on thy way, go thou not too fast,
Brandish not with thy head, nor with thy shoulders cast,[5]
Have not too many words, from swearing keep aloof,
For all such manners come to an evil proof.
   For he that catcheth to him an evil name,
   It is to him a foul fame,
     My lief child.

Go thou not into the town, as it were agaze,
From one house to another, for to seek the maze;[6]
Nor to sell thy russet,[7] to the market shalt thou go,
And then to the tavern to bring thy credit low.
   For they that taverns haunt
   From thrift soon come to want,
     My lief child.

And if thou be in any place where good ale is aloft,[8]
Whether that thou serve thereof or that thou sit soft,
Measurably thou take thereof, that thou fall in no blame,
For if thou be often drunk, it falleth to thy shame.
   For those that be often drunk—
   Thrift is from them sunk,
     My lief child.

Go not to the wrestling or shooting at the cock,
As it were a strumpet or a gigggelot[9];

[4] Giddy girl.
[5] Shake or shrug.
[6] Wonder?
[7] Coarse brown stuff, homespun, frieze.
[8] A-going.
[9] A giggling girl, expressively spelled.

Dwell at home, daughter, and love thy work much,
And so thou shalt, my lief child, wax the sooner rich.
    A merry thing 'tis evermore,
    A man to be served of his own store,
      My lief child.

Acquaint thee not with each man that goeth by the street,
Though any man speak to thee, swiftly [10] thou him greet;
By him do not stand, but let him his way depart,
Lest he by his villainy should tempt thy heart.
    For all men be not true
    That fair words can shew,
      My lief child.

Also, for covetousness gifts beware to take;
Unless thou know why else,[11] quickly them forsake;
For which gifts may men soon women overcome,
Though they were as true as steel or as stone.
    Bound forsooth is she
    That of any man takes fee,[12]
      My lief child.

And wisely govern thy house, and serving maids and men,
Be thou not too bitter or too debonaire with them;
But look well what most needs to be done,
And set thy people at it, both rathely [13] and soon.
    For ready is at need
    A foredone [14] deed,
      My lief child.

And if thy husband be from home, let not thy folk do ill,
But look who doeth well and who doeth nil;
And he that doeth well, quit him well his while,
But he that doeth other, serve him as the vile.
    A foredone deed
    Will another speed,
      My lief child.

And if thy time be strait and great be thy need,
Then like a housewife set to work with speed;
Then will they all do better that about thee stand,

[10] Curtly.
[11] Another reason.
[12] Gift.
[13] Quickly.
[14] Done betimes.

For work is sooner done that hath full many a hand.
    For many a hand and wight
    Makes a heavy work light;
    And after thy good service,
    Thy name shall arise,
      My lief child.

Whate'er thy household doth, about them must thou wend,
And as much as thou mayest, be at that one end;
If thou find any fault, make them soon amend,
As they have time and space, and may them defend.
    To compel a deed be done, if there be no space,
    It is but tyranny, without temperance and grace,
      My lief child.

And look that all things be well when they their work forsake,
Forget thou not the keys into thy ward to take
And beware to whom thou trustest, and for no fancy spare,
For much harm hath fallen to them that be not 'ware.
    But, daughter, look thou be wise, and do as I thee teach,
    And trust none better than thyself, for no fair speech,
      My lief child.

And give your household their hire at their term-day,
Whether they dwell still with thee, or they wend away.
Do well by them of the goods thou hast in hold,
And then shall they say well of thee, both the young and old.
    Thy good name to thy friends
    Great joy and gladness lends,
      My lief child.

And if thy neighbour's wife hath on rich attire,
Therefore mock not, nor let scorn burn thee as a fire.
But thank thou God in heaven for what He may thee give,
And so shalt thou, my daughter dear, a good life live,
    He hath ease in his power,
    Who thanks the Lord every hour,
      My lief child.

Housewifely thou shalt go on the working day,
For pride, rest, and idleness take thrift away;
But when the Holy Day is come, well clothéd shalt thou be,
The Holy Day to honour, and God will cherish thee.
    Have in mind to worship God alway,
    For much pride comes of the evil day,
      My lief child.

When thou art a wife, a neighbour for to be,
Love then well thy neighbours as God hath commanded thee.
It behoveth thee so for to do,
And to do to them as thou wouldst be done to.
> If any discord happen, night or day,
> Make it no worse, mend it if thou may,
>> My lief child.

And if thou art a rich wife, be not then too hard,
But welcome fair thy neighbours that come to-thee-ward
With meat, drink, and honest cheer, such as thou mayest bid,[15]
To each man after his degree, and help the poor at need.
> And also for hap that may betide,
> Please well thy neighbours that dwell thee beside,
>> My lief child.

Daughter, look that thou beware, whatsoever thee betide,
Make not thy husband poor with spending or with pride.
A man must spend as he may that hath but easy good,[16]
For as a wren hath veins, men must let her blood.
> His thrift waxeth thin
> That spendeth ere he win,
>> My lief child.

Borrow not too busily, nor take thine hire first,
This may make the more need, and end by being worst.
Nor make thee not to seem rich with other men's store,
Therefore spend thou never a farthing more.
> For though thou borrow fast,
> It must home again at last,
>> My lief child.

And if thy children be rebel and will not bow them low,
If any of them misdo, neither curse them nor blow;[17]
But take a smart rod and beat them in a row,
Till they cry mercy and their guilt well know.
> Dear child, by this lore
> They will love thee ever more,
>> My lief child.

And look to thy daughters that none of them be lorn;
From the very time that they are of thee born,

---

15 Offer.
16 Moderate means.
17 Scold.

Busy thyself and gather fast for their marriage,
And give them to spousing, as soon as they be of age.
 Maidens be fair and amiable,
 But in their love full unstable,
  My lief child.

Now have I taught thee, daughter, as my mother did me;
Think thereon night and day, that forgotten it not be,
Have measure and lowness, as I have thee taught,
Then whatever man shall wed thee will regret it naught.
 Better you were a child unbore
 Than untaught in this wise lore,
  My lief child.

Now thrift and speed be thine, my sweet bairn (near or far)!
Of all our former fathers that ever were or are,
Of all patriarchs and prophets that ever were alive,—
Their blessing may'st thou have, and well may'st thou thrive!
 For well it is with that child
 That with sin is not defiled,
  My lief child.

The blessing of God may'st thou have, and of His mother bright,
Of all angels and archangels and every holy wight! [18]
And may'st thou have grace to wend thy way full right,
To the bliss of heaven, where God sits in His might!

          AMEN

How to Behave Thyself in Going by the Street and in the School

In going by the way,
Thy cap put off,
In giving the way
It is a point
And thy way fortune
Let it not grieve thee
When to the school
This rule note well,
Thy master there being,

and passing the street,
salute those ye meet;
to such as pass by,
of civility.
so for to fall,
thy fellows to call.
thou shalt resort,
I do thee exhort:
salute with all reverénce,

[18] Creature.

Declaring thereby thy duty and obediénce;
Thy fellows salute in token of love,
Lest of inhumanity they shall thee reprove.
Unto thy place appointed for to sit,
Straight go thou to, and thy satchell unknit,
Thy bokes take out, thy lesson then learn,
Humbly thyself behave and govérn
Therein taking pain, with all thine industry,
Learning to get, thy book well apply.
All things seem hard when we do begin,
But labour and diligence yet both them win;
We ought not to reckon and count the thing hard,
That bringeth joy and pleasure afterward;
Leave off then labour and the lack rue,
Lament and repent when age doth ensue.
Deeds that deserved fame and great praise,
Buried had been, we see in old days,
If letters had not then brought them to light
The truth of such things who could now recite?
Apply thy mind to learning and science,
For learning in need will be thy defence.
Nothing to science compare we may well,
The sweetness whereof all things doth excel.
And Cato the wise this worthy saying hath,
That man wanting learning is as the image of death.
The roots of learning most bitter we deem;
The fruits at last most pleasant doth seem.
Then labour for learning while here thou shalt live,
The ignorant to teach, and good example give;
So shalt thou be thought a member most worthy
Thy commonwealth to serve in time of necessity.
Experience doth teach and show to thee plain
That many to honour by learning attain,
That were of birth but simple and base;
Such is the goodness of God's special grace.
For he that to honour by virtue doth rise,
Is double happy, and counted most wise.
If doubt thou dost, desire to be told,
No shame is to learn, being never so old;
Ignorance doth cause great errors in us
For wanting of knowledge doubts to discuss;
Then learn to discern the good from the ill,
And such as thee warn bear thou good will.
When from the school ye shall take your way,
Or orderly then go ye, two in array,

Your selves matching so equal as ye may,
That men it seeing may well of you say
In commending this, your laudable ways,
Which must needs sound to your great praise,
Not running in heaps as a swarm of bees,
As at this day every man it now sees;
Not using, but refusing, such foolish toys,
As commonly are used in these days of boys,
As whooping and hallooing, as in hunting the fox,
That men it hearing deride them with mocks.
This foolishness forsake, this folly eschewing,
And learn to follow this order ensuing.
In going by the way, neither talk nor jangle,
Gape not, nor gaze not at every new fangle,
But soberly go ye, with countenance grave;
Humbly yourselves toward all men behave;
Be free of cap and full of courtesy;
Great love of all men you shall win thereby.
Be lowly and gentle and of meek mood;
Then men can not but of you say good.
In passing the street, do no man no harm;
Use thou few words, and thy tongue charm,
Then men shall see that grace in thee groweth,
From whom virtues so abundantly floweth.
When thou art come where thy parents do dwell,
Thy leave then taking, bid thy fellows farewell;
The house then entering, in thy parents' présence,
Humbly salute them with all reverénce.

The Schoolmaster's Profession Through a Layman's Eyes

BERNARD DARWIN

BERNARD DARWIN, English writer, was born in 1876. He was educated at Eton and at Trinity College, Cambridge. He has been the golf correspondent to the Times *and* Country Life *for many years and has done other miscellaneous journalism.* The English Public School, *from which the following selection is taken, was published in 1929.*

IT is rather a singular thing about the schoolmaster's profession that while he himself loves it at least as often as other men love their occupations, few people envy him. Thousands of people in other walks of life wish, wish articulately or inarticulately, that they had chosen otherwise in their youth, before it was too late, but very few of them are heard to wish that they had been schoolmasters. On the other hand, men are frequently heard to thank heaven that they are not schoolmasters, and to assert that perpetually to look after boys would drive them crazy. The inference would seem to be that a man must have a call to be a schoolmaster. No doubt some of the best schoolmasters are born with a talent in that direction and could not have endured to be anything else; but the greater number, among whom are many who turn out equally successful, drift into the profession rather than choose it. They are offered a mastership at a time when they are at a loose end and have not made up their minds. It promises, on the surface, four things: an immediate income, in some cases quite a good one; life in what must be a pleasant place, and, in the case of their own school, perhaps the place they love best in the world; a long reprieve from the sorrow of giving up games and the delightfully long holidays. It would be difficult to put forward four reasons so likely to appeal to a man who has just taken his degree, on behalf of any other profession. The second and fourth reasons ought to remain good ones forever. The first and third grow less alluring with the passing of the years, for the income, though it does increase, seems to dwindle compared with that of middle-aged contemporaries in other walks of life, and even schoolmasters have to give up foot ball some day. No doubt all four of

The above selection from *The English Public School,* by Bernard Darwin, is here reprinted by permission of Longmans, Green and Company.

these reasons seem trivial and superficial ones, to the man who adores his work, but there is a great difference between this passionate adoration, which is rare in any profession, and the ordinary interest which an ordinarily sensible and conscientious man takes in his daily round.

A layman may thank goodness that he is not a schoolmaster; he may be fully conscious of what an extraordinarily bad one he would have made, and yet he may feel envious of one thing in a schoolmaster's life, namely, the never-ceasing opportunity of making friends. Other people may have more friends of their own generation, and may be able to see more of them, but in regard to friends of younger generations, the schoolmaster is likely to be far the richer. Moreover, as long as he is a schoolmaster he will, in this respect, grow with each year richer still, so that if he lives to a hundred he can never feel that all his companions are gone. Moreover, even if he has not, as some have, a genius for keeping friendship warm by letter-writing, he will never lose his friends altogether. They may be scattered to the ends of the earth but, sooner or later, they will come back to their school, and whenever they come their master will be there; there is no need to appoint a meeting place, since one party to the friendship is a fixed point; they cannot miss one another altogether. It is a kind of friendship that, without being sentimental, possesses a quality that can come rather near to tears, and it has an invaluable something which, as a rule, only belongs to friendships between contemporaries, namely, a common background to life. It is, in this case, one seen from different angles, but still it does belong to both parties and it is the feature of friendships that have such a background that they can always be taken up comfortably and easily where they left off. This is not always true of friendships made in grown-up life. If the parties do not meet for a long time, there is often something of embarrassment in their meeting; each reproaches himself a little for forgetting and wonders if the other is bored. School friendships, even though they may never have been very warm, seem to be able to stay at the same temperature without any kind of effort, and so can produce at least a calm pleasure free from self-consciousness. And, after all, it is no small bond, between two men or between a hundred, that they have been "at the best house of the best school in England."

On the Education of Children

RICHARD STEELE

RICHARD STEELE (1672-1729) was born in Dublin in the same year as Addison. At the age of five he was left an orphan and in 1684 was entered at the Charterhouse, where two years later he began a life-long friendship with Addison. In 1689 Steele entered Christ Church, Oxford, where he enjoyed a reputation as a scholar. Early in 1694 he left Oxford without a degree and enlisted in the Duke of Ormond's regiment. In 1701 he was captain in the Tower Guard, a companion of the wits and men-of-letters who frequented Will's Coffee-house, and the author of The Christian Hero *and a successful play,* The Funeral. *In 1706 he became gentleman waiter to Prince George of Denmark, a post he held until the death of Prince George two years later.*

In 1709 Steele started The Tatler, *a money-making enterprise but one which soon exerted a considerable influence. In 1711* The Tatler *came to an end, and with Addison's help Steele began* The Spectator, *which ran for five hundred and fifty-five numbers and had a circulation of ten thousand a week. This paper was followed by* The Guardian *in 1713 and by several others which were short lived. During the last decade of his life Steele's chief interests were in the theatre and in public affairs. In 1715 he was knighted. His last comedy* The Conscious Lovers *was produced in 1722. He died in 1729 at the age of fifty-seven.*

The following essays are taken from The Spectator.

I MUST confess I have very often with much sorrow bewailed the misfortune of the children of Great Britain, when I consider the ignorance and undiscerning of the generality of schoolmasters. The boasted liberty we talk of is but a mean reward for the long servitude, the many heart-aches and terrors, to which our childhood is exposed in going through a grammar-school. Many of these stupid tyrants exercise their cruelty without any manner of distinction of the capacities of children, or the intention of parents in their behalf. There are many excellent tempers which are worthy to be nourished and cultivated with all possible diligence and care, that were never designed to be acquainted with Aristotle, Tully, or Virgil; and there are as many who have great capacities for understanding every word those great persons have writ, and yet were not born to have any relish of their writings. For want of this common and obvious discerning in those who have the care of youth, we have so many hundred unaccountable creatures every age whipped up into great scholars, that are forever near a right understanding, and will never arrive at it. These are the scandal of letters, and these are generally the men who are to teach others. The sense of shame and honor is enough to keep the world itself in order, without corporal punishment,—much more to train the minds of uncorrupted and innocent children. It happens, I doubt not, more than once in a year, that a lad is chastised for a blockhead, when it is good apprehension that makes him incapable of knowing what his teacher means. A brisk imagination very often may suggest an error which a lad could not have fallen into if he had been as heavy in conjecturing as his master in explaining. But there is no mercy even towards a wrong inter-pretation of his meaning; the sufferings of the scholar's body are to rectify the mistakes of his mind.

I am confident that no boy who will not be allured to letters without blows, will ever be brought to anything with them. A great or good mind must necessarily be the worse for such indignities, and it is a sad change to lose of its virtue for the improvement of its knowledge. No one who has gone through what they call a great school, but must remember to have seen children of excellent and ingenuous natures (as has afterward ap-peared in their manhood)—I say no man has passed through this way of education, but must have seen an ingenuous creature, expiring with shame, with pale looks, beseeching sorrow, and silent tears, throw up its honest eyes, and kneel on its tender knees to an inexorable blockhead, to be forgiven the false quantity of a word in making a Latin verse. The child is punished, and the next day he commits a like crime, and so a third, with the same consequence. I would fain ask any reasonable man whether this lad, in the simplicity of his native innocence, full of shame and capable of any impression from that grace of soul, was not fitter for any purpose in this life, than after that spark of virtue is extinguished in him, though he is able to write twenty verses in an evening?

Seneca says, after his exalted way of talking, "As the immortal gods never learnt any virtue, though they are endued with all that is good, so there are some men who have so natural a propensity to what they should follow, that they learn it almost as soon as they hear it." Plants and vege-tables are cultivated into the production of finer fruits than they would yield without that care; and yet we cannot entertain hopes of producing a tender conscious spirit into acts of virtue, without the same methods as are used to cut timber, or give new shape to a piece of stone. It is wholly to this dreadful practice that we may attribute a certain hardness and ferocity which some men, though liberally educated, carry about them in all their behavior. To be bred like a gentleman, and punished like a male-factor, must, as we see it does, produce that illiberal sauciness which we see sometimes in men of letters.

The Spartan boy who suffered the fox, which he had stolen and hid under his coat, to eat into his bowels, I dare say had not half the wit or petulance which we learn at great schools among us; but the glorious sense of honor, or rather fear of shame, which he demonstrated in that action, was worth all the learning in the world without it.

It is, methinks, a very melancholy consideration that a little negligence can spoil us, but great industry is necessary to improve us. The most excellent natures are soon depreciated, but evil tempers are long before they are exalted into good habits. To help this by punishments is the same thing as killing a man to cure him of a distemper; when he comes to suffer punishment in that one circumstance, he is brought below the existence of a rational creature, and is in the state of a brute that moves only by the admonition of stripes. But since this custom of educating by the lash is suffered by the gentry of Great Britain, I would prevail only that honest heavy lads may be dismissed from slavery sooner than they are at present, and not whipped on to their fourteenth or fifteenth year, whether they expect any progress from them or not. Let the child's capacity be forthwith examined, and he sent to some mechanic way of life, without respect to his birth, if nature designed him for nothing higher; let him go before he has innocently suffered, and is debased into a dereliction of mind for being what it is no guilt to be—a plain man. I would not here be supposed to have said that our learned men of either robe, who have been whipped at school, are not still men of noble and liberal minds; but I am sure they would have been much more so than they are, had they never suffered that infamy.

A Plea for Better Schoolmasters

MR. SPECTATOR,

I send you this to congratulate your late choice of a subject, for treating of which you deserve public thanks; I mean that on those licensed tyrants the schoolmasters.[1] If you can disarm them of their rods, you will certainly have your old age reverenced by all the young gentlemen of Great Britain who are now between seven and seventeen years. . . .

I was bred myself, sir, in a very great school, of which the master was a Welshman, but certainly descended from a Spanish family, as plainly appeared from his temper as well as his name.[2] I leave you to judge what a sort of school-master a Welshman ingrafted on a Spaniard would make. So very dreadful had he made himself to me, that although it is above twenty years since I felt his heavy hand, yet still once a month at least I dream of him, so strong an impression did he make on my mind. 'Tis a

[1] *Spectator*, No. 157, also by Steele.
[2] Dr. Charles Roderick, Headmaster of Eton.

sign he has fully terrified me waking, who still continues to haunt me sleeping.

And yet I may say without vanity, that the business of the school was what I did without great difficulty; and I was not remarkably unlucky; and yet such was the master's severity, that once a month, or oftener, I suffered as much as would have satisfied the law of the land for a petty larceny.

Many a white and tender hand, which the fond mother has passionately kissed a thousand and a thousand times, have I seen whipped until it was covered with blood; perhaps for smiling, or for going a yard and a half out of a gate, or for writing an O for an A, or an A for an O. These were our great faults! Many a brave and noble spirit has been there broken; others have run from thence and were never heard of afterwards. It is a worthy attempt to undertake the cause of distressed youth; and it is a noble piece of knight-errantry to enter the lists against so many armed pedagogues. 'Tis pity but we had a set of men, polite in their behaviour and method of teaching, who should be put into a condition of being above flattering or fearing the parents of those they instruct. We might then possibly see learning become a pleasure, and children delighting themselves in that which now they abhor for coming upon such hard terms to them. What would be still a greater happiness arising from the care of such instructors, would be, that we should have no more pedants, nor any bred to learning who had not genius for it. I am, with the utmost sincerity,

Sir,

Your most affectionate,

HUMBLE SERVANT

Four Characteristics of the Successful Teacher

GEORGE HERBERT PALMER

GEORGE HERBERT PALMER (1842-1933) spent two years at Phillips Academy, Andover, and a year in the wholesale dry-goods business before entering Harvard in 1860. Following his graduation in 1864, he taught for a year at the Salem High School and then entered the Andover Theological Seminary, from which he received a degree in 1867. He traveled and studied abroad and on his return became a tutor in Greek at Harvard. From 1873 until his retirement in 1913 he taught philosophy at Harvard. He died in 1933 at the age of ninety-one, distinguished as a teacher and scholar.

The Ideal Teacher, from which the following selections are taken, was written out of an experience of nearly forty years of successful teaching.

FIRST, a teacher must have an aptitude for vicariousness; and second, an already accumulated wealth; and third, an ability to invigorate life through knowledge; and fourth, a readiness to be forgotten. Having these, any teacher is secure. Lacking them, lacking even one, he is liable to serious failure. But as here stated they have a curiously cabalistic sound and show little relation to the needs of any profession. They have been stated with too much condensation, and have become unintelligible through being too exact. Let me repair the error by successively expanding them.

The teacher's art takes its rise in what I call an aptitude for vicariousness. As year by year my college boys prepare to go forth into life, some laggard is sure to come to me and say, "I want a little advice. Most of my classmates have their minds made up about what they are going to do. I am still uncertain. I rather incline to be a teacher, because I am fond of books and suspect that in any other profession I can give them but little time. Business men do not read. Lawyers only consult books. And I am by no means sure that ministers have read all the books they quote. On the whole it seems safest to choose a profession in which books will be my daily companions. So I turn toward teaching. But before settling the matter I thought I would ask how you regard the profession." "A noble profession," I answer, "but quite unfit for you. I would advise you to become a lawyer, a car conductor, or something equally harmless. Do not turn to anything so perilous as teaching. You would ruin both it and yourself; for you are looking in exactly the wrong direction."

Such an inquirer is under a common misconception. The teacher's task is not primarily the acquisition of knowledge, but the impartation of it,—an entirely different matter. We teachers are forever taking thoughts out of our minds and putting them elsewhere. So long as we are content to keep them in our possession, we are not teachers at all. One who is interested in laying hold on wisdom is likely to become a scholar. And while no doubt it is well for a teacher to be a fair scholar,—I have known several such,—that is not the main thing. What constitutes the teacher is the passion to make scholars; and again and again it happens that the great scholar has no such passion whatever.

But even that passion is useless without aid from imagination. At every instant of the teacher's life he must be controlled by this mighty power. Most human beings are contented with living one life and delighted if they can pass that agreeably. But this is far from enough for us teachers. We incessantly go outside ourselves and enter into the many lives about us,—lives dull, dark, and unintelligible to any but an eye like ours. And this is imagination, the sympathetic creation in ourselves of conditions which belong to others. Our profession is therefore a double-ended one. We inspect truth as it rises fresh and interesting before our eager sight. But that is only the beginning of our task. Swiftly we then seize the lines of least intellectual resistance in alien minds and, with perpetual reference to these, follow our truth till it is safely lodged beyond ourselves. Each mind has its peculiar set of frictions. Those of our pupils can never be the same as ours. We have passed far on and know all about our subject. For us it wears an altogether different look from that which it has for beginners. It is their perplexities which we must reproduce and—as if a rose should shut and be a bud again—we must reassume in our developed and accustomed souls something of the innocence of childhood. Such is the exquisite business of the teacher, to carry himself back with all his wealth of knowledge and understand how his subject should appear to the meagre mind of one glancing at it for the first time.

. . .

Plainly, then, beside his aptitude for vicariousness, our ideal teacher will need the second qualification of an already accumulated wealth. These hungry pupils are drawing all their nourishment from us, and have we got it to give? They will be poor, if we are poor; rich if we are wealthy. We are their source of supply. Every time we cut ourselves off from nutrition, we enfeeble them. And how frequently devoted teachers make this mistake! dedicating themselves so to the immediate needs of those about them that they themselves grow thinner each year. We all know the "teacher's face." It is meagre, worn, sacrificial, anxious, powerless. That is exactly the opposite of what it should be. The teacher should be the big bounteous being of the community. Other people may get along tolerably by holding whatever small knowledge comes their way. A moderate stock will pretty well serve their private turn. But that is not our case. Supplying a multitude, we need wealth sufficient for a multitude. We should then be clutching at knowledge on every side. Nothing must escape us. It is a mistake to reject a bit of truth because it lies outside our province. Some day we shall need it. All knowledge is our province.

But the two qualifications of the teacher already named will not alone suffice. I have known persons who were sympathetically imaginative, and who could not be denied to possess large intellectual wealth, who still failed as teachers. One needs a third something, the power to invigorate life through learning. We do not always notice how knowledge naturally buffets. It is offensive stuff, and makes young and wholesome minds rebel. And well it may; for when we learn anything, we are obliged to break up the world, inspect it piecemeal, and let our minds seize it bit by bit. Now about a fragment there is always something repulsive. Any one who is normally constituted must draw back in horror, feeling that what is brought him has little to do with the beautiful world he has known. Where was there ever a healthy child who did not hate the multiplication table? A boy who did not detest such abstractions as seven times eight would hardly be worth educating. By no ingenuity can we relieve knowledge of this unfortunate peculiarity. It must be taken in disjointed portions. That is the way attention is made. In consequence each of us must be to some extent a specialist, devoting himself to certain sides of the world and neglecting others quite as important. These are the conditions under which we imperfect creatures work. Our sight is not world-wide. When we give our attention to one object, by that very act we withdraw it from others. In this way our children must learn and have their expansive natures subdued to pedagogic exigencies.

Because this belittlement through the method of approach is inevitable, it is all-important that the teacher should possess a supplemental dignity, replacing the oppressive sense of pettiness with stimulating intimations of high things in store. Partly on this account a book is an imperfect instructor. Truth there, being impersonal, seems untrue, abstract, and insignificant. It needs to shine through a human being before it can exert its vital force on a young student. Quite as much for vital transmission as for intellectual elucidation, is a teacher employed. His consolidated character exhibits the gains which come from study. He need not point them out. If he is a scholar, there will appear in him an augustness, accuracy, fulness of knowledge, a buoyant enthusiasm even in drudgery, and an unshakable confidence that others must soon see and enjoy what has enriched himself; and all this will quickly convey itself to his students and create attention in his classroom. Such kindling of interest is the great function of the teacher. People sometimes say, "I should like to teach if only pupils cared to learn." But then there would be little need of teaching. Boys who have made up their minds that knowledge is worth while are pretty sure to get it, without regard to teachers. Our chief concern is with those who are unawakened. In the Sistine Chapel Michael Angelo has depicted the Almighty moving in clouds over the rugged earth where lies the newly created Adam, hardly aware of himself. The tips of the fingers touch, the Lord's and Adam's, and the huge frame loses its inertness and rears itself into action. Such may be the electrifying touch of the teacher.

Too long I have delayed the fourth, the disagreeable, section of my paper. Briefly it is this: a teacher must have a readiness to be forgotten. And what is harder? We may be excellent persons, may be daily doing kindnesses, and yet not be quite willing to have those kindnesses overlooked. Many a man is ready to be generous, if by it he can win praise. The love of praise,—it is almost our last infirmity; but there is no more baffling infirmity for the teacher. If praise and recognition are dear to him, he may as well stop work. Dear to him perhaps they must be, as a human being; but as a teacher, he is called on to rise above ordinary human conditions. Whoever has followed me thus far will perceive the reason. I have shown that a teacher does not live for himself, but for his pupil and for the truth which he imparts. His aim is to be a colorless medium through which that truth may shine on opening minds. How can he be this if he is continually interposing himself and saying, "Instead of looking at the truth, my children, look at me and see how skilfully I do my work. I thought I taught you admirably to-day. I hope you thought so too." No, the teacher must keep himself entirely out of the way, fixing young attention on the proffered knowledge and not on anything so small as the one who brings it. Only so can he be vicarious, whole-hearted in invigorating the lives committed to his charge.

Jesus Teaches His Disciples

THE GOSPEL ACCORDING TO ST. MATTHEW

JESUS *was one of the world's greatest teachers; throughout the four Gospels He is presented as a teacher. His teaching methods were simple. He was, first of all, an incomparable story teller. He illustrated his teaching by parable and story, by concrete references to the life with which his hearers were familiar. His teaching, unlike that of the scribes, was not a learned commentary upon Scriptural texts but a direct and simple statement of truth. He taught with a freedom and spontaneity, an inspiration and power which made a deep impression on those who heard Him. His illustrations gave life and vitality to abstract ethical principles. Into a community concerned with legalistic interpretation of dogma He brought a new sense of ethical reality. He did not speculate about truth; He did not argue about truth; in simple act and story He demonstrated truth. And truth was not to Him something apart from the daily needs of men; it was light and guidance to men in their daily living. In His teaching there was none of the pedant's sterile pleasure in abstruse knowledge. In simple language He taught men how to live. Through His great gift of creative imagination He was able to discern the needs of men and to respond to their needs.*

Jesus never forgot that He was teaching men. His approach was that of a friend offering help, not that of a scholar imparting knowledge. To His wisdom and insight He added a simple kindliness and affection. If He talked of love, He demonstrated love in His life; if He taught the necessity of humility, He was Himself humble. With the transgressor He was always kindly and human, quick to reprove, quick to forgive, yet capable of wrathful indignation against wrongdoing and error.

His greatest gift as a teacher was, perhaps, His ability to make others think for themselves. In His teaching He was not handing down the law but revealing the truth which makes men free. He taught always as one who having a knowledge of truth wished to reveal it to others that they too might share its power and beauty. It is no wonder that those who heard Him felt that He spoke "as one having authority."

A ND seeing the multitudes, he went up into a mountain: and when he was set, his disciples came unto him. And he opened his mouth, and taught them, saying:

Blessed are the poor in spirit: for theirs is the kingdom of heaven. Blessed are they that mourn: for they shall be comforted. Blessed are the meek: for they shall inherit the earth. Blessed are they which do hunger and thirst after righteousness: for they shall be filled. Blessed are the merciful: for they shall obtain mercy. Blessed are the pure in heart: for they shall see God. Blessed are the peacemakers: for they shall be called the children of God. Blessed are they which are persecuted for righteousness' sake: for theirs is the kingdom of heaven. Blessed are ye, when men shall revile you, and persecute you, and shall say all manner of evil against you falsely, for my sake. Rejoice, and be exceeding glad: for great is your reward in heaven: for so persecuted they the prophets which were before you.

Ye are the salt of the earth: but if the salt have lost his savour, wherewith shall it be salted? it is thenceforth good for nothing, but to be cast out, and to be trodden under foot of men. Ye are the light of the world. A city that is set on an hill cannot be hid. Neither do men light a candle, and put it under a bushel, but on a candlestick; and it giveth light unto all that are in the house. Let your light so shine before men, that they may see your good works, and glorify your Father which is in heaven.

Think not that I am come to destroy the law, or the prophets: I am not come to destroy, but to fulfill. For verily I say unto you, Till heaven and earth pass, one jot or one tittle shall in no wise pass from the law, till all be fulfilled. Whosoever therefore shall break one of these least commandments, and shall teach men so, he shall be called the least in the kingdom of heaven: but whosoever shall do and teach them, the same shall be called great in the kingdom of heaven. For I say unto you, That except your righteousness shall exceed the righteousness of the scribes and Pharisees, ye shall in no case enter into the kingdom of heaven.

Ye have heard that it was said by them of old time, Thou shalt not kill; and whosoever shall kill shall be in danger of the judgment: But I say unto you, That whosoever is angry with his brother without a cause shall be in danger of the judgment: and whosoever shall say to his brother, Ra-ca, shall be in danger of the council: but whosoever shall say, Thou fool, shall be in danger of hell fire.

Therefore if thou bring thy gift to the altar, and there rememberest that thy brother hath ought against thee; leave there thy gift before the altar, and go thy way; first be reconciled to thy brother, and then come and offer thy gift. Agree with thine adversary quickly, whiles thou art in the way with him; lest at any time the adversary deliver thee to the judge, and the judge deliver thee to the officer, and thou be cast into prison. Verily I say unto thee, Thou shalt by no means come out thence, till thou hast paid the uttermost farthing. Ye have heard that it was said by them of old time, Thou shalt not commit adultery: but I say unto you, That whosoever looketh on a woman to lust after her hath committed adultery with her already in his heart. And if thy right eye offend thee, pluck it out, and cast it from thee: for it is profitable for thee that one of thy members should perish, and not that thy whole body should be cast into hell. And if thy right hand offend thee, cut it off, and cast it from thee: for it is profitable for thee that one of thy members should perish, and not that thy whole body should be cast into hell. It hath been said, Whosoever shall put away his wife, let him give her a writing of divorcement: but I say unto you, That whosoever shall put away his wife, saving for the cause of fornication, causeth her to commit adultery: and whosoever shall marry her that is divorced committeth adultery.

Again, ye have heard that it hath been said by them of old time, Thou shalt not forswear thyself, but shalt perform unto the Lord thine oaths: but I say unto you, Swear not at all; neither by heaven; for it is God's throne: nor by the earth; for it is his footstool: neither by Jerusalem; for it is the city of the great King. Neither shalt thou swear by thy head, because thou canst not make one hair white or black. But let your communication be, Yea, yea; Nay, nay; for whatsoever is more than these cometh of evil.

Ye have heard that it hath been said, An eye for an eye, and a tooth for a tooth: but I say unto you, That ye resist not evil: but whosoever shall smite thee on thy right cheek, turn to him the other also. And if any man will sue thee at the law, and take away thy coat, let him have thy cloke also. And whosoever shall compel thee to go a mile, go with him twain. Give to him that asketh thee, and from him that would borrow of thee turn not thou away.

Ye have heard that it hath been said, Thou shalt love thy neighbour, and hate thine enemy. But I say unto you, Love your enemies, bless them that curse you, do good to them that hate you, and pray for them which despitefully use you, and persecute you; that ye may be the children of your Father which is in heaven: for he maketh his sun to rise on the evil and on the good, and sendeth rain on the just and on the unjust. For if ye love them which love you, what reward have ye? do not even the publicans the same? And if ye salute your brethren only, what do ye more than others? do not even the publicans so? Be ye therefore perfect, even as your Father which is in heaven is perfect.

Take heed that ye do not your alms before men, to be seen of them: otherwise ye have no reward of your Father which is in heaven. Therefore when thou doest thine alms, do not sound a trumpet before thee, as the hypocrites do in the synagogues and in the streets, that they may have glory of men. Verily I say unto you, They have their reward. But when thou doest alms, let not thy left hand know what they right hand doeth: that thine alms may be in secret: and thy Father which seeth in secret himself shall reward thee openly.

And when thou prayest, thou shalt not be as the hypocrites are: for they love to pray standing in the synagogues and in the corners of the streets, that they may be seen of men. Verily I say unto you, They have their reward. But thou, when thou prayest, enter into thy closet, and when thou hast shut thy door, pray to thy Father which is in secret; and thy Father which seeth in secret shall reward thee openly. But when ye pray, use not vain repetitions, as the heathen do: for they think that they shall be heard for their much speaking. Be not ye therefore like unto them: for your Father knoweth what things ye have need of, before ye ask him. After this manner therefore pray ye: Our Father which art in heaven, Hallowed be thy name. Thy kingdom come. Thy will be done in earth, as it is in heaven. Give us this day our daily bread. And Forgive us our debts, as we forgive our debtors. And lead us not into temptation, but deliver us from evil: For thine is the kingdom, and the power, and the glory, for ever. Amen. For if ye forgive men their trespasses, your heavenly Father will also forgive you: but if ye forgive not men their trespasses, neither will your Father forgive your trespasses.

Moreover when ye fast, be not, as the hypocrites, of a sad countenance: for they disfigure their faces, that they may appear unto men to fast. Verily I say unto you, They have their reward. But thou, when thou fastest, anoint thine head, and wash thy face; that thou appear not unto men to fast, but unto thy Father which is in secret: and thy Father, which seeth in secret, shall reward thee openly.

Lay not up for yourselves treasures upon earth, where moth and rust doth corrupt, and where thieves break through and steal: but lay up for yourselves treasures in heaven, where neither moth nor rust doth corrupt, and where thieves do not break through nor steal: for where your treasure is, there will your heart be also. The light of the body is the eye: if therefore thine eye be single, thy whole body shall be full of light. But if thine eye be evil, thy whole body shall be full of darkness. If therefore the light that is in thee be darkness, how great is that darkness!

No man can serve two masters: for either he will hate the one, and love the other; or else he will hold to the one, and despise the other. Ye cannot serve God and mammon. Therefore I say unto you, Take no thought for your life, what ye shall eat, or what ye shall drink; nor yet for your body, what ye shall put on. Is not the life more than meat, and the body than raiment? Behold the fowls of the air: for they sow not, neither do they reap, nor gather into barns; yet your heavenly Father feedeth them. Are ye not much better than they? Which of you by taking thought can add one cubit unto his stature? And why take ye thought for raiment? Consider the lilies of the field, they grow; they toil not, neither do they spin: and yet I say unto you, That even Solomon in all his glory was not arrayed like one of these. Wherefore, if God so clothe the grass of the field, which to day is, and to morrow is cast into the oven, shall he not much more clothe you, O ye of little faith? Therefore take no thought, saying, What shall we eat? or, What shall we drink? or, Wherewithal shall we be clothed? (For after all these things do the Gentiles seek:) for your heavenly Father knoweth that ye have need of all these things. But seek ye first the kingdom of God, and his righteousness; and all these things shall be added unto you. Take therefore no thought for the morrow: for the morrow shall take thought for the things of itself. Sufficient unto the day is the evil thereof.

Judge not, that ye be not judged. For with what judgment ye judge, ye shall be judged: and with what measure ye mete, it shall be measured to you again. And why beholdest thou the mote that is in thy brother's eye, but considerest not the beam that is in thine own eye? Or how wilt thou say to thy brother, Let me pull out the mote out of thine eye; and, behold, a beam is in thine own eye? Thou hypocrite, first cast out the beam out of thine own eye; and then shalt thou see clearly to cast out the mote out of thy brother's eye.

Give not that which is holy unto the dogs, neither cast ye your pearls before swine, lest they trample them under their feet, and turn again and rend you.

Ask, and it shall be given you; seek, and ye shall find; knock, and it shall be open unto you: for every one that asketh receiveth; and he that seeketh findeth; and to him that knocketh it shall be opened. Or what man is there of you, whom if his son ask bread, will he give him a stone? Or if he ask a fish, will he give him a serpent? If ye then, being evil, know how to give good gifts unto your children, how much more shall your Father which is in heaven give good things to them that ask him? Therefore all things whatsoever ye would that men should do to you, do ye even so to them; for this is the law and the prophets.

Enter ye in at the strait gate: for wide is the gate, and broad is the way, that leadeth to destruction, and many there be which go in thereat: because strait is the gate, and narrow is the way, which leadeth unto life, and few there be that find it.

Beware of false prophets, which come to you in sheep's clothing, but inwardly they are ravening wolves. Ye shall know them by their fruits. Do men gather grapes of thorns, or figs of thistles? Even so every good tree bringeth forth good fruit; but a corrupt tree bringeth forth evil fruit. A good tree cannot bring forth evil fruit, neither can a corrupt tree bring forth good fruit. Every tree that bringeth not forth good fruit is hewn down, and cast into the fire. Wherefore by their fruits ye shall know them.

Not every one that saith unto me, Lord, Lord, shall enter into the kingdom of heaven; but he that doeth the will of my Father which is in heaven. Many will say to me in that day, Lord, Lord, have we not prophesied in thy name? and in thy name have cast out devils? and in thy name done many wonderful works? And then will I profess unto them, I never knew you: depart from me, ye that work iniquity.

Therefore, whosoever heareth these sayings of mine, and doeth them, I will liken him unto a wise man, which built his house upon a rock: and the rain descended, and the floods came, and the winds blew, and beat upon that house; and it fell not: for it was founded upon a rock. And every one that heareth these sayings of mine, and doeth them not, shall be likened unto a foolish man, which built his house upon the sand: and the rain descended, and the floods came, and the winds blew, and beat upon that house; and it fell: and great was the fall of it. And it came to pass, when Jesus had ended these sayings, the people were astonished at his doctrine: for he taught them as one having authority, and not as the scribes.

Of the Institution and Education of Children

MICHEL de MONTAIGNE

MICHEL de MONTAIGNE (1533-1592) was sent at the age of six to the College of Guienne at Bordeaux, where he was taught by several of the most eminent scholars of the day. At thirteen he left school to study law. In 1554 he received an appointment as councillor in the Parliament of Bordeaux; in 1559 he was at Bar-le-Duc with the court of Francis II, and in the year following he was present at Rouen to witness the declaration of the majority of Charles IX. He played an important part in the affairs of his day and was honored for his services by being admitted to the Order of St. Michael, the highest order of the French noblesse. In his thirty-eighth year, however, he resolved to dedicate the remaining years of his life to study and contemplation. He withdrew to his château and occupied himself with reading and reflection, setting down his thoughts as they occurred to him. These thoughts, published in 1580 under the title Essais, *conferred immortality on their author.*

Shortly after the publication of his Essais *Montaigne made a leisurely journey into Italy. While returning from this journey, he learned by letter that in his absence he had been elected mayor of Bordeaux. He held this office for four years, successfully maintaining peace between the two religious factions which at that time divided the town of Bordeaux. Once again Montaigne retired to his château, glad to be rid of civic duties and free to pursue his private interests. He died at his château in 1592, at the age of fifty-nine.*

To a gentleman borne of noble parentage, and heire of a house, that aymeth at true learning, and in it would be disciplined, not so much for gaine or commoditie to himselfe (because so abject an end is far unworthie the grace and favour of the Muses, and besides, hath a regard or dependencie of others) nor for externall shew and ornament, but to adorne and enrich his inward minde, desiring rather to shape and institute an able and sufficient man, than a bare learned man. My desire is therefore, that the parents or overseers of such a gentleman be very circumspect, and carefull in chusing his director, whom I would rather commend for having a well composed and temperate braine, than a full stuft head, yet both

will doe well. And I would rather prefer wisdome, judgement, civill cus-
tomes, and modest behaviour, than bare and meere literall learning; and
that in his charge he hold a new course. Some never cease brawling in
their schollers eares (as if they were still pouring in a tonell) to follow
their booke, yet is their charge nothing else, but to repeat, what hath
beene told them before. I would have a tutor to correct this part, and that
at first entrance, according to the capacitie of the wit he hath in hand,
he should begin to make shew of it, making him to have a smacke of all
things, and how to chuse and distinguish them, without helpe of others,
sometimes opening him the way, other times leaving him to open it by
himselfe. I would not have him to invent and speake alone, but suffer his
disciple to speake when his turne commeth. *Socrates,* and after him
Arcesilaus, made their schollers to speak first, and then would speake
themselves. *Obest plerumque iis qui discere volunt, auctoritas eorum qui
docent* (CIC. *De Nat. i.*). *Most commonly the authoritie of them that
teach, hinders them that would learne.*

It is therefore meet, that he make him first trot-on before him, whereby
he may the better judge of his pace, and so guesse how long he will hold
out, that accordingly he may fit his strength: for want of which proportion,
we often marre all. And to know how to make a good choice, and how far
forth one may proceed (still keeping a due measure) is one of the hardest
labours I know. It is a signe of a noble, and effect of an undanted spirit, to
know how to second, and how far forth he shall condescend to his
childish proceedings, and how to guide them. As for my selfe, I can better
and with more strength walke up, than downe a hill. Those which according to our common fashion, undertake with one selfe-same lesson, and
like maner of education, to direct many spirits of divers formes and different humours, it is no marvell if among a multitude of children, they
scarse meet with two or three, that reap any good fruit by their discipline,
or that come to any perfection. I would not only have him to demand an
accompt of the words contained in his lesson, but of the sense and substance thereof, and judge of the profit he hath made of it, not by the testi-
monie of his memorie, but by the witnesse of his life. That what he lately
learned, he cause him to set forth and pourtray the same into sundrie
shapes, and then to accommodate it to as many different and severall subjects; whereby he shal perceive, whether he have yet apprehended the
same, and therein enfoffed himself, at due times taking his instruction from
the institution given by *Plato*. It is a signe of cruditie and indigestion for
a man to yeeld up his meat, even as he swallowed the same: the stomacke
hath not wrought his full operation, unlesse it have changed forms, and
altered fashion of that which was given him to boyle and concoct.

* * *

. . . How wide are they, which go about to allure a childs mind to go
to his booke, being yet but tender and fearefull, with a stearne-frowning
countenance, and with handsfull of rods? Oh wicked and pernicious man-

ner of teaching! which *Quintillian* hath very wel noted, that this imperious kind of authoritie, namely, this way of punishing of children, drawes many dangerous inconveniences within. How much more decent were it, to see their school-houses and formes strewed with greene boughes and flowers, than with bloudy burchen-twigs? If it lay in me, I would doe as the Philosopher *Speusippus* did, who caused the pictures of Gladnesse and Joy, of *Flora*, and of the Graces, to be set up round about his school-house. Where their profit lieth, there should also be their recreation. Those meats ought to be sugred over, that are healthful for childrens stomackes, and those made bitter that are hurtfull for them.

Dr. Skinner of Roughborough

SAMUEL BUTLER

SAMUEL BUTLER was born in 1835, the eldest son of the Rev. Thomas Butler. He was educated at Shrewsbury School and at St. John's College, Cambridge. Unable because of his religious skepticism to accede to his father's wishes and enter the ministry, he studied music and drawing, but his father refused to allow him to follow either interest as a profession, and so he went to New Zealand and became a sheep-farmer. This venture prospered, and in 1864 Butler returned to England with a comfortable fortune and the determination to develop his interests in music, painting, and writing. In 1872 he published Erewhon, *a satire on English life and manners. This novel was followed by other satirical work in which Butler waged war against the hypocrisies and conventions which he saw around him. He died in 1902.*

The following selections are taken from The Way of All Flesh, *his greatest novel, published posthumously in 1903.*

I WILL give no more of the details of my hero's earlier years. Enough that he struggled through them, and at twelve years old knew every page of his Latin and Greek Grammars by heart. He had read the greater part of Virgil, Horace and Livy, and I do not know how many Greek plays: he was proficient in arithmetic, knew the first four books of Euclid thoroughly, and had a fair knowledge of French. It was now time he went to school, and to school he was accordingly to go, under the famous Dr. Skinner of Roughborough.

Theobald had known Dr. Skinner slightly at Cambridge. He had been a burning and a shining light in every position he had filled from his boyhood upwards. He was a very great genius. Every one knew this; they said, indeed, that he was one of the few people to whom the word genius could be applied without exaggeration. Had he not taken I don't know how many University Scholarships in his freshman's year? Had he not been afterwards Senior Wrangler, First Chancellor's Medallist and I do not know how many more things besides? And then, he was such a wonderful speaker; at the Union Debating Club he had been without a rival, and had, of course, been president; his moral character—a point on which so many geniuses were weak—was absolutely irreproachable; foremost of all, however, among his many great qualities, and perhaps more remarkable even than his genius was what biographers have called 'the simple-minded and childlike earnestness of his character,' an earnestness which might be perceived by the solemnity with which he spoke even about trifles. It is hardly necessary to say he was on the Liberal side in politics.

His personal appearance was not particularly prepossessing. He was about the middle height, portly, and had a couple of fierce grey eyes, that flashed fire from beneath a pair of great bushy beetling eyebrows and overawed all who came near him. It was in respect of his personal appearance, however, that, if he was vulnerable at all, his weak place was to be found. His hair when he was a young man was red, but after he had taken his degree he had a brain fever which caused him to have his head shaved; when he reappeared he did so wearing a wig, and one which was a good deal further off red than his own hair had been. He not only had never discarded his wig, but year by year it had edged itself a little more and a little more off red, till by the time he was forty, there was not a trace of red remaining, and his wig was brown.

When Dr. Skinner was a very young man, hardly more than five-and-twenty, the head-mastership of Roughborough Grammar School had fallen vacant, and he had been unhesitatingly appointed. The result justified the selection. Dr. Skinner's pupils distinguished themselves at whichever University they went to. He moulded their minds after the model of his own, and stamped an impression upon them which was indelible in after-life; whatever else a Roughborough man might be, he was sure to make every one feel that he was a God-fearing earnest Christian and a Liberal, if not a Radical, in politics. Some boys, of course, were incapable of appreciating the beauty and loftiness of Dr. Skinner's nature. Some such boys, alas! there will be in every school; upon them Dr. Skinner's hand was very properly a heavy one. His hand was against them, and theirs against him during the whole time of the connection between them. They not only disliked him, but they hated all that he more especially embodied, and throughout their lives disliked all that reminded them of him. Such boys, however, were in a minority, the spirit of the place being decidedly Skinnerian.

I once had the honour of playing a game of chess with this great man. It was during the Christmas holidays, and I had come down to Roughborough for a few days to see Alethea Pontifex (who was then living there) on business. It was very gracious of him to take notice of me, for if I was a light of literature at all it was of the very lightest kind.

It is true that in the intervals of business I had written a good deal, but my works had been almost exclusively for the stage, and for those theatres that devoted themselves to extravaganza and burlesque. I had written many pieces of this description, full of puns and comic songs, and they had had a fair success, but my best piece had been a treatment of English history during the Reformation period, in the course of which I had introduced Cranmer, Sir Thomas More, Henry the Eighth, Catherine of Aragon, and Thomas Cromwell (in his youth better known as the *Malleus Monachorum*), and had made them dance a break-down. I had also dramatized the *Pilgrim's Progress* for a Christmas Pantomime, and made an important scene of Vanity Fair, with Mr. Greatheart, Apollyon, Christiana, Mercy and Hopeful as the principal characters. The orchestra played music taken from Handel's best known works, but the time was a good deal altered, and altogether the tunes were not exactly as Handel left them. Mr. Greatheart was very stout and he had a red nose; he wore a capacious waistcoat, and a shirt with a huge frill down the middle of the front. Hopeful was up to as much mischief as I could give him; he wore the costume of a young swell of the period, and had a cigar in his mouth which was continually going out.

Christiana did not wear much of anything; indeed it was said that the dress which the Stage Manager had originally proposed for her had been considered inadequate even by the Lord Chamberlain, but this is not the case. With all these delinquencies upon my mind it was natural that I should feel convinced of sin while playing chess (which I hate) with the great Dr. Skinner of Roughborough—the historian of Athens and editor of Demosthenes. Dr. Skinner, moreover, was one of those who pride themselves on being able to set people at their ease at once, and I had been sitting on the edge of my chair all the evening. But I have always been very easily overawed by a schoolmaster.

The game had been a long one, and at half-past nine, when supper came in, we had each of us a few pieces remaining. 'What will you take for supper, Dr. Skinner?' said Mrs. Skinner in a silvery voice.

He made no answer for some time, but at last in a tone of almost superhuman solemnity, he said, first, 'Nothing,' and then 'Nothing whatever.'

By and by, however, I had a sense come over me as though I were nearer the consummation of all things than I had ever yet been. The room seemed to grow dark, as an expression came over Dr. Skinner's face, which showed that he was about to speak. The expression gathered force, the room grew darker and darker. 'Stay,' he at length added, and I felt that here at any rate was an end to a suspense which was rapidly becoming unbearable. 'Stay—I may presently take a glass of cold water—and a small piece of bread and butter.'

As he said the word 'butter' his voice sank to a hardly audible whisper; then there was a sigh as though of relief when the sentence was concluded, and the universe this time was safe.

Another ten minutes of solemn silence finished the game. The Doctor rose briskly from his seat and placed himself at the supper-table. 'Mrs. Skinner,' he exclaimed jauntily, 'what are those mysterious-looking objects surrounded by potatoes?'

'Those are oysters, Dr. Skinner.'

'Give me some, and give Overton some.'

And so on till he had eaten a good plate of oysters, a scallop shell of minced veal nicely browned, some apple tart, and a hunk of bread and cheese. This was the small piece of bread and butter.

The cloth was now removed and tumblers with teaspoons in them, a lemon or two and a jug of boiling water were placed upon the table. Then the great man unbent. His face beamed.

'And what shall it be to drink?' he exclaimed persuasively. 'Shall it be brandy and water? No. It shall be gin and water. Gin is the more wholesome liquor.'

So gin it was, hot and stiff too.

Who can wonder at him or do anything but pity him? Was he not headmaster of Roughborough School? To whom had he owed money at any time? Whose ox had he taken, whose ass had he taken, or whom had he defrauded? What whisper had ever been breathed against his moral character? If he had become rich it was by the most honourable of all means—his literary attainments; over and above his great works of scholarship, his *Meditations upon the Epistle and Character of St. Jude* had placed him among the most popular of English theologians; it was so exhaustive that no one who bought it need ever meditate upon the subject again—indeed it exhausted all who had anything to do with it. He had made £5,000 by this work alone, and would very likely make another £5,000 before he died. A man who had done all this and wanted a piece of bread and butter had a right to announce the fact with some pomp and circumstance. Nor should his words be taken without searching for what he used to call a 'deeper and more hidden meaning.' Those who searched for this even in his lightest utterances would not be without their reward. They would find that 'bread and butter' was Skinnerese for oyster-patties and apple tart, and 'gin hot' the true translation of water.

But independently of their money value, his works had made him a lasting name in literature. So probably Gallio was under the impression that his fame would rest upon the treatises on natural history which we gather from Seneca that he compiled, and which for aught we know may have contained a complete theory of evolution; but the treatises are all gone and Gallio has become immortal for the very last reason in the world that he expected, and for the very last reason that would have flattered his vanity. He had become immortal because he cared nothing about the most important movement with which he was ever brought into connection (I wish people who are in search of immortality would lay the lesson to heart and not make so much noise about important movements), and so, if Dr. Skinner becomes immortal, it will probably be for some reason very different from the one which he so fondly imagined.

Could it be expected to enter into the head of such a man as this that in reality he was making his money by corrupting youth; that it was his paid profession to make the worse appear the better reason in the eyes of those who were too young and inexperienced to be able to find him out; that he kept out of the sight of those whom he professed to teach material points of the argument, for the production of which they had a right to rely upon the honour of anyone who made professions of sincerity; that he was a passionate half-turkey-cock, half-gander of a man whose sallow, bilious face and hobble-gobble voice could scare the timid, but who would take to his heels readily enough if he were met firmly; that his *Meditations on St. Jude,* such as they were, were cribbed without acknowledgment, and would have been beneath contempt if so many people did not believe them to have been written honestly? Mrs. Skinner might have perhaps kept him a little more in his proper place if she had thought it worth while to try, but she had enough to attend to in looking after her household and seeing that the boys were well fed, and, if they were ill, properly looked after—which she took good care they were.

Ernest Meets Dr. Skinner

ERNEST had heard awful accounts of Dr. Skinner's temper, and of the bullying which the younger boys at Roughborough had to put up with at the hands of the bigger ones. He had now got about as much as he could stand, and felt as though it must go hard with him if his burdens of whatever kind were to be increased. He did not cry on leaving home, but I am afraid he did on being told that he was getting near Roughborough. His father and mother were with him, having posted from home in their own carriage; Roughborough had as yet no railway, and as it was only some forty miles from Battersby, this was the easiest way of getting there.

On seeing him cry, his mother felt flattered and caressed him. She said she knew he must feel very sad at leaving such a happy home, and going among people who, though they would be very good to him, could never, never be as good as his dear papa and she had been; still she was herself, if he only knew it, much more deserving of pity than he was, for the parting was more painful to her than it could possibly be to him, etc., and Ernest, on being told that his tears were for grief at leaving home, took it all on trust and did not trouble to investigate the real cause of his tears. As they approached Roughborough he pulled himself together, and was fairly calm by the time he reached Dr. Skinner's.

On their arrival they had luncheon with the Doctor and his wife, and then Mrs. Skinner took Christina over the bedrooms, and showed her where her dear little boy was to sleep.

Whatever men may think about the study of man, women do really believe the noblest study for womankind to be woman, and Christina was too much engrossed with Mrs. Skinner to pay much attention to anything else; I dare say Mrs. Skinner, too, was taking pretty accurate stock of Christina. Christina was charmed, as indeed she generally was with any new acquaintance, for she found in them (and so must we all) something of the nature of a cross; as for Mrs. Skinner, I imagine she had seen too many Christinas to find much regeneration in the sample now before her; I believe her private opinion echoed the dictum of a well-known head master who declared that all parents were fools, but more especially mothers; she was, however, all smiles and sweetness, and Christina devoured these graciously as tributes paid more particularly to herself, and such as no other mother would have been at all likely to have won.

In the meantime Theobald and Ernest were with Dr. Skinner in his library—the room where new boys were examined and old ones had up for rebuke or chastisement. If the walls of that room could speak, what an amount of blundering and capricious cruelty would they not bear witness to!

Like all houses, Dr. Skinner's had its peculiar smell. In this case the prevailing odour was one of Russia leather, but along with it there was a subordinate savour as of a chemist's shop. This came from a small laboratory in one corner of the room—the possession of which, together with the free chattery and smattery use of such words as 'carbonate,' 'hyposulphite,' 'phosphate,' and 'affinity,' were enough to convince even the most sceptical that Dr. Skinner had a profound knowledge of chemistry.

I may say in passing that Dr. Skinner had dabbled in a great many other things as well as chemistry. He was a man of many small knowledges, and each of them dangerous. I remember Alethea Pontifex once said in her wicked way to me, that Dr. Skinner put her in mind of the Bourbon princes on their return from exile after the battle of Waterloo, only that he was their exact converse; for whereas they had learned nothing and forgotten nothing, Dr. Skinner had learned everything and forgotten everything. And this puts me in mind of another of her wicked sayings about Dr. Skinner. She told me one day that he had the harmlessness of the serpent and the wisdom of the dove.

But to return to Dr. Skinner's library; over the chimney-piece there was a Bishop's half-length portrait of Dr. Skinner himself, painted by the elder Pickersgill, whose merit Dr. Skinner had been among the first to discern and foster. There were no other pictures in the library, but in the dining-room there was a fine collection, which the doctor had got together with his usual consummate taste. He added to it largely in later life, and when it came to the hammer at Christie's, as it did not long since, it was found to comprise many of the latest and most matured works of Solomon Hart, O'Neil, Charles Landseer, and more of our recent Academicians than I can at the moment remember. There were thus brought together and exhibited at one view many works which had attracted attention at the Academy Exhibitions, and as to whose ultimate destiny there had been some curiosity. The prices realized were disappointing to the executors, but, then, these things are so much a matter of chance. An unscrupulous writer in a well-known weekly paper had written the collection down.

Moreover there had been one or two large sales a short time before Dr. Skinner's, so that at this last there was rather a panic, and a reaction against the high prices that had ruled lately.

The table of the library was loaded with books many deep; MSS. of all kinds were confusedly mixed up with them,—boys' exercises, probably, and examination papers—but all littering untidly about. The room in fact was as depressing from its slatternliness as from its atmosphere of erudition. Theobald and Ernest as they entered it, stumbled over a large hole in the Turkey carpet, and the dust that rose showed how long it was since it had been taken up and beaten. This, I should say, was no fault of Mrs. Skinner's but was due to the Doctor himself, who declared that if his papers were once disturbed it would be the death of him. Near the window was a green cage containing a pair of turtle doves, whose plaintive cooing added to the melancholy of the place. The walls were covered with book-shelves from floor to ceiling, and on every shelf the books stood in double rows. It was horrible. Prominent among the most promiment upon the most prominent shelf were a series of splendidly bound volumes entitled 'Skinner's Works.'

Boys are sadly apt to rush to conclusions, and Ernest believed that Dr. Skinner knew all the books in this terrible library, and that he, if he were to be any good, should have to learn them too. His heart fainted within him.

He was told to sit on a chair against the wall and did so, while Dr. Skinner talked to Theobald upon the topics of the day. He talked about the Hampden Controversy then raging, and discoursed learnedly about "Praemunire"; then he talked about the revolution which had just broken out in Sicily, and rejoiced that the Pope had refused to allow foreign troops to pass through his dominions in order to crush it. Dr. Skinner and the other masters took in the *Times* among them, and Dr. Skinner echoed the *Times'* leaders. In those days there were no penny papers and Theobald only took in the *Spectator*—for he was at that time on the Whig side in politics; besides this he used to receive the *Ecclesiastical Gazette* once a month, but he saw no other papers, and was amazed at the ease and fluency with which Dr. Skinner ran from subject to subject.

The Pope's action in the matter of the Sicilian revolution naturally led the Doctor to the reforms which his Holiness had introduced into his dominions, and he laughed consumedly over the joke which had not long since appeared in *Punch*, to the effect that Pio "No, No," should rather have been named Pio "Yes, Yes," because, as the Doctor explained, he granted everything his subjects asked for. Anything like a pun went straight to Dr. Skinner's heart.

Then he went on to the matter of these reforms themselves. They opened up a new era in the history of Christendom, and would have such mo-mentous and far-reaching consequences, that they might even lead to a reconciliation between the Churches of England and Rome. Dr. Skinner had lately published a pamphlet upon this subject, which had shown great learning, and had attacked the Church of Rome in a way which did not promise much hope of reconciliation. He had grounded his attack upon the letters A.M.D.G., which he had seen outside a Roman Catholic chapel, and which of course stood for *Ad Mariam Dei Genetricem.* Could anything be more idolatrous?

I am told, by the way, that I must have let my memory play me one of the tricks it often does play me, when I said the Doctor proposed *Ad Mariam Dei Genetricem* as the full harmonies, so to speak, which should be constructed upon the bass A.M.D.G., for that this is bad Latin, and that the doctor really harmonised the letters thus: *Ave Maria Dei Genetrix.* No doubt the doctor did what was right in the matter of Latinity—I have forgotten the little Latin I ever knew, and am not going to look the matter up, but I believe the doctor said *Ad Mariam Dei Genetricem,* and if so we may be sure that *Ad Mariam Dei Genetricem* is good enough Latin at any rate for ecclesiastical purposes.

The reply of the local priest had not yet appeared, and Dr. Skinner was jubilant, but when the answer appeared, and it was solemnly declared that A.M.D.G. stood for nothing more dangerous than *Ad Majorem Dei Gloriam,* it was felt that though this subterfuge would not succeed with any intelligent Englishman, still it was a pity Dr. Skinner had selected this particular point for his attack, for he had to leave his enemy in possession of the field. When people are left in possession of the field, spectators have an awkward habit of thinking that their adversary does not dare to come to the scratch.

Dr. Skinner was telling Theobald all about his pamphlet, and I doubt whether this gentleman was much more comfortable than Ernest himself. He was bored, for in his heart he hated Liberalism, though he was ashamed to say so, and, as I have said, professed to be on the Whig side. He did not want to be reconciled to the Church of Rome; he wanted to make all Roman Catholics turn Protestants, and could never understand why they would not do so; but the Doctor talked in such a truly liberal spirit, and shut him up so sharply when he tried to edge in a word or two, that he had to let him have it all his own way, and this was not what he was accustomed to. He was wondering how he could bring it to an end, when a diversion was created by the discovery that Ernest had begun to cry—doubtless through an intense but inarticulate sense of a boredom greater than he could bear. He was evidently in a highly nervous state, and a good deal upset by the excitement of the morning; Mrs. Skinner therefore, who came in with Christina at this juncture, proposed that he should spend the afternoon with Mrs. Jay, the matron, and not be introduced to his young companions until the following morning. His father and mother now bade him an affectionate farewell, and the lad was handed over to Mrs. Jay.

O schoolmasters—if any of you read this book—bear in mind when any particularly timid, drivelling urchin is brought by his papa into your study,

and you treat him with the contempt which he deserves, and afterwards
make his life a burden to him for years—bear in mind that it is exactly in
the disguise of such a boy as this that your future chronicler will appear.
Never see a wretched little heavy-eyed mite sitting on the edge of a chair
against your study wall without saying to yourselves, "Perhaps this boy
is he who, if I am not careful, will one day tell the world what manner of
man I was." If even two or three schoolmasters learn this lesson and
remember it, the preceding chapters will not have been written in vain.

Economy

HENRY DAVID THOREAU

HENRY DAVID THOREAU was born in Concord, Massachusetts, in 1817. He grew up in Concord, attended the local schools, and in 1833 entered Harvard. He was graduated four years later at the age of twenty. For a while he taught school; for two years he lived in Emerson's household, chiefly as tutor and gardener; for a year he helped his father in his business of making lead pencils. Then in 1845 he built a shack on Walden Pond, and there he lived for a little more than two years to demonstrate his principle of simple living. After this experiment he lived the rest of his life at his father's house in Concord, lecturing, writing, carrying on his father's business, and in general following his own inclinations. He died of tuberculosis in 1862 at the age of forty-five.

The following selection is from Walden.

I THUS found that the student who wishes for a shelter can obtain one for a lifetime at an expense not greater than the rent which he now pays annually. If I seem to boast more than is becoming, my excuse is that I brag for humanity rather than for myself; and my shortcomings and inconsistencies do not affect the truth of my statement. Notwithstanding much cant and hypocrisy,—chaff which I find it difficult to separate from my wheat, but for which I am as sorry as any man,—I will breathe freely and stretch myself in this respect, it is such a relief to both the moral and physical system; and I am resolved that I will not through humility become the devil's attorney. I will endeavor to speak a good word for the truth. At Cambridge College the mere rent of a student's room, which is only a little larger than my own, is thirty dollars each year, though the corporation had the advantage of building thirty-two side by side and under one roof, and the occupant suffers the inconvenience of many and noisy neighbors, and perhaps a residence in the fourth story. I cannot but think that if we had more true wisdom in these respects, not only less education would be needed, because, forsooth, more would already have been acquired, but the pecuniary expense of getting an education would in a great measure vanish. Those conveniences which the student requires at Cambridge or elsewhere cost him or somebody else ten times as great a sacrifice of life as they would with proper management on both sides. Those things for which the most money is demanded are never the things which the student most wants. Tuition, for instance, is an important item in the term bill, while for the far more valuable education which he gets by associating with the most cultivated of his contemporaries no charge is made. The mode of founding a college is, commonly, to get up a subscription of dollars and cents, and then, following blindly the principles of a division of labor to its extreme,—a principle which should never be followed but with circumspection,—to call in a contractor who makes this a subject of speculation, and he employs Irishmen or other operatives actually to lay the foundations, while the students that are to be are said to be fitting themselves for it; and for these oversights successive generations have to pay. I think that it would be *better than this,* for the students, or those who desire to be benefited by it, even to lay the foundation themselves. The student who secures his coveted leisure and retirement by systematically shirking any labor necessary to man obtains but an ignoble and unprofitable leisure, defrauding himself of the experience which alone can make leisure fruitful. "But," says one, "you do not mean that the students should go to work with their hands instead of their heads?" I do not mean that exactly, but I mean something which he might think a good deal like that; I mean that they should not *play* life, or *study* it merely, while the community supports them at this expensive game, but earnestly *live* it from beginning to end. How could youths better learn to live than by at once trying the experiment of living? Methinks this would exercise their minds as much as mathematics. If I wished a boy to know something about the arts and sciences, for instance, I would not pursue the common course, which is merely to send him into the neighborhood of some professor, where anything is professed and practised but the art of life;—to survey the world through a telescope or a microscope, and never with his natural eye; to study chemistry, and not learn how his bread is made, or mechanics, and not learn how it is earned; to discover new satellites to Neptune, and not detect the motes in his eyes, or to what vagabond he is a satellite himself; or to be devoured by the monsters that swarm all around him, while contemplating the monsters in a drop of vinegar. Which would have advanced the most at the end of a month,—the boy who had made his own jackknife from the ore which he had dug and smelted, reading as much as would be necessary for this,— or the boy who had attended the lectures on metallurgy at the Institute in the meanwhile, and had received a Rogers' penknife from his father? Which would be most likely to cut his fingers? . . . To my astonishment I was informed on leaving college that I had studied navigation!—why, if I had taken one turn down the harbor I should have known more about it. Even the *poor* student studies and is taught only *political* economy, while that economy of living which is synonymous with philosophy is not even sincerely professed in our colleges. The consequence is, that while he is reading Adam Smith, Ricardo, and Say, he runs his father in debt irretrievably.

My Last Walk with the Schoolmistress

OLIVER WENDELL HOLMES

OLIVER WENDELL HOLMES was born at Cambridge, Massachusetts, in 1809. He attended Cambridge schools until 1824, when he entered Phillips Academy, Andover. He was at Harvard from 1825-1829. Following his graduation from Harvard, he studied law for a few months, soon forsook the law for medicine, in 1833 continued the study of medicine abroad. He received the degree of M.D. from Harvard in 1836 and two years later became Professor of Anatomy in Dartmouth College. In 1847 he became Professor of Anatomy and Physiology in the Harvard Medical School, a position which he held until his resignation in 1882. He died in 1894.

Holmes is a distinguished writer of light verse, a brilliant and urbane essayist, who is at his best in the Breakfast-Table *series.*

I CAN'T say just how many walks she and I had taken together before this once. I found the effect of going out every morning was decidedly favorable on her health. Two pleasing dimples, the places for which were just marked when she came, played, shadowy, in her freshening cheeks when she smiled and nodded good-morning to me from the schoolhouse-steps.

I am afraid I did the greater part of the talking. At any rate, if I should try to report all that I said during the first half-dozen walks we took together, I fear that I might receive a gentle hint from my friends the publishers, that a separate volume, at my own risk and expense, would be the proper method of bringing them before the public.

—I would have a woman as true as Death. At the first real lie which works from the heart outward, she should be tenderly chloroformed into a better world, where she can have an angel for a governess, and feed on strange fruits which will make her all over again, even to her bones and marrow.—Whether gifted with the accident of beauty or not, she should have been moulded in the rose-red clay of Love, before the breath of life made a moving mortal of her. Love-capacity is a congenital endowment; and I think, after a while, one gets to know the warm-hued natures it belongs to from the pretty pipe-clay counterfeits of them.—Proud she may be, in the sense of respecting herself; but pride, in the sense of

This selection from Holmes' *The Autocrat of the Breakfast Table* is here reprinted by permission of Houghton Mifflin Company.

contemning others less gifted than herself, deserves the two lowest circles of a vulgar woman's Inferno, where the punishments are Smallpox and Bankruptcy.—She who nips off the end of a brittle courtesy, as one breaks the tip of an icicle, to bestow upon those whom she ought cordially and kindly to recognize, proclaims the fact that she comes not merely of low blood, but of bad blood. Consciousness of unquestioned position makes people gracious in proper measure to all; but if a woman put on airs with her real equals, she has something about herself or her family she is ashamed of, or ought to be. Middle, and more than middle-aged people, who know family histories, generally see through it. An official of standing was rude to me once. Oh, that is the maternal grandfather,—said a wise old friend to me,—he was a boor.—Better too few words, from the woman we love, than too many: while she is silent, Nature is working for her; while she talks, she is working for herself.—Love is sparingly soluble in the words of men; therefore they speak much of it; but one syllable of woman's speech can dissolve more of it than a man's heart can hold.

—Whether I said any or all of these things to the schoolmistress, or not, —whether I stole them out of Lord Bacon,—whether I cribbed them from Balzac,—whether I dipped them from the ocean of Tupperian wisdom,—or whether I have just found them in my head, laid there by that solemn fowl, Experience (who, according to my observation, cackles oftener than she drops real live eggs), I cannot say. Wise men have said more foolish things,—and foolish men, I don't doubt, have said as wise things. Anyhow, the schoolmistress and I had pleasant walks and long talks, all of which I do not feel bound to report.

—You are a stranger to me, Ma'am.—I don't doubt you would like to know all I said to the schoolmistress.—I sha'n't do it;—I had rather get the publishers to return the money you have invested in these pages. Besides, I have forgotten a good deal of it. I shall tell only what I like of what I remember.

—My idea was, in the first place, to search out the picturesque spots which the city affords a sight of, to those who have eyes. I know a good many, and it was a pleasure to look at them in company with my young friend. There were the shrubs and flowers in the Franklin-Place front-yards or borders: Commerce is just putting his granite foot upon them. Then there are certain small seraglio-gardens, into which one can get a peep through the crevices of high fences,—one in Myrtle Street, or at the back of it,—here and there one at the North and South ends. Then the great elms in Essex Street. Then the stately horse-chestnuts in that vacant lot in Chambers Street, which hold their outspread hands over your head (as I said in my poem the other day), and look as if they were whispering, "May grace, mercy, and peace be with you!"—and the rest of that bene-diction. Nay, there are certain patches of ground, which, having lain neglected for a time, Nature, who always has her pockets full of seeds, and holes in all her pockets, has covered with hungry plebeian growths, which fight for life with each other, until some of them get broad-leaved and succulent, and you have a coarse vegetable tapestry which Raphael would not have disdained to spread over the foreground of his master-piece. The Professor pretends that he found such a one in Charles Street, which, in its dare-devil impudence of rough-and-tumble vegetation, beat the pretty-behaved flower-beds of the Public Garden as ignominiously as a group of young tatterdemalions playing pitch-and-toss beats a row of Sunday-school-boys with their teacher at their head.

But then the Professor has one of his burrows in that region, and puts everything in high colors relating to it. That is his way about everything. —I hold any man cheap,—he said,—of whom nothing stronger can be uttered than that all his geese are swans.—How is that, Professor?—said I; —I should have set you down for one of that sort.—Sir,—said he,—I am proud to say, that Nature has so far enriched me, that I cannot own so much as a *duck* without seeing in it as pretty a swan as ever swam the basin in the garden of the Luxembourg. And the Professor showed the whites of his eyes devoutly, like one returning thanks after a dinner of many courses.

I don't know anything sweeter than this leaking in of Nature through all the cracks in the walls and floors of cities. You heap up a million tons of hewn rocks on a square mile or two of earth which was green once. The trees look down from the hill-sides and ask each other, as they stand on tiptoe,—"What are these people about?" And the small herbs at their feet look up and whisper back,—"We will go and see." So the small herbs pack themselves up in the least possible bundles, and wait until the wind steals to them at night and whispers,—"Come with me." Then they go softly with it into the great city,—one to a cleft in the pavement, one to a spout on the roof, one to a seam in the marbles over a rich gentleman's bones, and one to the grave without a stone where nothing but a man is buried,—and there they grow, looking down on the generations of men from mouldy roofs, looking up from between the less-trodden pavements, looking out through iron cemetery-railings. Listen to them, when there is only a light breath stirring, and you will hear them saying to each other,—"Wait awhile!" The words run along the telegraph of those narrow green lines that border the roads leading from the city, until they reach the slope of the hills, and the trees repeat in low murmurs to each other,—"Wait awhile!" By-and-by the flow of life in the streets ebbs, and the old leafy inhabitants—the smaller tribes always in front—saunter in, one by one, very careless seemingly, but very tenacious, until they swarm so that the great stones gape from each other with the crowding of their roots, and the feldspar begins to be picked out of the granite to find them food. At last the trees take up their solemn line of march, and never rest until they have encamped in the market-place. Wait long enough and you will find an old doting oak hugging a huge worn block in its yellow under-ground arms; that was the corner-stone of the State-House. Oh, so patient she is, this imperturbable Nature!

—Let us cry!—

But all this has nothing to do with my walks and talks with the school-mistress. I did not say that I would not tell you something about them. Let me alone, and I shall talk to you more than I ought to, probably. We never tell our secrets to people that pump for them.

Books we talked about, and education. It was her duty to know something of these, and of course she did. Perhaps I was somewhat more learned than she, but I found that the difference between her reading and mine was like that of a man's and a woman's dusting a library. The man flaps about with a bunch of feathers; the woman goes to work softly with a cloth. She does not raise half the dust, nor fill her own eyes and mouth with it,—but she goes into all the corners and attends to the leaves as much as to the covers.—Books are the *negative* pictures of thought, and the more sensitive the mind that receives their images, the more nicely the finest lines are reproduced. A woman (of the right kind), reading after a man, follows him as Ruth followed the reapers of Boaz, and her gleanings are often the finest of the wheat.

But it was in talking of Life that we came most nearly together. I thought I knew something about that,—that I could speak or write about it somewhat to the purpose.

To take up this fluid earthly being of ours as a sponge sucks up water,— to be steeped and soaked in its realities as a hide fills its pores lying seven years in a tan-pit,—to have winnowed every wave of it as a mill-wheel works up the stream that runs through the flume upon its float-boards,— to have curled up in the keenest spasms and flattened out in the laxest languors of this breathing-sickness, which keeps certain parcels of matter uneasy for three or four score years,—to have fought all the devils and clasped all the angels of its delirium,—and then, just at the point when the white-hot passions have cooled down to cherry-red, plunge our experience into the ice-cold stream of some human language or other, one might think would end in a rhapsody with something of spring and temper in it. All this I thought my power and province.

The schoolmistress had tried life, too. Once in a while one meets with a single soul greater than all the living pageant which passes before it. As the pale astronomer sits in his study with sunken eyes and thin fingers, and weighs Uranus or Neptune as in a balance, so there are meek, slight women who have weighed all which this planetary life can offer, and hold it like a bauble in the palm of their slender hands. This was one of them. Fortune had left her, sorrow had baptized her; the routine of labor and the loneliness of almost friendless city-life were before her. Yet, as I looked upon her tranquil face, gradually regaining a cheerfulness which was often sprightly, as she became interested in the various matters we talked about and places we visited, I saw that eye and lip and every shifting lineament were made for love,—unconscious of their sweet office as yet, and meeting the cold aspect of Duty with the natural graces which were meant for the reward of nothing less than the Great Passion.

—I never addressed one word of love to the schoolmistress in the course of these pleasant walks. It seemed to me that we talked of everything but love on that particular morning. There was, perhaps, a little more timidity and hesitancy on my part than I have commonly shown among our people at the boarding-house. In fact, I considered myself the master at the breakfast-table; but, somehow, I could not command myself just then so well as usual. The truth is, I had secured a passage to Liverpool in the steamer which was to leave at noon,—with the condition, however, of being released in case circumstances occurred to detain me. The schoolmistress knew nothing about all this, of course, as yet.

It was on the Common that we were walking. The *mall,* or boulevard of our Common, you know, has various branches leading from it in different directions. One of these runs down from opposite Joy Street southward across the whole length of the Common to Boylston Street. We called it the long path, and were fond of it.

I felt very weak indeed (though of a tolerably robust habit) as we came opposite the head of this path on that morning. I think I tried to speak twice without making myself distinctly audible. At last I got out the question,—Will you take the long path with me?—Certainly,—said the schoolmistress,—with much pleasure.—Think,—I said,—before you answer: if you take the long path with me now, I shall interpret it that we are to part no more!—The schoolmistress stepped back with a sudden movement, as if an arrow had struck her.

One of the long granite blocks used as seats was hard by,—the one you may still see close by the Gingko-tree.—Pray, sit down,—I said.—No, no, she answered, softly,—I will walk the *long path* with you!

—The old gentleman who sits opposite met us walking, arm in arm, about the middle of the long path, and said, very charmingly,—"Good-morning, my dears!"

The Educational System of the Twentieth Century

EDWARD BELLAMY

EDWARD BELLAMY was born in 1850, at Chicopee Falls, Massachusetts, where for thirty-five years his father had been Baptist minister. He received his education in the public schools and at Union College, where he spent a few months as a special student of literature. A trip abroad in 1868 impressed him with the sad plight of the economically dispossessed in the slums of Europe, and caused him eventually to write Looking Backward *as a solution to economic evils. On his return to America he studied law, did newspaper work, and contributed stories to magazines. Following the publication of* Looking Backward *in 1888, Bellamy clubs were formed, and Bellamy found himself at the center of publicity and controversy. A retiring man, by nature a recluse, he was forced by the popularity of* Looking Backward *to become an enthusiastic propagandist for the theories he had advocated in his book. Never physically robust, he fell ill and died in 1898 at the age of forty-eight.*

The following selection from Looking Backward *gives some of Bellamy's ideas on education.*

IT had been suggested by Dr. Leete that we should devote the next morning to an inspection of the schools and colleges of the city, with some attempt on his own part at an explanation of the educational system of the twentieth century.

'You will see,' he said, as we set out after breakfast, 'many very important differences between our methods of education and yours, but the main difference is that nowadays all persons equally have those opportunities of higher education which in your day only an infinitesimal portion of the population enjoyed. We should think we had gained nothing worth speaking of, in equalizing the physical comfort of men, without this educational equality.'

'The cost must be very great,' I said.

'If it took half the revenue of the nation, nobody would grudge it,' replied Dr. Leete, 'nor even if it took it all save a bare pittance. But in

This selection from Edward Bellamy's *Looking Backward* is reproduced by permission of Houghton Mifflin Company.

truth the expense of educating ten thousand youth is not ten nor five times that of educating one thousand. The principle which makes all operations on a large scale proportionally cheaper than on a small scale holds as to education also.'

'College education was terribly expensive in my day,' said I.

'If I have not been misinformed by our historians,' Dr. Leete answered, 'it was not college education but college dissipation and extravagance which cost so highly. The actual expense of your colleges appears to have been very low, and would have been far lower if their patronage had been greater. The higher education nowadays is as cheap as the lower, as all grades of teachers, like all other workers, receive the same support. We have simply added to the common school system of compulsory education, in vogue in Massachusetts a hundred years ago, a half dozen higher grades, carrying the youth to the age of twenty-one and giving him what you used to call the education of a gentleman, instead of turning him loose at fourteen or fifteen with no mental equipment beyond reading, writing, and the multiplication table.'

'Setting aside the actual cost of these additional years of education,' I replied, 'we should not have thought we could afford the loss of time from industrial pursuits. Boys of the poorer classes usually went to work at sixteen or younger, and knew their trade at twenty.'

'We should not concede you any gain even in material product by that plan,' Dr. Leete replied. 'The greater efficiency which education gives to all sorts of labor, except the rudest, makes up in a short period for the time lost in acquiring it.'

'We should also have been afraid,' said I, 'that a high education, while it adapted men to the professions, would set them against manual labor of all sorts.'

'That was the effect of high education in your day, I have read,' replied the doctor; 'and it was no wonder, for manual labor meant association with a rude, coarse, and ignorant class of people. There is no such class now. It was inevitable that such a feeling should exist then, for the further reason that all men receiving a high education were understood to be destined for the professions or for wealthy leisure, and such an education in one neither rich nor professional was a proof of disappointed aspirations, an evidence of failure, a badge of inferiority rather than superiority. Nowadays, of course, when the highest education is deemed necessary to fit a man merely to live, without any reference to the sort of work he may do, its possession conveys no such implication.'

'After all,' I remarked, 'no amount of education can cure natural dullness or make up for original mental deficiencies. Unless the average natural mental capacity of men is much above its level in my day, a high education must be pretty nearly thrown away on a large element of the population. We used to hold that a certain amount of susceptibility to educational influences is required to make a mind worth cultivating, just as a certain natural fertility in soil is required if it is to repay tilling.'

'Ah,' said Dr. Leete, 'I am glad you used that illustration, for it is just the one I would have chosen to set forth the modern view of education. You say that land so poor that the product will not repay the labor of tilling is not cultivated. Nevertheless, much land that does not begin to repay tilling by its product was cultivated in your day and is in ours. I refer to gardens, parks, lawns, and, in general, to pieces of land so situated that, were they left to grow up to weeds and briers, they would be eyesores and inconveniences to all about. They are therefore tilled, and though their product is little, there is yet no land that, in a wider sense, better repays cultivation. So it is with the men and women with whom we mingle in the relations of society, whose voices are always in our ears, whose behavior in innumerable ways affects our enjoyment—who are, in fact, as much conditions of our lives as the air we breathe, or any of the physical elements on which we depend. If, indeed, we could not afford to educate everybody, we should choose the coarsest and dullest by nature, rather than the brightest, to receive what education we could give. The naturally refined and intellectual can better dispense with aids to culture than those less fortunate in natural endowments.

'To borrow a phrase which was often used in our day, we should not consider life worth living if we had to be surrounded by a population of ignorant, boorish, coarse, wholly uncultivated men and women, as was the plight of the few educated in your day. Is a man satisfied, merely because he is perfumed himself, to mingle with a malodorous crowd? Could he take more than a very limited satisfaction, even in a palatial apartment, if the windows on all four sides opened into stable yards? And yet just that was the situation of those considered most fortunate as to culture and refinement in your day. I know that the poor and ignorant envied the rich and cultured then; but to us the latter, living as they did, surrounded by squalor and brutishness, seem little better off than the former. The cultured man in your age was like one up to the neck in a nauseous bog solacing himself with a smelling bottle. You see, perhaps, now, how we look at this question of universal high education. No single thing is so important to every man as to have for neighbors intelligent, companionable persons. There is nothing, therefore, which the nation can do for him that will enhance so much his own happiness as to educate his neighbors. When it fails to do so, the value of his own education to him is reduced by half, and many of the tastes he has cultivated are made positive sources of pain.

'To educate some to the highest degree, and leave the mass wholly uncultivated, as you did, made the gap between them almost like that between different natural species, which have no means of communication. What could be more inhuman than this consequence of a partial enjoyment of education! Its universal and equal enjoyment leaves, indeed, the differences between men as to natural endowments as marked as in a state of nature, but the level of the lowest is vastly raised. Brutishness is eliminated. All have some inkling of the humanities, some appreciation of the things of the mind, and an admiration for the still higher culture they have fallen short of. They have become capable of receiving and imparting, in various degrees, but all in some measure, the pleasures and inspirations of a refined social life. The cultured society of the nineteenth century—what did it consist of but here and there a few microscopic oases in a vast, unbroken wilderness? The proportion of individuals capable of intellectual sympathies or refined intercourse, to the mass of their contemporaries, used to be so infinitesimal as to be in any broad view of humanity scarcely worth mentioning. One generation of the world to-day represents a greater volume of intellectual life than any five centuries ever did before.

'There is still another point I should mention in stating the grounds on which nothing less than the universality of the best education could now be tolerated,' continued Dr. Leete, 'and that is, the interest of the coming generation in having educated parents. To put the matter in a nutshell, there are three main grounds on which our educational system rests: first, the right of every man to the completest education the nation can give him on his own account, as necessary to his enjoyment of himself; second, the right of his fellow-citizens to have him educated, as necessary to their enjoyment of his society; third, the right of the unborn to be guaranteed an intelligent and refined parentage.'

I shall not describe in detail what I saw in the schools that day. Having taken but slight interest in educational matters in my former life, I could offer few comparisons of interest. Next to the fact of the universality of the higher as well as the lower education, I was most struck with the prominence given to physical culture, and the fact that proficiency in athletic feats and games as well as in scholarship had a place in the rating of the youth.

'The faculty of education,' Dr. Leete explained, 'is held to the same responsibility for the bodies as for the minds of its charges. The highest possible physical, as well as mental, development of every one is the double object of a curriculum which lasts from the age of six to that of twenty-one.'

The magnificent health of the young people in the schools impressed me strongly. My previous observations, not only of the notable personal endowments of the family of my host, but of the people I had seen in my walks abroad, had already suggested the idea that there must have been something like a general improvement in the physical standard of the race since my day, and now, as I compared these stalwart young men and fresh, vigorous maidens with the young people I had seen in the schools of the nineteenth century, I was moved to impart my thought to Dr. Leete. He listened with great interest to what I said.

'Your testimony on this point,' he declared, 'is invaluable. We believe that there has been such an improvement as you speak of, but of course it could only be a matter of theory with us. It is an incident of your unique position that you alone in the world of to-day can speak with authority on this point. Your opinion, when you state it publicly, will, I assure you, make a profound sensation. For the rest it would be strange, certainly, if the race did not show an improvement. In your day, riches debauched one class with idleness of mind and body, while poverty sapped the vitality of the masses by overwork, bad food, and pestilent homes. The labor required of children, and the burdens laid on women, enfeebled the very springs of life. Instead of these maleficent circumstances, all now enjoy the most favorable conditions of physical life; the young are carefully nurtured and studiously cared for; the labor which is required of all is limited to the period of greatest bodily vigor, and is never excessive; care for one's self and one's family, anxiety as to livelihood, the strain of a ceaseless battle for life—all these influences, which once did so much to wreck the minds and bodies of men and women, are known no more. Certainly, an improvement of the species ought to follow such a change. In certain specific respects we know, indeed, that the improvement has taken place. Insanity, for instance, which in the nineteenth century was so terribly common a product of your insane mode of life, has almost disappeared, with its alternative, suicide.'

"Good Morning, Miss Barton"

JEANNETTE COVERT NOLAN

JEANNETTE COVERT NOLAN was born in Evansville, Indiana, in 1897. She received her education in the public schools of Evansville, and at seventeen became a cub reporter on a local newspaper. Her first writing of fiction was a story for St. Nicholas. *She is best known for her short stories, biographies, and historical novels for young people. Four of her novels have been Junior Literary Guild Selections.*

The following selection from The Story of Clara Barton of the Red Cross *gives a glimpse of school life in a little red schoolhouse of the past.*

CLARA had the mumps.

She was more disgruntled than ill. What a dismally juvenile disease to contract when you're fifteen and just about to put your hair in a chignon and lengthen your skirts and be a young lady!

She lay on the sofa in the hall. In the next room, Mother was talking to Mr. L. N. Fowler, who had come to Oxford to lecture. There was nothing remarkable in Mr. Fowler's being in the parlor. Men and women of note were always calling on Mother and Father. Every town has its house to which distinguished visitors seem naturally to gravitate, and the Bartons' was such a house. Clara had been introduced to Mr. Fowler and liked him. He was a phrenologist. By placing his hands on your head and running his fingers lightly over your scalp, Mr. Fowler could tell you what sort of person you were and prophesy your future. He had put his hands on Clara's head—before the mumps had made her too grotesque to be seen in company.

But she realized after a moment that what was being said in the parlor was remarkable indeed. It was about Clara herself.

"A very comely and intelligent-looking girl," Mr. Fowler was saying. "Her wavy brown hair, her brown eyes and regular features, the broad brow and firm chin, these signify a forceful personality."

("Ah!" thought Clara.)

"She is little in stature, and slender; but her manner of walking, somewhat like an Indian's tread, never stooping her shoulders, gives her the appearance of height. I would not say that she speaks musically, but her voice has gentleness and some sweet tones."

("Well!" Clara smiled.)

"Her chief weakness of character," went on Mr. Fowler, "is an excessive sensitiveness, a tendency to draw away from people."

"That's it," Mrs. Barton said. "When anyone she doesn't know is here, Clara just shuts up like a clam. You'd think she was deaf and dumb."

("Humph!" muttered the eavesdropper.)

"She may always have this retiring nature. In my opinion, she will never assert herself *for herself*. She will tolerate any abuse of her own rights and privileges. But for others she will be perfectly fearless."

"What shall we do for her?" Mrs. Barton asked. "Our only desire is that she get the most out of life and the talents she was born with."

"She should have responsibilities," Mr. Fowler said. "She will not falter under them. I believe that all her earthly days Clara will fight injustice, cruelty, and oppression, and that her happiness will be in the contending more than in any victory she may win." He paused. "I see her future as extraordinary and good. Whatever she undertakes, she'll never fail."

When the dialogue was over, and even when Mr. Fowler had gone, Clara lay on the sofa, thinking, rehearsing his words in memory. Often and utterly she'd been disgusted with herself—and especially now that the hateful mumps made her comical as a figure in a cartoon. She knew also (and alas!) the truth of what Mother had said: she was absurdly timid with guests; probably many people thought she was a dummy. But Mr. Fowler had described her as another sort of person, a splendid person. *Very* splendid.

She listened again, for now Father was in the parlor.

"Stephen," Mother said, "I've been counseling with Mr. Fowler. He feels that as soon as she's old enough, Clara should have responsibilities."

"What kind?"

"Well, he suggested schoolteaching. But what annoys me is this: How much faith can we have in Mr. Fowler's prophecies?"

"My dear, phrenologists are not scientists," Father said. "I doubt that the size and shape of the human skull and the bumps on it are an index to the brain inside that skull, or that the soul can be deciphered, as Mr. Fowler professes to do. And yet he's a cut above other phrenologists; an educated man, something of a psychologist."

"His guess about Clara was uncannily accurate," Mother murmured. "If it *was* a guess."

"She might take the examinations, anyway," Father said. "Then in the spring I'll inquire around for a school. She'll be a young, inexperienced teacher, of course."

("She'll be a *good* teacher," breathed Clara in the hall. "And Mr. Fowler is a good prophet. . . . 'She'll never fail.' Hah!")

The school was in District Number 9, near Sally's home, where Clara was to board during the term. The instructor preceding Clara had resigned his position because the bigger boys among his pupils had locked him out of the schoolhouse for six consecutive days—which must have been vexing, to say the least. As she walked up the hill path through the dewy grass that May morning, Clara speculated what her own fate might be. She carried a parcel of books, including her Testament, a pocket of lunch, and, in her pocket, the certificate of an examination passed with flying colors.

At the top of the hill she stopped to scan the schoolyard. No one was in sight. Vivid sunshine spread serenely over everything—and silence.

She went to the door, foreboding assailing her as she turned the knob. But the door was not locked. It swung open, and she saw her charges, forty boys and girls of ages varying from four to thirteen, rosy-cheeked faces in smiling, expectant rows.

They stood up and chanted in cheerful singsong, "Good *morning*, Miss *Barton*."

But on a bench near the window were four boys who did not join the chorus. They were big boys, taller than the new teacher and, she felt, older too. One of them had a sullen mouth. And when Clara had hung her hat and shawl in the closet and seated herself at the desk, this one whispered something to his cronies, at which they all nudged one another and tittered. Clara didn't know what he had said, and had no wish to know; it was sure to be something uncomplimentary.

There was a lull. The children were waiting for her to begin the session. And, with a sensation of panic, she knew that she must act quickly. Forty pairs of eyes were on her, and the four loungers at the window were winking and grimacing.

"You may all sit down now," she said, steeling herself against the awkward moment. "And *you* may rise."

"Me?" The leader of the four got up, displeased at being made conspicuous. "Me?"

"Yes, you. What is your name? Nate Jones? Well, Nate, I want you to read some verses from the Bible." She handed him her Testament opened to the Sermon on the Mount.

"Out loud?"

"Yes, so that we may all enjoy them." As slowly, and most reluctantly, Nate droned through the verses, Clara thought of what she must do next. She couldn't let the children guess how dismayed she was. "Now you may tell us, Nate," she said when he had plodded to the end of the page, "the meaning of our Saviour's admonition to 'love your enemies.'"

But Nate had no intention of continuing as the center of things. He scowled and said, "I don't know."

"Does someone else know?"

Several hands fluttered, and one so emphatically that Clara said, "The little girl in the pink-checked pinafore."

"I'm Emily." The pink-checked pinafore bobbed a curtsy. "And I think Jesus meant that you must be good to everybody, Miss Barton, and mustn't quarrel or make nobody feel bad—and I'm going to try."

"That's right, Emily." Clare shot a glance at Nate Jones. If only *he* would try! "A splendid explanation, and thank you."

Somehow then (Clara never could imagine just how it was) a vociferous debate was launched in the schoolroom, with forty young Christians interpreting the Sermon on the Mount. Clara gave them each a hearing. She became intensely interested, gauging from what they said the amount of their information and whether or not they would be brilliant scholars or dull. The atmosphere was warm and informal, and when the morning had gone, so had her uneasiness.

But Nate Jones had not thawed. It would take more than this to impress him.

She went to see what could be causing the hubbub in the yard. That was at noon on her third day as a schoolmistress. If the yells now bursting forth were any indication, she had a ticklish situation before her. Would she be able to deal with it? Would she ever get the hang of a teacher's job?

The children were embroiled in a violent argument, with Nate Jones the prime troublemaker, as might have been expected. There was a horseshoe green. Nate had a game—

"But he won't let anybody play except his own chums, Miss Barton," said Edward Gates, a fifth-grade pupil. "And he plays all the time himself. It isn't fair!"

"No," Clara said, "it isn't fair. And Nate has no right to decide who is to be in the game. You must each have your turn, even the littlest ones."

Her words might have been a thunderbolt for the effect they produced. Profound quiet fell over the schoolyard. Clara picked up the horseshoes—and slouching forward, big Nate Jones glared at her.

"I'm the boss here," he said.

"You are? Why?"

"Because I'm the best pitcher." Nate despised all teachers, and one so small and slender as this was simply not to be endured. "Go mind your own business!"

The other children gasped.

"This is my business." Clara's knees trembled under her flounced skirt, but her voice was steady. "If you really *were* the best pitcher—"

"Who's better?"

"Well, I am, for one."

"*You?*" Nate snorted. "Shucks!"

"I think I can beat you at horseshoes, at lots of games," Clara said. "Shall we have a test?"

"I'd lick you!"

"Let's see you do it, Nate. Come, we'll have a game of horseshoes, and whichever of us wins will be the custodian of the green for the whole term. If you're the winner, then I'll never interfere again. But if I win, then I make the rules hereafter. How's that for a bargain?"

Nate scuffed the gravel. He thought the bargain was absurd, and Miss Barton obviously insane. But he had prestige, and he couldn't risk forfeiting it.

"Oh, well," he growled scornfully.

The green was cleared, the gallery for the match lining up on either side. Clara granted her opponent the first pitch. But some latent courtesy made him brusquely refuse.

So she took her place, toed the mark, flexed her arm. She said a silent little prayer—for much was at stake, far more than one game of horseshoes. ("I can't fail, I *won't*.")

She pitched, and there was the clang of metal on metal. And somebody cried, "A ringer!"

It was a thrilling contest, the score was close, but Clara was the better player.

More than once she had to exhibit her prowess in the recess hours. At such times she thought gratefully of David and Lovett Stimpson, for it was their coaching which made her rule supreme, outside the schoolroom as well as in.

And gradually Nate Jones was won over. Perhaps he would never be much of a scholar, but there was good in him and loyalty which he gave to Clara. She had hit upon the surest way of convincing him that she was not an unmitigated nuisance.

The county trustees came to District Number 9 on the last day of the term and conferred a badge upon Miss Barton and congratulated her on the discipline she had maintained. She hadn't had to suspend a pupil, or whip one, or rap any knuckles or switch any legs. "A fine record," said the trustees, beaming.

Miss Barton blushed and bowed. But she thought there was an error, somewhere. Discipline? She hadn't maintained it at all. She wouldn't have known how to. And it never had been necessary.

"They were such dear children," she said. "I learned as much from them as they learned from me. Maybe more."

The Social Value of the College-Bred

WILLIAM JAMES

WILLIAM JAMES (1842-1910), great American philosopher, was born in New York City and educated with his famous brother Henry by private tutors and at various schools in Europe. For a year he studied painting but in 1864 he entered the Harvard Medical School, receiving his degree in 1869. In 1872 he was appointed to the Harvard faculty and until his retirement in 1907 taught successively physiology, psychology, and philosophy. After his retirement from Harvard he continued to write and to. lecture. He was honored as the foremost American philosopher of his time.

OF what use is a college training? We who have had it seldom hear the question raised; we might be a little nonplussed to answer it off-hand. A certain amount of meditation has brought me to this as the pithiest reply which I myself can give: The best claim that a college education can possibly make on your respect, the best thing it can aspire to accomplish for you, is this: that it should *help you to know a good man when you see him.* This is as true of women's as of men's colleges; but that it is neither a joke nor a one-sided abstraction I shall now endeavor to show.

What talk do we commonly hear about the contrast between college education and the education which business or technical or professional schools confer? The college education is called higher because it is supposed to be so general and so disinterested. At the "schools" you get a relatively narrow practical skill, you are told, whereas the "colleges" give you the more liberal culture, the broader outlook, the historical perspective, the philosophic atmosphere, or something which phrases of that sort try to express. You are made into an efficient instrument for doing a definite thing, you hear, at the schools; but, apart from that, you may remain a crude and smoky kind of petroleum, incapable of spreading light. The universities and colleges, on the other hand, although they may leave you less efficient for this or that practical task, suffuse your whole mentality with something more important than skill. They redeem you, make you well-bred; they make "good company" of you mentally. If they find you with a naturally boorish or caddish mind, they cannot leave you so, as a technical school may leave you. This, at least, is pretended; this is what we hear among college-trained people when they compare their education with every other sort. Now, exactly how much does this signify?

It is certain, to begin with, that the narrowest trade or professional training does something more for a man than to make a skilful practical tool of him—it makes him also a judge of other men's skill. Whether his trade be pleading at the bar or surgery or plastering or plumbing, it develops a critical sense in him for that sort of occupation. He understands the difference between second-rate and first-rate work in his whole branch of industry; he gets to know a good job in his own line as soon as he sees it; and getting to know this in his own line, he gets a faint sense of what good work may mean anyhow, that may, if circumstances favor, spread into his judgments elsewhere. Sound work, clean work, finished work: feeble work, slack work, sham work—these words express an identical contrast in many different departments of activity. In so far forth, then, even the humblest manual trade may beget in one a certain small degree of power to judge of good work generally.

Now, what is supposed to be the line of us who have the higher college training? Is there any broader line—since our education claims primarily not to be "narrow"—in which we also are made good judges between what is first-rate and what is second-rate only? What is especially taught in the colleges has long been known by the name of the "humanities," and these are often identified with Greek and Latin. But it is only as literatures, not as languages, that Greek and Latin have any general humanity-value; so that in a broad sense the humanities mean literature primarily, and in a still broader sense the study of masterpieces in almost any field of human endeavor. Literature keeps the primacy; for it not only *consists* of masterpieces, but is largely *about* masterpieces, being little more than an appreciative chronicle of human master-strokes, so far as it takes the form of criticism and history. You can give humanistic value to almost anything by teaching it historically. Geology, economics, mechanics, are humanities when taught with reference to the successive achievements of the geniuses to which these sciences owe their being. Not taught thus literature remains grammar, art a catalogue, history a list of dates, and natural science a sheet of formulas and weights and measures.

The sifting of human creations!—nothing less than this is what we ought to mean by the humanities. Essentially this means biography; what our colleges should teach is, therefore, biographical history, that not of politics merely, but of anything and everything so far as human efforts and conquest are factors that have played their part. Studying in this way, we learn what types of activity have stood the test of time; we acquire standards of the excellent and durable. All our arts and sciences and institutions are but so many quests of perfection on the part of men; and when we see how diverse the types of excellence may be, how various the tests, how flexible the adaptations, we gain a richer sense of what the terms "better" and "worse" may signify in general. Our critical sensibilities grow both more acute and less fanatical. We sympathize with men's mistakes even in the act of penetrating them; we feel the pathos of lost causes and misguided epochs even while we applaud what overcame them.

Such words are vague and such ideas are inadequate, but their meaning is unmistakable. What the colleges—teaching humanities by examples which may be special, but which must be typical and pregnant—should at least try to give us, is a general sense of what, under various disguises, *superiority* has always signified and may still signify. The feeling for a good human job anywhere, the admiration of the really admirable, the disesteem of what is cheap and trashy and impermanent,—this is what we call the critical sense, the sense for ideal values. It is the better part of what men know as wisdom. Some of us are wise in this way naturally and by genius; some of us never become so. But to have spent one's youth at college, in contact with the choice and rare and precious, and yet still to be a blind prig or vulgarian, unable to scent out human excellence or to divine it amid its accidents, to know it only when ticketed and labeled and forced on us by others, this indeed should be accounted the very calamity and shipwreck of a higher education.

The sense for human superiority ought, then, to be considered our line, as boring subways is the engineer's line and the surgeon's is appendicitis. Our colleges ought to have lit up in us a lasting relish for the better kind of man, a loss of appetite for mediocrities, and a disgust for cheapjacks. We ought to smell, as it were, the difference of quality in men and their proposals when we enter the world of affairs about us. Expertness in this might well atone for some of our awkwardness at accounts, for some of our ignorance of dynamos. The best claim we can make for the higher education, the best single phrase in which we can tell what it ought to do for us, is, then, exactly what I said: it should enable us *to know a good man when we see him.*

That the phrase is anything but an empty epigram follows from the fact that if you ask in what line it is most important that a democracy like ours should have its sons and daughters skilful, you see that it is this line more than any other. "The people in their wisdom"—this is the kind of wisdom most needed by the people. Democracy is on its trial, and no one knows how it will stand the ordeal. Abounding about us are pessimistic prophets. Fickleness and violence used to be, but are no longer, the vices which they charge to democracy. What its critics now affirm is that its preferences are inveterately for the inferior. So it was in the beginning, they say, and so it will be world without end. Vulgarity enthroned and institutionalized, elbowing everything superior from the highway, this, they tell us, is our irremediable destiny; and the picture-papers of the European continent are already drawing Uncle Sam with the hog instead of the eagle for his heraldic emblem. The privileged aristocracies of the foretime, with all their iniquities, did at least preserve some taste for higher human quality, and honor certain forms of refinement by their enduring traditions. But when democracy is sovereign, its doubters say, nobility will form a sort of invisible church, and sincerity and refinement, stripped of honor, precedence, and favor, will have to vegetate on sufferance in private corners. They will have no general influence. They will be harmless eccentricities.

Now, who can be absolutely certain that this may not be the career of democracy? Nothing future is quite secure; states enough have inwardly rotted; and democracy as a whole may undergo self-poisoning. But, on the other hand, democracy is a kind of religion, and we are bound not to admit its failure. Faiths and utopias are the noblest exercise of human reason, and no one with a spark of reason in him will sit down fatalistically before the croaker's picture. The best of us are filled with the contrary vision of a democracy stumbling through every error till its institutions glow with justice and its customs shine with beauty. Our better men *shall* show the way and we *shall* follow them; so we are brought round again to the mission of the higher education in helping us to know the better kind of man whenever we see him.

The notion that a people can run itself and its affairs anonymously is now well known to be the silliest of absurdities. Mankind does nothing save through initiatives on the part of inventors, great or small, and imitation by the rest of us—these are the sole factors active in human progress. Individuals of genius show the way, and set the patterns, which common people then adopt and follow. *The rivalry of the patterns is the history of the world.* Our democratic problem thus is statable in ultra-simple terms: Who are the kind of men from whom our majorities shall take their cue? Whom shall they treat as rightful leaders? We and our leaders are the x and the y of the equation here; all other historic circumstances, be they economical, political, or intellectual, are only the background of occasion on which the living drama works itself out between us.

In this very simple way does the value of our educated class define itself: we more than others should be able to divine the worthier and better leaders. The terms here are monstrously simplified, of course, but such a bird's-eye view lets us immediately take our bearings. In our democracy, where everything else is so shifting, we alumni and alumnæ of the colleges are the only permanent presence that corresponds to the aristocracy in older countries. We have continuous traditions, as they have; our motto, too, is *noblesse oblige;* and, unlike them, we stand for ideal interests solely, for we have no corporate selfishness and wield no powers of corruption. We ought to have our own class-consciousness. *"Les Intellectuels!"* What prouder club-name could there be than this one, used ironically by the party of "redblood," the party of every stupid prejudice and passion, during the anti-Dreyfus craze,[1] to satirize the men in France who still retained

---

[1] Alfred Dreyfus, an artillery officer in the French Army, convicted of treason in 1894, was, after harrowing experiences, declared innocent by the highest court, in

some critical sense and judgment! Critical sense, it has to be confessed, is not an exciting term, hardly a banner to carry in processions. Affections for old habit, currents of self-interest, and gales of passion are the forces that keep the human ship moving; and the pressure of the judicious pilot's hand upon the tiller is a relatively insignificant energy. But the affections, passions, and interests are shifting, successive, and distraught; they blow in alternation while the pilot's hand is steadfast. He knows the compass, and, with all the leeways he is obliged to tack toward, he always makes some headway. A small force, if it never lets up, will accumulate effects more considerable than those of much greater forces if these work inconsistently. The ceaseless whisper of the more permanent ideals, the steady tug of truth and justice, give them but time, *must* warp the world in their direction.

This bird's-eye view of the general steering function of the college-bred amid the driftings of democracy ought to help us to a wider vision of what our colleges themselves should aim at. If we are to be the yeast-cake for democracy's dough, if we are to make it rise with culture's preferences, we must see to it that culture spreads broad sails. We must shake the old double reefs out of the canvas into the wind and sunshine, and let in every modern subject, sure that any subject will prove humanistic, if its setting be kept only wide enough.

Stevenson says somewhere to his reader: "You think you are just making this bargain, but you are really laying down a link in the policy of mankind." Well, your technical school should enable you to make your bargain splendidly; but your college should show you just the place of that kind of bargain—a pretty poor place, possibly—in the whole policy of mankind. That is the kind of liberal outlook, of perspective, of atmosphere, which should surround every subject as a college deals with it.

We of the colleges must eradicate a curious notion which numbers of good people have about such ancient seats of learning as Harvard. To many ignorant outsiders, that name suggests little more than a kind of sterilized conceit and incapacity for being pleased. In Edith Wyatt's exquisite book of Chicago sketches called *Every One His Own Way* there is a couple who stand for culture in the sense of exclusiveness, Richard Elliot and his feminine counterpart—feeble caricatures of mankind, unable to know any good thing when they see it, incapable of enjoyment unless a printed label gives them leave. Possibly this type of culture may exist near Cambridge and Boston. There may be specimens there, for priggishness is just like painter's colic or any other trade-disease. But every good college makes its students immune against this malady, of which the microbe haunts the neighborhood of printed pages. It does so by its general tone being too hearty for the microbe's life. Real culture lives by sympathies and admirations, not by dislikes and disdains; under all misleading wrap-

---

1903. The feeling for and against Dreyfus was bitter in the extreme, so that France was for many years torn into two factions.

pings it pounces unerringly upon the human core. If a college, through the inferior human influences that have grown regnant there, fails to catch the robuster tone, its failure is colossal, for its social function stops: democracy gives it a wide berth, turns toward it a deaf ear.

"Tone," to be sure, is a terribly vague word to use, but there is no other, and this whole meditation is over questions of tone. By their tone are all things human either lost or saved. If democracy is to be saved it must catch the higher, healthier tone. If we are to impress it with our preferences, we ourselves must use the proper tone, which we, in turn, must have caught from our own teachers. It all reverts in the end to the action of innumerable imitative individuals upon each other and to the question of whose tone has the highest spreading power. As a class, we college graduates should look to it that *ours* has spreading power. It ought to have the highest spreading power.

In our essential function of indicating the better men, we now have formidable competitors outside. *McClure's Magazine*, the *American Magazine, Collier's Weekly*, and in its fashion, the *World's Work*, constitute together a real popular university along this very line. It would be a pity if any future historian were to have to write words like these: "By the middle of the twentieth century the higher institutions of learning had lost all influence over public opinion in the United States. But the mission of raising the tone of democracy, which they had proved themselves so lamentably unfitted to exert, was assumed with rare enthusiasm and prosecuted with extraordinary skill and success by a new educational power; and for the clarification of their human sympathies and elevation of their human preferences, the people at large acquired the habit of resorting exclusively to the guidance of certain private literary adventures, commonly designated in the market by the affectionate name of ten-cent magazines."

Must not we of the colleges see to it that no historian shall ever say anything like this? Vague as the phrase of knowing a good man when you see him may be, diffuse and indefinite as one must leave its application, is there any other formula that describes so well the result at which our institutions *ought* to aim? If they do that, they do the best thing conceivable. If they fail to do it, they fail in very deed. It surely is a fine synthetic formula. If our faculties and graduates could once collectively come to realize it as the great underlying purpose toward which they have always been more or less obscurely groping, a great clearness would be shed over many of their problems; and, as for their influence in the midst of our social system, it would embark upon a new career of strength.

The Will

The teacher often is confronted in the schoolroom with an abnormal type of will, which we may call the 'balky will.' Certain children, if they do not succeed in doing a thing immediately, remain completely inhibited in regard to it: it becomes literally impossible for them to understand it if it be an intellectual problem, or to do it if it be an outward operation, as long as this particular inhibited condition lasts. Such children are usually treated as sinful, and are punished; or else the teacher pits his or her will against the child's will, considering that the latter must be 'broken.' "Break your child's will, in order that it may not perish," wrote John Wesley. "Break its will as soon as it can speak plainly—or even before it can speak at all. It should be forced to do as it is told, even if you have to whip it ten times running. Break its will, in order that its soul may live." Such will-breaking is always a scene with a great deal of nervous wear and tear on both sides, a bad state of feeling left behind it, and the victory not always with the would-be will-breaker.

When a situation of the kind is once fairly developed, and the child is all tense and excited inwardly, nineteen times out of twenty it is best for the teacher to apperceive the case as one of neural pathology rather than as one of moral culpability. So long as the inhibiting sense of impossibility remains in the child's mind, he will continue unable to get beyond the obstacle. The aim of the teacher should then be to make him simply forget. Drop the subject for the time, divert the mind to something else: then, leading the pupil back by some circuitous line of association, spring it on him again before he has time to recognize it, and as likely as not he will go over it now without any difficulty. It is in no other way that we overcome balkiness in a horse: we divert his attention, do something to his nose or ear, lead him round in a circle, and thus get him over a place where flogging would only have made him more invincible. A tactful teacher will never let these strained situations come up at all.

But such consequences as this, you instinctively feel, are erroneous. The more ideals a man has, the more contemptible, on the whole, do you continue to deem him, if the matter ends there for him, and if none of the laboring man's virtues are called into action on his part,—no courage shown, no privations undergone, no dirt or scars contracted in the attempt to get them realized. It is quite obvious that something more than the mere possession of ideals is required to make a life significant in any sense that claims the spectator's admiration. Inner joy, to be sure, it may *have*, with its ideals; but that is its own private sentimental matter. To extort

"The Will" and "The Gospel of Relaxation" are from *Talks to Teachers on Psychology* and *talks to Students on Some of Life's Ideals,* by William James; copyright, 1899, 1900, by William James; reprinted by permission of Henry Holt and Company.

from us, outsiders as we are, with our own ideals to look after, the tribute of our grudging recognition, it must back its ideal visions with what the laborers have, the sterner stuff of manly virtue; it must multiply their sentimental surface by the dimension of the active will, if we are to have *depth,* if we are to have anything cubical and solid in the way of character.

The significance of a human life for communicable and publicly recognizable purposes is thus the offspring of a marriage of two different parents, either of whom alone is barren. The ideals taken by themselves give no reality, the virtues by themselves no novelty. And let the orientalists and pessimists say what they will, the thing of deepest—or, at any rate, of comparatively deepest—significance in life does seem to be its character of *progress,* or that strange union of reality with ideal novelty which it continues from one moment to another to present. To recognize ideal novelty is the task of what we call intelligence. Not every one's intelligence can tell which novelties are ideal. For many the ideal thing will always seem to cling still to the older more familiar good. In this case character, though not significant totally, may be still significant pathetically. So, if we are to choose which is the more essential factor of human character, the fighting virtue or the intellectual breadth, we must side with Tolstoï, and choose that simple faithfulness to his light or darkness which any common unintellectual man can show.

The Gospel of Relaxation

They talk much in pedagogic circles to-day about the duty of the teacher to prepare for every lesson in advance. To some extent this is useful. But we Yankees are assuredly not those to whom such a general doctrine should be preached. We are only too careful as it is. The advice I should give to most teachers would be in the words of one who is herself an admirable teacher. Prepare yourself in the *subject so well that it shall be always on tap:* then in the class-room trust your spontaneity and fling away all further care.

My advice to students, especially to girl-students, would be somewhat similar. Just as a bicycle-chain may be too tight, so may one's carefulness and conscientiousness be so tense as to hinder the running of one's mind. Take, for example, periods when there are many successive days of examination impending. One ounce of good nervous tone in an examination is worth many pounds of anxious study for it in advance. If you want really to do your best in an examination, fling away the book the day before, say to yourself, "I won't waste another minute on this miserable thing, and I don't care an iota whether I succeed or not." Say this sincerely, and feel it; and go out and play, or go to bed and sleep, and I am sure the results next day will encourage you to use the method permanently.

On Knowledge of One's Own Country

WILLIAM COBBETT

WILLIAM COBBETT (1762-1835), political writer and reformer, was the son of a farm laborer. His education was self attained by reading. Until 1783 he worked in the fields. He then became a lawyer's clerk in London, but after a year he enlisted in the army. During his army days he spent all his spare time in study, particularly the study of grammar. On his discharge from the army in 1791 he aroused official wrath by calling attention to graft among officers and by advocating higher pay for privates. He fled to France, then to America, to Philadelphia, where he taught English to French refugees, mixed in politics, edited two little magazines, and became so involved in libel suits that he thought it wise to return to England. In London he founded Cobbett's Political Register, *in which he expressed his political views. For an article attacking the flogging of soldiers he was imprisoned. In time his paper became the organ of the new group of industrial workers. In 1832 he became a member of the House of Commons, where overwork brought on an illness from which he died three years later.*

The following selection is taken from Advice to Young Men, *published in 1829.*

HOPING that I have said enough to induce you to set resolutely about the study of *grammar,* I might here leave the subject of *learning;* arithmetic and grammar, both *well learned,* being as much as I could wish in a mere youth. But these need not occupy the whole of your spare time; and, there are other branches of learning which ought immediately to follow. If your own calling or profession require book-study, books treating of that are to be preferred to all others; for, the first thing, the first object in life, is to secure the honest means of obtaining sustenance, raiment, and a state of being suitable to your rank, be that rank what it may: excellence in your own calling is, therefore, the first thing to be aimed at. After this may come *general knowledge,* and of this, the first is a thorough knowledge of *your own country;* for, how ridiculous is it to see an English youth engaged in reading about the customs of the Chinese or of the Hindoos, while he is content to be totally ignorant of those of Kent or of Cornwall! Well employed he must be in ascertaining how Greece was divided and how the Romans parcelled out their territory, while he knows not, and apparently does not want to know, how England came to be divided into counties, hundreds, parishes and tithings.

609

School Days

ALBERT JAY NOCK

ALBERT JAY NOCK is so averse to personal publicity that little is known about his life beyond what he tells us in Memoirs of a Superfluous Man. *He is a graduate of St. Stephen's College. He lived in Brussels before 1914. His first book,* How Diplomats Make War, *was published in 1916. Following the close of World War I, Nock lived in New York and edited the* Freeman. *He contributed frequently to* Harper's *and the* Atlantic Monthly. *During the 1930's he conducted an anti-New Deal column in the* American Mercury *called* The State of the Nation.

Memoirs of a Superfluous Man *was published in 1943. Of this book Clifton Fadiman wrote: "I have not since the days of the early Mencken read a more eloquently written blast against democracy or enjoyed more fully a display of crusted prejudice. Mr. Nock is a highly civilized man who does not like our civilization and will have no part of it. He is a rare bird, one of an almost extinct species, and, as he very properly puts it, a superfluous man. We are not apt to see his like again."*

WHEN I was just turning fourteen I was sent off to boarding-school, a long way from home, down in the prairie country on the banks of the Illinois River, where again I was plumped into a brand-new set of physical and social surroundings. The town had about ten thousand people; it made its living out of agriculture and miscellaneous manufactures, the principal products being organs, ploughs, alcohol and corn whisky. It had been settled by 'forty-eighters, the best stock that Europe ever exported here, and the descendants of those superb people were keeping very closely to the old ways and traditions. All their social activities and amenities were German. They had three flourishing musical societies; a *Männerchor*, a *Liederkranz* of mixed voices, and a less formal *Gesangverein* of younger folk from whom in course of time I learned practically the whole *Kommersbuch* pretty well by heart. Also with the help of some of them I learned to read music as an extra-curricular activity, with no idea of doing anything with it in a practical way, but only with a vague notion of some day becoming musically literate. The theory and history of music has always interested me, and I have kept at them in a desultory fashion all my life. For some reason there was no instrumental music, except for the piano. In a town brimming over with vocal music of a high order, and harbouring excellent pianists, one would at least look for a string quartette of sorts, but I can not recall a single person who had ever scraped a string.

A great deal of social interest centred in the *Turnverein,* which was an exclusive institution. One had to have credentials running back as far as Henry the Fowler to belong to it, so I got my knowledge of its doings mainly by hearsay. It put on two or three really remarkable gymnastic exhibitions each winter, which were invitation-affairs, though a few plebeians with a "pull" were sometimes grudgingly allowed to crash the gate for standing-room, and were promptly hunted out again when the show was over and the festivities beginning. Some of the beauty and chivalry off the very top layer of two neighbouring cities were usually on hand to grace the occasion; and speaking of beauty, this region blossomed with more pretty girls than I would have supposed there were in the world. They were somewhat on the alfalfa-fed order, innocent of cosmetics, and making an excellent appearance, whether singly or in groups. They gave me the beginnings of a critical taste in such matters, for outside of my own family I had not seen any female beauty worth speaking of, except in some older women. Since then I have been in regions which I thought were a shade or two more productive, and the product rather better. Belgium, for example, seemed on long acquaintance to be keeping up to its mediæval record in this respect, as appears in the old monastic hexameters,

> *Gandavum laqueis, formosis Bruga puellis,*
> *Lovanium doctis, gaudet Mechlinia stultis.*

Of course one can't know exactly what sort of thing Bruges kept in stock to fluster the monks of the Middle Ages, but at any time these thirty years I would have put Brussels far and away ahead of Bruges or any other town in the kingdom. I understand, however, that connoisseurs unite *nem. con.* in giving the first prize for this pleasing commodity to Poland, but I have never been in Poland or seen more than a very few Polish girls, so I can have no opinion.

I also acquired, quite unconsciously, the beginnings of a creditable taste in beer. The town had a small brewery which brought forth a most superexcellent product, and the proprietor's son being a day-pupil in our school, its hospitalities were open to us. It was an impressive experience to go down to the brewery when the bock-beer season opened, and see a jury of grave old pundits assembled, austere colossi of learning, taciturn, profoundly scrupulous, sampling the new brew with reverent care and finally delivering judgement. With such a start, I quite naturally grew up in the prevailing superstition that all German beer is good, but when I went into Germany I found a great deal that was bad. I also found that our little brewery was an exception to the rule discussed by Herbert Spencer, that the worst place to look for a product is the place where it is produced. In my day Brussels imported beers from Munich and Dortmund that were beyond belief; they were too good to drink; yet in Munich and Dortmund the same brands of beer were not nearly so good. Thirty-five years ago, the dark beer one got at Lüchow's in New York, and especially the Bavarian black beer that Jansen imported, were far better than anything I found under the same name in Würzburg and Kulmbach, where they were made.

Our school ran to a dozen or fifteen boarders and as many day-pupils, all from good substantial families. It was a strange affair in some ways. Its material equipment was poor and primitive; well-to-do parents today would not dream of putting boys in such a place, though it was well-kept in the sense that nothing was let go dirty or slovenly. Our food was abundant and good; quite on the coarse side and thoroughly uninteresting, but we got on with it and saw no reason to complain. But our living-quarters, dormitory, schoolrooms, were bare, bleak, repellent, as anything one would find in a county jail. One could get up as tear-compelling a story as Copperfield's about our discomfort and wretchedness,—breaking a skin of ice in our wash-pitchers mornings, and all that sort of thing,—but it would hardly go down with us, for we were not conscious of being uncomfortable and wretched; on the contrary we were having a very good time out of our situation. We had all known better things, but not so much better that the contrast was heartbreaking. I sometimes think a superheated passion for the Uplift rather overplays the sense of hardship and misery ensuing upon circumstances like ours; at all events, we laboured under no such distress.

With regard to my studies at the school, my extraordinary luck still held good. Poor as the place would seem if judged by modern notions of the American standard of living, whatever that is, it was just the place for me. I wish now that I had thought to ask my parents how they came to hear of it and what had moved them to send me there. The head of the school was wise, capable, kind, hard-working, and had an excellent literary sense. He woke me up to the fact that Greek and Roman poetry really has some merit; he even caused my detestation of Homer and Virgil to fade out; and he introduced me casually to a great deal that is good in English verse. He had three assistants. One of them managed to sluice some arithmetic and algebra into my head, but it all promptly seeped out again, so that I had to do an extra year's preparatory work in order to enter college, which was humiliating. All I did in mathematics, then or ever, was done by sheer effort of unintelligent memory. Today I am unable to add a column of ten figures and get the same result twice, unless by chance, and the simplest sum in long division is as far beyond me as driving a locomotive.

Like my two friends at home, the other assistants gave the curious impression of not belonging where they were, and one could not help wondering how they had found their way there. One was a cripple, moving about on crutches. He bore one of the most distinguished names to be found in the academic circles of Massachusetts, and everything about him betokened the indefinable quality of distinction. His culture, manners, humour, easy affability, delightful conversation, all had the unmistakable mark of superiority. We had boundless respect for him, and great affection; whatever he might want from us was his. In return, he liked us, treating us as friends, and above all invariably as gentlemen. It was his influence in particular, even above that of the head-master, which set the social tone of the school.

The other master was a gentle-spirited young German, an excellent musician, (though he taught no music), who seemed always very sad. He was a capable teacher, but outside of his work and his music there seemed little that he had the heart to care for. He rather took to me, mainly on the score of music in the first instance, but we soon established a friendship on general grounds. His conversation taught me a great deal about music and musicians, and when I left school he gave me a book of musical exercises to remember him by, seeming to set a great deal of store by it, much more than the book was actually worth. It bore a blue bookplate with a woman's name printed in heavy, bold German script, *Welda Reichels.* I have sometimes wondered whether it was connected with some romance that had missed fire.

It appears to me now that the most unusual and salutary thing about our life in that school was its atmosphere of freedom. Within our hours of work the discipline was strict enough to keep things going as they should, but it was not unkind, unreasonable, or on a proper occasion, inflexible. Out of hours we had all the range there was, free to wander in the fields, row on the river, hob-nob with the townspeople, and strike up acquaintances where we chose. The policy worked well enough. We were never cautioned against putting beans up our noses, or subjected to any snivelling talk about being on our honour, or keeping up the credit of the dear old school, or any such odious balderdash. Nevertheless we somehow managed to behave decently, no doubt because we had no overweening inducements to behave otherwise. I do not recall any pranks serious enough to come in for more than a good-natured reprimand. Yet we were not holding any brief for Condorcet's or Rousseau's views on the essential goodness of human nature. There was always plenty to do that was legitimate and more interesting than anything likely to land us in trouble, so why get in trouble? This was all there was to it; this was the sum of our ethical imperative.

Not so long afterwards I began to suspect that this might also be the sum of the ethical imperative affecting the conduct of mankind-at-large. What first drew my attention that way was the very eloquent and splendid passage of poetry in which Juvenal contrasts the social behaviour of other animals with that of man.[1] On a first reading it struck me that for

[1] Sat. xv, 159-171.

a first-class satirist Juvenal must have been a shocking poor observer. When he said that there is greater concord among serpents than among men, that the stronger lions and boars always spare the weaker, he was saying something which I made bold to believe simply wasn't so.

> *Indica tigris agit rabida cum tigride pacem*
> *Perpetuam.*

—but, I said to myself, that is just what she doesn't do. She keeps the peace only unless and until some circumstance arises which in her opinion justifies her in breaking it. I thought that if Juvenal had been a better observer he could not have helped seeing that his tigresses and bears behave precisely as men and women do, and for the same reason. There seemed to me to be some principle at work here, some general law of conduct prevailing throughout the animal world. But all this was casual at the time, something that popped into my head and at once popped out again to stay gone for years. I scribbled a ribald note on the margin of a Tauchnitz text, and was amused by it in my subsequent re-readings of Juvenal, but gave the matter no further thought. My mind reverted to it immediately, however, when long afterwards I learned that there is indeed such a law, though its universality had not been established at that time, nor its implications fully apprehended. I found that Aristippus, Epicurus, Aristotle and St. Augustine had brushed elbows with this law without clearly recognising it, and so in modern times had Bishop Butler. Bentham and Mill had occasional glimpses of it. Spencer's view of it and Henry George's was clear but limited; they did not go the full length it should have led them. Not for a long time did I come upon a competent exposition of that law and its effects; and when I did, curiously, I did not get it from an academic philosopher, but from a retired businessman. I shall have something more to say of this hereafter.

College Days

ERNEST POOLE

ERNEST POOLE, American novelist, was born in Chicago, in 1880. He was graduated from Princeton in 1902. He then did settlement work in New York and in 1904 was publicity agent for the strikers in the Chicago stockyards strike. Out of his knowledge of tenement life and labor conditions came his best-known novel, The Harbor.

THE first thing I needed in college was a good thorough dressing down. And this I got without any delay. In the first few weeks my artist's ears and eyes and soul were hazed to a frazzle. From "that boy who will go far" I became "you damn young freshman." I was told to make love to a horse's hind leg, I was made to perch on a gatepost and read the tenderest passages of "Romeo and Juliet," replacing Romeo's name by my own, and Juliet's by that of stout Mrs. Doogan, who scrubbed floors in a dormitory close by. Refusals only made matters painful. Besides, I was told by a freshman friend that I'd better fit in or I'd "queer" myself.

This dread of "queering" myself at first did me a world of good. Dumped in this community of over a thousand callow youths, three hundred in my class alone and each one absorbed in getting acquainted, fitting in, making friends and a place for himself, I was soon struggling for a foothold as hard as the rest. Within a month the thing I wanted above all else was to shed my genius and become "a good mixer" in the crowd.

This drew me at first from books to athletics. Though still slight of build I was wiry, high-strung and quick of movement. I had a snub nose and sandy hair, and I was tough, with a hard-set jaw. And I now went into the football world with a passion and a patience that landed me at the end of the season—one-of the substitute quaterbacks on the freshman team. I did not get into a single game, I was only used on the "scrub" in our practice. This made for a wholesome humility and a real love of my college.

The football season over, I tried for the daily paper. One of the freshman candidates for the editorial Spring elections, I became a daily reporter slave. Here at first I drew on my "queer" past, turning all my "descriptive powers" to use. But a fat senior editor called "Pop" inquired one day with a sneer, "For God's sake, Freshman, why these flowers?" And the flowers forthwith dropped out of my style. At all hours, day and night, to the almost entire neglect of studies, I went about college digging up news—not the trivial news of the faculty's dull, puny plans for the development of our minds, but the real vital news of our college life, news of the things we were here for, the things by which a man got on, news of all the athletic teams, of the glee, mandolin and banjo clubs, of "proms," of class and fraternity elections, mass meetings and parades. Ferreting my way into all nooks and crannies of college life, ears keen for hints and rumors, alert to "scoop" my eighteen reporter rivals—the more I learned the better I loved. And when in the Spring I was one of the five freshman editors chosen, the conquest was complete. No more artist's soul for me. I was part and parcel of college life.

Together with my companions I assumed a genial tolerance toward all those poor dry devils known to us as "profs." I remember the weary sighs of our old college president as he monotoned through his lectures on ethics to the tune of the cracking of peanuts, which an old darky sold to us at the entrance to the hall. It was a case of live and let live. He let us eat and we let him talk. With the physics prof, who was known as "Madge the Scientist," our indulgence went still further. We took no disturbing peanuts there and we let him drone his hour away without an interruption, except perhaps an occasional snore. We were so good to him, I think, because of his sense of humor. He used to stop talking now and then and with a quizzical hopeless smile he would look about the hall. And we would all smile broadly back, enjoying to the full with him the droll farce of our presence there. "Go to it, Madge," someone would murmur. And the work of revealing the wonders of this material universe would limp quietly along. In examinations Madge gave no marks, at least not to the mass of us. If he had, over half of us would have been dropped, so he "flunked" the worst twenty and let the rest through.

The faculty, as a whole, appeared to me no less fatigued. Most of them lectured as though getting tired, the others as though tired out. There were a few lonely exceptions but they had to fight against heavy odds.

The hottest fighter of all against this classic torpor was a tall, joyous Frenchman who gestured not only with his hands but with his eloquent knees as well. His subject was French literature, but from this at a moment's notice he would dart off into every phase of French life. There was nothing in life, according to him, that was not a part of literature. In college he was considered quite mad.

I met him not long ago in New York. We were both hanging to straps in the subway and we had but a moment before he got off.

"I have read you," he said, "in the magazines. And from what you write I think you can tell me. What was the trouble with me at college?" I looked into his black twinkling eyes.

"Great Scott!" I said suddenly. "You were alive!"

"Merci! Au revoir, monsieur!"

What a desert of knowledge it was back there. Our placid tolerance of the profs included the books they gave us. The history prof gave us ten books of collateral reading. Each book, if we could pledge our honor as gentlemen that we had read it, counted us five in examination. On the night before the examination I happened to enter the room of one of our football giants, and found him surrounded by five freshmen, all of whom were reading aloud. One was reading a book on Russia, another the life of Frederick the Great, a third was patiently droning forth Napoleon's war on Europe, while over on the window-seat the other two were racing through volumes one and two of Carlyle's French Revolution. The room was a perfect babel of sound. But the big man sat and smoked his pipe, his honor safe and the morrow secure. In later years, whatever might happen across the sea would find this fellow fully prepared, a wise, intelligent judge of the world, with a college education.

"This reminds me," he said, "of last summer—when I did Europe in three weeks with Dad."

The main idea in all courses was to do what you had to but no more. One day an English prof called upon me to define the difference between a novel and a book of science.

"About the same difference," I replied, "as between an artist's painting and a mathematical drawing."

"Bootlick, bootlick," I heard in murmurs all over the hall. I had answered better than I had to. Hence I had licked the professor's boots. I did not offend in this way again.

• • •

But early in my sophomore year, when the novelty had worn away, I began to do some thinking. Was there nothing else here? My mother and I had had talks at home, and she had told me plainly that unless I sent home better reports I could not finish my four years' course. And after all, she wasn't a fool, there was something in that idea of hers—that here in this quiet old town, so remote from the harbor and business, a fellow ought to be getting "fine" things, things that would help him all his life.

"But look what I've got!" I told myself. "When I came here what was I? A little damn prig! And look at me now!"

"All right, look ahead. I'm toughened up, I've had some good things knocked into me and a lot of fool things knocked out of me. But that's just it. Are all the fine things fool things? Don't I still want to write? Sure I do. Well, what am I going to write about? What do I know of the big things of life? I was always hunting for what was great. I'm never hunting for it now, and unless I get something mighty quick my father will make me go into his business. What am I going to do with my life?"

At first I honestly tried to "pole," to find whether, after all, I couldn't break through the hard dry crust of books and lectures down into what I called "the real stuff." But the deeper I dug the drier it grew. Vaguely I felt that here was crust and only crust, and that for some reason or other it was meant that this should be so, because in the fresh bubbling springs and the deep blazing fires whose presence I could feel below there was something irritating to profs and disturbing to those who paid them. These profs, I thought confusedly, had about as much to do with life as had that little "hero of God" who had cut such a pitiful figure when he came close to the harbor. And more pitiful still were the "polers," the chaps who were working for high marks. They thought of marks and little else. They thrived on crust, these fellows, cramming themselves with words and rules, with facts, dates, theorems and figures in order to become professors themselves and teach the same stuff to other "polers." There was a story of one of them who stayed in his room and crammed all through the big football game of the season, and at night when told we had won remarked blithely,

"Oh, that's splendid! I think I'll go out and have a pretzel!"

God, what a life, I thought to myself! None of that for me! And so I left the "polers."

But now in my restless groping around for realities in life that would thrill me, things that I could write about, I began trying to test things out by talking about them with my friends. What did a fellow want most in life—what to do, what to get and to be? What was there really in business beside the making of money? In medicine, law and the other professions, in art, in getting married, in this idea of God and a heaven, or in the idea I vaguely felt now filtering through the nation, that a man owed his life to his country in time of peace as in time of war. The harbor with rough heavy jolts had long ago started me thinking about questions of this kind. Now I tackled them again and tried to talk about them.

And at once I found I was "queering" myself. For these genial companions of mine had laid a most decided taboo upon all topics of this kind. They did so because to discuss them meant to openly think and feel, and to think or feel intensely, about anything but athletics and other things prescribed by the crowd, was bad form to say the least.

Bad form to talk in any such fashion of what we were going to make of our lives. Nobody cared to warm up on the subject. Many had nothing at all in sight and put off the whole idea as a bore. Others were already fixed, they had positions waiting in law and business offices, in factories, mines, mills and banks, and they took these positions as settled and sure.

"Why?" I would argue impatiently. "How do you know it's what you want most?"

"Oh, I guess it'll do as well as another."

"But damn it all, why not have a look? We can have a big look now, we've got a chance to broaden out before we jump into our little jobs— to see all the jobs and size 'em up and look at em as a part of the world!"

"Oh, biff." I got little or no response. The greater part of these decent likable fellows could not warm up to anything big, they simply hadn't it in them.

"Why in hell do you want me to get all hot?" drawled one fat sluggard of a friend. "I'll keep alive when the time comes." And he and his kind set the standard for all. Sometimes a chap who could warm up, who had the real stuff in him, would "loosen up" about his life on some long tramp with me alone. But back in college his lips were sealed. It was not exactly that he was ashamed, it was simply that with his college friends such talk seemed utterly out of place.

"Look out, Bill," said one affectionately. "You'll queer yourself if you keep on."

The same held true of religion. An upper classman, if he felt he had to, might safely become a leader of freshman in the Y. M. C. A. But when one Sunday evening I disturbed a peaceful pipe-smoking crowd by wondering why it was that we were all so bored in chapel, there fell an embarrassing silence—until someone growled good-humoredly, "Don't bite off more'n you can chew." Nobody wanted to drop his religion, he simply wanted to let it alone. I remember one Sunday in chapel, in the midst of a long sermon, how our sarcastic old president woke us up with a start.

"I was asked," he said, "if we had any free thinkers here. 'No,' I replied. 'We have not yet advanced that far. For it takes half as much thinking to be a free thinker as it does to believe in God.'"

And I remember the night in our sophomore club when the news came like a thunderclap that one of our members had been killed pole-vaulting at a track meet in New York. It was our habit, in our new-found manliness, to eat with our hats on, shout and sing, and speak of our food as "tapeworm," "hemorrhage," and the like. I remember how we sat that night, silent, not a word from the crowd—one starting to eat, then seeing it wasn't the thing to do, and staring blankly like the rest. They were terrible, those stares into reality. That clutching pain of grief was real, so real it blotted everything out. Later some of us in my room began to talk in low voices of what a good fellow he had been. Then some chap from the Y. M. C. A. proposed timidly to lead us in prayer. What a glare he got from all over the room! "Damn fool," I heard someone mutter. Bad form!

Politics also were tabooed. Here again there were exceptions. A still fiery son of the South could rail about niggers, rapes and lynchings and the need for disenfranchising the blacks. It was good fun to hear him. Moreover, a fellow who was a good speaker, and needed the money, might stump the state for either political party, and his accounts were often amusing. But to sit down and talk about the trusts, graft, trade unions, strikes, or the tariff or the navy, the Philippines, "the open door," or any other of the big questions that even then, ten years ago, were beginning to shake the country, and that we would all be voting on soon? No. The little Bryan club was a joke. And one day when a socialist speaker struck town the whole college turned out in parade, waving red sweaters and firing "bombs" and roaring a wordless Marseillaise! We wanted no solemn problems here!

Finally, it was distinctly bad form to talk about sex. Not to tell "smutty stories," they were welcomed by the average crowd. But to look at it squarely, as I tried to do, and get some light upon what would be doubtless the most vital part of our future lives—this simply wasn't done. What did women mean to us, I asked. What did prostitutes mean at present? What would wives mean later on? And all this talk about mistresses and this business of free love, and easy divorces and marriage itself—what did they all amount to? Was love really what it was cracked up to be, or had the novelists handed us guff? When I came out with questions like these, the chaps called "clean" looked rather pained; the ones who weren't, distinctly bored.

For this whole intricate subject was kept in the cellars of our minds, cellars often large but dark. Because "sex" was wholly rotten. It had nothing to do, apparently, with the girls who came chaperoned to the "proms," it had to do only with certain women in a little town close by. Plenty of chaps went there at times, and now and then women from over there would come to us on the quiet at night. But one afternoon I saw a big crowd on the front campus. It grew every moment, became a mob, shoving and surging, shouting and jeering. I climbed some steps to look into the center, and saw two painted terrified girls, hysterical, sobbing, swearing and shrieking. So they were shoved, a hidden spectacle, to the station and put on the train. Nothing like that on our front campus! Nothing like "sex" in the front rooms of our minds. The crowd returned chuckling. Immoral? Hell, no. Simply bad form.

·   ·   ·

"What am I going to write about?"

"Games," said the college. "Only games. Don't go adventuring down into life."

Qualifications of a Schoolmaster

OLIVER GOLDSMITH

OLIVER GOLDSMITH (1728-1774), when six years old, was sent to the village school described in The Deserted Village. *In 1744 he was entered at Trinity College, Cambridge, from which he obtained his degree in 1749. Following his graduation, he helped in his brother's school, told stories, played the flute, and threw the hammer at village sports. In 1752 he went to Edinburgh to study medicine but soon decided to finish his studies on the continent. He did little study but he traveled widely, visiting Paris, Germany, Switzerland, Italy, and returning penniless to England in 1756. For a time he was an usher in a school; he contributed miscellaneous articles to the* Monthly Review; *he tried to get an appointment as a physician in a factory but he was found "not qualified," and so he became a literary hack. He continued contributing to magazines, and in 1760 appeared the first of his essays called the* Chinese Letters.*

About 1764 he became a member of Dr. Johnson's famous club. In 1766 he published The Vicar of Wakefield. *The success of this novel established Goldsmith's reputation as a man of letters. In 1770 he published* The Deserted Village, *a poem so popular it went through five editions within a few months.* She Stoops to Conquer *was performed at Covent Garden in 1773.*

The first of the following selections is from The Vicar of Wakefield; *the second from* The Deserted Village.*

U PON my arrival in town, Sir, my first care was to deliver your letter of recommendation to our cousin, who was himself in little better circumstances than I. My first scheme, you know, Sir, was to be usher at an academy; and I asked his advice on the affair. Our cousin received the proposal with a true sardonic grin. "Ay," cried he, "this is indeed a very pretty career that has been chalked out for you. I have been an usher at a boarding school myself; and may I die by an anodyne necklace, but I had rather be an under-turnkey in Newgate. I was up early and late: I was browbeat by the master, hated for my ugly face by the mistress, worried by the boys within, and never permitted to stir out to meet civility abroad. But are you sure you are fit for a school? Let me examine you a little. Have you been bred apprentice to the business?"—"No."—"Then you won't do for a school. Can you dress the boys' hair?"—"No."—"Then you won't do

for a school. Have you had the smallpox?"—"No."—"Then you won't do
for a school. Can you lie three in a bed?"—"No."—"Then you will never
do for a school. Have you got a good stomach?"—"Yes."—"Then you will
by no means do for a school. No, sir: if you are for a genteel, easy profession, bind yourself seven years an apprentice to turn a cutler's wheel;
but avoid a school by any means. . . ."

The Village Schoolmaster

Beside yon straggling fence that skirts the way
With blossom'd furze, unprofitably gay,
There, in his noisy mansion, skill'd to rule,
The village master taught his little school:
A man severe he was, and stern to view,
I knew him well, and every truant knew;
Well had the boding tremblers learn'd to trace
The day's disasters in his morning face;
Full well they laugh'd with counterfeited glee
At all his jokes, for many a joke had he;
Full well the busy whisper, circling round,
Convey'd the dismal tidings when he frown'd;
Yet he was kind, or if severe in aught,
The love he bore to learning was in fault;
The village all declared how much he knew,
'Twas certain he could write and cipher too;
Lands he could measure, terms and tides presage,
And e'en the story ran that he could gauge:
In arguing too, the parson own'd his skill,
For e'en though vanquish'd, he could argue still;
While words of learned length and thundering sound
Amazed the gazing rustics ranged around;
And still they gazed, and still the wonder grew
That one small head could carry all he knew.

What Is Education?

THOMAS HENRY HUXLEY

THOMAS HENRY HUXLEY (1825-1895), biologist, teacher, and writer, was born into a schoolmaster's family. He attended his father's school until he was ten. He had no further formal schooling until he began the study of medicine in 1841. In 1842 he entered Charing Cross Hospital on a scholarship. Three years later he received his M.B. degree. Badly in need of money, he took the naval examination and was assigned to naval duty. From 1846-1850 he was assistant-surgeon on the S. S. Rattlesnake, *which had been sent to explore Australia. It was during this voyage that Huxley laid the foundations of his career as an original investigator. In 1852 he gave the first of the lectures on scientific and philosophical subjects for which he became famous. In 1854 he resigned from the navy and devoted his time to lecturing and scientific investigation. He was active in the defense and exposition of Darwinian evolution. During the last decade of his life he withdrew from the lecture platform and spent his time in Biblical criticism.*

The following essay on education is taken from A Liberal Education; and Where to Find It, *published in 1868.*

WHAT is education? Above all things, what is our ideal of a thoroughly liberal education?—of that education which, if we could begin life again, we would give ourselves—of that education which, if we could mold the fates to our own will, we would give our children? Well, I know not what may be your conceptions upon this matter, but I will tell you mine, and I hope I shall find that our views are not very discrepant.

Suppose it were perfectly certain that the life and fortune of every one of us would, one day or other, depend upon his winning or losing a game of chess. Don't you think that we should all consider it to be a primary duty to learn at least the names and the moves of the pieces; to have a notion of a gambit, and a keen eye for all the means of giving and getting out of check? Do you not think that we should look with a disapprobation amounting to scorn, upon the father who allowed his son, or the state which allowed its members, to grow up without knowing a pawn from a knight?

Yet it is a very plain and elementary truth, that the life, the fortune, and the happiness of every one of us, and, more or less, of those who are connected with us, do depend upon our knowing something of the rules of a game infinitely more difficult and complicated than chess. It is a game which has been played for untold ages, every man and woman of us being one of the two players in a game of his or her own. The chessboard is the world, the pieces are the phenomena of the universe, the rules of the game are what we call the laws of Nature. The player on the other side is hidden from us. We know that his play is always fair, just and patient. But also we know, to our cost, that he never overlooks a mistake, or makes the smallest allowance for ignorance. To the man who plays well, the highest stakes are paid, with that sort of overflowing generosity with which the strong shows delight in strength. And one who plays ill is checkmated—without haste, but without remorse.

My metaphor will remind some of you of the famous picture in which Retzsch has depicted Satan playing at chess with man for his soul. Substitute for the mocking fiend in that picture a calm, strong angel who is playing for love, as we say, and would rather lose than win—and I should accept it as an image of human life.

Well, what I mean by Education is learning the rules of this mighty game. In other words, education is the instruction of the intellect in the laws of Nature, under which name I include not merely things and their forces, but men and their ways; and the fashioning of the affections and of the will into an earnest and loving desire to move in harmony with those laws. For me, education means neither more nor less than this. Anything which professes to call itself education must be tried by this standard, and if it fails to stand the test, I will not call it education, whatever may be the force of authority, or of numbers, upon the other side.

It is important to remember that, in strictness, there is no such thing as an uneducated man. Take an extreme case. Suppose that an adult man, in the full vigour of his faculties, could be suddenly placed in the world, as Adam is said to have been, and then left to do as he best might. How long would he be left uneducated? Not five minutes. Nature would begin to teach him, through the eye, the ear, the touch, the properties of objects. Pain and pleasure would be at his elbow telling him to do this and avoid that; and by slow degrees the man would receive an education which, if narrow, would be thorough, real, and adequate to his circumstances, though there would be no extras and very few accomplishments.

And if to this solitary man entered a second Adam, or, better still, an Eve, a new and greater world, that of social and moral phenomena, would be revealed. Joys and woes, compared with which all others might seem but faint shadows, would spring from the new relations. Happiness and sorrow would take the place of the coarser monitors, pleasure and pain; but conduct would still be shaped by the observation of the natural consequences of actions; or, in other words, by the laws of the nature of man.

To every one of us the world was once as fresh and new as to Adam. And then, long before we were susceptible of any other modes of instruction, Nature took us in hand, and every minute of waking life brought its educational influence, shaping our actions into rough accordance with Nature's laws, so that we might not be ended untimely by too gross disobedience. Nor should I speak of this process of education as past for any one, be he as old as he may. For every man the world is as fresh as it was at the first day, and as full of untold novelties for him who has the eyes to see them. And Nature is still continuing her patient education of us in that great university, the universe, of which we are all members—Nature having no Test-Acts.

Those who take honours in Nature's university, who learn the laws which govern men and things and obey them, are the really great and successful men in this world. The great mass of mankind are the "Poll," who pick up just enough to get through without much discredit. Those who won't learn at all are plucked; and then you can't come up again. Nature's pluck means extermination.

Thus the question of compulsory education is settled so far as Nature is concerned. Her bill on that question was framed and passed long ago. But, like all compulsory legislation, that of Nature is harsh and wasteful in its operation. Ignorance is visited as sharply as willful disobedience— incapacity meets with the same punishment as crime. Nature's discipline is not even a word and a blow, and the blow first; but the blow without the word. It is left to you to find out why your ears are boxed.

The object of what we commonly call education—that education in which man intervenes and which I shall distinguish as artificial education —is to make good these defects in Nature's methods; to prepare the child to receive Nature's education, neither incapably nor ignorantly, nor with willful disobedience; and to understand the preliminary symptoms of her pleasure, without waiting for the box on the ear. In short, all artificial education ought to be an anticipation of natural education. And a liberal education is an artificial education which has not only prepared a man to escape the great evils of disobedience to natural laws, but has trained him to appreciate and to seize upon the rewards, which Nature scatters with as free a hand as her penalties.

That man, I think, has had a liberal education who has been so trained in youth that his body is the ready servant of his will, and does with ease and pleasure all the work that, as a mechanism, it is capable of; whose intellect is a clear, cold, logic engine, with all its parts of equal strength, and in smooth working order; ready, like a steam engine, to be turned to any kind of work, and spin the gossamers as well as forge the anchors of the mind; whose mind is stored with a knowledge of the great and fundamental truths of Nature and of the laws of her operations; one who, no stunted ascetic, is full of life and fire, but whose passions are trained to come to heel by a vigorous will, the servant of a tender conscience; who has learned to love all beauty, whether of Nature or of art, to hate all vileness, and to respect others as himself.

Such an one and no other, I conceive, has had a liberal education; for he is, as completely as a man can be, in harmony with Nature. He will make the best of her, and she of him. They will get on together rarely; she as his ever beneficent mother; he as her mouthpiece, her conscious self, her minister and interpreter.

All This Does the Public-School and College Boy Learn

WILLIAM MAKEPEACE THACKERAY

WILLIAM MAKEPEACE THACKERAY (1811-1863) was born at Calcutta, India, where his father was in the Indian Civil Service. In 1816 the elder Thackeray died, and in the following year the boy was sent to a school in England. He was not happy at this school nor at Charterhouse, which he next attended. Some account of his experience at Charterhouse under its tyrannical headmaster is given in Pendennis. *In 1829 Thackeray entered Trinity College, Cambridge, but at the end of the Easter term a year later he withdrew and went abroad, traveling in Europe until 1831, when he returned to London and began the study of law. This study soon lost its interest for him. He became a newspaper correspondent in Paris but soon gave up this work and turned to the study of art. He returned to London in 1837, his fortune gone and his living to make. He settled down to write. For the following ten years he was a contributor to the magazine* Punch *and other journals. In 1840 he published* A Shabby Genteel Story *in* Fraser's Magazine. Vanity Fair, *published serially in 1847-1848, at first attracted little attention, though Currer Bell's eulogistic dedication of the second edition of* Jane Eyre *to Thackeray helped to turn the tide of public opinion in his favor.*

In 1852-1853 and again in 1855-1856 Thackeray visited the United States on a lecture tour. From 1860-1862 he was editor of the Cornhill Magazine. *He died in 1863.*

Go, my son, for ten years to a public school, that "world in miniature"; learn "to fight for yourself" against the time when your real struggles shall begin. Begin to be selfish at ten years of age; study for other ten years; get a competent knowledge of boxing, swimming, rowing, and cricket, with a pretty knack of Latin hexameters and a decent smattering of Greek plays,—do this and a fond father shall bless you—bless the two thousand pounds which he has spent in acquiring all these benefits for you. And, besides, what else have you not learned? You have been many hundreds of times to chapel, and have learned to consider the religious service performed there as the vainest parade in the world. If your father is a grocer, you have been beaten for his sake, and have learned to be ashamed of him.

You have learned to forget (as how should you remember, being separated from them for three-fourths of your time?) the ties and natural affections of home. You have learned, if you have a kindly heart and an open hand, to compete with associates much more wealthy than yourself; and to consider money as not much, but honour—the honour of dining and consorting with your betters—as a great deal. All this does the public-school and college boy learn; and woe be to his knowledge! Alas, what natural tenderness and kindly clinging filial affection is he taught to trample on and despise!

At School and at Home

I dined yesterday with three gentlemen, whose time of life may be guessed by their conversation, a great part of which consisted of Eton reminiscences and lively imitations of Dr. Keate. Each one, as he described how he had been flogged, mimicked to the best of his power the manner and the mode of operating of the famous doctor. His little parenthetical remarks during the ceremony were recalled with great facetiousness: the very *hwhish* of the rods was parodied with thrilling fidelity, and after a good hour's conversation, the subject was brought to a climax by a description of that awful night when the doctor called up squad after squad of boys from their beds in their respective boarding-houses, whipped through the whole night, and castigated I don't know how many hundred rebels. All these mature men laughed, prattled, rejoiced, and became young again, as they recounted their stories; and each of them heartily and eagerly bade the stranger to understand how Keate was a thorough gentleman. Having talked about their floggings, I say, for an hour at least, they apologised to me for dwelling upon a subject which after all was strictly local; but, indeed, their talk greatly amused and diverted me, and I hope, and am quite ready, to hear all their jolly stories over again.

Be not angry, patient reader of former volumes by the author of the present history, if I am garrulous about Grey Friars, and go back to that ancient place of education to find the heroes of our tale. We are young but once. When we remember that time of youth, we are still young. He over whose head eight or nine lustres have passed, if he wishes to write of boys, must recall the time when he himself was a boy. Their habits change; their waists are longer or shorter; their shirt-collars stick up more or less; but the boy is the boy in King George's time as in that of his royal niece— once our maiden queen, now the anxious mother of many boys. And young fellows are honest, and merry, and idle, and mischievous, and timid, and brave, and studious, and selfish, and generous, and mean, and false, and truth-telling, and affectionate, and good, and bad, now as in former days.

The Steps of a Good Man

The custom of the school is, that on the 12th of December, the Founder's Day, the head gownboy shall recite a Latin oration, in praise *Fundatoris Nostri,* and upon other subjects; and a goodly company of old Cistercians is generally brought together to attend this oration; after which we go to chapel and hear a sermon; after which we adjourn to a great dinner, where old condisciples meet, old toasts are given, and speeches are made. Before marching from the oration-hall to chapel, the stewards of the day's dinner, according to old-fashioned rite, have wands put into their hands, walk to church at the head of the procession, and sit there in places of honour. The boys are already in their seats, with smug fresh faces, and shining white collars; the old black-gowned pensioners are on their benches; the chapel is lighted and Founder's Tomb, with its grotesque carvings, monsters, heraldries, darkles and shines with the most wonderful shadows and lights. There he lies, *Fundator Noster,* in his ruff and gown, awaiting the Great Examination Day. We oldsters, be we ever so old, become boys again as we look at that familiar old tomb, and think how the seats are altered since we were here, and how the doctor—not the present doctor, the doctor of our time—used to sit yonder, and his awful eye used to frighten us shuddering boys, on whom it lighted; and how the boy next to us *would* kick our shins during service time, and how the monitor would cane us afterwards because our shins were kicked. Yonder sit forty cherry cheeked boys, thinking about home and holidays to-morrow. Yonder sit some threescore old gentlemen pensioners of the hospital, listening to the prayers and the psalms. You hear them coughing feebly in the twilight— the old reverend blackgowns. Is Codd Ajax alive, you wonder?—the Cistercian lads called these old gentlemen Codds, I know not wherefore— I know not wherefore—but is old Codd Ajax alive, I wonder?- or Codd Soldier? or kind old Codd Gentleman? or has the grave closed over them? A plenty of candles lights up this chapel, and this scene of age and youth, and early memories, and pompous death. How solemn the well-remembered prayers are, here uttered again in the place where in childhood we used to hear them! How beautiful and decorous the rite; how noble the ancient words of the supplications which the priest utters, and to which generations of fresh children, and troops of bygone seniors have cried Amen under these arches! The service for Founder's Day is a special one; one of the psalms selected being the thirty-seventh, and we hear—

23. The steps of a good man are ordered by the Lord, and he delighteth in his way.
24. Though he fall, he shall not be utterly cast down, for the Lord upholdeth him with His hand.

25. I have been young, and now am old, yet have I not seen the righteous forsaken, nor his seed begging their bread.

As we came to this verse, I chanced to look up from my book towards the swarm of black-coated pensioners: and amongst them—amongst them—sat Thomas Newcome.

His dear old head was bent down over his Prayer-book; there was no mistaking him. He wore the black gown of the pensioners of the Hospital of Grey Friars. His Order of the Bath was on his breast. He stood there amongst the poor brethren, uttering the responses to the psalm. The steps of this good man had been ordered hither by Heaven's decree: to this Alms-house! Here it was ordained that a life all love, and kindness and honour, should end. I heard no more of prayers, and psalms, and sermon, after that.

On a Lazy Idle Boy

There was a sweet pretty river walk we used to take in the evening and mark the mountains round glooming with a deeper purple; the shades creeping up the golden walls; the river brawling, the cattle calling, the maids and chatterboxes round the fountains babbling and bawling; and several times in the course of our sober walks we overtook a lazy slouching boy, or hobbledehoy, with a rusty coat, and trousers not too long, and big feet trailing lazily one after the other, and large lazy hands dawdling from out the tight sleeves, and in the lazy hands a little book, which my lad held up to his face, and which I dare say so charmed and ravished him, that he was blind to the beautiful sights around him: unmindful, I would venture to lay any wager, of the lessons he had to learn for to-morrow; forgetful of mother waiting supper, and father preparing a scolding;—absorbed utterly and entirely in his book.

What was it that so fascinated the young student, as he stood by the river shore? Not the *pons asinorum*. What book so delighted him, and blinded him to all the rest of the world, so that he did not care to see the apple-woman with her fruit, or (more tempting still to sons of Eve) the pretty girls with their apple cheeks, who laughed and prattled round the fountain? What was the book? Do you suppose it was Livy, or the Greek grammar? No; it was a NOVEL that you were reading you lazy, not very lean, good-for-nothing, sensible boy. It was D'Artagnan locking up General Monk in a box, or almost succeeding in keeping Charles the First's head on. It was the prisoner of the Château d'If cutting himself out of the sack fifty feet under water (I mention the novels I like best myself—novels without love or talking, or any of that sort of nonsense, but containing plenty of fighting, escaping, robbery, and rescuing)—cutting himself out of the sack and swimming to the island of Monte Cristo. O Dumas! O thou brave kind gallant old Alexandre! I hereby offer thee homage, and give thee thanks for many pleasant hours. I have read thee (being sick in bed) for thirteen hours of a happy day, and had the ladies of the house fighting for the volumes. Be assured that lazy boy was reading Dumas (or I will go so far as to let the reader here pronounce the eulogium, or insert the name of his favourite author); and as for the anger, or, it may be, the verberations of his schoolmaster, or the remonstrances of his father, or the tender pleadings of his mother that he should not let the supper grow cold —I don't believe the scapegrace cared one fig. No! Figs are sweet, but fictions are sweeter.

Football

OWEN JOHNSON

OWEN JOHNSON was born in New York City in 1878, the son of Robert Underwood Johnson, editor, diplomat, and poet. His literary career began early: at six he published a story in St. Nicholas *and at twelve put out a paper. At Lawrenceville School he founded and edited the* Lawrenceville Literary Magazine, *and in 1909 he published* The Eternal Boy, *his first novel of school life. At Yale, Johnson was chairman of the* Yale Literary Magazine. *He was graduated from Yale in 1901; ten years later he published* Stover at Yale, *a novel which berated the senior societies and the lack of intellectual interests among undergraduates.*

> Oh, we'll push her over
> Or rip the cover
>   Too bad for the fellows that fall!
> They must take their chances
> Of a bruise or two
>   Who follow that jolly football.

So sang the group on the Kennedy steps, heralding the twilight; and beyond, past the Dickinson, a chorus from the Woodhull defiantly flung back the challenge. For that week the Woodhull would clash with the Kennedy for the championship of the houses.

The football season was drawing to a close, only the final game with Andover remained, a contest awaited with small hopes of victory. For the season had been disastrous for the 'Varsity; several members of the team had been caught in the toils of the octopus examination and, what was worse among the members, ill-feeling existed due to past feuds.

Stover, in the long grueling days of practice, had won the respect of all. Just how favorable an impression he had made he did not himself suspect. He had instinctive quickness and no sense of fear—that was something that had dropped from him forever. It was not that he had to conquer the impulse to flinch, as most boys do; it simply did not exist with him. The sight of a phalanx of bone and muscle starting for his end to sweep him off his feet roused only a sort of combative rage, the true joy of battle. He loved to go plunging into the unbroken front and feel the shock of bodies as he tried for the elusive legs of Flash Condit or Charley DeSoto.

This utter recklessness was indeed his chief fault; he would rather charge interference than fight it off, waiting for others to break it up for him and so make sure of his man.

Gradually, however, through the strenuous weeks, he learned the deeper lessons of football—how to use his courage and the control of his impulses.

"It's a game of brains, youngster, remember that," Mr. Ware would repeat day after day, hauling him out of desperate plunges. "That did no good; better keep on your feet and follow the ball. Above all, study the game."

His first lesson came when, at last being promoted to end on the scrub, he found himself lined up against Tough McCarty, the opposing tackle. Stover thought he saw the intention at once.

"Put me against Tough McCarty, eh?" he said, digging his nails into the palms of his hands. "Want to try out my nerve, eh? I'll show 'em!"

Now McCarty did not relish the situation either; foreseeing as he did the long weeks of strenuous contact with the one boy in the school who was vowed to an abiding vengeance. The fact was that Tough McCarty, who was universally liked for his good nature and sociable inclination, had yielded to the irritation Stover's unceasing enmity had aroused and had come gradually into something of the same attitude of hostility. Also, he saw in the captain's assigning Stover to his end a malicious attempt to secure amusement at his expense.

For all which reasons, when the scrub first lined up against the 'Varsity, the alarum of battle that rode on Stover's pugnacious front was equaled by the intensity of his enemy's coldly-calculating glance.

"Here's where I squash that fly," thought McCarty.

"Here's where I fasten to that big stuff," thought Dink, "and sting him until the last day of the season!"

The first direct clash came when the scrubs were given the ball and Dink came in to aid his tackle box McCarty for the run that was signaled around their end.

Tough made the mistake of estimating Stover simply by his lack of weight, without taking account of the nervous, dynamic energy which was his strength. Consequently, at the snap of the ball, he was taken by surprise by the wild spring that Stover made directly at his throat and, thrown off his balance momentarily by the frenzy of the impact, tripped and went down under the triumphant Dink, who, unmindful of the fact that the play had gone by, remained proudly fixed on the chest of the prostrate tackle.

"Get off," said the muffled voice.

Stover, whose animal instincts were all those of the bulldog, pressed down more firmly.

"Get off of me, you little blockhead," said McCarty growing furious as he heard the jeers of his teammates at his humiliating reversal.

"Hurry up there, you Stover!" cried the voice of the captain, unheeded, for Dink was too blindly happy with the thrill of perfect supremacy over the hated McCarty to realize the situation.

"Stover! ! !"

At the shouted command Dink looked up and at last perceived the play was over. Reluctantly he started to rise, when a sudden upheaval of the infuriated McCarty caught him unawares and Tough's vigorous arm flung him head over heels.

Down went Dink with a thump and up again with rage in his heart. He rushed up to McCarty as in the mad fight under the willows and struck him a resounding blow.

The next moment not Tough, but Cockrell's own mighty hand caught him by the collar and swung him around.

"Get off the field!"

Dink, cold in a minute, quailed under the stern eye of the supreme leader.

"I did sling him pretty hard, Garry," said Tough, taking pity at the look that came into Dink's eyes at this rebuke.

"Get off!"

Dink, who had stopped with a sort of despairing hope, went slowly to the side-lines, threw a blanket over his head and shoulders and squatted down in bitter, utter misery. Another was in his place, plunging at the tackle that should have been his, racing down the field under punts that made the blood leap in his exiled body. He did not understand. Why had he been disgraced? He had only shown he wasn't afraid—wasn't that why they had put him opposite Tough McCarty, after all?

The contending lines stopped at last their tangled rushes and straggled, panting, back for a short intermission. Dink, waiting under the blanket, saw the captain bear down upon him and, shivering like a dog watching the approach of his punishment, drew the folds tighter about him.

"Stover," said the dreadful voice, loud enough so that every one could hear, "you seem to have an idea that football is run like a slaughter-house. The quicker you get that out of your head the better. Now, do you know why I fired you? Do you?"

"For slugging," said Dink faintly.

"Not at all. I fired you because you lost your head; because you forgot you were playing football. If you're only going into this to work off your private grudges, then I don't want you around. I'll fire you off and keep you off. You're here to play football, to think of eleven men, not one. You're to use your brains, not your fists. Why, the first game you play in some one will tease you into slugging him and the umpire will fire you. Then where'll the team be? There are eleven men in this game on your side and on the other. No matter what happens don't lose your temper, don't be so stupid, so brainless—do you hear?"

"Yes, sir," said Dink, who had gradually retired under his blanket until only the tip of the nose showed and the terror-stricken eyes.

"And don't forget this. You don't count. It isn't the slightest interest to the team whether some one whales you or mauls you! It isn't the slightest interest to you, either. Mind that! Nothing on earth is going to get your mind off following the ball, sizing up the play, working out the weak points—nothing. Brains, brains, brains, Stover! You told me you came out here because we needed some one to be banged around—and I took you on your word, didn't I? Now, if you're going out there as an egotistical, puffed-up, conceited individual who's thinking only of his own skin, who isn't willing to sacrifice his own little, measly feelings for the sake of the school, who won't fight for the team, but himself——"

"I say, Cap, that's enough," said Dink with difficulty; and immediately retired so deep that only the mute, pleading eyes could be discerned.

Cockrell stopped short, bit his lip and said sternly: "Line up now. Get in, Stover, and don't let me ever have to call you down again. Tough, see here." The two elevens ran out. The captain continued: "Tough, every chance you get to-day give that little firebrand a jab, understand? So it can't be seen."

The 'Varsity took the ball and for five minutes Dink felt as though he were in an angry sea, buffeted, flung down and whirled about by massive breakers. Without sufficient experience his weight was powerless to stop the interference that bore him back. He tried to meet it standing up and was rolled head over heels by the brawny shoulders of Cheyenne Baxter and Doc Macnooder. Then, angrily, he tried charging into the offenses and was drawn in and smothered while the back went sweeping around his unprotected end for long gains.

Mr. Ware came up and volunteered suggestions:

"If you're going into it dive through them, push them apart with your hands—so. Keep dodging so that the back won't know whether you're going around or through. Keep him guessing and follow up the play if you miss the first tackle."

Under this coaching Dink, who had begun to be discouraged, improved and when he did get a chance at his man he dropped him with a fierce, clean tackle, for this branch of the game he had mastered with instinctive delight.

"Give the ball to the scrubs," said the captain, who was also coaching.

Stover came in close to his tackle. The third signal was a trial at end. He flung himself at McCarty, checked him and, to his amazement, received a dig in the ribs. His fists clenched, went back and then stopped as remembering, he drew a long breath and walked away, his eyes on the ground; for the lesson was a rude one to learn.

"Stover, what are you doing?" cried the captain, who had seen all.

Dink, who had expected to be praised, was bewildered as well as hurt.

"What are you stopping for? You're thinking of McCarty again aren't you? Do you know where your place was? Back of your own half. Follow up the play. If you'd been there to push there'd been an extra yard. Think quicker, Stover."

"Yes, sir," said Stover, suddenly perceiving the truth. "You're right, I wasn't thinking."

"Look here, boy," said the captain, laying his hand on his shoulders. "I have just one principle in a game and I want you to tuck it away and never forget it."

"Yes, sir," said Dink reverently.

"When you get in a game get fighting mad, but get cold mad—play like a fiend—but keep cold. Know just what you're doing and know it all the time."

"Thank you, sir," said Dink, who never forgot the theory, which had a wider application than Garry Cockrell perhaps suspected.

"You laid it on pretty strong," said Mr. Ware to Cockrell, as they walked back after practice.

"I did it for several reasons," said Garry; "first, because I believe the boy has the makings of a great player in him; and second, I was using him to talk to the team. They're not together and it's going to be hard to get them together."

"Bad feeling?"

"Yes, several old grudges."

"What a pity, Garry," said Mr. Ware. "What a pity it is you can only have second and third formers under you!"

"Why so?"

"Because they'd follow you like mad Dervishes," said Mr. Ware, thinking of Dink.

Stover, having once perceived that the game was an intellectual one, learned by bounds. McCarty, under instructions, tried his best to provoke him, but met with the completest indifference. Dink found a new delight in the exercise of his wits, once the truth was borne in on him that there are more ways of passing beyond a windmill than riding it down. Owing to his natural speed he was the fastest end on the field to cover a punt, and once within diving distance of his man he almost never missed. He learned, too, that the scientific application of his one hundred and thirty-eight pounds, well timed, was sufficient to counter-balance the disadvantage in weight. He never loafed, he never let a play go by without being in it, and at retrieving fumbles he was quick as a cat.

Meanwhile the house championships had gone on until the Woodhull and the Kennedy emerged for the final conflict. The experience gained in these contests, for on such occasions Stover played with his House team, had sharpened his powers of analysis and given him a needed acquaintance with the sudden, shifting crises of actual play.

Now, the one darling desire of Stover, next to winning the fair opinion of his captain, was the rout of the Woodhull, of which Tough McCarty was the captain and his old acquaintances of the miserable days at the

Green were members—Cheyenne Baxter, the Coffee-colored Angel and Butsey White. This aggregation, counting as it did two members of the 'Varsity, was strong, but the Kennedy, with P. Lentz and the Waladoo Bird and Pebble Stone, the Gutter Pup, Lovely Mead and Stover, all of the scrub, had a slight advantage.

Dink used to dream of mornings, in the lagging hours of recitation, of the contest and the sweet humiliation of his ancient foes. He would play like a demon, he would show them, Tough McCarty and the rest, what it was to be up against the despised Dink—and dreaming thus he used to say to himself, with suddenly tense arms:

"Gee, I only wish McCarty would play back of the line so I could get a chance at him!"

But on Tuesday, during the 'Varsity practice, suddenly as a scrimmage ended and sifted open a cry went up. Ned Banks, left end on the 'Varsity, was seen lying on the ground after an attempt to rise. They gathered about him with grave faces, while Mr. Ware bent over him in anxious examination.

"What is it?" said the captain, with serious face.

"Something wrong with his ankle; can't tell yet just what."

"I'll play Saturday, Garry," said Banks, gritting his teeth. "I'll be ready by then. It's nothing much."

The subs carried him off the field with darkened faces—the last hopes of victory seemed to vanish. The gloom spread thickly through the school, even Dink, for a time, forgot the approaching hour of his revenge in the great catastrophe. The next morning a little comfort was given them in the report of Doctor Charlie that there was no sprain but only a slight wrenching, which, if all went well, would allow him to start the game. But the consolation was scant. What chance had Banks in an Andover game? There would have to be a shift; but what?

"Turkey Reiter will have to go from tackle to end," said Dink, that afternoon, as in football togs they gathered on the steps before the game, "and put a sub in Turkey's place."

"Who?"

"I don't know."

"I guess you don't."

"Might bring Butcher Stevens back from center."

"Who'd go in at center?"

"Fatty Harris, perhaps."

"Hello—here's Garry Cockrell now," said P. Lentz. "He don't look particular cheerful, does he?"

The captain, looking indeed very serious, arrived, surveyed the group and called Stover out. Dink, surprised, jumped up, saying:

"You want me, sir?"

"Yes."

Cockrell put his arm under his and drew him away.

"Stover," he said, "I've got bad news for you."

"For me?"

"Yes. I'm not going to let you go in the Woodhull game this afternoon."

Stover received the news as though it had been the death of his entire family, immediate and distant. His throat choked, he tried to say something and did not dare trust himself.

"I'm sorry, my boy—but we're up against it, and I can't take any risks now of your getting hurt."

"It means the game," said Dink at last.

"I'm afraid so."

"We've no one to put in my place—no one but Beekstein Hall," said Stover desperately. "Oh, please, sir, let me play; I'll be awfully careful. It's only a House game."

"Humph—yes, I know these House games. I'm sorry, but there's no help for it."

"But I'm only a scrub, sir," said Stover, pleading hard.

"We're going to play you at end," said Cockrell suddenly, seeing he did not understand, "just as soon as we have to take Banks out; and Heaven only knows when that'll be."

Dink was aghast.

"You're not going—you're not going——" he tried to speak, and stopped.

"Yes, we've talked it over and that seems best."

"But—Turkey Reiter—I—I thought you'd move him out."

"No, we don't dare weaken the middle; it's bad enough now."

"Oh, but I'm so light."

The captain watched the terror-stricken look in his face and was puzzled.

"What's the matter? You're not getting shaky?"

"Oh, no, sir," said Dink, "it's not that. It—it seems so awful that you've got to put me in."

"You're better, my boy, than you think," said Cockrell, smiling a little, "and you're going to be better than you know how. Now you understand why you've got to keep on the side-lines this afternoon. You're too fragile to take risks on."

"Yes, I understand."

"It comes hard, doesn't it?"

"Yes, sir, it does; very hard."

When the Kennedy and the Woodhull lined up for play an hour later little Pebble Stone was at end in place of Stover, who watched from his post as linesman the contest that was to have been his opportunity. He heard nothing of the buzzing comments behind, of the cheers or the shouted entreaties. Gaze fixed and heart in throat, he followed the swaying tide of battle, imprisoned, powerless to rush in and stem the disheartening advance.

The teams, now more evenly matched, both showed the traces of tense nerves in the frequent fumbling that kept the ball changing sides and prevented a score during the first half.

In the opening of the second half, by a lucky recovery of a blocked kick, the Kennedy scored a touchdown, but failed to kick the goal, making the score four to nothing. The Woodhull then began a determined assault upon the Kennedy's weak end. Stover, powerless, beheld little Pebble Stone, fighting like grim death, carried back and back five, ten yards at a time as the Woodhull swept up the field.

"It's the only place they can gain," he cried in his soul in bitter iteration.

He looked around and caught the eye of Captain Cockrell and sent him a mute, agonizing, fruitless appeal.

"Kennedy's ball," came the sharp cry of Slugger Jones, the umpire.

Dink looked up and felt the blood come back to his body again—on the twenty-five yard line there had been a fumble and the advance was checked. Twice again the battered end of the Kennedy was forced back for what seemed certain touchdowns, only to be saved by loose work on the Woodhull's part. It was getting dark and the half was ebbing fast— three minutes more to play. A fourth time the Woodhull furiously attacked the breach, gaining at every rush over the light opposition, past the forty-yard line, past the twenty-yard mark and triumphantly, in the last minute of play, over the goal for a touchdown. The ball had been downed well to the right of the goal posts and the trial for goal was an unusually difficult one. The score was a tie, everything depended on the goal that, through the dusk, Tough McCarty was carefully sighting. Dink, heart-broken, despairing, leaning on his linesman's staff, directly behind the ball, waited for the long, endless moments to be over. Then there was a sudden movement of McCarty's body, a wild rush from the Kennedy and the ball shot high in the air and, to Stover's horror, passed barely inside the farther goalpost.

"No goal," said Slugger Jones. "Time up."

Dink raised his head in surprise, scarcely crediting what he had heard. The Woodhull team were furiously disputing the decision, encouraged by audible comments from the spectators. Slugger Jones, surrounded by a contesting, vociferous mass, suddenly swept them aside and began to take the vote of the officials.

"Kiefer, what do you say?"

Cap Kiefer, referee, shook his head.

"I'm sorry, Slugger, it was close, very close, but it did seem a goal to me."

"Tug, what do you say?"

"Goal, sure," said Tug Wilson, linesman for the Woodhull. At this, jeers and hoots broke out from the Kennedy.

"Of course he'll say that!"

"He's from the Woodhull."

"What do you think?"

"Justice!"

"Hold up, hold up, now," said Slugger Jones, more excited than any one. "Don't get excited; it's up to your own man. Dink, was it a goal or no goal?"

Stover suddenly found himself in a whirling, angry mass—the decision of the game in his own hands. He saw the faces of Tough McCarty and the Coffee-colored Angel in the blank crowd about him and he saw the sneer on their faces as they waited for his answer. Then he saw the faces of his own teammates and knew what they, in their frenzy, expected from him.

He hesitated.

"Goal or no goal?" cried the umpire, for the second time.

Then suddenly, face to face with the hostile mass, the fighting blood came to Dink. Something cold went up his back. He looked once more above the riot, to the shadowy post, trying to forget Tough McCarty, and then, with a snap of his jaws, he answered:

"Goal."

Stonehenge

LOGAN PEARSALL SMITH

LOGAN PEARSALL SMITH (1865-1946), essayist, was graduated from Haverford College in 1884. He spent a year at Harvard and a year in his father's business, leaving the latter to go to England, where he established residence and lived, chiefly in London, for the remainder of his life. He has written essays, short stories and literary criticism. He is best known as the author of Trivia, *a collection of aphoristic, witty, ironic essays, seldom more than one paragraph in length.*

THEY sit there forever on the dim horizon of my mind, that Stonehenge circle of elderly disapproving Faces—Faces of the Uncles and Schoolmasters and Tutors who frowned on my youth.

In the bright centre and sunlight I leap, I caper, I dance my dance; but when I look up, I see they are not deceived. For nothing ever placates them, nothing ever moves to a look of approval that ring of bleak and contemptuous Faces.

A Letter to S. S. Drury

JOHN JAY CHAPMAN

JOHN JAY CHAPMAN (1862-1933) was graduated from Harvard in 1884, travelled abroad after graduation, studied law, and was admitted to the bar in 1888. He practiced law for ten years but disliked the profession. He was interested chiefly in politics, in which he was active for most of his life.

Chapman wrote verse, plays, critical essays, and letters. He has been called the best letter writer of his time. What he thought of schoolboys the following letter to Dr. Drury, then headmaster of St. Paul's School, at Concord, New Hampshire, will show.

Barrytown, N. Y.
Nov. 26: 1916

MY DEAR DR. DRURY

Do you really think that if I *had* any ideas on the parent and the child question I'd waste them on you? But just now I am taking a loaf and trying to forget the whole subject. Is the education of the young the whole of life? I hate the young—I'm worn out with them. They absorb you and suck you dry and are vampires and selfish brutes at best. Give me some good old rumsoaked club men—who *can't* be improved and make no moral claims—and let me play chequers with them and look out of the Club window and think about what I'll have for dinner.

Yours faithfully

JOHN JAY CHAPMAN

This letter is from *John Jay Chapman and His Letters*, edited by M. A. De Wolfe Howe; copyright, 1937, by M. A. De Wolfe Howe; reprinted by permission of Houghton Mifflin Company.

On the Education of a Lady of Quality

LADY MARY WORTLEY MONTAGU

LADY MARY WORTLEY MONTAGU (1688-1762), daughter of Evelyn Pierrepont, Duke of Kingston, and wife of Edward Wortley Montagu, Ambassador to Constantinople in 1716, showed early aptitude for intellectual pursuits. In her youth she studied Greek and Latin and read widely in drama and romance. During her residence in Constantinople she learned Turkish and observed with discernment the life around her. The letters she wrote from Constantinople commenting on Turkish life and customs were collected and published after her death. On her return to London she was not only a leader in London society but also a figure of importance in literary circles. In 1742 she settled in Avignon, where she lived in an old mill remodeled into a dwelling. Later she established residence in a decayed palace in Brescia and while there wrote letters to her daughter, Lady Bute, commenting on Italian society and discussing the books she had read. She returned to England in 1762 and died in the same year.

M<small>Y</small> own was one of the worst in the world, being exactly the same as Clarissa Harlowe's; her pious Mrs. Norton so perfectly resembling my governess, who had been nurse to my mother, I could almost fancy the author was acquainted with her. She took so much pains, from my infancy, to fill my head with superstitious tales and false notions, it was none of her fault I am not at this day afraid of witches and hobgoblins, or turned methodist. Almost all girls are bred after this manner. I believe you are the only woman (perhaps I might say, person) that never was either frighted or cheated into anything by your parents. . . . I could give many examples of ladies whose ill conduct has been very notorious, which has been owing to that ignorance which has exposed them to idleness, which is justly called the mother of mischief. There is nothing so like the education of a woman of quality as that of a prince: they are taught to dance, and the exterior part of what is called good breeding, which if they attain, they are extraordinary creatures in their kind, and have all the accomplishments required by their directors. The same characters are formed by the same lessons, which inclines me to think (if I dare say it) that nature has not placed us in an inferior rank to men, no more than the females of other animals, where we see no distinction of capacity; though, I am persuaded, if there was a commonwealth of rational horses (as Dr. Swift has supposed), it would be an established maxim among them, that a mare could not be taught to pace.

"And Suddenly There Shined Round About Him a Light from Heaven"

WILLIAM ALLEN WHITE

WILLIAM ALLEN WHITE (1868-1944) was born in Emporia, Kansas. In 1884 he was graduated from high school. He entered Kansas State University but left without a degree to take a job as business manager on the Eldorado *Republican. For a few years he was an editorial writer on the* Kansas City *Star. In 1895 he bought the Emporia* Gazette *and in the following year became famous following the publication of an editorial* "What's the Matter with Kansas?" *In addition to his editorials White has written short stories, novels, and biographies.*

THE College of Emporia, in the autumn of 1884, was without a building. It was located on the third floor of a brick structure at the corner of Sixth and Commercial in the throbbing heart of Emporia, which then held six or seven thousand people. There the college opened in half a dozen rooms. Seventy-five boys and girls were herded by six or eight teachers. I met a minor shame on the opening day. I had played the cabinet organ in high school often for singing, and in high school at the organ I marched them out playing "General Persifor F. Smith's Grand March" and "Garfield's Funeral March," so lugubrious but highly popular, and the March from "Lucia di Lammermoor," all of which I had learned by ear. So, when they wanted someone to volunteer to play the cabinet organ for the opening day of college, I took a chance and volunteered. I thought I knew all the gospel hymns, but they rang a new one in on me which was hard to fake. It was "All Hail the Power of Jesus' Name," and while I had a whistling acquaintance with it, the harmony was over my head for a first shot. I knew I was making a terrible mess out of it, which did not help me. But I got through it and learned my lesson. The college marked me for an unmasked smart aleck. It took me a week or ten days to live that down. Only when I showed the boys that I could chin a pole nineteen times, did I restore lost ground.

For the first time in my life I encountered home cooking in another woman's home. I lived with a widow, a preacher's widow, Mrs. Jones, who had a boy my age. She was Welsh and knew how to feed boys. And her son Bob and I kept Mrs. Jones and her two little daughters busy feeding us. I got very little out of that college. I had a year of third-year Latin and my first year of Greek, which I presumed that naturally all college students had to have. There was no nonsense in the curriculum of the College of Emporia to disabuse me. I tried a term of French. I had been through Hill's Rhetoric twice in high school—once to learn it and the second time to enjoy it, and probably to show off my knowledge of it. So I took it again in college, and had advanced algebra and a little primitive physics. There was no chemistry laboratory, and they did not teach chemistry. And of course, I had English literature, an advanced course over the high-school course, which I enjoyed.

I brought from Eldorado to college a small box of books: my Red Line poets; a pirated edition of Longfellow's early poems; "The Wandering Jew," by Eugène Sue; the Deerslayer stories, and a one-volume condensed copy of the Works of Thomas De Quincey. The last contained the "Confessions of an English Opium Eater," which that year was my favorite literary diversion. And, however poor the college was as an intellectual stimulus, Bob Jones—the preacher's widow's son—was a joy and stimulation to me. He read my books and I read his, for a preacher's son generally has books. And we roamed the woods together Saturdays with our lunch— gay sixteen-year-olders. We carried a sack for walnuts and a club with which to knock them from the tree; also always a book or two. So we rowed on the Cottonwood and stripped betimes and jumped in and stretched out on our bellies, kicking our toes in the mold in the woods, reading Tennyson and Byron, talking bashful big talk that little boys in their teens enjoy. In his diary, after his death, I read an entry of November 1, 1884: "Went swimming with Bill White this morning, thin scum of ice." And, reading it, I recall that it was so cold that my measles came out and I was scared for a bit. But if Bob and I meet again in heaven we can never have lovelier hours than those Saturdays we spent in the woods, on the river, roving the fields, enjoying God's unfolding universe where youth sees so many new, strange, and lovely things.

And of course, despite the fact that Agnes Riley and I had a sweet and bashful parting, as though I were going to the ends of the earth when I left for college, and that I carried her picture in my trunk and put it on the table in my room, still there were fair girls in the College of Emporia. Mostly perhaps because of my pimples, which still bore me down, I viewed them from afar.

But the lifelong blessing which the College of Emporia gave me was a boy—Vernon Kellogg. The thing that brought us together was that he also was buying books from John B. Alden. So far as I know, he was the only boy in the College of Emporia who had much bookish interest. He was my height, a scant five feet seven and five-eighths. He wore the same size hat, seven and a half, and the same size shoes, six and a half on a wide last or seven on a narrower. We both came from the ruling class. It was his father, as the president of the State Normal School, who had ridden into Emporia in '65 on the stage with my mother. The president had studied law, had become probate judge of the county, was elected state senator the year I came to college; and his stepmother also was a lawyer, her husband's partner. And their house, when I entered it to visit Vernon, was the first house full of books that I had ever seen—bookcases around the walls, books on the table. So I walked in the new heaven and the new earth. And I became in the College of Emporia the willing slave of Vernon, a few months my senior. His brother Fred, who was a year my junior, also interested me, but not as Vernon did. The two boys lived in a little house outside their parents' home on the wide lawn under the shading elms and maples. There they had their own way. It was a rule that they should make their own beds, pick up their own things, run their own ménage. And after four o'clock in the day it looked it, though they did manage to get their beds made before breakfast. But to that little house came like-minded boys from all over town, who were interested in books and bugs and birds. Vernon hunted (which I never did), but only for birds to classify and stuff. And the Kellogg boys built boats in the barn, homemade canoes under rules that came out of a boys' book of boats. And maybe because he was slight and well muscled, and maybe because he had no pimples and was not going "to die or go crazy or be an idiot," and because he was lithe and trim and wiry in those days, Vernon had no use for girls, which was good for me, and we cleaved to each other as brothers. When I got home to Lew Schmucker, Albert Ewing, Agnes Riley, and Alice Murdock, I poured forth stories of the prowess and grandeur of Vernon Kellogg. For I was ever a blabby kid and never self-contained—and always loved heroes.

In 1884 I got a lesson that lasted me all my life by scaring the daylights out of me. James G. Blaine was running against Grover Cleveland. I was supposed to be a Democrat. I fought, bled, and died on the school grounds in Eldorado for the Democrats. And I was hoping heartily for Cleveland's election, particularly as I remember standing up in school, amid the hoots of the high-school partisans in '82, and predicting that Cleveland would be the next President. But the day after the election, Blaine seemed to have won. A great crowd surged on Emporia's Commercial Street and Sixth Avenue as the news came seeping in, and the Democrats, for all the Republican clamor of delight, were still cocky, and were still betting on Cleveland. That morning I had received from my mother the twenty dollars to last me through the month of November. It was in four five-dollar bills. Treacherously but greedily, thinking to make money out of the foolish Democrats, I bet five dollars on Blaine and lost. Five dollars out of a twenty-dollar allowance was a burden too grievous to be borne. I have never made an election bet of over fifty cents since. Experience is a dear school, and fools learn in no other; and I have always had to get my experience in the foolish way. I was ashamed to tell my mother that I had bet on her candidate. I just sweated it out!

When I came home for Thanksgiving, I learned a story that shamed me more. When Cleveland's election was finally beyond a doubt the week following, the Democrats in Eldorado put on a great torchlight parade and hired the band, indeed a couple of bands from neighboring towns, and literally tore the roof off of Eldorado. It was their first victory since Buchanan in '56. While I was betting on Blaine my mother had been rejoicing in every way a woman can. But the night of the big Cleveland torchlight procession and jubilee, she was heartbroken. She believed that the rebels were coming up out of the South to run the country. But she knew how my father would feel. So that festive night she put a lighted candle in every one of the forty windows in our house except the kitchen. There she pulled down the curtains, blew out the light, and sat and rocked in sorrow, yet I suppose in a certain proud glamour of loyalty that his house, his big house with a hundred and forty-four feet of porch, where the band stopped three times and serenaded that night, his house was with him—all lighted up in jubilation at the victory. She was the kind of woman who would enjoy the emotional stimulus of that kind of situation.

I remember little about that first year in Emporia College, except that it was fun to get the best of old Dr. Cruickshank, the Greek professor, who slammed us into Xenophon's "Anabasis," six months after we had achieved the Greek alphabet, and I stumbled through the year of Greek as thick-headed a blunderer as ever thumbed a pony. But my Latin was good. And there again I went through Hill's Rhetoric the third time and knew it by heart. Curiously, the quotations and examples of rhetorical forms and figures of speech attracted me as much as the instruction in the book. There I first met verses from Omar Khayyám's "Rubáiyát," and Wordsworth, and Coleridge, and Ossian. And this is funny: In the footnotes where the author's verses were accredited, I found the words "Anon" and "Ibid" and thought they were names of authors also, and not until Vernon Kellogg lifted the scales from my eyes, did I know better. But that year the big thing that Vernon Kellogg did for me was to take me across the street from the college into the second floor of the bank building, where the City Library was housed. The gray-haired librarian, Mrs. Carpenter, who was a glamorous figure for me because her husband had been killed in the Quantrill Raid, let me loaf there and brought me books. In Eldorado I had been thrilled by Emerson's line in the essay on Self-Reliance: "Trust thyself: every heart vibrates to that iron string." And I asked Mrs. Carpenter for the essay. It was on a snowy February day when I had just turned seventeen; and as I read that essay my spirit expanded as though I had heard the trumpet call of life. I was thrilled and stirred and literally overturned. I doubt if I have ever been moved so deeply by anything else that I have read. So I read all the essays and other Emersonian books, and was glad to live and proud to feel that I was beginning to understand something of the puzzle of life. The Emporia City Library was a vastly different place from the Eldorado Library; more books, better books, and a fulltime librarian were in Emporia, and all of the magazines that one could want, even from England, and illustrated papers: Harper's, Leslie's, the London Illustrated News, Puck, Judge. To add warmth to the glamour, often across the table sat Vernon Kellogg and we whispered and giggled; and when he found a sentence in a bird book, or bug book, or zoology book that pleased him, he shoved it across the table. And I did the same when a poem or essay pleased me. I found there all the books of De Quincey, who was my especial delight in those days. It made little difference to me whether the college across the street kept or not. I was not bold enough to skip classes, but I doubt if I learned much from them.

But that winter the college students, because there were a hundred of them, could do what the Spring Chickens in Eldorado could not do. Often a sled—a great hayrack on runners—was hired, and we all sat in the bottom, boys and girls, and tangled our legs together and felt very warm and wicked as we slyly held hands, slipped arms about each other, and were quite sinful in our own Presbyterian eyes. I had qualms about Agnes Riley, but I went every time I was asked. Vernon went also, and I often wondered if he got the same kind of fun out of it that I did; but our confidences, though deep in philosophy and science, never went quite that far. I was too shy; he was too wise and canny.

During vacations, of course, I went home; indeed I went home between vacations, sometimes over week ends, and always brought back literally trunks full of food. My mother did not realize how Bob Jones's mother was stuffing me—how good a cook she was. So, to keep my soul and body together, my mother baked cakes and pies and roasted a chicken, and tucked in doughnuts and glasses of jelly. Craftily I widened the circumference of my college influence by inviting boys to my room, where we devoured the feasts that I brought from Eldorado. So I had some distinction in the college which had nothing to do with my scholarship, and other boys deferred to me. I had sense enough never to invite Emporia boys to these feasts, but boys from other towns who keenly appreciated the food. For they lived in cheap boarding houses mostly. Board could be had in that day for from one dollar and seventy-five cents to three dollars a week, half a room for three or four dollars and a fine room for 'en.

So, in college, I bribed my way into leadership of a sort as in Eldorado my big barn, my turning pole, my trapeze, my swinging rings, my red sled, and my boughten wagon gave me, from the first, the bribe-giver's power over my fellows. In a way I probably knew it and did not take the shame that should have been mine for my advantage. Without these things, which are granted to boys from the ruling class, I would probably have been just a little bashful, measly-looking boy, afraid to say his soul was his own and craven at heart. Instead of which, I read Emerson's "Self-Reliance" and had my first rebirth on earth.

For Emerson seemed to correlate all the world for me, the spiritual world. Deep within me a philosophy was forming. Probably I was just imposing Emersonian transcendentalism upon the theology of the Sunday school of my childhood, and the protracted meetings, pupil poundings and howling of the itinerant preachers who came along through my childhood at home. Nor did Emerson, who probably justified my rambunctiousness by preaching self-reliance, make me less of a conceited ass. But he did give me courage, always backed up by Vernon Kellogg, to survive a Moody revival which shook the school. Vernon and I were scared stiff that it would get us, and pledged ourselves to stand against it. We were like two mules crossing a rattling iron bridge who leaned against each other and shuffled in trembling timidity through the clamor. But we did come scot-free out of the orgy. It took the town as well as the school, and I can remember Moody yet—a soft-voiced man with a high and lovely tenor singsong to his incantations, a bearded man, paunchy, with fat jowls and wonderful eyes, and with all that a really spiritual face. He looked like a kind of over-stuffed angel when he was going well in his exhortations. Of course, Vernon and I heard him time and again. I had two roommates who knelt and prayed every night by the bedside; and, like a soldier upheld by Emerson, I ducked into bed and turned my face to the wall and said my little "Now I lay me's" in secret, scorning what seemed to me the profanation of their public promiscuity with God.

But after the revival I noticed the college gradually slumped back to its normal life. I can remember still the curious spiritual squint-eyed, wordless questioning I put to Rankin Hendy, the president's son, who, being a preacher's son, the devil's dear and mischievous child, proposed to illustrate some precept in our psychology class, wherein we were studying "surprise." He picked up a three-legged chair in the back of the room, a discarded recitation chair, and when I asked him what he was going to do, he went to the open window there on the third floor above the busy street, and said:

"Let me show you some surprise and see how it reacts."

He balanced the chair a minute on the window sill and I stood beside him, wondering what was in his mind. We both looked out and down into the street. It was almost deserted. Fifty feet to the westward of us, going east, was old man Cross, a pompous banker with side whiskers, who wore a high, sawed-off, stiff felt hat and swung a cane which he flicked at dogs and boys who got in his way. And as he approached, Hendy said to me: "Now look!" And he dropped the chair three stories down on the sidewalk, not a dozen feet in front of old man Cross, who literally jumped into the air, threw his cane in the gutter and, hearing the thing crash and seeing it splinter, ran for his life. It was a noble sight, and I can laugh at it yet after nearly sixty years. And I know now how surprise works as a biological process. But a second after we had ducked back from the window I thought: "Hendy's a hell of a Christian." I told Vernon later, and we

both laughed and agreed that Hendy was in truth "a hell of a Christian"—
a phrase that we preserved in our intimacy as a tag for many years.

The spring semester found me grinding away with the college fresh-
man classical course. I cared little for any of it except English literature,
English composition, and Virgil's "Aeneid"; but I was tremendously interested in books and magazines. Occasionally Lew Schmucker and I, in
Eldorado, had bought Scribner's and Harper's and the Century; but in
Emporia the Atlantic Monthly was placed in my hands by the librarian.
And there I had my first taste of William Dean Howells, possibly following an advertisement, or possibly a suggestion of the librarian. I read
Howells's "A Modern Instance" and realized that I was opening a new
door. Here was a novel different from the Dickens I adored, a novel by a
writer whose methods were in conscious opposition to those other writers,
Scott and Cooper and the authors of "The Scottish Chiefs" and "Thaddeus
of Warsaw," and "The Children of the Abbey," and Eugène Sue, whose
"Wandering Jew" I was reading for the second or third time. Mr. Howells
some way fitted into the Emersonian pattern of my youthful philosophy.
And to look ahead for a few pages, when I got home to Eldorado that summer, I bought his book and tried to get Lew Schmucker and Agnes Riley
and my mother interested in the story—but with little success. Lew, who
doted on "Lalla Rookh," "Nick Carter," "Tom Sawyer," and "The Pickwick Papers" and "Seth Luvengood," found "A Modern Instance" dry.
Agnes could not get interested, and my mother was frankly critical of its
realism. But that spring in Emporia I read it and reread it, and some way
felt that I had made a great discovery. Mr. Howells was not anywhere near
the zenith of his fame in the spring of 1885. I was always proud that I
spotted him early. When he came to Emporia I asked him to write in my
book, and when I told him how I had found him and taken him to my
heart, he wrote in my book: "W. D. Howells—Mr. White's discovery!"

I was a seventeen-year-old boy and was passing out of gangdom and
becoming an individual. Looking back now, I know why I made long and
lonesome walks into the country. That spring I walked seven miles to
Americus once or twice to visit friends, often wandered over the townsite
of Emporia; and even Vernon Kellogg, or Bob Jones, whom I got along
with so well, seemed to be too much company for me. Probably what I
really needed to do was to go fishing; but I never cared to fish. I liked
to row the boat and take care of the minnow-pail bait when others were
fishing for bass. But, as for fishing alone, neither fishing nor hunting appealed to me then; and they never did interest me. Yet I remember that I
was often alone. Sundays I went to the Congregational Church to hear
the Reverend Frank Ingalls, brother of the Kansas Senator of that day,
deliver his erudite, passionless spiritual essays, rather on the Emersonian
pattern, or to hear him tell about his trip to the Holy Land. But also I went
to a young men's Bible class in the Presbyterian Church, which had a
marvelous teacher. He gave me the first glimpse of a higher criticism when

he told us that Jeremiah was probably written by two or three men, that
the books of the Gospel were first taken out of tradition into writing probably fifty or a hundred years after Matthew, Mark, Luke, and John were
dead, and indicated that Moses had made many mistakes of chronology.
All these revelations did not shake my faith; but it interested me, as an
Emersonian, to know that my theory of spiritual gravitation toward the
triumph of righteousness in human relations was not dependent upon any
script or text.

One Sunday night in the early spring I was walking alone, because I felt
it was too hot to go to church. I plodded up Commercial Street with my
hands behind me, as is my wont today when I am mildly curious and interested about the universe and the immediate environment thereof. Along
came a man whom I had never seen before and have never seen since, but
have remembered for a lifetime—a slim, good-looking, well dressed,
ready-speaking man. I thought he was a traveling man—probably a salesman. He boarded me with some light remark, slowing down his pace and
catching step with me, and we began to talk about Heaven knows what.
But before we had gone much more than a block we began to talk religion. Because he was a stranger I unbuttoned my heart to him, and he
sensed that I was in some sort of conflict. I myself do not remember what
it was. For an hour we walked, and he talked and set me right with the
world. Whatever religious faith I have is based upon his wise words. And
the wise thing he said was that it made little difference how the Bible was
put together but a great deal of difference that it had held up through the
centuries and for many thousands of years, because its wisdom some way
matched and covered human experience. I remember also that he said not
to fret too much about the miracles and the story of the virgin birth, that
the same stories would be found in many religions. He talked about the
tragedy of the life and death of Jesus, pictured him as a young man who
found his country and his people in bondage and sought to free them by
pointing their way to a philosophy of peace through humility, through
tolerance, through charity, rather than by appeal to arms. He held Jesus
up to me as the greatest hero in history and asked me to read the story of
the two thousand years that had followed his death and to watch how
slowly and yet how inexorably the world had changed, veering to human
happiness as it accepted little by little, phrase by phrase, the philosophy he
preached and made it a part, even a small part, of human institutions. Then
my companion turned our talk to a discussion of the futility of force and the
ultimate triumph of reason in human affairs. He explained his theory that
Jesus died to save the world by demonstrating, through his crucifixion and
the symbol of his resurrection, the indestructibility of truth.

My ears had been opened by Emerson. That unknown man turned over
the sod of my spirit and uncovered an understanding heart. That, to my
youth, was the night of the Great Light. Yet it was only the seed and not
the harvest of the truth that came to me as the unknown sower walked with

me on that evening's pilgrimage along Commercial Street toward "the way, the truth, and the life"! He may have been a preacher and not a traveling salesman at all. Or, more likely, he was some young divinity student in his early twenties. And I have often wondered whence he came and whither he went. But because I was seventeen, because youth opens its heart in those days to the great mysteries, the faith this stranger preached has been with me through all the years.

So at last I was on the road to Damascus!

I Open School

ELLA ENSLOW AND ALVIN F. HARLOW

ELLA ENSLOW is the pen name of Lena Davis Murray. The story of her experiences as a young teacher in a difficult school in the Tennessee mountains is told in Schoolhouse in the Foothills, *written in collaboration with Alvin Fay Harlow.*

ALVIN FAY HARLOW was born in Sedalia, Missouri, in 1875. In 1899 he was graduated from Franklin College, Indiana. He has been a special writer for various business magazines, has produced motion pictures of life in the southern Appalachian Mountains, and has written historical and biographical narratives.

Schoolhouse in the Foothills, *from which the two following selections are taken, was written as the result of a coincidence. While reading the correspondence of the Save-a-Child Fund, Alvin Harlow came across three letters from Ella Enslow asking for aid for "her people." He determined to meet Ella Enslow and hear the full story of her experiences at Shady Cove. As a result of the meeting* Schoolhouse in the Foothills *was written.*

ON the Monday morning early in August when my school was to open I was ready to rise shortly after dawn, for I had slept poorly, seeing dread prophetic visions whenever I did fall into a doze. It gave promise of being a hot day. Wood thrushes were trilling their morning song on the wooded hillsides and a cardinal was whistling from a pasture clump—all far happier and freer from apprehension than I. I got through my breakfast somehow and started on the two-mile hike to my school. During the first three winters I walked nearly all the time, firstly, because there was no place at the school to house the modest car that I had bought out of my earnings, and secondly, because it would be a clear case of malicious destruction of property to take any car over that road—frightfully rough, twisting, deeply gullied, thigh-deep in mud in winter and spring, taking to the creek bed here and there, and likely to be cut off any time when a hard shower brought a freshet in the creek.

Pinch up with the fingers of one hand a fold in a piece of cloth, and the little pouch where the fold begins will represent the site of Dawyer, my home town. It is there that one branch of Little Shady Creek rises; the sprinkle of houses which constitute Dawyer are scattered up and down the slopes of this cul-de-sac. Of the two railroads which pass through the hamlet one cuts through the ridge at the head of the hollow, the other emerges from a tunnel right under the station of the first.

My father has for many years been a section foreman on one of these railroads, and no egregious boasting is involved when I say that we live in perhaps the largest and most pretentious house in the village. Of course it is very near the railroad tracks. From its door one may look down the rapidly descending glen of Little Shady Creek—which is nearly straight for the better part of a mile, then becomes narrower and more winding— and see some of the nearest homes of my school children. But for the ugliness of some of man's "improvements", there would be a beauty in the view, approaching grandeur. The odd thing is that living there almost within sight of it, as I did for so many years, I had never before visited Shady Cove School.

The school and its surroundings were picturesque enough from an artistic point of view, but appalling to the eye of a modern educator; an old log building of one room with a tiny belfry thrust through its decaying clapboard roof—nothing more, though the building was seated proudly upon the most appropriate site in the Cove for an institution of learning— one which symbolized the importance that learning should play in the life of a community. From the ridge forming the west wall of the winding dale a half-round knoll thrust itself well out into the bed of the valley, its crest more than a hundred feet above the creek, while the road swept in a great arc around the outcropping ledges at its base. It was a natural site for a great statue or memorial; and failing that, a school, as a beacon of knowledge, was next appropriate. Unfortunately the poor little school had never been able to live up to its site.

Immediately back of and above the schoolyard was a cemetery which climbed the slope for another hundred yards or so to the door of a plain little church of which it was the appendage; a Baptist church, to which nearly all pious citizens of the Cove adhered. They can't be Primitive or Hard-Shell Baptists, for they don't believe in congregational foot-washing. A cemetery is a doubly pathetic spot in our mountain region, for the sculptured stones are few and starkly plain. Some cannot afford even these, and many graves are marked with mere rough slabs or splinters of stone, with plank, or nothing at all; but every family knows and cherishes its own little plot.

I had received the regular issue of supplies with which our county equips every country school—namely, a box of chalk and a broom—but I didn't take them with me that morning. On the way I rehearsed again my opening speeches and the plans I was going to outline; I tried to guess at possible contingencies. My teaching hitherto had been in towns; small towns, to be sure, but I had not yet encountered anything so primitive as what I must grapple with in Shady Cove. The country school-teacher in the mountains must be a social-service worker as well as a pedagogue; the few who can't or won't take on that additional function are not successes as teachers. In the past two springs I have lectured on school hygiene in a college in the mountain region, and didn't learn nearly as much from books as I did from personal experience on Little Shady Creek.

I suspected that many of the parents would be present that morning, and I was right. The opening of school, the storm center of the community —and with a slender young woman as its new pedagogical experiment— was an event not to be missed. I knew almost none of the people of the Cove, but many of them knew me by sight or reputation. My father's long tenure of so public a job as section boss on a railroad whose track many of the Coveites used as a highway on their trips to "town" (Dawyer); our neatly painted two-story home with its large, trim lawn, shade trees and flower beds which mother and we girls so carefully tended, the bathroom in which—so it was rumored in the Cove—we washed ourselves every day; these were regarded as evidences of affluence far beyond the personal dreams of anyone along Little Shady Creek. I was a native of Whittis County, but the fact that in childhood I had lived briefly in a Western state, that I had had a few spring semesters in college and had visited some of the great cities of the North—these made me a prodigy of learning and a world traveler to a people, few of whom had seen the big city of our mountain region, Southmont, only forty miles distant; nay, some of whom had never even set foot in Teviston.

I had timed my arrival at the school for seven o'clock, expecting to be first on the ground; but here I received a disconcerting repulse. Under the great oaks and hickories among whose gently swaying boughs the doves were mourning, a horde of people were scattered over the hillside. Bony horses and mules hitched to trees, lank hounds scratching or snoring, men whittling or talking in groups, mothers carrying babies and shepherding children to school for the first time, old folks gabbling toothless gossip, and the school children themselves, too excited over the coming ceremonial to play—every one of these fixed me with an eager appraising stare as I came up the slope.

My emotions, I fancy, somewhat resembled those of a mouse compelled to bluff its way through an assemblage of cats. There might have been latent hostility in some of those eyes, but I am convinced that it was mostly mere curiosity which looked out of them. I knew only two or three of the gathering; I exchanged greetings with them and spoke to others. Scarcely any of the men had sufficient acquaintance with urban courtesy to touch their hats. But I knew from long experience that most mountain folk have an innate courtesy which is not revealed in conventional forms.

The schoolhouse itself was the most horrifying part of the picture. Every pane of glass in it was broken, and in some windows even the frame was partly or wholly smashed. There were various psychological elements which entered into this vandalism. To begin with, mountain boys don't play games as lowland boys do. They have so long lacked any paraphernalia for games that they have been reduced to stone-throwing, wrestling and scuffling or whittling—when they have knives to whittle with, which isn't always. Stone-throwing, at any sort of mark or for distance, is perhaps the commonest outlet for energy. Anyone who knows boys or has been a boy, whether in city or country, knows that there is no more voluptuously satisfying crash in all nature than that of a pane of glass yielding to a stone thrown by oneself. And finally, the schoolhouse was a fair target; a hunter's quarry, an opponent to be beaten, whether in the person of the teacher or in the unresisting building itself, in what had come to be a sort of game of wits and brawn, cherished because there were no other games. And so the lights were broken out of Shady Cove School over and over again, until the county had tired of buying glass.

The last retiring teacher had nailed the door shut; a superfluous precaution in view of the certainty that the windows would soon be smashed. Two or three of the men helped me to prize it open and I entered alone, the crowd politely remaining outside until invited in. The interior of the room beggars description. The poor little benches and desks were battered, carved, broken and covered with dust, the floor was littered with broken glass, sticks, stones and leaves which had drifted in. Birds, looking the building over in the spring, had conceived it to be a deserted ruin, and had taken up their abode inside. I wished I had brought my new broom, but as I hadn't I could only pick up the worst of the sticks and stones and heave them outside. Then, as all the community was assembled and there didn't seem to be any reason for waiting until eight o'clock, the legal hour —I don't suppose there was a person in the crowd who had the faintest notion as to what time it was, anyhow—I rang the bell. How the boys had happened to overlook cutting off the bell rope and putting it to other uses, I can't imagine.

Slowly and solemnly they came in, the men awkwardly pulling off their tattered felt hats—no real mountaineer ever wears a straw hat—and turning to the left at the door, the women drifting to the right, just as they sit in church. The children crowded the benches, some elders sitting with them or on desks; some sat on the window sills or stood; some of the men squatted—a favorite attitude—or sat on the floor. Not all the crowd could comfortably get inside the little building, and a few looked in through the cavities which had been windows. There was a strong effluvium of unbathed bodies and of the soil, but I was used to that after four years of teaching in mining camps and some twenty-five years of living in the mountains.

As they came in, one kindly disposed woman whispered to me, "Brother Flathead, thar, is a preacher, if you want any prayin' done."

"Brother Flathead?" I repeated.

"Yes; him yonder with the scars on his neck." She pointed.

My first thought when I looked at him was, "What a coincidence! How singularly appropriate his name."

Some circumstance of his birth, possibly the ignorance of a mountain midwife, might have been responsible for that curious cranial malformation. Not until some time afterward did I learn that his name really is Higson; the other is a descriptive nickname, one of the sort applied with naïve callousness by primitive folk, and finally coming to be a commonplace. Like it? He has to like it!

I had decided to do my own praying, however—in fact, I had planned a considerable portion of my prayer. I stood up by the rickety table on the low rostrum and asked the children what song they knew. No one answered; they just sat there, staring at me or turning their eyes away uneasily, stiff with embarrassment, fright and ineptitude.

"Does anyone know a song they would like to help me sing?" I asked, looking around at the elders. Still no voice replied. "Oh, if I could only unlock these shut-up souls," I thought, "and let them move about with a little freedom—"

At last I said, "If no one knows a song, I'll try to sing one for you. Later I hope we can all learn to sing together." They sang in church—I knew that—but singing in so unaccustomed a place as the schoolhouse, and under a woman's leadership, was something else again.

At this juncture Brother Flathead made bold to ask, "Do you know Ameriky? Seems to me that's a mighty good school song."

"Yes, sir, it is," I agreed; and I thereupon sang America, as a solo, for no voice, not even the preacher's, chimed in to help me. I remembered the words, but as to voice and artistry, I'm no Jenny Lind; though I don't suppose my listeners realized that.

After the song, I read a chapter from the Bible, in Proverbs it was, as best suited to my audience; and then I did a thing revolutionary for Shady Cove, where St. Paul's "Let your women keep silence in the churches" was still considered sound up-to-date law. I said, "Let us pray."

Brother Flathead, naturally regarding himself as the only person in the room qualified to address God, considered this a summons, cleared his throat and was about to begin, but I beat him to it. I had things that I wanted to lay before my earthly audience as well as the Most High in that prayer, and I didn't propose to be done out of it. So the preacher kept silent—no doubt an amazed and outraged silence, though I must say I have never been aware of any hostility in his attitude toward me since.

As I prayed, I felt more and more at my ease. We mountain folk have the gift of speech when we are on our feet; words, whether meaty or not, come to us readily. In my prayer I more or less deftly put a share of the responsibility for my success with the school on the parents who were listening to me. I asked that we all be given a kindly, willing, helpful spirit, so that we might labor together for the good of Shady Cove. When

I ended, there were a few muttered "Amens!" from the men's side; but when I opened my eyes, there was that same intense, fascinated gaze of every other eye in the house still fixed on me. I don't believe any of them had bowed their heads or closed their eyelids during the prayer. The spectacle of a woman praying in public was too novel, too interesting to miss. Possibly most of them doubted that it was a legitimate prayer, anyhow, being offered by one of the wrong sex. But as I looked around the room I somehow knew that I had made a strong impression.

"Now, if you will let me talk awhile," said I, "I will tell you something of my plans, and then I should like to hear what you think of them." I set forth my idea of a school and its relation to a community, with all the citizens cooperating to help the teacher in her task and make the schoolhouse a center for social life and betterment, which, in the mountain region, it is or may be if the teacher is the right sort. The church almost never assumes such a function. To begin with, the poor and sometimes ignorant and inept circuit-riding preacher may not come around more than once a month, if that often; and furthermore, he is usually opposed to the church's dabbling in social service. Religion pure and simple is, in his opinion, the only commodity that should be vended from the church house.

I told them that I didn't want to fight my way through school—in fact, I couldn't. I wanted it to be a school ruled by kindness and fairness. After I had had my say, I asked for comments. A long, dead silence ensued. Finally Brother Flathead stepped into the breach and talked at length about nothing in particular; after which another silence fell. I called upon the two men I knew by name, and they spoke a few halting words, opining that the school was a good thing and hoping I would succeed. Finding the men still shy, I turned to the women and said, with my best smile, "Won't some of you ladies tell me that you're glad to see me here and that you'll help me in my work?"

Another moment's pause, and then a woman slowly arose from a window sill; a pioneer, if ever there was one.

"I don't know how to talk in public," she said, "fur I ain't never done none of it. But I just want to say that my young-uns allus has trouble with the teachers, and the teachers is allus a-beatin' on 'em. But I reckon the trouble is we jist ain't never had one before that knowed nothin'. Seems like you air a-startin' out different. My young-uns is mean and you'll have to whoop 'em, but you're welcome to do it. Hit ain't that I don't want 'em learnt."

The Bully

When school had been in session a week and I hadn't whipped anybody there was some head-shaking in the community, and fears were expressed that I would prove to be a failure after all. The pioneer dogma "No lickin', no larnin'" had a strong hold on the minds of Shady Cove. Under the regime of some of the men who had preceded me the swish and thwack of the hickory sprout was heard in the schoolroom daily. I found that some of the boys, with the pride of medieval flagellants, had been keeping score of their penances on the outer wall of the schoolhouse. One boy who claimed 110 lickings was the "champeen," and was regarded with a sort of Spartan admiration amounting almost to envy by his fellows.

But the time finally came when I had to administer a whipping, and it probably saved my reputation, besides being one of the most important events of my four years' incumbency. If we had had a newspaper in Shady Cove, it would have been front-page stuff. After my school had been in session several days, a big handsome six-footer with wavy dark hair and brown eyes, weighing about one hundred and eighty pounds, sauntered into the schoolroom one morning and announced himself as a new pupil, name Floyd Harbison, age twenty-four. Some of the pupils warned me that Floyd was there for no good. He had been in the habit of dropping in for no more than two or three days a week just after each new teacher arrived, to bully the youngsters, start trouble and take the lead in driving the teacher out. A favorite whimsy of his was throwing a dead animal of some sort through a window while school was in session.

His father had lost control of him long before he reached his majority. It was his boast that "I ain't never had no whoopin'." Instead, he had prevailed in physical combat with some of my male predecessors. To run up against a mere willow wand of a young-woman teacher was a new experience, and no doubt he had much curiosity to see how it would work out. Perhaps he thought to charm me as he had some of the mountain belles; for he was a bit of a Lothario, as might be expected of that face and figure. He had served a term in reform school for burglary in his teens, which, of course, only added to his dreadful fascination for the impressionable young ladies of the hills.

He assumed a defiant attitude from the start, giving me to understand that he wasn't there to work. As he came in for his second session he brought a club about the size of a baseball bat, which he rapped heavily on the floor as he walked. He sprawled in his seat, looked impudently about him; he whispered and even talked in an audible voice, and altogether was a highly disorganizing influence.

For the first three days I was completely baffled by him. If mine had been a city school—but of course this couldn't have happened in a city school. The mountain bravo is a dangerous animal to tamper with, and I must admit that I had a certain amount of wholesome fear of Floyd Harbison. I might have had him removed by the county authorities because he was over age, but I was tolerating others who were over age, so that would be illogical and detrimental, for I was anxious to serve the older illiterates as well as the children. Not knowing what else to do I simply ignored Floyd, even when, on Friday, he lighted his pipe and smoked it at his desk. It was ignoble of me, but up to that time I hadn't screwed my courage up to the point of grasping the situation by the horns.

But pondering the problem over the weekend, I saw that I must do something. His defiance and my toleration of it were causing me to lose face with my other pupils, and upsetting my regimen generally. I knew that the pickle must be the subject of gossip in every home in the Cove. And finally, I myself had had enough of it. I resolved that on Monday I would have a show-down with him. I didn't know just how it would be brought about or what would be the result, but something had to break.

As it happened, Floyd himself supplied the cue. In an effort to provide the boys with some other amusement than stone-throwing, I had collected from here and there some wooden and iron hoops and two or three small iron machinery wheels and toy-wagon wheels, which I lent to the younger children with instructions in hoop-rolling; for most of them had never done such a thing before. I happened to be near the door before the session began on Monday morning and saw Floyd seize a wheel which a little boy was rolling and hurl it far down the slope toward the creek. That was the necessary spark; it fired me as nothing else had done.

Striding toward the bully, I said, feeling my face blazing, but keeping my voice calm:

"Go and get that wheel!"

The young man stared at me, plainly unable to believe his ears. He wasn't used to being addressed like that, and to hear it from one so much smaller than himself was cataclysmic. I waited a moment or two, and then said quietly, "I never ask boys but once to do a thing for me."

Instead of retorting, "And what do you do then?" for which gibe I had given him an excellent opening, he merely stared a moment longer; then his face relaxed slightly. With a cunning twinkle in his very nice brown eyes he conceded, "I'll bring it back this time, but I won't never do it again."

"Thanks," said I. "And now, because of conduct unbecoming a gentleman, you may bring a good-sized switch back with you when you come."

His humorous expression broadened. He ambled at a leisurely pace down the hill and took his time at selecting the switch. I have often wondered if he had fleeting thoughts of using it himself—on me. Play was quickly suspended in the yard, and the whole student body, numbering some twenty-five or thirty, gathered at a respectful distance to witness the contest between David and Goliath. If the original David was as nervous as I was, it's a wonder his aim was so good.

At last Floyd came slowly back up the hill with his switch and wheel, and tossed the latter on the ground.

"No," said I, "not there, but exactly where you got it. Give it back to Lije"—the child he took it from.

He hesitated, his face flushing slightly. This was getting to be humiliating. Nevertheless, some strange persuasion—I shall never know what— moved him to pick the wheel up—though sullenly—and hand it to the little boy. I felt my first thrill of triumph, a feeling of psychological power. I knew that the effect on the other pupils, who stood frozen at attention, open-mouthed, about us, would be salutary.

"Now you may give me the switch," said I, "and come inside."

He looked around at the children with a leer, as if to say, "Here's where the fun begins," and followed me into the building. Once inside I closed the door and said:

"Now, Floyd, don't imagine I'm foolish enough to think that I can whip you if you don't want me to. I know I can't. Why, you are twice my size and have four times my strength. But in spite of that you have a licking coming to you, and you're going to get it; simply because you are man enough to know when you have done wrong, and man enough to take your punishment."

That was to him an unexpected approach; it conquered him as perhaps nothing else would have done. I think it probable that when he came in, he had expected to best me laughingly in a combat which would be no more than a flip of the wrist for him. But to put his punishment on a voluntary basis, to appeal to his honor as a gentleman, was a new experience for him. It touched and shamed him—showing that he had good stuff in him, after all. His gaze dropped to the floor; he stood with bent head for a few moments, no longer a mountain Mars but just a big, awkward, shame-faced boy.

At last he mumbled, "I been actin' like a fool, I reckon, but I won't do it no more."

It was a heroic thing for Floyd Harbison to make that confession, and my heart softened toward him—as what woman's would not? I doubt that he had ever before admitted having been morally wrong. But the teacher within me knew that I could not afford to let him off. I sternly recalled to myself the humiliation to which he had subjected me, and for the sake of my prestige and the maintenance of discipline, I stood firm.

"I'm glad to hear that," said I. "And now, turn around."

I did not spare my arm or his feelings, but laid on heavily, distributing the blows over his back and legs. The weather was hot, he wore no coat, and I saw him flinch and his face and neck flush as the switch bent itself around his broad back, where the one thin shirt was feeble insulation. There was dead silence outside; all the children were listening intently.

Whether any of them peeped through the windows, I do not know. But whether they got the lesson by eye or ear, it was of high value. I was building for the future with every stroke. I was warning Shady Cove that discipline must be maintained; that, although I was a peaceful female, abhorring violence, yet if pushed just so far I would show my teeth.

When my arm was tired I stopped and said, somewhat breathlessly, "That will do. You may go now." He shambled out, and, as I afterward heard, took some of the boys down behind the hill, pulled his shirt up and displayed the welts on his back to their still half-incredulous eyes with a sort of pride akin to that of the boys who kept score on the schoolhouse wall—and yet different, too: he had proved that he was a good sport, that he could "take it" when put upon his honor, and that, instead of breaking the young-woman teacher between his fingers like a butterfly, he had been patient, magnanimous and chivalrous with her. Everyone knew or ought to know that I couldn't have whipped him without his consent.

That episode put an end, I think, to much of the doubt in the Cove as to my fitness for the job. When, instead of starting in moderately by switching a few puny little boys, I suddenly electrified the community by licking the biggest and toughest pupil in school, I unintentionally gave myself publicity such as I could have acquired in no other way. It was as if an unpromising candidate for the heavyweight championship instead of trying to earn a reputation by meeting several minor fighters had picked a quarrel with Jim Braddock on the street, and knocked him cold. I have never favored whipping, and I did comparatively little of it during my five years' stay in Shady Cove. I didn't have to; everybody knew that David had conquered Goliath, without half trying, and therefore might be presumed to fear no lesser paladins.

That incident also ended Floyd's insurgency. He buckled down at once to study, and his deportment was well-nigh ideal. On Wednesday afternoon, when the other pupils left, he remained in his seat.

"Did you want to see me about something, Floyd?" I asked, wondering whether his reform of the past three days had proved too much of a strain to be endured longer.

"Nothin' particular," he drawled with a touch of diffidence, "I jest thought I'd ask—a—if you was comin' to prayer meetin' tonight. I'll walk home with you if you will."

Here was a facer. I had begun the previous week to identify myself with Shady Cove by attending the Wednesday-night prayer meeting in the little church beside the schoolhouse. But now to be asked to walk home through the dark with this bully, whose reputation with women was pretty shady, was a ticklish matter. What was behind the invitation? Had I made a conquest of his heart by whipping him? Or did he meditate some extremely unpleasant revenge upon me for humiliating him? Of course a refusal would be easy. I didn't have to attend prayer meeting every week; I could just say that I was doing something else that evening. But if, as had seemed likely for the past three days, Floyd was really repentant and trying to be more of a man, I wanted to help him. I knew the high sensitivity of the mountain man, and to show that I didn't trust him or didn't care for his company would not further that aim. And after all, at the bottom of my soul, I had a prideful little notion that Floyd really admired me and would like to please me. I insisted upon believing that he meant me no harm.

I doubt that my long hesitation was as embarrassing to him as it was to me. At last I brought myself to say, "Yes, I think I'll come. And thank you, Floyd."

My family were naturally alarmed when they heard of my proposed escort, and predicted the worst. But their opposition only increased my steadfastness to my engagement. "I'll come back as good as new," I assured them as I hurried away through the afterglow, for prayer meeting in summer begins before nightfall.

Nevertheless I must admit that my nerves were a bit tense when Floyd said, "Good evenin', Miss Ella," and fell in beside me after the benediction. I believe that every eye in the little congregation was upon us; at least, I felt so. The conjectures as to the status and possible outcome of the relations between Floyd and me would no doubt have made an interesting symposium.

A waning moon was just rising above the hills to eastward and whipporwills were crying over beyond the cemetery as we turned our steps toward Dawyer. We did not go down past the schoolhouse to the road. From the church it was more convenient to go toward town by a trail along the ridge. Floyd did not take my arm or even my hand, which latter is the social mode for young couples walking in the mountains. He just stalked respectfully by my side.

"Warm evenin'," was, I think, his opening remark.

I agreed that it was.

"Need rain," he commented.

I admitted that too. "How's your corn looking?" I asked.

"Hit'll be all right if we git a rain this week. Been comin' along purty good."

And so we rambled on, discussing the little vital banalities of life in the Cove, and the events of school. Later he drifted into telling me of the most interesting yet most maddening experience of his life—his term in reform school. He told—all in a sort of fatalistic strain, as if it were an accident that had happened to him—why he had been sent; how he had broken into a store at Coaldale, emptied the cash drawer and taken some candy and goods. The long train ride to the reformatory was to him like a journey to another world. He gained a few snatches of knowledge there, but suffered continuously from the mountaineer's bitter rebellion; not only against the disgrace of punishment, of being under duress, but against the restraint of the absolute freedom of will which seems vital to his feral spirit, which he cherishes as a basic prerogative.

The rising moon faintly lighted our way while we were in the open, but when we came to a tract of woodland where velvety black shadow laced with silver obscured the path, and owls quavered and hooted in the eerie dusk, my heart beat more rapidly. Here, if anywhere, I was in danger. But Floyd was more than ever the rustic gentleman.

"Lemme go ahead," he said, when the path narrowed. "I know the way." And on he strode, while I, like the true mountain woman, trailed behind, his soft drawl still leisurely progressing through that epoch in his life when he was supposedly being reformed. "Take keer o' that rock," he would break in to warn me, or "Look out; little rough here." When we came to a fence across the trail where a sort of stile had been arranged by sloping a plank up from each side as a ramp, he took my elbow and gently steadied me over the hazard—the only time he touched me during the walk. He did not even do so when we scrambled down the steep bank to the railroad: a fearsome place, especially at night, because the track comes curving out of a tunnel there and forms a mere notch on a steep hillside, so that when trains dart out of the black bore unexpectedly one is either the quick or the dead.

During the mile and a half walk thence along the cinder-path at the trackside into Dawyer, Floyd either strode in front of me, or hopped and skipped along the ties beside me. At our gate he spoke a few awkwardly polite words of leave-taking. I thanked him heartily for his courtesy, he gave a pull at his hat brim, said, "Good evenin' to you, Miss Ella," and turned to trudge over his solitary four-mile journey back home.

My family were much concerned lest this be the beginning of a "case" with the mountain Adonis. But though I had a decidedly soft spot in my heart for him, and felt no shame for it, the affair did not develop. In fear of it, however, I may have assumed a little more of the pedagogical and less of the social manner toward him. I fancy, too, that his escorting me from church was not entirely because of admiration for me; it was in part a gesture to show the Cove that the episode at the school was just an ordinary problem between friends which had been worked out amicably and without prejudice; that his submission to the whipping had been voluntary, and that he still stood high in my regard.

For four months Floyd attended school, seldom missing a session, and was almost a model pupil. But meanwhile he fell a victim of the wiles of a woman at Coaldale, a common woman of the mining camps, nearly twice his age; and just before Christmas he married her. That made it necessary for him to quit school and go to work. In January he found a three-days-a-week job in the mines, and he and his wife took up residence in one of a row of the ugly, flimsy frame shacks that the miners in such camps call home. Two months later he fell into a dispute with one Jim Gribble, the man who lived in the cabin next to his, over a party wire which supplied light for their two houses. And so it was that appalling news greeted me one morning when I came to school.

"Floyd Harbison was killed last night at Coaldale," one of the boys told me.

"Killed!" I gasped. "Good heavens! How did it happen?"

"Feller named Jim Gribble blowed half his head off with a shotgun."

Inspired Teaching

ESTHER CLOUDMAN DUNN

ESTHER CLOUDMAN DUNN, a teacher of English in Smith College, was born in Portland, Maine, in 1891. She received her A.B. from Cornell University in 1913 and her Ph.D. from the University of London in 1922. Before going to England to study, she had taught at Bryn Mawr College for several years. She was appointed to the faculty of Smith College in 1917 and has taught there ever since.

Pursuit of Understanding, from which the following selection is taken, is an account of the author's own education.

THE room where our first Greek class met is not clear in my memory nor, at first, the teacher; though it was this man who would do more for my ideas and method of learning than any other single figure in what now seems a lifetime of teachers. But the textbook we used, *Ball's Elements of Greek,* I took to myself at once. It was bound in yellow-green cloth and my copy was significantly clean and white. In 1907 the Greek books did not have hard usage in public schools; not one of the five copies we used had been rebound. The paper had a smooth finish and took with precision the imprint of the delicate Greek letters.

I remember the Greek coin, the two sides of which were reproduced on one of the early pages. It was an Athenian obol; on one side stared Athena's owl with its crude round eyes and meticulously placed feathers; on the other the helmeted goddess in profile looked out imperiously from her Olympian height. The imperfect circle of that coin, with the bevel worn off on one side like a waning moon, made Greek feel real. I saw and believed in a world where Greek was the only language in which to whisper, sing, buy and sell, make jokes, order one's shoes resoled. Avaricious thumbs had clasped that coin, light fingers had picked it from a pocket, extravagant hands had let it slip through them, all in the ordinary course of the days. Enough of those days, enough of those fingers handling it over greedily or generously, had worn it off. If this coin had been so actually and mercilessly used, so had those strange words in unfamiliar letters which surrounded it on the page.

Thus Greek became a live language with human voices shouting it to one another across streets in the noonday glare, just as 'the girls'' German was live to them. Let them proclaim 'der Apfel auf dem Tisch'; I knew something, too. As we mounted the hill going home from school, we looked out across the harbour. I knew that it was $\vartheta\acute{a}\lambda a\sigma\sigma a$, the ageless, timeless wine-dark element that lapped the shores of ancient Athens. Athens had a harbour, too, not unlike the bay below me with its six-masters and its lighthouses.

The incident of the Greek coin with the worn edge shows what magic is in the greatest teaching. I do not remember how the unevenness of the obol was called to our attention. It was done so naturally and so vividly that it was just there in our consciousness, a part of our equipment, a talisman by which all at once, then and forever after, the Greek world became alive and ours to return to, to roam about in, to love as long as we lived.

Gradually bit by bit the person and personality of the Greek teacher were borne in upon us. He spoke to us in his own variation of a Harvard accent. It had been Maine's best, to begin with. It staunchly refused to give up entirely a fastidious reverberation through his high-cut nostrils. The words came out elegantly tinged with Maine nasality. He was my first teacher who maintained his authority without speaking to us as if we were an audience in a public hall. The class seemed rather like a meeting in a hotel lobby or a club. There was no chasm that separated teacher from taught.

The desk itself was merely a point of reference, not a fixed centre. He would stray to the window, pull aside the cord on the shade and look out. He knew just as we did, even in the midst of recitation, that there was another world, our actual world, waiting just outside. Some of his brightest flashes came back over his shoulder as he looked across the roofs to the clanging trolley cars on the main street. Or he would lean slightly sideways, the fingers of one hand brushing the bottom of his coat aside and tipping themselves into the slit of his trousers' hip pocket.

He was thus elegantly at ease in the midst of a fine point of Greek grammar. His authority rested on deeper foundations than the maintenance of a rigid upright position in front of a class. He was always blowing the chalk-dust from his lean fingers as if it were an element with which he had only a casual contact. Teaching Greek, writing with chalk on blackboards was merely one of the many ways in which his knowledge of the meaning of life, of the scope of human achievement, past with present in unbroken continuity, expressed itself, made contact with the particular human lives around him.

The rest of my high-school career, three years of it, becomes in memory a single piece of experience. I still was one of the quartet; we still shared adolescent pleasures in clothes, beaux, dances and house-parties. But along with this outward conformity to the usual pattern of the middle 'teens, went something immediately and continuously my own. It was so with all four of us; we each began to show at that moment in our lives the faint beginnings of our individual pattern, as differentiated from the pattern which we shared in common with others of our generation. Gertrude began to think of herself as a potential musician; Adelaide as a potential woman of the world. The focus of our private lives became clearer; the choice among the immediate alternatives of each day, week and month, was made by each of us half consciously, in accordance with its usefulness in achieving this ultimate individual pattern.

The centre for me was an idea of knowing the ancient world of Greece and Rome, mastering it, living by it, and probably teaching it. The idea was always there gradually disclosing vistas toward which it and I might go. The only thing needed was patience to acquire a gradually increasing power to read Greek and Latin. It was like the glimpse of ultimate perfection that flashes upon an amateur golfer. He sees himself and the ball and the necessary sticks moving, on some happy future day, with brilliant rightness over the most beautiful and difficult golf course in the world. Just so I might some day move with facility among the Greek words which waited there in their black grace upon the white page. I could then re-create the Greek world and exist within it. As it seemed to me the most beautiful, witty and right world, no price was too high to pay to win my way into it.

This idea with its beckoning power was the creation of the Greek teacher. He did not put it into words. Neither he nor any great teacher could or would do that. Rather a real teacher feels his way, day by day, hour by hour, adapting his specific matter to the mood and need of particular pupils on particular days. He is like a gardener to whom the summer's task has regular stages and series of things to do; planting, weeding, spraying, staking, pruning. No gardener could tell at the beginning of the summer the order and date when each of these things should be done. He must feel his way; consider the weather, the unexpected in shade or light, in quality of soil, in presence of unsuspected rock at root. The variation between one plant and another, set in the same row and at the same time, would not escape his flexible garden knowledge. So it was with my Greek teacher.

I remember less of the actual business of vocabulary, grammar and translation, in the early stages, than of the teacher's asides. They illumined with vision the long grind of learning to read Greek. The day we found the Greek word for 'red' in the vocabulary, the teacher seemed to take it up in his hand. He turned it over, like the faceted jewel it was, and showed us its hidden brilliance. The word, he said, showed in its origin how the Greeks made their red-purple dye from a shell fish. It was precious, used for the garments and carpets of kings. When Clytemnestra, conscious of her guilty love affair with Aegisthus, waited for her husband, Agamemnon, to come home from the Trojan War, she decked the palace stairs with carpets of this red dye to welcome him. It was a royal purple compliment beneath which lurked a bloody warning of his coming murder.

We heard how the Greek dramatist, Aeschylus, had used this word, making it flash out again and again through the metrical lines of his great tragedy. The teacher did not tell us that Aeschylus was a classic which we should admire. Instead he re-created, through that word for *red,* a fearful and violent moment in a great love story. He let us hear a few unintelligible but rolling lines through which the familiar word recurred. He paused when he came to it and pronounced it meticulously. We had by this delicate legerdemain already entered into Aeschylus' *Agamemnon.* It was not a classic but a heightened moment of life. The inference that some day we should easily and familiarly understand all of the words, if we stuck to the daily grind, he left to take root and grow, almost unconsciously, in our minds.

There was a whole series of these inspired tricks to make the past come alive for us. In the long dark school hall hung a plaster cast of a Greek soldier, the hoplite. He easily balanced his great upright spear before his slender young body. 'We four' in our recess throngings had for two years passed it without being really aware of it. We only knew it as one of those things which convey the atmosphere of 'school.' Now that the word for 'soldier' had turned up in the vocabulary, I saw as if for the first time the graceful pleating of that short skirt falling over the soldier's lean muscular flanks. How rhythmically those pleats would sway as he ran lightly forward into battle or lose their vertical creases as he lounged at ease with his fellows in the shade of the portico at the public baths.

The school library had been unplumbed before now, except as the anteroom to the principal's office. It was a hushed little place, smelling of carpet and varnish. The dead air was fanned into life from time to time by the ominous opening and closing of the principal's door as some culprit was tossed into the pit or tossed out again, subdued and mute. But now, under the Greek teacher's direction, we found the section of shelves on which stood the books of classical archaeology.

'Classical archaeology,' what a meaningless mouthful of words till we found that it was just another of those adult stupidities for obscuring from our young imaginations things we were interested in! Classical archaeology meant books full of pictures of everyday objects in the Greek and Roman worlds; safety pins, lamps, beds, wine jars and bowls, which the Greeks and Romans had made or used with fingers as warm and living as ours that held the book.

A volume of architect's plans for the Parthenon destroyed the stale sepia unreality of the photograph of this famous building which I had often seen in public libraries and hotel lobbies. These architect's plans put the Parthenon into the future; it was yet to be built according to the designs of a Greek named Ictinus. He planned the upright columns with a slight bulge in the centre, allowing for just that oddity in human eyesight which would, by this irregularity, make the columns look straight. Such cleverness as this was Greek; by it, he no doubt outstripped the local architects who were building our new City Hall.

Our teacher made us aware, outside of the school building, too, of moments of recognition of and identity with the Greek world. As the Sicilian harbour of Trapani has turned up in dispatches on air action in the Second World War, I am sure that at least five Americans, who sat in that Greek class over thirty years ago, have, among the unfamiliar foreign places, seized with relief upon Trapani for their own. All five of us have known it well ever since that winter day in 1907 when a bark from Trapani with a cargo of salt anchored in our harbour. She was grey and needed painting. Her foreign flag looked bright and southern in the steely winter harbour.

We might have noticed her arrival of our own accord. But it took that genius in the business of teaching which gathers all kinds of common places to itself and transmutes them for its purpose, to make the arrival of this patched grey bark an event for the Greek class. The eye of our teacher, scanning the thin local newspaper, so crampingly provincial, had no doubt turned for room to the shipping news. There he found recorded the arrival of a Sicilian bark. He put this little happening into contact with his own memories of Sicily and thence transferred it backward in his mind to ancient Greek Sicily with its singing goatherds. And thus he produced for us, like a rabbit from a hat, the flocks and songs, the shade and running water, of ancient Mediterranean hillsides. Theocritus, the Greek poet, had recorded them. His poetry was beyond our present skill to translate. But it would be there, waiting for us, when our grammar and vocabulary had caught up with it.

My father, seeing how warmly the wind blew from Mediterranean shores, made contributions of his own from the same quarter. With overcoat collar turned up against the raw east wind, he would sometimes be waiting for me at the corner of the school alley and the main street. The large brown paper-bag under his arm, would, likely as not, in this stage of my enthusiasm, hold wreaths of dusty grey-brown figs, strung on straw and tins of olive oil with the names of Italian canners on their chrome yellow labels. The figs were really dusty and had to be slipped off their straw strings and soaked in warm water before they could be eaten. The olive oil, turned out of its tin into a Mason jar, revealed a thick dark sediment at the bottom. But never was the 'peck of dirt' consumed with less harm to a young stomach or more sustenance for a young imagination.

Caesar and Xenophon as war reporters did not interest me. Perhaps for the boys in the class it might have been different. But Xenophon's account of the education of King Cyrus was real enough. His games took place in the royal park outside the palace. The Greek word for that park was *paradise*. The paradise of the Bible, of the Sunday hymns in church, had

an unpleasantly cold and alien connotation. There would be no inducement to be good here on earth for the reward of living in such a paradise.
But a Greek park full of great trees, long avenues, deer flecked with light
under the shadow of leafy branches, and young Cyrus cantering down
the sward on his Persian pony, such a destination might have turned my
unbelieving soul toward religion.

Cicero's *Orations* were not much better than Caesar's *Gallic Wars*. There
was too much in them of election shouting as I knew it in Maine. His
defence of Archias was more congenial. Archias was a Greek and a poet.
In defending such a client, Cicero found opportunity to say things which
he felt about poetry and art. I liked this better than his excoriating oratory
directed against dishonesty and bribery in public life. I had already heard
more than enough about those things in the torrent of Republican violence
against the rare Democrat who won public office in Maine.

The Cicero of the Archias mood turned up again in a tall copy of his
Letters which my father had picked up in a junk-shop. His daily walks
to his office lay through the poor foreign section which existed even in a
Maine city and in the earliest part of the twentieth century. The Italian
fruit-shop which yielded figs and olive oil stood between junk-shops where
the flotsam and jetsam of Victorian New England came temporarily to
rest behind dusty, small-paned windows.

Father always kept a nickel or a thin silver dime in his right waistcoat
pocket. With it, when he had the leisure, he angled skilfully, in these old
junk-shops, among bound volumes of sermons, gilded gift books, old
Bibles with metal clasps. Sometimes he found the rare volume that, if his
bargaining was as successful as his coin was meagre, might come home in
his bulging pocket to assume a worthy place on his choice library shelves.

The tall copy of Cicero's *Letters* in pebbled black cloth aged to a dusty
brown, was such a find. Some Bowdoin or Harvard man had purchased it
in a long-ago, undergraduate enthusiasm and brought it home from college
to rust silently in the dark oblivion of a tall old bookcase while he lived,
loved, married, had children and died. Then his old library was cast out
again from its long quiet to move upon the chance currents of a twentieth
century junk dealer's world.

I could hardly claim that the volume of Cicero's *Letters* came into its
own again in my immature and inexpert hands. There was not yet enough
Latin in me to read it with any ease. The style was often unstudied, with
colloquialisms. My experience with the solid formation in which the sentences of the orations advanced down the textbook page was of little use
among these supple, private phrases. But the very fact that he wrote personal letters did something for my idea of Cicero. The rolling periods of
those public speeches were pronounced from a rostrum by a statuesque
figure in a toga. Its public correctness needed to be balanced by that other
impression of the genial, fluent letter-writer.

In the senior year, our Greek teacher took over Virgil as well as Homer.

Only then did Latin become a vehicle for a real and beautiful story. When Dido first appeared to Aeneas, our teacher showed how Virgil had a special verb for her graceful entrance, *incessit*. Our imagination made up some happy combination of floating and walking for *incessit*. When night fell to terminate a long day of battle and harangue in Troy, it fell quickly, it rushed down, *ruit . . . nox*. It was the sharp, tropical opposite of the austere, slow twilights of our northern New England. Dido, the queen of Carthage who nearly beguiled Aeneas from his stern task of being the hero of the Latin people, was to Virgil in his Roman superiority *Phoenissa*, a gipsy.

Such classroom comment as this was too good to be lost. It evoked a magic world; it must be preserved. Father had a copy of the text of *Aeneid* interleaved and bound on tapes, as law students' books were interleaved for annotation. Every Sunday morning, on those thin interleaves, was inscribed in immature round handwriting the seasoned wit and ripe perception which Virgil's hexameters had called up, day by day, in the teacher's comment.

Homer's *Iliad* and *Odyssey*, read at the same time and under the same master's baton, were less vivid. One missed the urbanity of the conscious Roman epic. I was not sufficiently mature to feel the elemental grandeur of the Greek poem. The heroes seemed long-winded and the lists of names boring. The repetition of stock epithets, looking out familiarly from the text, time after time, was no boon. They seemed cheats, fillers up of space that might have been illumined by something new. This was heresy, never consciously realised by me nor discovered by the teacher. But the annotation of Homer went by the board while the *Aeneid* notes flourished, neatly and persistently, through the whole first six books of the poem.

Yet the Homer hour was often a lovely one. The five original Greek beginners had survived for three years, intact. We met in an improvised room, made out of a corner of the great study-hall. A dozen panelled and hinged doors were unfolded and turned into walls. The teacher did the unfolding. His action, not unlike the movement of an accordion player, seemed to produce a kind of music, though inaudible. The expanding contraption was still a schoolroom; the panelled doors gleamed with the thick yellow varnish in which all schoolrooms since earliest days had been preserved. But the resinous trimness, so well contrived to close in the airless routine of the usual classroom, enclosed now the fresh, free empyrean of inspired teaching.

Index by Authors

675